FUNDAMENTALS OF PHYSICAL GEOGRAPHY

McGRAW-HILL SERIES IN GEOGRAPHY

EDWARD J. TAAFFE AND JOHN W. WEBB, *Consulting Editors*

Broek and Webb   A Geography of Mankind

Carlson   Africa's Lands and Nations

Conkling and Yeates   Man's Economic Environment

Cressey   Asia's Lands and Peoples

Demko, Rose, and Schnell   Population Geography: A Reader

Detwyler   Man's Impact on Environment

Eliot Hurst   Transportation Geography: Comments and Readings

Fryer   Emerging Southeast Asia: A Study in Growth and Stagnation

Kolars and Nystuen   Geography: The Study of Location, Culture, and Environment

Kolars and Nystuen   Human Geography: Spatial Design in World Society

Kolars and Nystuen: Physical Geography: Environment and Man

Lanegran and Palm   An Invitation to Geography

Mather   Climatology: Fundamentals and Applications

Murphy   The American City: An Urban Geography

Pounds   Political Geography

Raisz   General Cartography

Raisz   Principles of Cartography

Starkey, Robinson, and Miller   The Anglo-American Realm

Thoman and Corbin   The Geography of Economic Activity

Trewartha   An Introduction to Climate

Trewartha, Robinson, and Hammond   Elements of Geography: Physical and Cultural

Trewartha, Robinson, and Hammond   Physical Elements of Geography (A republication of Part I of the above)

Trewartha, Robinson, Hammond, and Horn   Fundamentals of Physical Geography

Van Riper   Man's Physical World

Watts   Principles of Biogeography: An Introduction to the Functional Mechanisms of Ecosystems

Yeates   An Introduction to Quantitative Analysis in Economic Geography

Yeates   Quantitative Analysis in Human Geography

FUNDAMENTALS OF PHYSICAL GEOGRAPHY

Third Edition

Glenn T. Trewartha

Professor Emeritus of Geography
University of Wisconsin

Arthur H. Robinson

Professor of Geography
University of Wisconsin

**Cartography by
Randall D. Sale**

Professor of Geography
University of Wisconsin

Edwin H. Hammond

Professor of Geography
University of Tennessee

Lyle H. Horn

Professor of Meteorology
University of Wisconsin

McGRAW-HILL BOOK COMPANY
New York   St. Louis   San Francisco   Auckland   Bogotá   Düsseldorf   Johannesburg   London
Madrid   Mexico   Montreal   New Delhi   Panama   Paris   São Paulo   Singapore   Sydney   Tokyo   Toronto

FUNDAMENTALS
OF PHYSICAL
GEOGRAPHY

1234567890 VHVH 7832109876

This book was set in Century Schoolbook by Black Dot, Inc. The editors
were Stephen D. Dragin, Janis M. Yates, and David Dunham;
the designer was Joseph Gillians; the production supervisor was Joe Campanella.
Von Hoffmann Press, Inc., was printer and binder.

Design and artwork for the Special World Maps was done
by Michael L. Czechanski and Clifford H. Wood.

Library of Congress Cataloging in Publication Data
Main entry under title:

Fundamentals of physical geography.

   First-2d editions by G. T. Trewartha, A. H. Robinson,
and E. H. Hammond.
   Bibliography: p.
   Includes index.
   1.   Physical geography—Text-books—1945-
I.   Trewartha, Glenn Thomas, date
GB55.T73   1977   551   76-27841
ISBN 0-07-065183-3

CONTENTS

PREFACE

This third edition of *Fundamentals of Physical Geography*, which is markedly different from the second edition, keeps pace with major modern changes in attitudes toward the physical environment and in the study of it. The much increased concern about human occupance of the earth and the intense study of what is happening to our planet have greatly enlarged our knowledge. Nevertheless, subject matter for the text has been selected, as before, to serve a one-semester, one-quarter, or two-quarter introductory, college survey course. The major focus remains on the primary elements of the earth environment and their interrelation, namely the atmosphere and the weather and climate it supplies, water in the seas and on the land, the solid earth and its dynamic surface, and the natural vegetation and soils of the lands. Missing from this edition is a section on mineral resources, deleted to make space for new material on other elements and with the thought that the topic is more appropriate as a part of the study of economic geography.

A major innovation in this edition is the systems approach. The physical geography of the earth involves many dynamic phenomena, all of which are interrelated in their functioning and distribution. These systems, such as the circulation of the atmosphere, the hydrologic cycle, or the molding of the surface forms of the land, are powered by energy inputs and regulated by feedback. A prime objective has been to describe the major subsystems which together constitute the geosystem.

The treatment of the subject matter has been thoroughly modernized. The opening chapter includes a description of systems, a section introducing the student to physical geography, and a description of the earth's behavior as a satellite of the sun, our major source of energy. Methods of location, mapping, and reckoning time are also introduced.

The section describing the operation of the atmosphere and how it produces weather has been completely redone and modernized, although the basic scheme of climatic classification has been retained. The treatment of climates is approached as resulting from a synthesis of weather. Greater attention is given to the impact of human activity on climate and to the weather events which impart particular characteristics to a climatic region.

The waters of the seas and the land have become an increasingly critical element of the environment, necessitating an increased analysis of these great circulating systems.

The understanding of the forces at work in modifying the solid earth and its surface, from plate tectonics to geomorphological processes, has advanced rapidly in recent years, requiring a thorough revision of this major section. New material has been added, especially on major crustal features and current functioning of the land surface in different environments. Organizational changes emphasize relationships among processes at some expense of descriptive detail.

The sections on natural vegetation and soils have been recast to include a modernized treatment of the vegetation cover of the land. The old scheme of soil classification has been replaced with the modern terminology and diagnostic elements now used by the scientists of the Soil Conservation Service of the U.S. Department of Agriculture.

In the interest of convenience and cost, the four-color world maps of the previous editions have been replaced by two-color maps placed in the text. A new world map of the major structural characteristics of the earth has been added to complement the extended treatment of world structure and plate tectonics, and the world maps of natural vegetation and soils have been completely redone.

Four other innovations are worth noting. First, a new author has been added. Second, in all appropriate instances, measurements are given in metric units with the customary equivalent measures in the United States included in parentheses. Third, a set of review questions has been included at the end of each chapter, and fourth, the lists of selected references have been annotated.

The physical geography of the earth involves a fascinating variety of fundamental processes which interact to cause a systematic variation in the character of the environment from place to place. There is a surprising amount of order in the environmental patterns. From the geographical point of view, neither the processes nor the patterns should be studied in isolation. In this book we have tried to help the student understand the major and minor processes involved, the energy flows that power them, and the environmental patterns that result, all with the basic principle in mind that on our earth, all things are related.

Glenn T. Trewartha
Arthur H. Robinson
Edwin H. Hammond
Lyle H. Horn

The Physical Environment and Geography

ENVIRONMENT AND SYSTEMS

Like all creatures, people must live in harmony with the environment in order to survive. The environment is the whole earth, and it is necessary to study it in order to appreciate its complex diversity and to understand how it functions as a life-support system.

There are two ways to study the earth. One is to focus on a restricted grouping of phenomena and processes, such as those having to do with the solid earth (geology) or the gaseous earth (meteorology). Another way is to study the variations and interrelations of environmental phenomena from place to place. Since the time of the ancient Greeks this has been called *geography* (Gr. *geo*, earth + *graphos*, description).

The Study of Geography

Geography, like history, is not restricted to a selected group of phenomena as are such disciplines as geology and meteorology. In theory geography is concerned with all environmental phenomena, and the uniqueness of geography derives from its aims and methods in the study of these phenomena. History emphasizes chronology and the interrelation of things in time, while geography emphasizes location and the interrelation of things in earth space.

Geographical Principles

The geographical study of the environment is based upon five principles that may be described briefly as follows:

1. All parts of the earth are different. Although this may seem quite obvious, it is a fact of enormous importance. From it arises the functional interaction of a multitude of inorganic and organic phenomena. In everyday language, the "geography" of an area usually means the description of its environmental characteristics.

Description is an important objective of all sciences, and in geography, the description of the earth is accomplished by mapping in addition to verbal and quantitative characterization.

2. Each phenomenon varies from place to place. If we survey any one environmental element, such as

1

the land form or precipitation or population density or industrial production, we find that it has its own pattern of variation which can be mapped and analyzed.

3. The spatial variation of each element of the environment is functionally related to the other elements. In the broad sense everything is related to everything: individual things and processes on earth are never independent. Some of the linkages are relatively simple, such as the swirl of storms produced by winds on the rotating earth, while others are much less direct, such as the decomposition and erosion of the land surface. Some, including those things created by people, are very complex indeed.

The interrelationships among the earth phenomena and among their patterns of variation may be studied at various levels of detail. These can range from a detailed focus on local variations to more generalized considerations on a worldwide level.

4. There is a continual interaction among parts of the earth. Heat flows from equatorial areas toward the polar; water is moved from the oceans to the land, whence it flows back to the seas; agricultural areas trade products with industrial areas; and so on. The geographical patterns of such interactions are important both as consequences of place-to-place differences and as distinctive spatial phenomena in their own right.

5. The earth is dynamic. Nothing on earth ever remains exactly the same. In the short run, for example, in some parts of the earth there is an annual change of the seasons with marked rhythmic modifications of the environment. In the longer run, there are such profound developments as climatic variations, the increase of population, and the erosion of the land. Many of the longer-run changes are nonperiodic, progressive, and in some cases irreversible, but this presently seems to be characteristic also of some short-run changes being initiated by people, such as the pollution of the atmosphere and the waters of the land.

Furthermore, the physical earth functions as a dynamic life-support mechanism. The combinations of conditions at the interface or contact zone between the atmosphere and the solid-liquid surface are such that a great variety of organic life can exist there.

This life is continually changing, not only in the short run with seasonal changes, but over the long run as well. Plant and animal species (which include people) evolve, and perhaps adapt, or migrate, or decline, or they may even disappear. This interaction between the organic and inorganic world is incredibly complex.

The Study of Physical Geography

Physical geography, which focuses upon those phenomena that are not primarily of human making, parallels human geography as one of the traditional topical subdivisions of the field. Each element of physical geography, namely, the atmosphere, the land surface, the waters of the seas and the lands, vegetation, and soils, is characterized by marked regional differences and by notable variations in the functioning of its primary constituents. Furthermore, the place-to-place variations within each of these physical classes are intimately related to the distributional patterns of the others; consequently, the study of physical geography is also concerned with these interrelations and their explanation.

To study the physical environment scientifically, one must consider the processes involved in the interaction of the various elements in place. In this respect there is inevitably a two-way overlap between geography and other earth sciences. The difference lies chiefly in emphasis: the geographer's fundamental concern is with spatial distribution—local, regional, and worldwide—the relations among patterns, the interactions among the phenomena that establish the physical character of areas, and the interactions between areas that arise from their differences. In scholarship there are, of course, no fences around fields of study. There are geographically minded geologists, soil scientists, and botanists, just as there are many geographers who have contributed to the other earth sciences.

While there are traditional and practical justifications for splitting geography into physical and human sections for teaching, the practice also has its drawbacks. Geography does not readily lend itself to a clear division, for however much people in the past may have considered themselves apart from and conquerors of nature, nonetheless people are a part of it, and they are now finding that, like other kinds of creatures, they must learn to live in harmony with the environment. The patterns of people's many activities and distribution on earth partly reflect these efforts to come to terms with a highly diverse "natural" world that simply cannot be treated as if it were everywhere the same.

Although the study of physical geography deals with natural phenomena, people are always involved—as evaluators, users, and modifiers. When people till the soil, irrigate a crop, extract a mineral deposit, build shelters from the cold, dam or foul streams, starve from drought, clear the forests from half a continent, pour noxious gases into the air, introduce new crops into a region, or avoid huge sections of the earth as being too costly or too trying to handle, they are living with and are a part of the physical geography of the earth. Consequently, physical geography studies the earth phenomena from the human point of view.

As it becomes ever more clear that the world is neither limitless nor secure against irreparable damage, it also becomes clear that we desperately need to know far more about all aspects of the natural world.

The Systems Model

The study of anything requires an organized approach to the assembly of facts and the analysis of their relationships. This is especially necessary when the object of the study is dynamic, that is, characterized by interrelated functioning phenomena, whether organic or inorganic. Clear understanding often requires the development of a simplified characterization by which one can observe the relations of the parts, the energy inputs and outputs, and the consequences of changes in any of the factors involved. Such a basic characterization is called a *model*.

Because the environment is so complex, it is desirable to employ a general scheme for the modeling which is readily applicable to the great diversity of earth phenomena. In the last several decades a broad framework, called *systems analysis*, has been employed with great success in many investigations in science and technology. By looking at the diversity of earth phenomena in a similar fashion one is better able to understand the relationships among the various forces and conditions. Because the systems approach to modeling supplies a useful framework for

the study of physical geography, a general description of the nature of systems is introduced here. The more specific application of the concepts will appear in the following chapters.

The attributes of systems. A system consists of a set of things which interact with one another to function as a viable structure. In its simplest form a system consists of three elements: (1) a functioning set of things, (2) a flow of energy which powers the functioning, and (3) a procedure for the internal regulation of the functioning, called *feedback*. A familiar, man-made example of an uncomplicated system, an electric refrigerator, will illustrate the concept. It consists of a box, a mechanism for removing heat from inside the box and dissipating it outside the box, and a set of controls. There are several sources of energy which enter into the functioning of the system, such as heat flux through the walls of the box, heat in the substances placed inside the box, heat that enters with the exchange of air when the door is opened, and electrical energy to operate the heat-removing mechanism and the control system. The feedback is provided by a thermally controlled switching device (thermostat), which, if the temperature inside the box rises to a set maximum, will start the heat-removing mechanism and, when the temperature drops to a set minimum, will turn it off.

In the above example, so long as the refrigerator remains operable and its surroundings remain normal, the feedback mechanism tends toward maintaining the temperature inside the box at an equilibrium, a balance between the heat that enters the box and that expelled by the operating of the heat-removal mechanism. In the operation of systems this aim toward an equilibrium is termed a *steady state*.

Steady state. The concept of "steady state" derives from the principles of the conservation of mass, momentum, and energy. It is assumed that the functioning of natural systems tends toward the maintenance of steady states through the operation of feedback.

An example of a tendency toward steady state and the feedback control in the environment is the temperature of the water in a lake. The water receives solar energy, which warms it. The more heat it receives, the warmer it gets; but the warmer it gets, the more heat it loses by radiation, conduction, evaporation from the surface, etc. Theoretically, through the operation of feedback, the water ultimately would reach a temperature where the energy input would be balanced by the output. This would be a steady state temperature. Many similar examples are provided in the biological world where a particular species depends on a particular food supply as its source of energy to maintain its viability. If the population increases beyond the capability of the environment to provide its food supply, the population will decrease until, other things remaining the same, there will be a balance, a steady state. The regulatory mechanism, feedback, operates in diverse ways.

Although all natural systems tend toward a steady state, it is important to keep in mind that the earth is dynamic both from the short-run and the long-run point of view. Consequently, the steady state condition toward which the systems tend is constantly changing, sometimes rapidly, as with the changing of the seasons, or slowly, as with the growth of a mountain range.

Open and closed systems. There are two kinds of systems: a *closed system* is one in which the flow of energy originates and remains within the system, and the other, an *open system*, is one in which the energy input originates largely outside the system and from which the output of energy leaves the system. In physical geography the only significant closed system is the solar system. We are not concerned with the energy which drives it, but we are very much concerned with its operation, for many of the phenomena on earth vary as a consequence of the earth-sun-moon relationships within the system. All the other major systems of consequence in physical geography are open systems.

Forms of energy. Without going into the subject in detail, it is useful in this introductory section to review briefly the major forms and sources of the energy which powers the open earth system (sometimes called the *geosystem*) and its subsystems. In the various processes that take place in the systems of the environment, energy in one form is often converted to another form. For example, the evaporation of water—its conversion from a liquid to a gaseous state—requires heat, which is retained by the water vapor in a form called *latent heat*; the carriage of the vapor aloft is accomplished by the addition of the

kinetic energy of motion; when condensation occurs, the latent heat is released, thus warming the air; the kinetic energy of the water that falls on the land as precipitation is changed to the potential energy of its position on the land above the ocean from which it came; when the water flows downhill, the potential energy of position is transformed to the kinetic energy of motion; and so on.

The more obvious forms of energy involved in the systems of the environment are heat, kinetic energy, and potential energy. Heat is the energy of molecular activity of materials; kinetic energy is the energy of motion; and potential energy is the energy of position relative to gravitational attraction. There are other forms of energy which are very important but not so obvious, such as the energy that is a consequence of chemical reactions, either inorganic or organic. In the latter case, as with food, it is often referred to as *chemical energy*. The various forms of energy are involved in the production of work, ranging from the circulation of the atmosphere and the erosion of the land to the biologic activity of all forms of life.

Efficiency of energy use. The conversion of one form of energy to another as it passes through a system is never perfectly efficient in the sense that all the energy of one form is converted to another form. For example, when a raindrop falls through air the frictional drag of the air converts part of the kinetic energy into heat. The biotic world provides another example. Plants use about one-sixth of the radiant energy they receive for their own metabolism; the remaining five-sixths is stored and is available, so to speak, for consumers of the plants. A herbivore eating the plant as food employs this five-sixths of the original radiant energy in several ways: to fuel its own metabolism, for growth, and as metabolic waste products, and some passes through its system unused. Actually, it turns out that only about half the energy stored in the plant is in turn stored by the herbivore. A meat eater who consumes the herbivore will repeat the process in a similar fashion, further diminishing the stored supply. The rapid shrinkage of stored energy as it passes from one organism to another accounts for the fact that food chains in nature rarely have more than five links.

It bears repeating that the inefficiency of energy conversion in a system does not mean that the energy is lost: it may simply be dissipated into other forms and subsystems and be unavailable to perform work in the system in which it first entered, or it may be stored, as in the case of the fossil fuels, upon which we now depend so heavily. The more complex a system is, the greater is the amount of chaos or inefficiency, sometimes called *entropy*, in its operation.

Sources of energy. If we discount the negligible amounts of energy received by the earth from starlight and other cosmic radiations, the functioning of the systems of the earth is powered essentially from only three sources of energy: (1) electromagnetic radiation from the nuclear fusion occurring in the sun, (2) gravitational attraction of the masses of the earth, sun, and moon, and (3) endogenetic energy arising from radioactive decay and other sources in the interior of the earth. It is well to put the sources in perspective.

The second and third together produce such major accomplishments as the movement of continental blocks, the raising or lowering of rock masses as in mountain building, the heating of the rocks and water in the crustal section of the earth, and its most obvious manifestation, volcanic activity. The assessment of the amounts of gravitational and endogenetic energy involved in earth systems over long periods is difficult, but it is clearly prodigious. On the other hand, the current contribution of endogenetic energy to the surface of the earth is so small, relatively, that it can be ignored.

By far the most important source of energy in the daily and annual functioning of the surface systems of the earth is the radiation from the sun. The amount of solar energy absorbed and then reradiated to space each year approximates 8.5×10^{23} gram calories, that is, about 1.15×10^{17} kilowatts or 1.7 billion billion horsepower.[1] Because the earth is in a nominally steady state with respect to temperature, the incoming and outgoing radiation essentially balance one another over an extended period.

Only a small amount, less than 1 percent, of the solar energy receipt is involved with the erosional

processes of landform development. This is largely fluvial through the lifting of water to the land. Photosynthesis in plants, the process by which green plants convert light to chemical energy and synthesize organic compounds, likewise takes less than 1 percent in the aggregate. The remaining vast amount of solar energy powers the great transport systems of the earth, namely, the circulation of the atmosphere and the oceans and the transport of water from the oceans to the land and back.

Mass exchanges and budgets. One of the notable consequences of the enormous amount of energy involved in the powering of earth systems is the continual exchange of materials from one part of the earth to another. For example, there is at all times in the atmosphere as water vapor the equivalent of about 15,000 cu km of liquid water. Solar energy incident upon the ocean surfaces powers the evaporation of much liquid, changing it to vapor. The vapor is transported along with the other gases of the atmosphere until some occurrence causes the water vapor to condense and some to fall as precipitation. Much of this falls back into the oceans, but a share falls on land, where it starts its movement back to the oceans. This exchange between ocean and land supplies the requisite water for all the biological activity on the land.

In a similar, but much slower, process of movement, vast amounts of solid material on the land are transferred from one place to another. Largely moved by running water either in suspension or in solution, but in some degree as airborne dust, the total mass involved is enormous. Some of it simply goes from one part of the land to some other place, but a great deal is transported to the oceans, to be deposited as sedimentary strata, whence ultimately it may again appear as land through crustal uplift. Many other examples, large and small, of the mass exchanges continually taking place could be cited, such as the movement of huge crustal plates and the flow of molten rock beneath the earth's surface, and the erosional movements of the solid materials within a single drainage basin. They all serve to remind us that the earth is dynamic.

When looked at in detail, the exchanges of mass and energy are seen to be variable and complex. The variations can range from the temperature differences resulting from the different amounts of solar

---

[1]One gram calorie is the amount of heat required to raise the temperature of one gram of water from 15° to 16° at 1 atmospheric pressure. (It is $1/1000$ of the food calorie.) One gram calorie equals 4.184 joules, and 1 joule/sec equals 1 watt.

energy received during the 24 hours of a day to the annual variations in precipitation. Fortunately, there is sufficient regularity in most regimes so that one can construct a summary in the form of a budget. The manner in which the solar energy received by the earth is changed in form, enters as inputs into the various subsystems, and leaves again by radiation to space, called the *energy budget*, as described in Chapter 3, is an example. The monthly variation in the manner in which water is made available to the soil and used by plants during the course of a year (also called the *water balance*) is another example of a budget.

Earth systems. When considered as a whole, the earth system with all its subsystems has a complexity that is formidable, and its comprehension requires breaking it into its major parts or subsystems. Although, as pointed out above, everything is related to everything, some of the subsystems have sufficient unity from the human point of view to permit them to be studied separately. These are the basic circulatory systems of the atmosphere, water, and the solid materials of the earth. They are all open systems and tend toward the steady state. The inorganic world and the organic world interact in the vegetation and soils that mantle most of the earth. These, too, are systems which, although constantly changing through time, also tend toward a steady state.

In the consideration of the earth systems it is well to keep in mind that people are a part of, not separate from, a life-support system composed of the elements of physical geography that operate together as a viable complex. Such a functioning assemblage of any size is called an *ecosystem* and its study is named *ecology*. The whole earth can be thought of as one vast, incredibly complicated ecosystem, and humanity's recent proliferation and greatly increased technological activities have for the first time in history made it a significant agent in the operation of the biosphere—the living portion of the earth—and in the feedback mechanisms which control its character and mode of change. People have suddenly reached a level in numbers and activity where they have significantly modified the near steady states of the recent past to the end that there may very soon be different steady states for many of the systems of the environment. Whether people will consider these as destructive or constructive can only be told by the passage of time.

THE EARTH AS A SATELLITE

The earth is a satellite (planet) in the solar system, and it follows a definite pattern in its spatial relations: It is a regular, rotating body which orbits a central star, the sun, from which it receives the electromagnetic energy that drives its many organic and inorganic systems.

A great many important phenomena (such as the seasons and night and day) and numerous everyday concepts (such as distance and direction) have their origin in the form and size of the earth and its relations with the sun. The appreciation of the diversity of the earth's environment begins with these fundamentals.

Form of the earth. The earth is a smooth, ball-like object whose outer portion is composed of a surrounding sea of gas overlying a solid and liquid surface. The solid-liquid surface departs from being truly spherical in several ways.

The spheroid. The earth is plastic and rotating. Because of this it assumes the general shape of an ellipsoid of revolution, being bulged a little in the equatorial region and flattened a little in the polar, so that a cross section through the poles would be slightly elliptical. The flattening is not great; the polar diameter is some 43 km (27 mi) shorter than an equatorial diameter.

Several slightly different spheroids are used for mapping in various parts of the earth. In North America, mapmakers employ the Clarke spheroid of 1866, which assigns the following dimensions to the earth:

Dimension	Kilometers	Miles
Equatorial radius	6,378.2	3,963.3
Polar semiaxis	6,356.6	3,949.7
Equatorial circumference	40,075	24,900
Surface area (approx.)	510,900,000 (sq km)	197,260,000 (sq mi)

The geoid. Because the concept of horizontal at the earth's surface is important in mapping, one minor way the earth departs from being a smooth spheroid is a consequence of minor surface irregularities (mountains, etc.) and variations in the density of its components. These cause the direction of gravity to depart from pointing precisely toward the center of the earth at all points. The geoid is the surface to which the direction of gravity would everywhere be perpendicular, and it is the shape that would be approximated by the waters of the ocean and in a network of sea-level canals through the land areas. The geoid departs from the spheroid only by a few tens of meters at most.

Surface irregularities. People are impressed by even modest mountains and ocean depths, and, because these differences may seem profound, the actual relative smoothness of the earth is not generally appreciated. The disparity in elevation between the highest mountain and the lowest ocean deep is only about 21 km (13 mi), or less than $1/600$ of the earth's diameter. If the earth were reduced proportionately to the size of a very large globe with a diameter of 1.0 m (3.3 ft), the Rocky Mountains in the United States would be only about 0.3 mm (0.14 in.) above the general surface level. On an ordinary desk globe they could hardly be felt at all. For its size the earth is as smooth as a bowling ball.

Beneath the atmosphere most of the relatively smooth solid surface is covered by water, and the 29 percent that does protrude above water does so only very slightly. The average elevation of the land surface above sea level is about 0.8 km (0.5 mi), and on this low-lying restricted land area mankind makes its home (Fig. 1.1).

The earth as a sphere. The irregularities in the shape of the earth are important in many ways. They affect the measurement of distances and angles, mapping accuracy, navigation, and the orbiting of satellites. Nevertheless, for understanding several aspects of physical geography, the near sphericity of the earth is far more important than are its slight departures from being a perfect sphere.

A large number of the variations in the earth environment from place to place are related to its spherical form. Accordingly, it is important to be familiar with some of the geometric properties of the sphere, the circle, and the arc.

Great circles and small circles. If one were to shine a flashlight on a ball in a dark room, several of

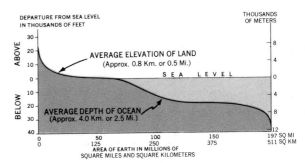

Figure 1.1 A cumulative graph showing the relative amounts of water and land surface on the earth and the average elevation and depth of the solid surface in relation to sea level.

the more fundamental consequences of the earth's spherical form (Fig. 1.2) would be demonstrated. First, one would be showing how the earth intercepts the solar energy which drives many of the earth's systems. Second, one would exhibit the concept of a great circle, for the line separating the dark from the light is a great circle.

A *great circle*, geometrically defined, is the path of the intersection of a spherical surface with any plane which includes the center of the sphere

Figure 1.2 The earth ball, primarily lighted from the sun, is always half dark and half light; the division is a great circle.

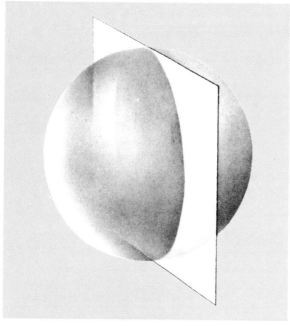

Figure 1.3 The trace of the intersection of a plane and a sphere is a great circle whenever the plane includes the center of the sphere.

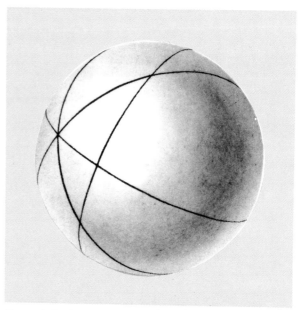

Figure 1.4 Any two points on the surface of a sphere may be "connected" by a great circle, which is the shortest possible course over the surface between the two.

(Fig. 1.3). A great circle has many important characteristics, such as that it is the largest possible circle on a sphere, it divides the earth's surface into hemispheres, any two points on a sphere can be "connected" by a part of a great circle, the course along the arc is the shortest course (Fig. 1.4), and any great circle bisects any other great circle.

The intersection of the surface of a sphere with a plane that does not include the center of the sphere also makes a circle, but it is called a *small circle* (Fig. 1.5). Small circles have none of the characteristics of great circles listed above. Moreover, small circles can be parallel to one another. A view around the horizon, whether from fairly close to the surface or from an orbiting satellite, is a small circle.

Distance and direction. It is not easy to specify distance on a spherical surface, and until a century or so ago there was immense confusion among countries using different units. Since the surface of a sphere is uniformly curved, it is possible to state the distance

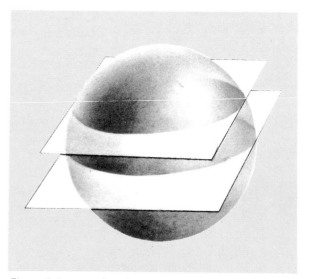

Figure 1.5 A small circle on a sphere results from its intersection by a plane that does not include the center of the earth. Whenever the planes are parallel, the resulting circles, either small or great, will be parallel.

from one place to another on it as the number of degrees, minutes, and seconds included in the great-circle arc that connects the two (Fig. 1.6). The arc distance can then be translated into other units by calculating the size of the sphere. This is done by measuring a small arc distance with precision and then extending the result to the entire great circle. Such a calculation was first carried out more than 2,000 years ago with some success.

Today the relationships are known with considerable exactness, and because the earth is not quite a perfect sphere, average values must be employed. The relation between angular and linear measure on the earth is most easily described by saying that one minute of arc (one-sixtieth of a degree) of a great circle is practically equal to the distance recognized as the international nautical mile. The relation of the nautical mile to other measures is shown below.

Unit	Meters	Feet
International nautical mile	1,852.00	6,076.10
Kilometer	1,000.00	3,280.84
Statute mile	1,609.34	5,280.00

Direction on a sphere is more difficult to specify than distance, because direction on such a curved surface is quite arbitrary. A method that is generally useful over a good part of the earth's surface is based on the familiar parallels and meridians of the spherical-coordinate referencing system and is described later in this chapter.

Principal movements of the earth. When the earth is considered as a satellite of the sun, its primary movement is termed its *revolution*, and this is simply its circuit or orbit around the sun. The orbit takes place in an imaginary plane called *the plane of the ecliptic*. The orbiting earth has a second major movement, *rotation*, which refers to the fact that it spins constantly while orbiting. Revolution and rotation are quite different motions and should not be confused.

In addition to the two primary motions, the surface of the earth maintains some critical directional relationships with the sun. These are best summed

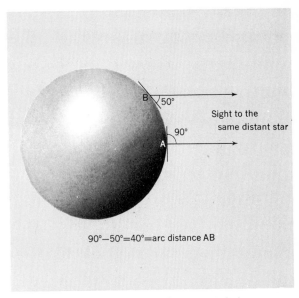

Figure 1.6   Arc distance along the great circle between two points is obtained by observing the difference in the astronomical altitude of a celestial object, real or imaginary, which lies in the plane of the great circle.

up in the terms *inclination* and *parallelism*. "Inclination" refers to the fact that the axis of the earth's rotation maintains an inclination of about $66\frac{1}{2}°$ from the plane of the ecliptic (or $23\frac{1}{2}°$ from perpendicular to it). This position is virtually constant. "Parallelism" refers to the fact that all the while the earth is orbiting the sun, the direction of its axis remains parallel to the axis' direction elsewhere in the orbit. These relationships are illustrated in Figure 1.7.

A remarkable number of things depend on the fundamental motions of revolution and rotation and the relationships of inclination and parallelism. They determine phenomena ranging from the seasons to night and day, and from our methods of reckoning time to the methods by which we specify location.

Revolution. The rotating earth revolves in a slightly elliptical orbit about the sun, from which it keeps an average distance of about 93 million miles. During the northern winter, the earth is a little closer to the sun, but the difference between perihelion (the position closest to the sun) and aphelion (position farthest from the sun) is only a small percentage of the total distance.

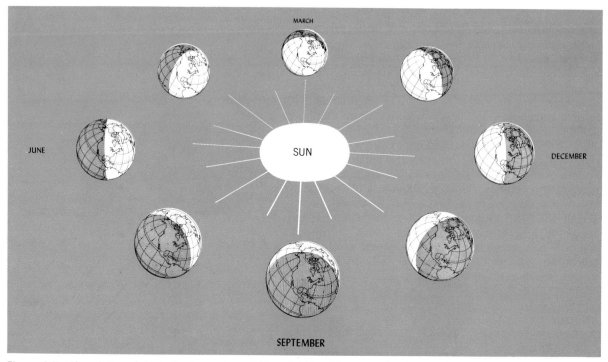

Figure 1.7   The relation of the inclination and parallelism of the earth's axis to the change of the seasons. For this drawing the observer is far outside the earth's orbit and slightly above the plane of the ecliptic.

The average time required for the earth to pass once completely around its orbit fixes the length of the year. During one year the earth rotates very nearly 365¼ times, thus determining the number of days in the year. The basic motions and relationships combine to produce a rhythmic seasonal change in the amounts of energy which enter the systems in different parts of the earth. During the northern summer, for example, the northern half of the earth's surface (called *Northern Hemisphere*) is inclined toward the sun, while in the winter it is inclined away (Fig. 1.7).

Rotation.   The earth rotates about an axis, and the poles represent the intersections of the axis with the surface. The time required for the earth to rotate once with respect to the sun is designated as one day. During one day, most places on the sphere turn alternately toward and away from the sun, thus going through a period of energy receipt and a period of loss. Consequently, they are twice passed through the twilight zone, the great-circle boundary between light and dark (the circle of illumination)—once at sunrise and again at sunset.

The earth rotates toward the direction we call *east*, and this fact has broad significance (Fig. 1.8). Not only does it determine the direction in which the sun, moon, and stars appear to move across the sky, but it is intimately related to the general circulation of the atmosphere and oceans.

LOCATION, MAPS, AND TIME

Systems of Geographical Location

The concept of relative location on the earth stems from the fundamental attributes of distance and direction. The importance of the specification of location in a systematic way was recognized more than 2,000 years ago, and the system devised then is still standard today.

Were there a perfect sphere with a uniform surface, alone in space, there would be no natural

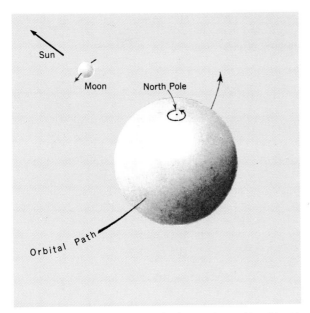

Figure 1.8 Assuming one were looking at the earth's orbit with the northern part of the earth uppermost, then the earth would be seen to orbit counterclockwise and rotate the same way. The moon also orbits the earth this way.

starting points from which to reckon the relative distance and direction of other points. Fortunately, the earth contains innumerable environmental contrasts, and it moves in a regular fashion with respect to other celestial bodies. Singly or in combination, these factors make it possible to relate one position to another. Some systems depend only upon celestial observation, some only upon ground comparisons, and some upon a combination of the two.

The Spherical (Geographical) Coordinate System

The early Greek geographers utilized a kind of grid system to describe position in the Mediterranean region. They based it upon the apparent movements of the sun and stars with respect to the earth, and the method evolved to a coordinate system based upon the sphericity and rotation of the earth. The fundamental reference points of the plan are the geographical poles.

The system is similar to the familiar rectangular coordinate arrangement on cross-section paper,

except for modifications necessary to fit the spherical earth. A line around the earth lying everywhere midway between the poles is called the *equator*, and any number of other lines parallel to the equator may be placed on the earth (Fig. 1.9). These lines, together with the equator, are all called *parallels*, and directions along them are east, toward the sunrise, and west, toward the sunset.

Since all parallels are parallel with the equator, it follows that every point on a given parallel will be the same distance to the north or to the south of the equator. The concept of position north or south in the earth coordinate system is called *latitude* and is expressed by identifying the appropriate parallel.

Needless to say, a statement of latitude is not enough to locate a position, since a parallel is a continuous line. Distance east and west, called *longitude*, is expressed by a second set of lines which are arranged so as to lie everywhere at right angles to the parallels. On the sphere, since these lines intersect the parallels at right angles, they must necessarily converge at each pole. These lines, called *meridians*,

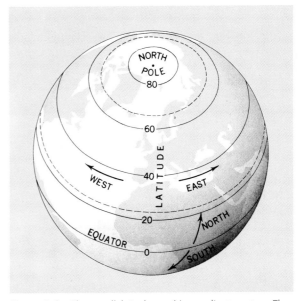

Figure 1.9 The parallels in the earth's coordinate system. They are identified by numbering from the equator to each pole. Parallels define the directions east and west, and their arrangement provides a method for specifying north-south position. Only a few of the infinite number possible are shown here.

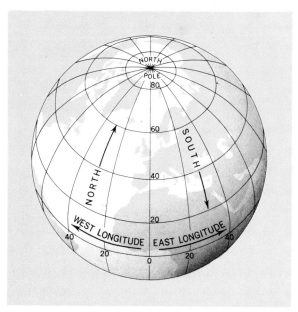

Figure 1.10 *The meridian system of the earth's coordinate graticule defines the directions north and south, and provides a method for specifying east-west position.*

run north and south (Fig. 1.10). A meridian circle is, of course, a great circle, but because of the numbering system used for them, each meridian great circle is treated as two semicircles extending from one pole to the other on opposite sides of the earth.

Latitude. In the earth's coordinate system, the single great circle formed by a matching pair of meridians is divided into quadrants, the points of division being the two poles and the two intersections with the equator. Each meridional quadrant is thus divided into 90° of latitude, and the numbering of the latitude proceeds from the equator (0° Lat) to each pole (90° Lat). Location along a meridian is established by noting its intersection with a particular parallel.

The lengths of the degrees of latitude are not quite identical along a meridian. The latitude of a point is determined by observing, at the point in question, the angular difference between horizontal and the elevation of some celestial body, such as Polaris (the North Star) or the sun. A degree of latitude is, therefore, the distance one must move along a meridian in order to observe a 1° change in this angle. Because of the slight flattening of the

earth in the polar regions, one must go farther along a meridian there to obtain a change of 1°. The first degree of latitude from the equator covers a distance of 110.6 km (68.7 mi), while the first degree away from either pole is 111.7 km long (69.4 mi).

Each degree of latitude is divided into 60 minutes ('), and each minute into 60 seconds ("). An average minute of latitude is about 1 nautical mile and about 1.85 km (1.15 statute mi), and 1 second of latitude is about 31 m (101 ft). The length of the meter is very nearly one ten-millionth of the distance along a great-circle arc from the equator to the pole.

Commonly only a few of the infinite number of meridian and parallel circles are shown on maps, such as those of the multiples of 5° or 10°. Often, however, four important parallels in addition to the equator are emphasized. Because of the inclination and parallelism of the earth's axis with respect to the plane of the ecliptic, the sun at noon appears at different elevations above the horizon in different latitudes. The parallels of 23$\frac{1}{2}$° N and S from the equator are called the *Tropics of Cancer* and *Capricorn*, respectively. They mark the limits of the zone near the equator within which the sun ever appears directly overhead. The parallels of 66$\frac{1}{2}$° N and S from the equator are called the *Arctic* and *Antarctic Circles*, respectively. They mark the limits of the polar area in each hemisphere within which the sun may appear above the horizon continuously for 24 hr or more or, at the same time in the opposite hemisphere, may remain below the horizon for 24 hr or more.

Longitude. Longitude is distance east and west, and it is reckoned in degrees, minutes, and seconds along the parallels. There is no particular meridian marked by nature from which the system of numbering longitude may be started (as the equator is for specifying latitude), since all meridians are exactly alike. In fact, for several centuries many countries designated some meridian that lay within their own borders as 0° Long. So much confusion resulted that the meridian passing through Greenwich Observatory (near London, England) was chosen in 1884 by international agreement to be 0° Long. It is called the *prime meridian*. The degrees of longitude in each parallel are numbered to the east and to the west from the prime meridian to 180° (Fig. 1.10). The prime meridian and the meridian of 180° together make a great circle.

All the parallels, except the equator, are

small circles, and they become progressively smaller poleward. Each parallel, regardless of size, is divided into 360° of longitude, and consequently the length of 1° of longitude decreases with higher latitude. On the equator (which is a great circle), 1° of longitude has about the same length as an average degree of latitude. The following table shows the decreasing lengths of the degrees of longitude at various latitudes from the equator to the pole.

At Latitude of	Length of 1° of longitude	
	Kilometers	Statute miles
0°	111.32	69.17
15°	107.56	66.83
30°	96.49	59.96
45°	78.85	49.00
60°	55.80	34.67
75°	28.90	17.96
90°	0.00	0.00

Direction on the earth. The relative location of places on the earth's surface may be indicated in directional terms as well as by identifying their latitudes and longitudes. The expression of precise direction on the earth is more complex than most people realize, because the earth is a sphere and its coordinate system is spherical instead of rectangular.

The path along a great circle is the most direct course between any two points A and B on the surface of the earth, and it is analogous to the straight line on a plane. The direction from A to B is specified by stating the angle between the meridian at A and the great-circle arc from A to B. The angle may be given either as the bearing of the great circle, e.g., NE, or as an azimuth, that is, a statement of the number of degrees in the angle between the meridian and the great circle, usually reckoned clockwise from north, such as NE = 45° azimuth. Another way of stating the same bearing would be N45°E.

When people think of bearings, they commonly think of the compass. The needle of the compass aligns itself with the forces emanating from that great magnet, the earth.[2] Unfortunately, only in limited areas does the magnetic needle actually parallel the meridian; in most places the needle comes to

[2]Contrary to popular belief, at most places the compass does not "point to the north magnetic pole."

rest at an angle with it. This angle varies considerably from place to place, and the magnitude of the variation at any point is called the *compass declination* of the point. For example, Figure 1.11 shows the lines of equal compass declination in the United States. East of the line marked 0°, the compass has a west declination, i.e., it points west of true north. The compass declination varies widely from place to place, and in both polar regions it is extreme.

Plane Coordinate Systems

Most maps used in the study of physical geography show a selection of the parallels and meridians of the geographical coordinate system. In this century, however, another type of system based on plane coordinates also appears frequently on detailed maps along with the geographical coordinate system. Plane coordinates are very much simpler. In a *plane coordinate system* the curved surface of the earth is first mapped on a plane, and then a simple rectangular coordinate system (like that on cross-section paper) which uses decimals is placed on the map (Fig. 1.12). It is easier to specify a position by its abscissa (distance in the direction of the x axis) and ordinate (distance in the direction of the y axis), that is, by the intersection of decimal rectangular coordinates, than it is to find its latitude and longitude to degrees, minutes, and seconds. However, a spherical surface cannot be transformed to a plane without introducing some kinds of distortion, and therefore plane coordinates can conveniently be extended to only a limited area.

In a rectangular coordinate system the x distances are called *eastings* and the y distances are called *northings*. The decimal divisions and numbering of the map coordinates are fitted to convenient land distances on the individual map, so that one can designate position to the nearest 100,000, 10,000, 1,000, etc., meters or feet. In Figure 1.12, for example, if each square formed by the broken black lines were 100,000 meters on a side, the position of point A could be stated as having an x value of 445 and a y value of 530. This would locate it on the earth's surface within a 1,000-m square. An additional digit added to each value would describe the position of point A within a 100-m square. In giving such a position, one does not identify x or y; instead, a grid reference is always a number with an even number of digits and *the easting value is always the first half* and the northing value the second: thus point A is at 445530. A simple rule is

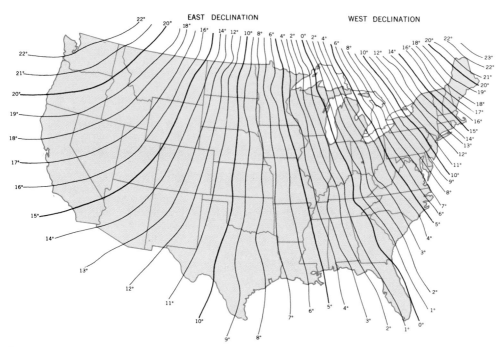

Figure 1.11 Lines of equal magnetic declination in the conterminous United States as mapped in 1965. The magnetic field constantly shifts at a slow rate. For example, the annual change is zero in northern New England, 76 minutes westward in Florida, and less than 3 minutes westward over most of western United States.

that to give or locate a grid reference properly, one must "read right up."

There are many different plane coordinate systems in use by various national surveys, but they all use the principles outlined above. In the United States the modern detailed maps published by the U.S. Geological Survey show two such systems on each map, although older maps do not. The two are known as the *State Plane Coordinate system* and the *Universal Transverse Mercator system (UTM)*. The former employs feet as the unit of distance and is shown by black ticks around the margins of the map, while the UTM system employs meters and is shown by blue ticks. Each state employs a unique State Plane Coordinate system fitted especially to cover

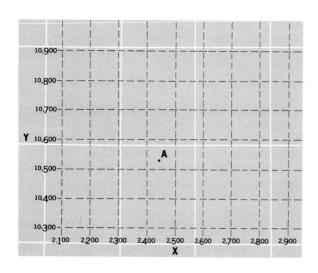

Figure 1.12 A plane coordinate grid (broken black lines) placed over parallels and meridians (solid white lines). The numbers designate the distance of the lines of the plane coordinate grid from its origin in, say, meters, but ordinarily only the bolder digits are used to begin each half of the grid reference. Therefore point A would be described as being at 445530 in the plane coordinate grid (445 easting and 530 northing). Note that magnetic north, geographical north, and grid north might all be different, and consequently, bearings as related to each system could all be different.

only that state. The UTM system is a worldwide
system which divides the earth into 60 zones, each 6°
of longitude wide and having its own system. Consequently, some states fall in two adjacent zones.

Ground Referencing Systems

The geographical coordinate system (latitude and
longitude) is the fundamental basis for establishing
relative location on the earth, but it is cumbersome
for bounding and designating small areas. Throughout the world the most widely used method of describing sections of land is known as *metes and bounds.* In
this method an arbitrary point, such as an iron stake
or other identifiable object, is designated as a point of
beginning. From this point the parcel of land in
question is bounded by a series of lines having given
lengths and true (not compass) directions. In most
parts of the world the bounding lines are more or less
fortuitous. They lead to no consistent regularity in
the pattern of fences, hedges, and roads which commonly separate properties. This may be seen in detailed maps of many areas, including parts of North
America such as Texas and New England.

  In contrast to the essentially unplanned subdivision used in most parts of the earth, some areas
have been subdivided according to a system of rectangular survey, including large parts of the United
States and Canada, where rectangular subdivision
was used in almost all the region lying to the west of
the earlier settled eastern seaboard (Fig. 1.13). All

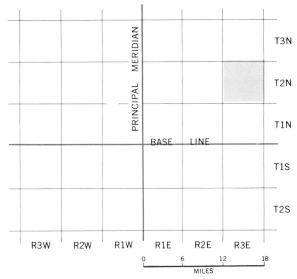

Figure 1.14 The system of designating government-survey
townships by township and range numbers with respect to a
principal meridian and a base line. The colored township is T2N,
R3E.

detailed maps of these areas of the United States
carry lines and numbers referring to this rectangular
survey system, which is described briefly below.

U.S. Public Land Survey system. This system
employs a framework based on a selection of approximately north-south and east-west lines. The north-
south lines are called *principal meridians*, and the
east-west ones are called *base lines* (Fig. 1.13). Based
on these lines the land is divided into essentially
rectangular blocks called *government* or *survey townships*, which are approximately 6 mi on a side. The
locations of the blocks are indicated by numbered
townships (north-south) and ranges (east-west), as
shown in Figure 1.14.[3]

  The ranges are 6-mile-wide north-south
strips or columns of land, each numbered to the east
or west of a particular principal meridian, and each
range is divided into a row or tier of townships by
east-west lines 6 miles apart, each township being

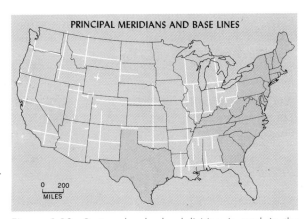

Figure 1.13 Rectangular land subdivision is used in the
light-colored areas of the United States. The principal meridians
and base lines of the Public Land Survey system are shown in
white. The system is also used in Alaska.

[3]But note that the civil, organized towns, townships, or
incorporated municipalities into which counties in the United States are divided are units of political administration,
and they may or may not coincide with survey townships,
which exist for purposes of land identification.

numbered north or south from its base line (Fig. 1.14). Owing to the fact that north-south lines converge poleward, certain corrections, offsets, and allowances must be made.

The usual survey township is divided into 36 sections, each approximately 1 mile square. The sections are numbered, beginning at the northeastern corner and ending at the southeastern, as shown in Figure 1.15. The locations of the township and section corners were originally marked on the ground by a stake, stone, mound, tree, or other device.[4]

[4]Since each section is supposed to be 1 mile square, its area should be 640 acres. The section may be divided into quarters, each containing 160 acres, and the quarter sections may be further divided into parcels of 80 or 40 acres each. The quarter sections are indicated by the points of the compass. To describe and locate a place, therefore, one might say that it is in the NE 1/4 of SW 1/4 of Sec 20, T44N, R5E, of the particular principal meridian to which the range number referred. This statement would then be followed by the names of the administrative districts—for example, the township or city, county, and state in which the area is located.

Wherever such a basic survey framework has been employed, it has left an indelible imprint on the landscape—a pattern of patchwork rectangularity easily seen from the air (Fig. 1.16). It is even reflected in road maps, since the minor roads (along with field boundaries) tend to be oriented with the cardinal directions.

Maps

Maps are a reduction of earth space and allow the scientist to bring selected aspects of a large area, or even of the entire earth, into view at once. This operation is as necessary for students of earth science as is microscopic enlargement for some other scientists. With the aid of maps, the geographer may observe how individual earth phenomena vary from place to place, develop hypotheses concerning the association of environmental factors, and, in general, study the distribution, organization, and spatial correlation of the elements and processes that comprise the earth system.

Maps are nearly infinite in variety but their construction generally conforms to basic rules. Students of geography should learn to "read" this sort of graphic display. Specifically, they should become familiar with three basic characteristics of every map: (1) the *map scale*, that is, the relation between the various dimensions on a map and the corresponding dimensions on the earth, (2) the system of *map projection* employed in transforming the spherical surface of the earth to the plane surface of the map sheet, and (3) the *map symbols*, that is, the various kinds of marks employed to represent the earth elements on the map.[5]

Map Scale

A globe represents the simplest kind of reduced representation of the earth. The size of the globe can be compared to the size of the earth and the relationship of the corresponding dimensions is expressed as a ratio. This ratio is the *scale* of the globe. For example,

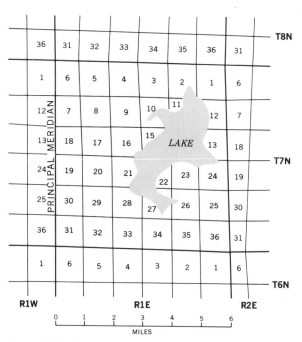

Figure 1.15 The sections are numbered within a township, in this case of the township T7N, R1E. Because of survey problems, sections are not always 1 sq mile.

[5]Cartography, or mapmaking, is a field of study in itself. Only the barest fundamentals necessary for using maps can be treated in a book devoted to physical geography. For the student who wishes more information, additional references on cartography are listed at the end of this chapter.

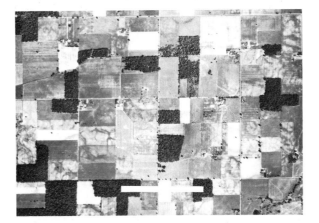

Figure 1.16 Contrasting landscapes, as seen from the air, that have resulted from rectangular and nonrectangular survey. These two areas, otherwise almost alike, are in central Ohio. *(Based upon Norman J. W. Thrower. Original Survey and Land Subdivision . . . Monograph 4, Assoc. Amer. Geographers and Rand McNally & Company, Chicago, 1966.)*

the earth has a diameter of about 500,000,000 in., so that a globe with a diameter of 25 in. has a scale ratio of 25 to 500,000,000—or, more simply, of 1 to 20,000,000. The ratio is, of course, independent of any kind of unit, since it is equally applicable to inches, centimeters, feet, etc. This ratio is commonly called the *Representative Fraction*, or *RF* for short.

Flat maps, like globes, always have a scale relationship to the area being portrayed. Sometimes the scale is given in the form of the RF; occasionally it is expressed in words—for instance, "One inch represents one mile," but most often it is indicated by a

"graphic scale," that is, by a measured line showing the map lengths of earth distances, as in Figure 1.15. A map may have any scale, but the convenience of using round numbers and the particular advantages of some map dimension–earth dimension relationships have given rise to a number of preferred scales. Some of the more common maps scales are these:

RF	1 cm represents	1 in. represents
1:10,000	100 m	833.3 ft
1:20,000	200 m	1,666.6 ft
1:24,000	240 m	2,000 ft
1:25,000	250 m	2,083 ft
1:50,000	500 m	4,167 ft
1:62,500	625 m	5,208 ft
1:63,360	634 m	1.00 mi
1:100,000	1.00 km	1.58 mi
1:500,000	5.00 km	7.89 mi
1:1,000,000	10.00 km	15.78 mi

Maps are often described as being large-, medium-, or small-scale; the distinction is important. Large-scale maps are those in which the fraction stated by the *RF* is relatively large; for instance, the fraction $1/25,000$ is twenty times larger than the fraction $1/500,000$. As a rough guide, one can say that small maps of large areas, such as the maps of the world in this book, are small-scale maps, while large maps of small areas, such as topographic maps, are large-scale maps. Of course, there are always those in between, which are classed as medium-scale.

The significant differences among small-, medium-, and large-scale maps are due both to the differences in the amount of information they can show, and also to the lesser amount of detail (greater degree of generalization) that can be shown on smaller-scale maps. Small maps of states or countries, to say nothing of the world as a whole, are highly generalized and should be read as such.

The scale of a globe is the same all over, since it is just a straightforward reduction of the earth. But when the spherical surface of the earth is transformed to the plane of a flat map, the scale will be reduced unequally. Whatever the *RF* or graphic scale may "say" on a map, it can never be precisely that ratio everywhere on the map in every direction. The differences are generally insignificant and unnoticeable in large-scale maps, but they become very important in small-scale ones.

Map Projections

A map projection is a system of transforming the spherical surface of the earth to a plane on which to make a map. Some surfaces can be bent into others without modifying the geometric relationships among the points on the surfaces. Thus a cylinder or a cone may be cut and then laid out flat to form a plane, and neither distance nor directional relationships across the surface will be changed. A spherical surface, however, cannot be transformed to a plane without differential stretching and shrinking. Thus all map projections result in changing the scale unequally and, consequently, in distorting the distance and directional relationships among points on the earth. Even so, the many practical advantages of a flat map over a bulky globe usually far outweigh the disadvantages that come from differential stretching and compression.

There are an infinite number of ways one can distribute the deformation which is inescapable in a flat map. Not very many ways of distributing the deformation are in common use, however. Map projections may be designed so as to have one or more specific useful characteristics, each of which is called a *property*. Since the properties of a projection may not be indicated in its name, sometimes the map reader must consult a treatise on cartography to find a description. The two most widely employed and important properties are those known as *equivalence* (or *equal-area*) and *conformality*. They are mutually exclusive; that is, they cannot exist together in the same system of projection.

Equivalence. An *equal-area* projection is one in which at any point the maximum stretching in one direction is balanced by a reciprocal compression in the direction perpendicular to it. The consequence is that the surface area of any region on the map is shown in its correct size in relation to the surface area of any other region.

Over most of an equal-area projection the scale is different in different directions at each point, and this causes shapes of areas, even small ones, to be deformed. Indeed, equivalent projections always de-

form shapes, in some instances to a very large degree. Various equivalent projections arrange the scale departures in different ways so that the deformation may be concentrated in the less-used portions of the map. The map reader must be alert to make allowances for this. Figure 1.17, the equal-area map projection used for most of the world maps in this book, shows how the greatest deformation of shape has been relegated to the peripheral areas of the map.

Conformality. The property of maintaining correct directional relationships around each point, called *conformality*, is valuable in maps on which directions at points are important—for example, maps used for navigation, surveying, or plotting wind directions. To obtain conformality, the scale is arranged in such a way that, whatever the scale may be at any point on the projection, it is the same in all directions at that point.

Shapes of small areas are well represented on conformal projections, but the shapes of large areas are considerably deformed, as they are on all projections. Furthermore, just as equivalent projections must modify angular relationships, so conformal projections must modify size relationships.

Map Symbols

A large variety of marks, colors, and shadings is employed on maps to represent the various earth phenomena. Most of these symbols are self-explanatory or may easily be deduced from the names on the map. For example, coastlines, roads, cities, houses, shaded terrain, lakes, swamps, and so on, are usually rather obvious, but if not, they may be identified by reference to a legend or description of the meanings of the marks, or *conventional signs*, as they are commonly called. Even such lines as boundaries of various sorts or survey section lines may be identified by the enclosed names or numbers.

Much of the information placed on a map must be generalized—that is, selected, simplified, and graded as to the visual emphasis it should be given relative to the other data. Therefore the map reader must be careful not to "read into" the map symbols a greater degree of accuracy, precision, or prominence than is warranted by their nature or by the scale of the map. For example, many of the maps in this book indicate the distribution of things by showing abrupt

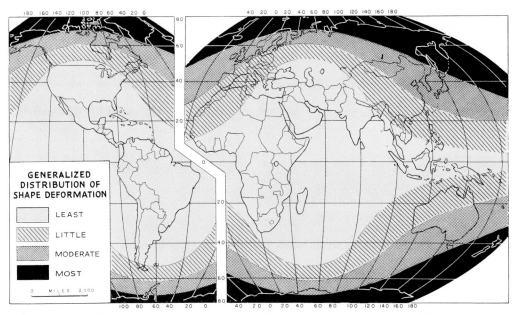

Figure 1.17 The flat polar equal-area projection used for many of the world maps in this book, showing the areas where the shape deformation has been concentrated. The darker the shading, the more the shape deformation.

changes in coloring or shading, or merely by using lines to separate areas. Yet such changes and boundaries frequently lie in transition zones and represent only average conditions. Similarly, coastlines, boundaries, landform regions, soil areas, average rainfall amounts, and other such information must be greatly simplified on most small-scale maps.

Isarithms. One of the frequently used, but not self-explanatory, symbolic ways to show distributions of quantity on maps is by means of successive lines, each of which is drawn through all points having a particular numerical value (Fig. 1.18). Such lines are called *isarithms*, *isopleths*, or *isolines*. They are used to delineate the surface configuration of a variety of distributions. Isarithms employed in connection with a particular class of phenomena are frequently identified by combining the prefix *iso* with a term derived from the type of data. Hence one speaks of *isotherms* (temperature) and *isobars* (air pressure).

Most isarithmic maps should be read in much the same way that one reads a contour map, which is a map showing the configuration of the land surface by means of isarithms of elevation.

Contours. *Contours* are widely used on large-scale topographic maps. A particular contour line on a map passes through all points which have the same elevation above sea level.

The idea of contour lines (isarithms), the significance of their comparative spacing, and their

Figure 1.18 An isarithmic map showing the variation over the United States of the number of days with snow cover. In the northeastern part of the map where the interval is 30 days, the closer together the lines are, the steeper is the gradient.

arrangements and shapes can be clarified by a simple illustration. In an open tank one may place an oval, hill-like mound of modeling clay approximately $6\frac{1}{2}$ in. high, steeply sloping at one end and gently sloping at the other (Fig. 1.19). To make the hill more realistic, a pair of gullies can be added on one side. If 6 in. of water is then permitted to flow into the tank, less than 1 in. of the mound will protrude. The position of the horizontal edge of the water (the shore) upon the clay can be marked with a sharp point. Next the water level can be lowered by 1-in. stages and the position of each stage similarly marked in the clay. The lowest will be everywhere 1 in. above the bottom of the tank, the next 2 in., and so on to the sixth, as shown in Figure 1.19. These marks will appear as contour lines on the mound. If the mound is viewed from directly above, as is the case with a map, the arrangement of the contour lines will look like that shown in Figure 1.20. On this small model, the successive water levels, and therefore the contour lines, have a vertical separation of 1 in. This is the contour interval.

The model in Figure 1.19, the contours in Figure 1.20, and the map and drawing in Figure 1.21 illustrate some general rules for the interpretation of any kind of isarithmic map. The most important is that isarithms show *gradient*, namely, the change or difference in value per unit of horizontal distance. Thus where the slope of the surface is steep—i.e., where the gradient is high—the isarithms are close together on the map, and they become more widely spaced as the slope or gradient becomes less. It will also be seen that the contour lines follow along the side of a gully, cross its bottom, and return along its

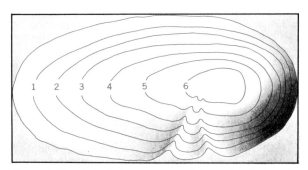

Figure 1.20   A shaded contour map of the model hill shown in Fig. 1.19. The contour interval is 1 in.

other side. One may then observe that when isarithms cross a trough or valley in a distribution, they do so by forming a bend whose closed end points in the upslope direction.

The principles just stated—(1) the closer the isarithms, the steeper the gradient, and (2) successive bent isarithms pointing upslope indicate a trough—are applicable no matter what phenomenon is being represented.

Topographic Maps

For some 200 years people have been carefully surveying the land surface with its complex of natural and cultural phenomena and have been preparing detailed maps from these data. Such maps are called *topographic* maps. They represent the basic geographical data from which many other maps of smaller scale are derived. Topographic maps are a prerequisite to the careful scientific study of the physical geography of an area. So far, perhaps half the land areas of the earth have been adequately mapped. Because it is a more difficult operation, the detailed mapping of the sea bottom is not nearly as far advanced.

Hundreds of series of topographic maps are produced by the national surveys of the different countries. They are made on a variety of projections, at a multitude of scales, and with somewhat different systems of symbols.

United States topographic maps.   At present the three most commonly used scales in the topographic maps of the United States are 1:24,000, 1:62,500, and

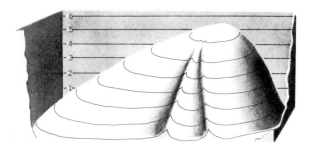

Figure 1.19   An imitation hill with two gullies, which has been modeled from clay and placed in a tank. The colored lines show the successive positions of the horizontal "shorelines" if water in the tank were lowered 1 in. at a time.

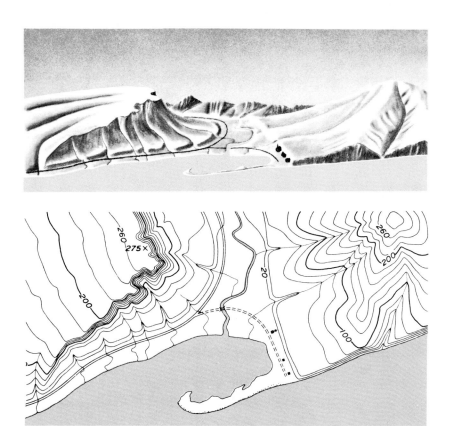

Figure 1.21 A perspective view of a land surface with the corresponding topographic map below it. Note the spacings and shapes of the contours in relation to the surface configuration. *(Modified from U.S. Geological Survey.)*

1:250,000. (Maps of Alaska are 1:63,360.) The standard detailed maps are the 1:24,000 for a quadrangle of 7.5 min of latitude and longitude and the 1:62,500.

      The maps are printed in colors. Black is commonly used for features classed as cultural, i.e., features which have human origin—such as roads, houses, towns, place names, boundary lines, and parallels and meridians. All water features, both natural and man-made—such as canals, streams, marshes, lakes, and seas—are blue. Red is used for built-up areas and sometimes for survey lines and roads. The contour lines and other symbols relating to the elevation of the land surface are shown in brown, and woodlands are occasionally shown in green. In recent years shading has been applied to the maps in order to provide a realistic impression of the terrain.

      In addition to the conventional topographic maps described above, a new kind of topographic map is being produced for selected areas. These are called *orthophotomaps* and display the earth's surface as it appears to the aerial camera with added line information, such as contours and boundaries.

      Each topographic map contains a place title, parallels and meridians, plane grid coordinates, and (where they exist) the section and township lines of the Public Land Survey. Each also gives a scale and a statement of the contour interval used on that map. The contour intervals employed usually are 10, 20, 50, or 100 ft, or even 1 ft; but on maps of rugged mountains, intervals are sometimes as much as 250 ft. Both the map scale and the contour interval of each map must be read and considered carefully.[6]

[6]U.S. topographic maps are "going metric" but the conversion is costly and, by necessity, slow.

Time on the Earth

The movement of the earth relative to the sun and the other stars provides the basis for two systems of measuring time. One is called *clock time* and is reckoned with respect to the period of average rotation relative to the sun. The other system of reckoning time is called *calendar time* and is reckoned with respect to the period of average revolution about the sun.

Clock time. The period of one average rotation of the earth is divided into 24 hr. Therefore the earth rotates through 1° every 4 min, or 15° every hour. Midday, or noon, at a place is when the sun reaches its highest point (culmination) there in its daily passage, and at that instant it is already 1 hr later (1:00 P.M.) 15° to the east and it lacks 1 hr of noon (it is 11:00 A.M.) 15° to the west. For the moment, it is noon on the meridian of that place only; but it is noon on that meridian from the North Pole to the South Pole. Four minutes later, it will be noon on the meridian 1° farther west.

In the past, each place set its clock by the time of its own meridian, and this time was called *apparent solar time* or, more commonly, *sun time.* When relatively rapid travel grew possible during the nineteenth century, the multitude of different local times became increasingly confusing, and more and more attempts were made to standardize time. Individual systems of standard time were adopted by various countries and railroads, and ultimately in 1884 general agreement was reached that the meridian of Greenwich (just outside London, England) would be the meridian on which a worldwide system of standard time would be based.

The system calls for all parts of a north-south zone 15° wide to adopt the solar time of the central meridian of that zone. Changing the clock would then be necessary only when crossing the boundary of a zone, and each change would be exactly 1 hr. The clock would be set forward (i.e., later, as from 3:00 to 4:00) in traveling east, and back (i.e., earlier, as from 3:00 to 2:00) in traveling west. For convenience the zones commonly are bounded by irregular lines approximating meridians, the locations of which are determined by administrative action. Figure 1.22 shows the present standard time zones of the United States as established by the Department of Transportation.

Figure 1.22 Standard-time zones in the conterminous United States as of 1972, as defined by the U.S. Department of Transportation.

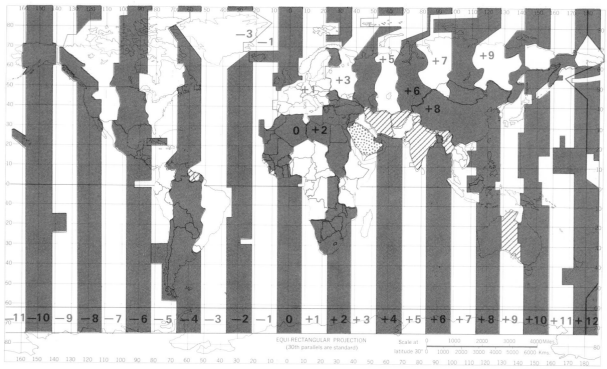

Figure 1.23   Simplified map showing world standard time zones. The times in the circles show the number of hours later (+) or earlier (−) the time of each 15° zone is in relation to Greenwich Mean Time (mean solar time at 0° longitude). The lined areas differ from the appropriate zone by a fraction, usually a half hour. The dotted area in Saudi Arabia uses sun time, i.e., clocks are set each day. The solid brown line at the far right is the Date Line.

For the whole earth there should be 24 standard-time zones, each extending from pole to pole and each differing from Greenwich time by an integral number of hours. In practice it is not so simple (Fig. 1.23). A few zones employ standard meridians that are not multiples of 15 and therefore do not differ from Greenwich time by exact hours, and many zones make regular or irregular use of daylight saving time (i.e., clocks set ahead, as from 1:00 to 2:00). Consequently, the map of world time zones related to Greenwich time is complicated and changes frequently.

Calendar time.   One rotation of the earth relative to the sun is termed *one day*, and the completion of one average orbit is termed a *year*. Because the number of rotations during one orbit includes a fraction of a day (about ¼), minor adjustments (leap years) must regularly be made in the calendar so as to

keep the equinoxes and solstices at about the same time on the calendar.

The modern calendar of the Western world which divides the year into 12 months is a rather mixed-up heritage of many modifications during the past 2,000 years. For example, September, October, November, and December are *named* for the seventh, eighth, ninth, and tenth months, but they are now actually the ninth, tenth, eleventh, and twelfth months. Also, the year now "begins" with January being the first month rather than March (the spring equinox in the Northern Hemisphere) as it used to be; consequently, the odd day of leap year is now added to February, our second month, rather than at the end of the year. Originally established by Julius Caesar and changed and adjusted several times since, the plan now known as the *Gregorian calendar* has generally been adopted, although the U.S.S.R. did not accept it until 1918.

The date line. The concept of the day at various places on the earth at the same instant is confusing. For example, if one assumes it is noon on Wednesday to an observer at Greenwich, then it must be midnight on the opposite side of the earth 180° away. But midnight between what two days? If the observer were to imagine the times of day at various places to his or her *west*, they would of course be progressively earlier in that day—Wednesday, until at 180° away it would seem to be midnight between the observer's Tuesday already past and his or her Wednesday to be. If, on the other hand, one were to conceive of the times at points to one's *east*, then at the same 180° away it would turn out to be midnight between one's Wednesday past and Thursday yet to be. If two people were actually to go east and west in this fashion, their personal calendars actually would turn out to be one day different. This caused great confusion in the past when people began to travel.

The solution may be visualized if one remembers that if someone makes an east-west circuit of the earth, that person will either add or cancel a day (one rotation of the earth relative to the sun),

depending on the direction he or she travels. Therefore that person will either gain or lose one day relative to the calendar of the people who remained in one place.

By international agreement the days are specified to begin and end at the Date Line, a line extending from pole to pole in the area of the Pacific approximating the 180th meridian (Fig. 1.24). Only if one crosses this line is it necessary to adjust the calendar: one adds a day—i.e., repeats a day—when crossing it going eastward, and one drops a day—e.g., Wednesday would be followed by Friday—when crossing it going westward.

REVIEW QUESTIONS

1. How might the geographical study of water in an area differ from its study by a hydrologist?
2. What are some illustrations of different levels of generalization?
3. What is meant by a geographical "pattern of distribution"? Give local, regional, and worldwide examples.
4. Suggest examples of differences between regions which result in an exchange.
5. Describe the essential elements of some simple systems such as space heating or cooling.
6. Try to analyze the sources, flows, and conversions of energy in some systems.
7. Give examples of man as an integral part of feedback in some human-natural system, such as water impoundment for hydroelectric production or flood control.
8. The length of a degree of a great circle which includes the poles is not the same everywhere along that great circle. Where is the degree longer and shorter, and why?
9. Passage through the circle of illumination is faster near the equator than it is farther poleward, and hence the length of the twilight period is shorter near the equator. Why?
10. The lengths of day and night are always the same (12 hr) at the equator. Why?
11. The Northern Hemisphere is closer to the sun in winter than in summer, yet it is colder in winter. Why?
12. What advantages do flat maps have over globes?
13. Which is a larger scale, 1:50,000 or 1:250,000? Why?

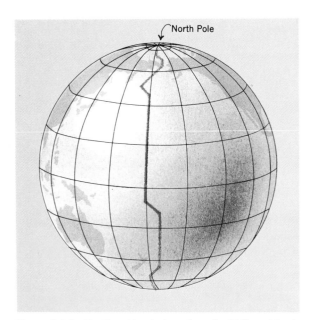

Figure 1.24 The Date Line deviates from the 180° meridian in order not to divide inconveniently into two calendar days those areas or island groups that lie along it.

14. If one were to follow the direction northeast on the earth, what would the course be like and where would it end?

15. How do maps help the scientist to observe things?

16. If it is 2:00 P.M. Wednesday at 90° West Longitude, what time and day is it at 90° East Longitude?

17. Describe the periods of daylight and darkness that would occur to people in an airplane or space vehicle that could orbit the earth at the equator in exactly 24 hours if they went westward. If they went eastward. What would happen to their calendars? How long would their "days" and "nights" be?

SELECTED REFERENCES

Department of Transportation. *Standard Time in the United States*. U.S. Government Printing Office, Washington, D.C., 1970. A history of standard and daylight saving time in the United States.

Dury, G. H. *Map Interpretation*. Sir Isaac Pitman & Sons, Ltd., London, 1972. Individual examples of analysis of topographic maps employing British maps. Emphasis on landforms.

Greenhood, D. *Mapping*. The University of Chicago Press, Chicago, 1971. A readable, general introduction to maps and map use. Well illustrated.

Grids and Grid References. U.S. Army TM 5-241-1 Headquarters, Department of the Army, Washington, D.C., 1967. Thorough explanation of the Universal Transverse Mercator (UTM) and Universal Polar Stereographic (UPS) grid systems.

Hewitt, K., and F. K. Hare. *Man and Environment*. Commission on College Geography, Association of American Geographers, Washington, D.C., 1973. Conceptual ideas in an approach to man-environment problems.

Maling, D. H. *Coordinate Systems and Map Projections*. George Philip & Son, Ltd., London, 1973. A basic treatment of the subject of coordinate transformations; moderately mathematical. An excellent reference.

Mitchell, H. C., and L. G. Simmons. *The State Coordinate Systems*. U.S. Coast and Geodetic Survey, Special Publication No. 235. U.S. Government Printing Office, Washington, D.C., 1945.

Robinson, A. H., and R. D. Sale. *Elements of Cartography*, 3d ed. John Wiley & Sons, Inc., New York, 1969. Fourth ed. in process. Covers the fundamentals of modern mapmaking. Useful reference for the beginning student.

An Introduction to the Atmosphere

While people live on the land surface of planet earth and occasionally travel on the surface of its oceans, they constantly live within its atmosphere. Their very existence is dependent on the quality of the air in which they live, and their way of life is in many ways influenced by the climate and weather of the atmosphere. In fact, among the elements that comprise the natural environment, climate is of singular importance, since it plays such a vital role in influencing the characteristics of the vegetation, soil, and water resources of a region. In addition, it is of great importance in sculpturing surface landform features. Areas with similar climates are likely to have significant resemblances in vegetation, soils, and, in some cases, terrain features. In turn, the characteristics of the soil and vegetation and the roughness of the land influence the weather and climate of the atmosphere above them.

In oceanic areas the prevailing wind systems are the major driving force for the great ocean current systems. The oceans in turn act as an enormous stabilizer of temperature and are the major source of the atmosphere's moisture. Thus the atmospheric system continually and intimately interacts with the oceans and the surface of the continents. It is at this interface, where the land-water surface is in contact with the atmosphere, that life has evolved and has itself become an intricate part of the interactions.

The Vertical Extent of the Atmosphere

The atmosphere is a mixture of gases surrounding the land-sea surface of the spherical earth. Unlike the continents and oceans, the atmosphere has no definite upper surface; rather, it thins with increasing height, eventually fading into the extremely thin outer atmosphere of the sun. While the spherical earth has a radius of nearly 6,400 km (4,000 mi), about 99 percent of the mass of the atmosphere is confined to the first 32 km (20 mi) above the earth. The atmosphere, which is bound to the earth by gravitation, is compressed, especially in its lower layers, by the weight of the air above. Thus in its lower portion the density of the atmosphere decreases more rapidly with increasing height than farther aloft. In fact, one-half of the mass of the atmosphere is found below a height of about 5,500 m (18,000 ft), an elevation which is exceeded by many mountaintops. On the other hand, traces of atmospheric gases along with charged parti-

Figure 2.1   Photo from *Gemini V*, August 22, 1965, looking south over Florida. The thin, bright fringe (above the dashed line) is produced by sunlight being scattered from the atmosphere and represents the thickness of the atmosphere. Note that the cumulus clouds are much more evident over the land. Some cumulonimbus are present in the upper part of the photo south of Florida. *(Courtesy NASA.)*

cles emitted from the sun and trapped within the earth's magnetic field extend to distances of 65,000 km (40,000 mi) and more above the earth's surface. However, at these great elevations the distance be-

tween particles is so large that the density of the atmosphere is less than that of the best vacuum achieved in laboratories. The shallowness of the main mass of the atmosphere is suggested by Figure 2.1, in which the thin, bright fringe extending above the earth's horizon represents the significant mass of the atmosphere. The molecules of the atmospheric gases scatter light from the sun, producing the bright fringe. If the photo were in color, the bright fringe would be blue, the color of the sky. Above the main mass of the atmosphere is the blackness of space.

Atmospheric layers.   The atmosphere can be divided into distinct layers. The more significant layers and the change of temperature with height within them are shown in Figure 2.2. The lowest layer, extending from the earth's surface to about 8 km (5 mi) above polar regions and 16 km (10 mi) above the tropics, is the *troposphere*. Its upper boundary is called the *tropopause*. The troposphere is a region in which the temperature normally decreases with height and in which the wind speed usually increases with height. Practically all of the atmosphere's water vapor is found in the troposphere. It is the layer in

which weather occurs and is thus the layer with which people are most directly concerned.

Above the troposphere are a number of other recognizable layers, but their combined mass is considerably less than the mass of the troposphere. The *stratosphere*, in which the temperature increases with height, extends from the tropopause to an elevation of about 50 km (30 mi). The warm layer near 50 km is the result of the photochemical absorption of sunlight, especially its ultraviolet portion. The photochemical processes produce and maintain the gas ozone (O_3), which shields us from the intense and harmful ultraviolet radiation of the sun. Ozone is such an effective absorber of ultraviolet radiation that the maximum heating occurs near the top of the ozone layer. Between 50 and 80 km is the *mesosphere*, a layer in which the temperature decreases with height. Above the mesosphere are layers in which the relative number of charged particles (protons or electrons) is large. The *ionosphere*, extending from 80 to 480 km (50 to 300 mi), reflects certain radio waves and is thus important in long-distance radio communications. Above the ionosphere is found the *magnetosphere*, a region which has been explored only since 1958 by satellite probes. Its upper limit is not clearly defined, but over the equator it extends to at least 65,000 km (40,000 mi).

At times when the sun emits large quantities of charged particles, many of the particles become trapped in the magnetosphere and are funneled toward lower parts of the atmosphere over the earth's magnetic poles. At lower elevations, most frequently near 100 km (60 mi), their collisions with molecules of atmospheric gases cause the molecules to emit light, producing the aurora borealis (northern lights) in the Northern Hemisphere and aurora australis (southern lights) in the Southern Hemisphere.

Composition of the Atmosphere

Through much of its depth the earth's atmosphere is a uniform mixture of permanent gases called *dry air* plus varying amounts of water vapor and both inorganic and organic impurities such as dust, smoke, and pollen. Pure dry air is invisible and odorless. By volume it consists of about 78 percent nitrogen, 21 percent oxygen, 0.93 percent argon, and 0.03 percent carbon dioxide and traces of numerous other gases.

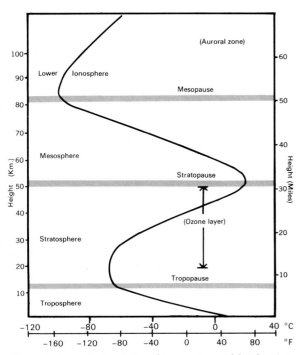

Figure 2.2   Typical variation of temperature with height. Note that the major atmospheric layers are defined according to whether the temperature decreases or increases with height.

Water vapor, which is also an invisible and odorless gas, is highly variable in amount, ranging from practically nothing in the high, cold regions of the atmosphere to as much as 3 or 4 percent of the total volume of air in hot, humid regions. Since water vapor is added to the atmosphere through evaporation of water from the earth's surface, it is concentrated in the lower atmosphere. The importance of water vapor is far greater than its percentage would indicate, for it not only is the source of clouds and precipitation but it also absorbs some solar radiation and is a very effective absorber of radiant heat emitted from the earth's surface. Furthermore, the large amount of heat that is used to evaporate surface water is released within the atmosphere when the water vapor condenses to form clouds and precipitation.

Some of the atmospheric impurities play an important role in the formation of clouds and precipitation by acting as nuclei around which condensation occurs. However, most other impurities, particularly those introduced by the burning of fossil fuels, are detrimental to life. Because of the growth of industrial activity, the use of the automobile, and, in general, the expanding population, the amount of impurities has greatly increased since the early part of the century. Atmospheric pollution, which has become one of the major problems of our time, will be discussed in Chapter 4 in terms of the weather and climatic conditions which lead to its concentration.

Origin of Atmospheric Gases

Evidence from the physical and biological sciences indicates that the development of the atmosphere and the evolution of life have been intimately related. Sometime in its early history, perhaps 4 or 5 billion years ago, the earth was without an atmosphere, much as the moon is today. During the time of its formation the earth may have been enveloped in an atmosphere rich in gases such as hydrogen and helium; but if such an atmosphere did exist, it was driven off to space because of the heating that accompanied consolidation of the planet. It is thought that our present atmosphere had its beginning with the volcanic release of gases formed in the earth's crust, a process which is called *out-gassing*. Analysis of the composition of present-day volcanic gases shows water vapor to be the dominant gas but with substantial amounts of carbon dioxide and nitrogen also present. From an early atmosphere with such a composition, enormous rains could be expected to fall, gradually filling the ocean basins. Much of the carbon dioxide either was dissolved in the ocean waters or combined with earth materials to form carbonate rocks, leaving nitrogen the dominant gas in the residual atmosphere. Since oxygen (O_2) is not present in volcanic gases, atmospheric oxygen must be of secondary origin.

Atmospheric oxygen. The original source of atmospheric oxygen (O_2) is not definitely known. The breakdown of water molecules (H_2O) in the oceans or water vapor molecules (also H_2O) in the atmosphere by the ultraviolet portion of sunlight may have been an early source of some small amounts of oxygen. However, the presence of even a very small supply of atmospheric oxygen leads to the formation of ozone (O_3), a gas which screens out much of the ultraviolet radiation. Thus the breakdown of water molecules by ultraviolet radiation is self-limiting. The fermentation process associated with some primitive bacteria may also have contributed to the early production of traces of oxygen. Both of these processes, however, were probably responsible for only a very small fraction of the present level of atmospheric oxygen.

The major portion of the oxygen is attributed to green plants. About three billion years ago the first green plants (algae) developed in the oceans, and through photosynthesis carbon dioxide and water were consumed and oxygen was released to the oceans, with some escaping to the atmosphere. By about 400 million years ago plant life spread to the land, and the rate of oxygen production increased. Since about as much oxygen is consumed in the decay of organic substances as they originally produced, it appears that only through the burial of vast amounts of organic matter could the quantity of atmospheric oxygen have significantly increased.

Coal and oil deposits represent buried organic matter. An interesting aspect of the photosynthesis hypothesis as the primary source of oxygen is that the estimated quantities of coal and oil and all forms of buried organic matter can account for only a small percentage of the present oxygen content of the atmosphere. At the present time there appears to be a balance between the production of oxygen by plants and its use by animal life and other oxidation processes. Thus there may exist vastly larger quantities of buried organic material than are known, or the present quantity of atmospheric oxygen was achieved by processes other than photosynthesis.

Atmospheric nitrogen.   The present-day nitrogen level of the atmosphere is also maintained by a balance between processes which deplete the supply and others which renew it. Lightning discharges and some plants remove atmospheric nitrogen. On the other hand, volcanic gases and the action of certain bacteria, which break down nitrogen compounds in the soil and seas, add nitrogen to the atmosphere. Thus the evolution and maintenance of both atmospheric oxygen and nitrogen provide examples of the complex ecological system which is responsible for the unique physical composition of the earth's atmosphere.

The Future Atmosphere

Since 1900 there has been about a 15 percent increase in the level of atmospheric carbon dioxide; however, the total carbon dioxide content is but a small fraction of 1 percent of dry air. The rise is attributed to the great increase in combustion resulting from the rapid industrialization of the earth. Since carbon dioxide is an effective absorber of the radiation (heat) given off by the earth, there is some concern that a continued increase in the carbon dioxide content may lead to a rather drastic warming of the earth's climate. On the other hand, there is speculation that the increased dirtiness of the polluted atmosphere causes more sunlight to be reflected and thus causes a general cooling of the climate. However, there are many factors—some human-induced, others natural—that can cause changes in the climate, and the role of each is not yet adequately understood to predict what the future climate will be.

It is equally difficult to predict the future composition of the atmosphere. While human activity may play an important role in future changes, the potential for naturally induced changes is far greater, particularly with regard to the major constituents, nitrogen and oxygen. It appears that the greatest influence of human activity on the composition of the future atmosphere may be in adding impurities and changing the amounts of the less abundant, but important, gases such as carbon dioxide and ozone. Recent investigations have suggested that supersonic aircraft which operate within the ozone layer and certain aerosols from spray cans may interfere with ozone production. Although the aerosols are released at the bottom of the atmosphere, they gradually mix upward, eventually reaching the ozone layer.

Elements of Weather and Climate

People have always been acutely aware of the condition of their atmospheric environment. Primitive people, unclothed and often without shelter, were especially vulnerable to the extremes of temperature and also to wind and precipitation. Modern people, clothed and often living in centrally heated and air-conditioned houses, are well sheltered, yet they, too, are affected by the condition of the atmosphere. Only an inch of snow falling, with the temperature just below freezing, during the evening rush hour can cause traffic jams on the main arteries of a city. The weak winds and sinking air associated with a stagnant high-pressure weather system can lead to dangerously high concentrations of atmospheric pollutants in urban areas. The approach of a hurricane may result in the evacuation of the entire population from low-lying coastal areas, or the sighting of a tornado funnel cloud may send the inhabitants of a community to their basements for shelter. Certainly modern society, with its complex technology, is as susceptible to the condition of the atmosphere as were its ancient forerunners.

Weather

Weather is the condition of the atmosphere at a given time and place; it is described by a combination of several weather elements, which are also called *atmospheric variables*. To our senses the most obvious are usually temperature, sunlight, moisture (humidity and precipitation), and the wind. To these must be added atmospheric pressure, which is of great significance in determining the characteristics of the other elements. The distribution of atmospheric pressure largely determines the direction and speed of the wind, and it is the wind which carries air masses of contrasting temperature and moisture to a locality. Although air moves mainly horizontally, it also moves very slightly upward in some areas and downward in other places. The regions in which the motion is upward are likely to be regions in which there are cloudiness and precipitation, while the regions of downward motion have fair skies.

Weather varies from day to day and from place to place. On a given day there may exist greatly varying weather conditions within an area as large as the United States, for example, warm and humid in Texas, snow and moderately cold in the Midwest, and clear and very cold in Montana. These widely varying conditions can be portrayed on a weather map, such as that shown in Figure 4.20. On the map the weather elements are plotted for many stations for a certain time. The map provides a *synoptic* ("as seen together") view of the weather across the country at a fixed time. The weather conditions are closely related to the location of various regions of high or low atmospheric pressure. These pressure patterns and their ac- companying weather are constantly changing, some- times rapidly, at other times sluggishly. It is these transient and mobile systems—highs and lows— which are the major contributors to day-to-day weather changes.

Climate

While the weather of any place is the sum total of its atmospheric conditions for a short period of time, climate is a composite of the variety of day-to-day weather conditions. It is the cumulative expression of the brief atmospheric patterns associated with the transient weather systems. Averages of the weather elements (temperature, precipitation, wind, etc.) are fundamental to the descriptions of climate. However, climate is not just "average weather," for the varia- tions from the mean or average are often as impor- tant as the mean itself.

Although weather, especially its extremes, most often makes the news, climate has a more important influence on the way people live. They adapt their agriculture and housing to the climate of the region, and also, to some extent, their transporta- tion systems and recreation. Minor changes in cli- mate often have a profound effect on the population of a region. For example, the turn toward a drier climate in the southwestern plains region of the United States in the 1930s led to a major migration of people from this "dust bowl" region to California. Steinbeck has vividly described the effects of the drought and the resulting migration in *The Grapes of Wrath.*

Throughout history people have responded not only to climate but to its changes as well.

The Controls of Weather and Climate

A primary goal of geography is to describe and explain the world distribution of climate and its relation to other aspects of the environment such as vegetation, soil, and landforms. For example, the distribution of mean annual precipitation shown in Figure 5.11 is described, and an effort is made to explain why the pattern exists. In order to accomplish such a task, it is necessary to first understand the processes which control weather and climate.

The basic cause of both weather and climate is the unequal heating and cooling of the atmosphere. While the system as a whole loses as much heat to space as it gains from the sun, some portions experi- ence a net gain and some a net loss. The unequal heating and cooling occurs on a wide variety of geographical scales. There are differences between continents and oceans, between snow-covered and snow-free areas, between cities and the surrounding countryside, but, most importantly, between high- and low-latitude regions. The heating differences and the air motions (winds) which they induce are funda- mental in controlling weather and climate. The na- ture of these controls is determined by various geo- graphical factors. They are briefly noted below and are then treated more fully in the following chapter.

Latitudinal variation of solar radiation.   The lat- itudinal variation of solar radiation is the most fun- damental climatic control. In low latitudes the sun is high in the sky, the solar radiation is intense, and the climate is tropical, while in high latitudes the sun is lower in the sky, the solar radiation weaker, and the climate colder. Global maps of mean temperature show that the *isotherms* (lines connecting places that have the same temperature) are oriented mainly east-west with cold temperatures in polar regions and warm temperatures in the tropics. (See Figs. 5.8 and 5.9.)

Distribution of continents and oceans.   Con- tinental areas heat and cool more rapidly than do oceanic areas. Consequently, continental areas expe- rience more intense seasons than oceanic areas (i.e., the summers are warmer and the winters colder than over the oceans). Coastal regions of continents, particularly those on the windward side, have less intense seasons than do the interiors of the continents. The *difference* between the mean monthly temperatures of the warmest and coldest months in London, England (52°N), for example, is only 14°C (25°F), while in Minneapolis, Minnesota (45°N), the *difference* is nearly 33°C (60°F).

Pressure systems. The differences in the heating and cooling between various regions of the earth, particularly between polar and tropical latitudes, lead not only to major temperature contrasts but also to differences in pressure. The pressure differences then cause air motions (winds). The wind transports heat from regions of net heat gain to regions of net loss, and water vapor from the oceans to the continents.

Because of the earth's rotation most atmospheric motions occur as *vortices*, that is, air moving in a somewhat circular manner around an area of low or high pressure. Just as there is a whole variety of geographical scales (sizes) of differential heating and cooling, so is there a variety of scales of atmospheric motion. They range from huge vortices centered aloft over the polar regions with their westerly winds encircling the middle-latitude regions of the entire globe to the small but extremely intense tornado.

Embedded within the largest and more permanent scales of motion are the smaller, transient low- and high-pressure systems which bring day-to-day weather changes. These smaller systems tend to develop in the vicinity of jet streams, which are narrow zones of stronger winds found within the global circulation patterns. The frequency of occurrence and the paths followed by these smaller mobile systems are significant factors in determining climate. Some pressure systems, particularly the major high-pressure areas over the subtropical oceans, tend to be semipermanent in position and are thus also of great climatic significance.

Ocean currents. The ocean currents, which are largely controlled by the major wind systems, are also an important climatic control. They aid in the transport of heat from low to high latitudes and in so doing give certain regions distinct climates. For example, the northern coast of Norway, well north of the Arctic Circle, is bathed by a warm ocean current that gives this coastal area a mean January temperature warmer than that of northern Illinois (42°N).

Major terrain features. In general, places situated at higher elevations have colder temperatures and more precipitation than adjacent lowland regions. Furthermore, windward sides of mountain ranges tend to have heavier precipitation than the lee sides. In some areas high mountain ranges block the movement of air masses. The Himalaya Mountains, for example, effectively prevent the intrusion of cold arctic air from northern Asia into India.

Local features. Finally, the climate of a place is affected by such local features as the slope of the land, the characteristics of the vegetation and soil, and the density of population. In the Northern Hemisphere south-facing slopes have a warmer climate than north-facing slopes; cities are usually warmer than the countryside; other factors being equal, areas with sandy, loosely packed soil experience more frosts than do areas with hard-packed soil; valleys have more frequent frosts than the adjacent hillsides.

Climate is indeed determined by the interaction of a complex set of controls. While the major characteristics are controlled by factors such as latitude and position on a continent, local geographical features also leave their imprint on the climate. In the next two chapters the processes which control weather and climate are examined. Once the controls are understood, it is possible to classify climates and study their distribution over the face of the earth.

REVIEW QUESTIONS

1. The surface of the moon is pock-marked with many craters. Why is the earth's surface not marked by many craters?
2. Contrast the depth of the major mass of the atmosphere with the radius of the solid earth. An attempt to draw the two depths to scale provides a contrast.
3. Why can the atmosphere be considered as the product of an enormous and continuing ecosystem?
4. Why is the gas ozone so important even though it is present in the atmosphere in only minute quantities?

5. Give several reasons why water vapor is an important atmospheric gas.
6. Contrast weather and climate.
7. What is the cause for the relatively warm temperatures found at an elevation of about 50 km?
8. Cite examples, other than those given in this chapter, of modern society's susceptibility to the condition of the atmosphere (i.e., air quality, weather, or climate).
9. The various climatic controls have been noted in this chapter. Use the climate of your city to illustrate the influence of each of the controls.
10. What would be the effect of a long-term decrease of 30 percent in the annual precipitation of your area? What effect would there be if this decrease were confined to the growing season?

SELECTED REFERENCES

Anthes, R. A., H. Panofsky, J. Cahir, and A. Rango. *The Atmosphere.* Charles E. Merrill Books, Inc., Columbus, Ohio, 1975. Pp. 189–208. The chapter on air pollution in this text provides a concise summary of the nature and possible effects of atmospheric pollution.

Berkner, L. V., and L. C. Marshall. "The Rise of Oxygen in the Earth's Atmosphere with Notes on the Martian Atmosphere." *Advances in Geophysics*, Vol. 12, pp. 309–333. Academic Press, New York, 1967. A rather advanced-level discussion of the evolution of the earth's atmosphere; however, for the student who has had some chemistry, this review article provides excellent source material.

Petterssen, S. *Introduction to Meteorology.* McGraw-Hill Book Company, New York, 1969. Pp. 26–52. The interaction between the atmospheres of the sun and the earth are treated in this chapter.

Scientific American, Vol. 223, No. 3, September, 1970. This issue of the magazine is devoted to the biosphere with a number of articles dealing with the exchange of energy, water, oxygen, nitrogen, and carbon between the atmosphere and the biosphere.

Steinbeck, John. *The Grapes of Wrath.* The Modern Library, Random House, New York, 1939. This novel provides a masterful description of the influence of the atmospheric environment on humans and their courage in responding to it.

Stewart, George R. *Storm.* The Modern Library, Random House, New York, 1941. The heroine of this novel is a cyclone that forms in the western Pacific and which eventually moves into California, influencing the daily lives of a broad range of Californians.

Van Valen, L. "The History and Stability of Atmospheric Oxygen." *Science*, Vol. 171, No. 3970, pp. 439–443, 1971. The article deals with the natural regulation of the concentration of atmospheric oxygen and points to the great difficulty that is encountered when attempts are made to explain the initial development of oxygen.

The Energy of
the Atmosphere

CHARACTERISTICS OF ATMOSPHERIC ENERGY

Practically all of the energy of the earth system is derived from the energy emitted by the sun and absorbed either within the atmosphere or at the surface of the earth's continents and oceans. Unquestionably, solar energy and the way in which it is distributed and absorbed within the earth system compose the principal climatic control. Solar energy not only strongly controls air temperature but is the ultimate cause of atmospheric motions. Since the earth system as a whole is neither warming nor cooling, the system returns as much energy to space as it receives from the sun. However, within the system, energy is transferred between regions and may be transformed from one form to another. Before examining the way in which weather and climate result from the system's energy processes, some general characteristics of atmospheric energy will be noted.

Energy Forms

Energy, which may appear in various forms, is the property of a system which enables it to do work. It makes systems run, whether the system be a person,

an automobile, a refrigerator, or the atmosphere. The principal forms of atmospheric energy are internal energy, gravitational potential energy, kinetic energy, and latent energy.

Internal energy. The *internal energy* of a parcel of air (or any gas) manifests itself in the random motions of its molecules. Since temperature is a measure of molecular activity, it is a measure of internal energy. If the temperature of a parcel of air is increased, the internal energy of the air is increased; if the temperature is decreased, the internal energy is decreased. The terms *thermal energy* and *heat* are often used in place of "internal energy."

Gravitational potential energy. The *gravitational potential energy* of a parcel of air is a stored form of energy resulting from the position of the parcel above the surface of the earth. It requires work (i.e., energy) acting against gravity to raise a parcel of air from one height to another. An amount of energy equal to that used in raising the parcel will remain stored in the parcel by virtue of its higher elevation. If the parcel eventually moves back to its original height, that same amount of energy will be released but will manifest itself as some other form of energy. In the atmosphere there is a close relationship between internal energy and gravitational potential energy, particularly in a column of air extending through the entire depth of the atmosphere. If the column of air is heated, the internal energy of the air is increased; at the same time, the heating causes the air to expand upward, thereby raising some of its mass and increasing its gravitational potential energy. Because the amounts of internal and gravitational potential energy generally occur in a fixed ratio, the term *total potential energy* is often used to denote their sum. It is often more convenient to speak of "total potential energy" rather than "gravitational potential energy plus internal energy."

Kinetic energy. *Kinetic energy* is energy of motion. In the atmosphere wind represents kinetic energy. For a given parcel of air it is proportional to the square of the wind speed. Since air motions are mainly horizontal, nearly all of the kinetic energy is associated with the horizontal wind. Although the kinetic energy of the upward and downward motion of the air is small, these motions are very important in producing weather and climate.

Latent energy. In the atmosphere the presence of water vapor, an invisible gas, represents *latent energy*. In the liquid state water molecules are packed closely together, while in the vapor state the molecules are widely separated. During the evaporation of water, heat (internal energy) is used to increase the separation of the molecules. When the water vapor condenses to form clouds and precipitation, the molecules return to their more packed state, and the energy which originally was used to separate them is released as heat.

Energy Transformations

An advantage in studying the workings of the atmosphere in terms of its energy is that energy is neither created nor destroyed within the earth system.[1] Al-

[1]In the sun or in the explosion of an atomic or hydrogen bomb there is a creation of energy from mass; however, such processes do not normally occur within the atmosphere. A small amount of energy is also created by the radioactive decay of certain materials within the solid earth; but with regard to atmospheric processes, the amount is only a few hundredths of 1 percent of that provided by the sun.

though energy is conserved, it may change from one form to another. In fact, one of the most basic principles of physical science is that energy in the form of heat is capable of producing motion (i.e., kinetic energy). For example, some of the heat (internal energy) produced in a gasoline combustion engine is transformed into the motion (kinetic energy) of an automobile.

By examining the transformation of energy from one form to another within the atmospheric system, it is possible to gain a better understanding of the processes which produce weather and climate. In the next chapter there is a discussion of the cause of atmospheric motion (wind). At this point, it is sufficient to note that the kinetic energy of the wind is produced through a transformation of total potential energy to kinetic energy; that is, an increase in wind, and thus kinetic energy, occurs at the expense of total potential energy. In turn, the kinetic energy is dissipated through friction, and the energy again changes form; in this case, it returns to its internal energy form (heat). This is consistent with the common experience that friction produces heat.

Energy Transfer

Because of the unequal heating of the atmosphere, there is a transfer of energy from warmer to colder regions. This transfer of heat, which is an integral part of weather and climate, is accomplished by radiation, conduction, or convection.

Radiation. Of the three transfer processes, radiation is most fundamental, for all of the energy the earth system receives from the sun and all of the energy it emits to space is transferred through radiation. Radiation consists of electromagnetic waves which travel at the speed of light. While all objects emit radiation, hot objects emit much more than do cooler objects. The radiant energy emitted from hot objects, such as the sun, is concentrated at short wavelengths; while the emission from cooler objects, such as the earth, occurs mainly at longer wavelengths. Radiation is the only way that energy is transferred through the emptiness of space, since it requires no medium for its propagation. When radiant energy encounters some medium, it may be either *transmitted* through the medium, *reflected* from it, or *absorbed* by it. The sunlight which passes through the atmosphere is an example of transmission, while the sunlight reflected from freshly fallen snow is an example of reflection. When radiation is absorbed, the absorbing material is warmed; that is, its internal energy is increased by an amount equal to the radiation it absorbs. In the case of transmission or reflection, there is no heating, for the radiant energy continues in transit.

Conduction. If one end of a metal rod is heated, the opposite end will gradually become warmer due to the conduction of heat through the rod. The faster-moving molecules at the heated end will impart some of their increased speed to neighboring molecules, and gradually the increased molecular speeds will extend to the full length of the rod. Likewise, whenever two objects are in contact, heat will be conducted from the warmer to the colder until both have the same temperature.

When warm air lies above a cooler land (or water) surface, there is some conduction of heat from the air to the surface, or vice versa, if the air is cooler than the surface. Since air is a poor conductor of heat, conduction is not a particularly effective energy transfer process within the atmosphere.

Convection. On the other hand, convection is a very effective energy transfer mechanism in the atmosphere and oceans. Convection involves the transfer of energy through the movement of air and water masses. In atmospheric studies the term *advection* is used for the horizontal transfer motions and the word *convection* is usually reserved for motions which are principally vertical. The advection of heat (internal energy) and water vapor (latent energy) by the wind is responsible for many of the day-to-day weather changes. For instance, in the middle latitudes of the Northern Hemisphere warm, moist southerly winds represent a poleward advection of both internal and latent energy.

The vertical transport of heat and moisture by atmospheric convection occurs at a variety of scales (sizes), ranging from very small turbulent eddies to towering thunderstorm clouds to extensive low- and high-pressure systems. All of these scales are important in transporting energy and in producing weather and climate.

Convection occurs in liquids as well as in gases. The movement of water masses in the form of

ocean currents accomplishes a transfer of energy. Warm currents carry heat from the tropics toward higher latitudes, and cold currents return cooler water toward the tropics, where the water is heated before it again flows poleward. (See Fig. 7.9.)

THE ENERGY BUDGET OF THE ATMOSPHERE
The Global Radiation Balance

As noted earlier, the sun is the source of nearly all of the atmosphere's energy. All of the other sources, such as conduction of heat from the earth's interior, moonlight, and man-made combustion, together account for no more than a very small fraction of 1 percent of the energy supplied by the sun. From the sun, which has a surface temperature of about 6,000°C, there streams outward into space an enormous and continuous flow of short-wave radiant energy. The earth, 150 million km (93 million mi) distant, intercepts only an infinitesimally small fraction of the sun's total energy output. Yet this minute fraction is enough to maintain the earth's atmospheric processes as well as other important physical and biological processes of the earth's system.

On a surface oriented perpendicular to the sun's rays and located at the mean distance the earth is from the sun, there arrives an average of 2.0 calories of heat (energy) on each square centimeter of the surface each minute. This quantity (2.0 cal/cm²/min) is known as the *solar constant* for the earth. For planets located closer to the sun, the solar constant is larger, and for the more distant planets it is smaller; the value varies inversely with the square of the distance from the sun. The solar constant is slightly greater in January, when the earth is nearest the sun, and slightly smaller in July, when it is at its most distant position. If the surface oriented perpendicular to the sun's rays is chosen to be a circular disc with a radius equal to the radius of the earth, its sun-facing side will intercept the same amount of solar radiation as does the earth. (See Fig. 3.1.) Because the earth rotates once each 24 hr and revolves about the sun once each year, various parts of the earth face the sun at different times. Thus the 2.0 cal/cm²/min of solar energy are actually spread over the spherical surface of the earth system. Since the area of a sphere is four times the area of one side of

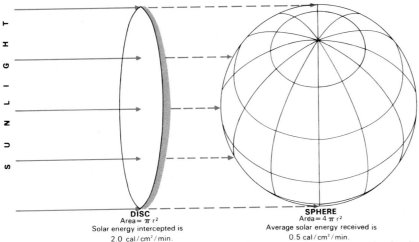

Figure 3.1   The area of the surface of the earth is four times as large as one side of a disc having the same radius as the earth. Thus, one-fourth as much solar energy reaches each square centimeter of the "top" of the atmosphere as would reach a disc the same distance from the sun as the earth.

the disc, the *global annual average* of solar energy arriving at the top of the atmosphere is 0.5 cal/cm²/min (one-quarter of the solar constant).

For the earth system as a whole about 30 percent of the intercepted solar radiation is reflected back to space and thus does not contribute to the energy processes of the system. The term *albedo* is used to denote the ratio of the reflected radiation to the total incoming radiation; thus the global albedo is 0.30. The main reflection occurs from cloud tops, although there is also reflection from the earth's surface, especially from light-colored areas such as snowfields or light-colored sands. A small amount of the reflection is also produced by dust and molecules of air which scatter some of the radiation back to space.

Since air is relatively transparent to short-wave radiation, only about 20 percent of the solar energy is directly absorbed and converted into total potential energy within the atmosphere. The remaining 50 percent is transmitted through the atmosphere and absorbed at the earth's surface. Eventually, most of this 50 percent indirectly heats the atmosphere through the processes discussed in the next section.

Of the solar energy intercepted by the earth system, 70 percent (20 percent plus 50 percent) heats the system. For the global annual average, this amounts to 0.35 cal/cm²/min (0.7 × 0.5 cal/cm²/min).

Since the earth system as a whole is neither warming nor cooling, it must emit an average of 0.35 cal/cm²/min of energy to space. Because the earth's surface and atmosphere are much cooler than the sun, they emit *long-wave radiation* (sometimes called *terrestrial* or *infrared* radiation). Some of this long-wave radiation is emitted directly to space from the earth's surface, but most is emitted from the atmosphere (Fig. 3.2).

Although there is a global annual balance between the incoming short-wave radiation and outgoing long-wave radiation, there are variations within the system, both in time and space, in the amounts of incoming and outgoing radiation. It is these variations that are of primary importance in producing weather and determining the patterns of the earth's climates.

How Solar Energy Heats the Atmosphere

The earth's land-water surface plays an important role in the heating of the atmosphere, since much of the solar radiation reaching the outer limits of the atmosphere is transmitted through the atmosphere and absorbed at the surface. The heated surface then transfers energy to the atmosphere via *radiation, evaporation,* and *conduction,* as shown in Figure 3.2.

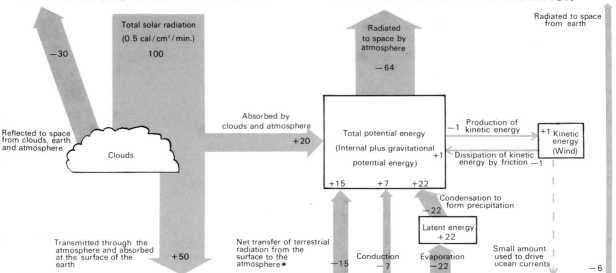

Figure 3.2 A schematic sketch of the average annual energy budget for the entire atmosphere. The incoming solar radiation (0.5 cal/cm²/min) is assigned a value of 100 units. A total of 70 units is absorbed by the system and an equal amount is radiated to space as terrestrial radiation. *

*The terrestrial radiation emitted from the surface is *about seven times greater* than the *net* transfer to the atmosphere, but because of the greenhouse effect much of this energy is reradiated from the atmosphere back to the earth. Thus, there is only a modest *net* transfer (15 units) to the atmosphere. Only 6 units are radiated directly to space from the earth's surface.

Terrestrial radiation. The radiation emitted from the surface is long-wave radiation, in contrast to the short-wave radiation it receives from the sun. While the atmosphere absorbs only about 20 percent of the incoming short-wave radiation, certain gases, particularly carbon dioxide and water vapor, absorb more than 90 percent of the outgoing long-wave radiation. The atmosphere acts like the glass in a greenhouse or automobile, letting through much of the incoming solar radiation but absorbing much of the outgoing long-wave radiation. This is called the *greenhouse effect.* If it were not for the greenhouse effect, the temperature of the atmosphere would be much lower than it is, for the heat added at the surface would be radiated directly back to space without warming the atmosphere. The analogy between the atmosphere and a greenhouse should not be carried too far because the glass of a greenhouse mainly acts as a barrier, preventing the warm air inside from rising (convection) and carrying the heat away.

Land-surface color contrasts. The amount of heat added to the atmosphere by long-wave radiation depends on the temperature of the earth's surface. In turn, the temperature of the surface depends on the amount of solar energy it absorbs. Light-colored surfaces, such as snow and some sands, have large albedos, reflecting much of the solar energy they receive. Thus they do not warm as much as darker surfaces, which readily absorb solar radiation. On a bright, sunny day following a fresh snowfall, the air temperature may rise very little during the day because much of the solar radiation is reflected to space rather than being absorbed by the surface and reradiated as long-wave radiation to the atmosphere.

Land-water contrast. In the lower 3,000 m (10,000 ft) of the atmosphere, the temperature varies much less between seasons and between night and day over the oceanic areas than over continental areas. For several reasons, land surfaces heat and cool more rapidly than water surfaces, even when both absorb the same amount of solar radiation. The most important reason is that the fluid character of water permits it to mix, and as a result the heat added to the water is distributed over a greater depth than the heat added to a land surface. Similarly, when a water surface cools, the surface water becomes heavier and begins to sink, allowing warmer water to rise to the surface.

In addition, water surfaces warm more slowly than land surfaces because water is somewhat transparent to solar radiation. Some of the sun's rays penetrate the water to a considerable depth, thus distributing their energy through a relatively deep layer. On the other hand, the opaqueness of land concentrates the absorption of solar energy at the surface, causing relatively rapid and intense heating. Also of significance is the fact that to raise the temperature of a mass of water 1°C requires more than twice as much energy as is needed to raise the temperature of a mass of land 1°C. Finally, it should be noted that in oceanic areas, more of the solar energy goes into evaporating water and thus is not available for warming the water.

As a consequence of these differences between land and water, the surface temperature, and thus the amount of heat transferred to the atmosphere, remains more uniform in oceanic areas. It is little wonder, then, that continental areas characteristically have much larger daily and seasonal extremes of air temperatures, becoming alternately hot and cold, whereas oceanic areas have more moderate climates with only small seasonal and daily temperature changes.

Evaporation and condensation. A significant portion of the solar energy absorbed at the land-water surface of the earth is used in the evaporation of water. In the atmosphere, the condensation of the water vapor to form precipitation is accompanied by a release of heat. Nearly 600 cal of heat are used to change just 1 gram (g) of liquid water to water vapor. When the water vapor condenses, an amount of energy equal to that used in its evaporation is released as internal energy, warming the atmosphere. However, only the rain or snow which falls to the earth contributes to the *net* heating of the atmosphere in this manner. Cloud droplets which remain suspended in the atmosphere eventually evaporate and an amount of energy equal to that released during condensation is consumed in their evaporation.

Conduction. At the interface where the atmosphere is in contact with the land-water surface, some heat is conducted from the surface to the atmosphere. The amount of conduction depends not only on the temperature difference between the surface and the air (if there is no temperature difference, there is no conduction) but also on the vigor of the convective processes.

Convective processes. Although convective processes are not in themselves capable of transferring energy from the heated surface to the atmosphere, they are important in contributing to the effectiveness of conduction and evaporation. Once water vapor (latent energy) and heat (internal energy) are added to the air by evaporation or conduction, the convective processes can be very effective in transporting these energy forms to higher levels in the atmosphere. When the earth's surface is considerably warmer than the air immediately above it, as it usually is on sunny days, convection in the form of turbulent eddies is quite strong. By carrying the heat and moisture away from the surface, the turbulent eddies maintain large *gradients* (i.e., differences) of temperature and moisture between the surface and the lowest layers of the atmosphere. Large gradients promote evaporation and conduction.

At night, when the earth's surface is usually cooler than the air, there is a transfer of heat, and sometimes moisture, from the air to the surface. The formation of dew or frost, which represents the condensation (or deposition) of atmospheric water vapor on the surface, adds heat to the surface. However, when the surface is cooler than the air, the convective processes are weak and the downward heat transfer is small compared to the upward transfer during the day. The net effect is that, while heat and moisture may be transferred toward or away from the surface, the transfer away from the surface is larger. This leads to a *net* (or average) transfer of heat and moisture from the surface to the atmosphere.

Latitudinal and Seasonal Variations of Solar Radiation

Disregarding the effects of the atmosphere and its clouds, the amount of solar energy that any latitude on the earth's surface receives is determined by two factors: (1) the *intensity* of solar radiation, which depends on the angle at which the rays of sunlight reach the earth's spherical surface, and (2) the *dura-*

tion of solar radiation, which is determined by the length of day compared with night.

Because of the great distance between the sun and the earth, the rays of sunlight received by the earth are essentially parallel. But because of the earth's curved surface, the rays reach different latitudes at different angles. Moreover, since the earth's axis is tilted, the angle at which the sun's rays reach the earth changes with the seasons. Since an oblique solar ray is spread over a larger segment of the earth's surface than a vertical one, it delivers less energy per unit area. (See Fig. 3.3.) An oblique ray is weaker also because it has passed through a thicker layer of scattering, absorbing, and reflecting air. Outside the tropics, therefore, winter sunlight is much weaker than the sunlight of summer. For the same reasons, on any given day the sunlight is much

more intense at noon than in the early-morning or late-afternoon hours.

As for the duration of solar radiation, obviously the longer the sun shines (i.e., the longer the day), the greater the amount of solar energy received, all other conditions being equal (Fig. 3.4). Thus it is quite understandable that in the middle latitudes summer temperatures are much higher than those of winter; not only are the summer sun's rays less oblique, but summer days are much longer.

Since on any one day both the length of day and the angle of the sun's rays are equal along any parallel of latitude, it follows that all parts of a parallel receive identical amounts of solar energy both in a day and in a whole year (allowing, of course, for differences in the transparency of the atmosphere). Different parallels receive unlike amounts of solar radiation, the annual amount decreasing from equator to poles. Thus if solar energy were the only control of weather and climate, all places at the same latitude would have identical climates. Although obviously they do not, there are strong temperature resemblances within latitude belts which testify to the dominant, although not exclusive, influence of sun control.

Earth and sun relations. The rotation and revolution of the earth and the inclination and parallelism of its axis were discussed in Chapter 1. The following section shows how these earth motions and axis positions produce the changing lengths of day and the varying angles of the sun's rays, which in turn are the causes of the seasons.

Equinoxes: spring and fall. Twice during the yearly period of revolution, on about March 21 and September 23, the sun's noon rays are directly overhead, or vertical, at the equator (Fig. 3.4). On these dates, therefore, the circle of illumination, marking the position of the sun's tangent rays, passes through both poles and cuts all the earth's parallels exactly in half. One-half of each parallel (180°) is in light and the other half is in darkness, and days and nights are equal (12 hr each) over the entire earth. Because of this fact the two dates March 21 and September 23 are called the *equinoxes* (derived from Latin words meaning "equal night"). At these times the maximum solar energy is received in equatorial latitudes; it diminishes regularly toward either pole, where it becomes zero.

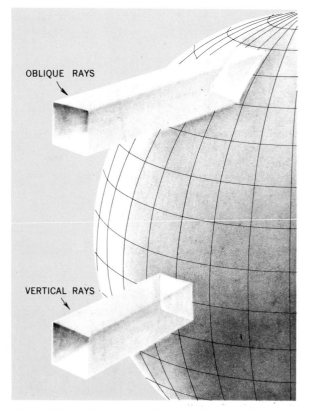

OBLIQUE RAYS

VERTICAL RAYS

Figure 3.3 Oblique rays deliver less energy at the earth's land-water surface than vertical rays, both because the energy of oblique rays is spread over a larger surface and because they must pass through a thicker layer of atmosphere.

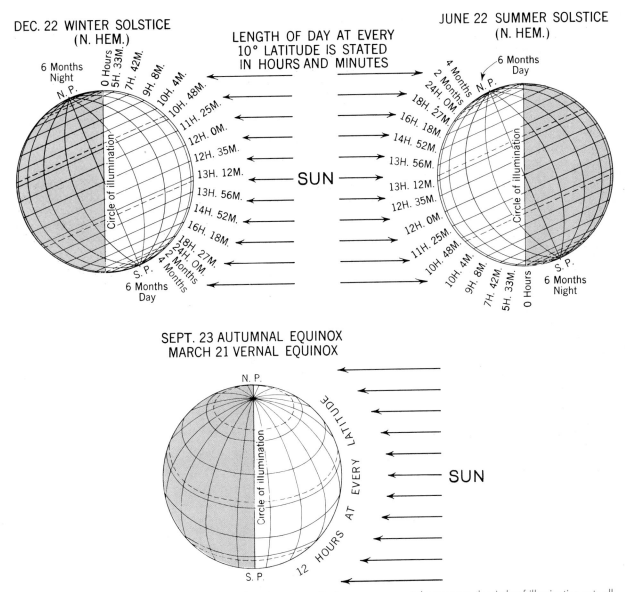

Figure 3.4 At the times of the two equinoxes, when the sun's vertical noon rays are at the equator, the circle of illumination cuts all parallels in half, so that days and nights are equal (12 hr) over the whole earth. At the times of the solstices, the sun's vertical noon rays have reached their greatest poleward displacement, 23$^{1}/_{2}$° north or south. The circle of illumination then cuts all parallels except the equator unequally, so that days and nights are unequal in length except at latitude 0°.

Solstices: summer and winter. On about June 22 the earth is approximately midway in its orbit between the equinoctial positions, and the North Pole is inclined 23$^{1}/_{2}$° toward the sun (Fig. 3.4). As a result of this axial inclination, the sun's rays are shifted northward the same number of degrees, so that the noon rays are vertical at the Tropic of Cancer (23$^{1}/_{2}$°N), and the tangent rays in the Northern Hemisphere pass over the pole and reach the earth 23$^{1}/_{2}$° of latitude beyond it, at the Arctic Circle (66$^{1}/_{2}$°N). In the Southern Hemisphere the tangent rays do not reach the pole but terminate at the Antarctic Circle, $23\frac{1}{2}°$ short of it. Thus while all parts of the earth north of the Arctic Circle are in constant daylight, similar latitudes in the Southern Hemisphere (poleward from the Antarctic Circle) are entirely without sunlight. All parallels, except the equator, are cut unequally by the circle of illumination. Those in the Northern Hemisphere have the larger segments of their circumferences toward the sun, so that days are longer than nights. Longer days, plus a greater angle of the sun's rays, make for a maximum receipt of solar energy in the Northern Hemisphere at this time. Summer, with its associated high temperatures, is the result, and north of the equator June 22 is known as the *summer solstice*. In the Southern Hemisphere all these conditions are reversed: nights are longer than days and the sun's rays are relatively oblique, so that solar radiation is at a minimum and winter conditions prevail.

On about December 22, when the earth is in the opposite position in its orbit, it is the South Pole that is inclined $23\frac{1}{2}°$ toward the sun. The noon rays are then vertical over the Tropic of Capricorn ($23\frac{1}{2}°$S), and the tangent rays pass over the South Pole to the Antarctic Circle $23\frac{1}{2}°$ beyond ($66\frac{1}{2}°$S.). Consequently, south of $66\frac{1}{2}°$S there is constant light, while north of $66\frac{1}{2}°$N there is none. All parallels of the earth except the equator are cut unequally by the circle of illumination, with days longer and the sun's rays more nearly vertical in the Southern Hemisphere. This, therefore, is summer south of the equator but winter in the Northern Hemisphere (*winter solstice*).

Latitudinal distribution of solar energy. Assuming there were no clouds and no absorption or scattering by the atmospheric gases, the solar radiation arriving at the earth's surface for the year as a whole would be greatest at the equator. It diminishes toward the poles, the Northern and Southern Hemispheres sharing equally in the annual amounts of solar energy received. At the time of the equinoxes the distribution of solar radiation is symmetric about the equator; however, for the solstices, the radiation curves are quite asymmetric (Fig. 3.5). At the solstices, when the sun's noon rays are vertical $23\frac{1}{2}°$ poleward from the equator and the length of day increases toward one pole and decreases toward the

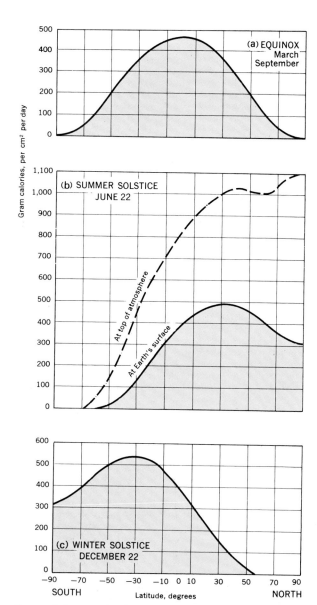

Figure 3.5 Latitudinal distribution of solar energy at the earth's surface (solid lines). At the two equinoxes, solar energy is symmetrically distributed in the Northern and Southern Hemispheres. There is a maximum in equatorial latitudes and minima at the North and South Poles. At the solstices, solar energy is very unequally distributed, with the summer hemisphere receiving two or three times the amount that the winter hemisphere does. Panel (b) shows that at high latitudes much more radiation reaches the top of the atmosphere (dashed line) than reaches the earth's surface.

other, the summer hemisphere receives two to three times as much solar radiation as the winter hemisphere. The summer hemisphere is the hemisphere that has summer. In July it is the Northern Hemisphere; in January it is the Southern Hemisphere. In the summer hemisphere there is a broad maximum of solar energy in the latitude belt extending between 20° and 50°, while latitude 60° receives as much as the equator. It is not surprising, then, that the warmest air temperatures in summer occur over the interior of continents at latitudes 30°–40° and not at the equator. During the year the zone of maximum heating shifts by about 60° of latitude. This shift has a profound effect upon the seasonal temperatures and, as we shall later see, upon the location of the major wind and precipitation belts. It is also significant that the gradient of solar radiation (i.e., its rate of change with latitude) is much steeper in the winter than in the summer hemisphere. As a result there are not only steeper gradients of temperature in the winter hemisphere than in the summer hemisphere, but also greater storminess and greater weather variability.

The amount of variation of solar radiation during the year depends on latitude. In Figure 3.6 are curves showing the annual march of the solar radiation reaching the top of the atmosphere at three different latitudes. The curve for the equator has only slight maxima at the two equinoxes and minima at the solstices. In general, the small seasonal variation in solar radiation is typical of the region between the Tropics of Cancer and Capricorn. The curve for 40°N,

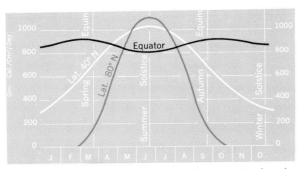

Figure 3.6 Annual march of solar radiation received at the outer limits of the earth's atmosphere at different latitudes. In the very low latitudes close to the equator, the amount of solar energy received at the top of the atmosphere is large and varies little throughout the year. In the middle and higher latitudes, there are great seasonal differences in receipts of solar energy.

on the other hand, has a pronounced seasonal variation with a single maximum at the time of the summer solstice. This is typical of the middle-latitude regions. In high-latitude regions the annual variation of solar radiation is very large, as is shown in the curve for 80°N. During the period from late October to late February the region receives no solar energy, while during the period near the summer solstice the sun is above the horizon throughout the 24-hour day, producing the highest value of solar energy for the three latitudes. However, it should be remembered that the three curves represent the solar radiation arriving at the outer fringe of the atmosphere. As was shown in Figure 3.5, the amount reaching the surface of the earth is reduced from having passed through a great thickness of atmosphere. This is particularly true for high latitudes, where the solar rays are very oblique. Furthermore, very high-latitude regions are perpetually snow- or ice-covered. Because of the large albedo of these surfaces, much of the solar radiation is reflected into space. Consequently, at the summer solstice these high-latitude regions do not warm as much as latitudes nearer the equator.

The Need for a Poleward Transport of Energy

Since the mean annual temperature of the earth as a whole gets neither higher nor lower, it is clear that the heat gained from solar radiation is balanced by a loss of terrestrial radiation to space. But this balance does not hold for individual latitudes. In low latitudes, equatorward of about 40°, the annual average incoming solar radiation exceeds the outgoing terrestrial radiation, whereas poleward from about latitude 40° the reverse is true. In Figure 3.7, which portrays these imbalances, the curve for the outgoing radiation (black line) varies less with latitude than does the solar radiation curve (brown line). If it were not for the greenhouse effect, the two curves would be approximately coincident and there would not be any imbalance of radiation at individual latitudes. At each latitude there would be as much energy emitted to space as is received from the sun. However, for the earth, with an atmosphere containing carbon dioxide and water vapor, a greenhouse effect exists. As a result the earth is not only warmer than it would otherwise be, but there are also large latitudinal differences in heating and cooling. *These differences*

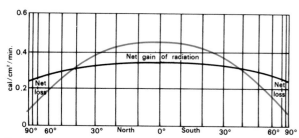

Figure 3.7 Average annual latitudinal distributions of solar radiation (brown line) absorbed by the earth system and terrestrial radiation (black line) emitted to space. The latitude scale is adjusted so that the distance between parallels is proportional to the area of the earth's surface between parallels.

are the fundamental cause of the earth's weather and climate.

Within the atmosphere and oceans there is a continuous transport of energy from the low-latitude regions, where there is a net surplus of radiant energy, to the high latitudes, where there is a net deficit; if there were not, the low-latitude regions would continually grow warmer while the high latitudes would grow colder. Within the atmosphere, energy is transported (i.e., advected) poleward by the winds. At high levels there is a substantial transport of gravitational potential energy, while at lower levels the transport is principally accomplished by the advection of internal energy (heat) and latent energy (water vapor).

Within the oceans the great current systems advect warm water poleward and cold water equatorward, thus producing a net poleward transport of heat. The ocean currents are mainly driven by the large-scale wind systems associated with extensive semipermanent high-pressure systems centered over the subtropical oceans. Regions such as Scandinavia, western Europe, and the coastal regions of Alaska and British Columbia benefit from the northward-flowing warm-water branches of the ocean current systems and are warmer than would be expected considering their high-latitude locations. On the other hand, the relatively cool coastal regions of California and northwestern Africa are under the influence of cool, equatorward-flowing currents. (See Fig. 7.9.)

Temporal variation of radiation and temperature. The average temperature of any month, sea-

son, year, or even long period of years is determined by using the mean daily temperature as a basic unit. This is the average of the highest and lowest temperatures recorded during the 24-hr period.

The daily march of temperature, or the rhythm of day and night temperatures, is obtained by plotting the temperature for each hour of the day. Chiefly it reflects the balance between incoming solar radiation and outgoing terrestrial radiation (Fig. 3.8). From shortly after sunrise until about 3:00 P.M., energy is supplied by incoming solar radiation faster than it is lost by terrestrial radiation, so that the daily temperature curve usually rises (Figs. 3.8 and 3.9). Conversely, from about 3:00 P.M. to sunrise, loss by terrestrial radiation exceeds receipt of solar energy, and the temperature curve usually falls. Often, however, clouds or the advection of cold or warm air modify this symmetrical rise and fall of the temperature curve. For example, in Figure 3.9 the temperature on December 22 did not fall in the evening because of the onset of southerly winds and warm-air advection.

The annual march of temperature is obtained by plotting the mean temperature for each month. It reflects the increase in solar energy (and hence in internal energy) from midwinter to midsummer, and the corresponding decrease from midsummer to midwinter (Fig. 3.10). Over large land masses the period of maximum (and minimum) temperature usually lags about a month behind the period of maximum (and minimum) solar energy. This seasonal lag is even greater over oceans and along windward coasts in middle latitudes, where in the Northern Hemisphere August may be the warmest month and February the coldest. As noted earlier, marine loca-

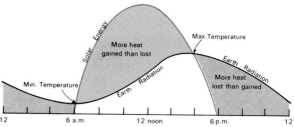

Figure 3.8 The march of incoming solar radiation and of outgoing earth radiation for a daily 24-hr period near the date of an equinox, showing their combined effects upon the times of daily maximum and minimum temperatures.

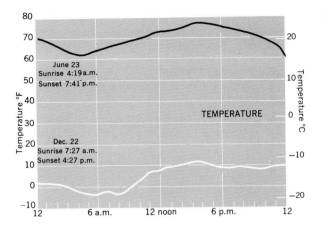

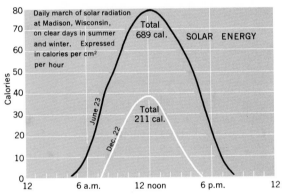

Figure 3.9 Daily march of solar radiation and temperature on cloudless days at the times of the summer and winter solstices at Madison, Wisconsin. The total solar energy recorded was 3.27 times as great on June 23 as on December 22. Note that temperature lags somewhat behind solar radiation. Advection by southerly winds prevented normal night cooling on December 22.

tions have smaller annual temperature variations than continental locations, just as their daily temperature variations are less.

Vertical variation of temperature. Since the major portion of the solar energy received by the earth-atmosphere system is absorbed at the surface of the earth, the highest air temperatures are normally found near the ground. Usually there is a decrease of temperature with increasing elevation up to the tropopause, which is typically found at a height of about 8 km (5 mi) in polar regions and 16 km (10 mi) in tropical regions. The rate of decrease of temperature

with height, called the *lapse rate*, is not uniform but varies with time of day, season, and location. It averages about 6.5°C for each kilometer of elevation (3.6°F per 1,000 ft); however, in the first few meters above the surface on a sunny day the lapse rate may exceed 10°C per kilometer, while at other times the temperature may actually increase with height.

Temperature inversions. An increase of temperature with altitude is referred to as a *temperature inversion*. Such a reversal of the normal lapse rate can occur in the layer of air next to the land surface or at various levels above it. (See Fig. 3.11.)

Inversions which occur above the surface layers are often the result of the slow sinking or *subsidence* of a layer of air aloft. Sinking leads to a warming of the air due to compression. When a layer of air sinks, the top of the layer experiences greater compression and more warming than the bottom, thus producing an inversion. The subsidence of air is characteristic of high-pressure systems, especially the slow-moving or stationary ones. Other inversions above the surface are found in the sloping transition zones which separate air masses of different temperatures. In the transition zones, the colder, more dense air is found at the lower levels with the warmer air aloft. (See Fig. 4.17.) The topics of subsidence and transition zones will be discussed in more detail in Chapter 4.

Perhaps the most common type of inversion is that which forms near the land surface at night. During the night there is no incoming solar radiation, so the outgoing terrestrial radiation dominates. Because the earth's surface radiates heat more efficiently than does air, it can become colder than the air immediately above it. The layer of air near the surface then can lose its heat to the colder land surface and eventually becomes colder than the air at somewhat higher levels. Clear skies and dry air favor strong nighttime cooling because the terrestrial radiation is lost to space without being absorbed by water vapor (a gas that favors the greenhouse effect) or clouds. If, in addition, the air is nearly calm, so that there is little mixing, stratification of the air occurs, with the coldest air at the surface. When a snow cover is present, the inversion may become especially pronounced, since the snow acts as an insulating blanket reducing the conduction of stored heat from the soil to the surface to replace the heat lost by radiation. This

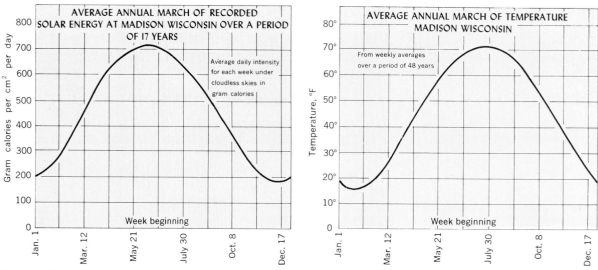

Figure 3.10   Note that temperature lags a month or more behind solar radiation. The solar radiation curve has been smoothed slightly.

is why nighttime temperatures in snow-covered areas are colder than in snowless areas.

Surface inversions occur at all latitudes, although in moist tropical regions they are weak. On the other hand, over the snow-covered polar regions during the winter season, the surface inversions are

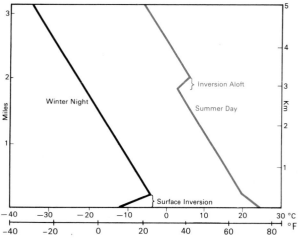

Figure 3.11   Examples of the vertical variation of temperature in the lower atmosphere. At night, especially in winter, surface inversions often occur; while during the day, especially in summer, the temperature near the surface may decrease very rapidly with height. Inversions aloft can occur in any season.

very pronounced and may extend to elevations of 3,000 m (10,000 ft) above the surface. In middle latitudes, calm, clear weather produces nighttime surface inversions in both summer and winter; however, the winter ones are generally stronger and more persistent.

While surface inversions occur over flat land surfaces, they tend to be best developed over low spots. As the air near the surface is cooled, it becomes more dense and flows, under the influence of gravity, toward lower areas. Because of this drainage of cold air, nighttime temperatures in valleys or bottomlands on clear, relatively calm nights are lower than on adjacent hillsides. As a consequence, frost and also fog more often occur in the lowlands.

Frost.   Frost occurs when the temperature falls to freezing (0°C, 32°F) or below. On some nights the surface of the earth (or a house roof or an auto top) may cool to below freezing, while the air temperature less than a meter above the surface remains above freezing. On such nights the surfaces may be covered with a white frost even though the air temperature as measured by a thermometer above the surface remains above freezing.

Because of their water content, many plants are sensitive to frost. The *growing season* for a locality is defined as the period between the last killing frost in the spring and the first in the fall. Conventionally, an air temperature of 0°C (32°F) is used to define a *killing frost*. Throughout the middle latitudes, frost is the most serious menace to crops in spring and fall, that is, near the beginning and end of the growing season. In the more subtropical areas, such as Florida and Southern California, winter frosts are critical, since many crops are grown throughout the relatively mild winter in these areas.

The same conditions which favor the development of surface inversions favor the occurrence of frost, provided the general air-mass temperature is not far above freezing. When there has been advection of cold, dry air during the day, farmers and gardeners are especially watchful for clearing skies and dying winds during the late afternoon or evening hours as indicators that frost may occur. When there is a frost, the effects on plants are often quite patchy, with the greatest damage occurring on the lowlands. Even very small variations in the terrain can have a noticeable effect on the cold-air drainage and frost formation. Sensitive crops such as fruits are commonly planted on hillsides rather than on lowlands to reduce the frost danger.

REVIEW QUESTIONS

1. Why is the conservation of energy an important concept to bear in mind when studying the workings of the atmosphere in terms of energy?
2. Why can the internal energy and gravitational potential energy of a column of air often be combined into a single quantity, the total potential energy?
3. Give examples from your everyday experience of the transfer of heat by conduction, convection, and radiation.
4. Define the solar constant. In studying the global energy budget, why is a value of one-quarter the solar constant used for the incoming solar energy?
5. The solar constant for a hypothetical planet is 6.0 cal/cm²/min. If the planet has an albedo of 0.50 and its mean temperature is neither increasing nor decreasing, what is the average rate of energy loss from the planet to space?
6. Why is the diurnal range of temperature (i.e., the difference between night and day temperatures) greater in desert regions than in humid regions at the same latitude?

7. At New York City, located at latitude 40°N, the noon sun at the time of the autumnal equinox is 50° above the southern horizon. How high above the horizon is the noon sun at New York at the time of the winter solstice?
8. Why does the noon sun in winter provide less heat to the earth's surface than the noon sun in summer?
9. Why are convective processes important in the transfer of energy from the earth's surface to the atmosphere?
10. Explain why it can be said that the atmosphere is heated directly by the earth and only indirectly by the sun.
11. During their respective summers, the North and South Polar regions have 24 hr of possible sunshine each day. Why are their summers not as warm as summers in lower-latitude regions which receive fewer hours of sunshine each day?
12. How do we know that there must be a net annual transport of heat from low-latitude to high-latitude regions of the earth?
13. What conditions favor the formation of surface-temperature inversions?

SELECTED REFERENCES

Anthes, R. A., H. Panofsky, J. Cahir, and A. Rango. *The Atmosphere.* Charles E. Merrill Books, Inc., Columbus, Ohio, 1975. Pp. 19–35. The properties of radiation are well illustrated in these pages.

Bonner, F. T., and M. Phillips. *Principles of Physical Science.* Addison-Wesley Publishing Co., Reading, Mass., 1957. Pp. 195–288. The concepts of energy and the properties of gases are dealt with at a basic level. There are many other elementary physical science and physics texts which also treat these concepts.

Petterssen, S. *Introduction to Meteorology,* 3rd ed. McGraw-Hill Book Company, New York, 1969. Pp. 53–73. The heat balance of the atmosphere is described by one of the world's great meteorologists.

Scientific American, Vol. 224, No. 3, September, 1971. This issue has energy as a central theme. The articles by Freeman Dyson (pp. 50–59) and David Gates (pp. 88–103), which treat the energy of the universe and the flow of energy in the biosphere, provide considerable additional depth to the subject of the atmosphere's energy.

The Atmosphere
in Motion

The great sea of air which envelops the earth is a restless sea. Its restlessness is revealed by a great variety of motions, some encompassing whole continents, others no more than the area of a city. Some motions persist for entire seasons, others for but a few moments. The larger and more persistent motions are of great significance in producing climate, while some of the smaller, more transitory motions are responsible for the day-to-day weather events. All of the motions of the atmospheric system owe their existence to the energy processes described in Chapter 3.

Within the atmospheric system, air moves both horizontally (parallel to the surface) and vertically (up or down). The horizontal motions, commonly called the *wind*, are typically 100 to 1,000 times as strong as the vertical motions. They are of great importance to weather and climate, since they transport water vapor from the oceans to the continents and energy from low latitudes where there is a surplus of radiant energy to high latitudes where there is a deficit. Although the vertical motions are usually very weak, they largely determine whether the sky is clear or cloudy and rainy. Areas of sinking motion normally have fair weather, while areas of rising motion are likely to have clouds and precipitation.

In studying atmospheric motion, it is helpful to divide the motion into its horizontal and vertical parts even though the two are intimately related. While the patterns of horizontal motion are extensive and easily recognizable, it is difficult to directly measure the vertical motion. However, the sense of the vertical motion (i.e., whether the air is rising or sinking) can usually be inferred from the type of horizontal motion that is present. In the first portion of this chapter, the cause of the wind (horizontal motion) is discussed. Then later in the chapter the upward and downward motions are related to the horizontal motion and to the type of weather they produce.

CAUSES OF THE WIND

The movement of air is controlled by forces due to (1) gravity, (2) differences in atmospheric pressure, (3) friction with the earth's surface, and (4) the rotation of the earth. Of the four forces, the one due to differences in pressure is most fundamental, for it is this force which sets air in motion. Consequently, the nature of atmospheric pressure will be discussed before the individual forces are taken up.

Atmospheric Pressure

Atmospheric pressure, which is simply the weight of the air above some level, is measured by barometers. At sea level the average air pressure is 14.7 lb/in.^{2} (i.e., a 1-in.-square column of air extending from sea level to the "top" of the atmosphere weighs 14.7 lb). In metric units the average sea-level pressure is 1,013,200 dynes/cm^2, or 1013.2 millibars (mb), 1 mb being equal to 1,000 dynes/cm^2. At sea level this *average* weight of air is equal to the weight of a column of mercury 29.92 in. or 760 mm tall[1]. Consequently, on home barometers the scale of pressure is often marked in inches, or sometimes millimeters, of mercury. In the remainder of this text the units of millibars will be used. For the reader who is accustomed to thinking in terms of inches of mercury rather than millibars, a conversion scale is shown in Figure 4.1.

Atmospheric pressure is not everywhere uniform. It not only decreases with increasing height, but at a fixed height it also varies from place to place and from time to time.

Vertical variation of pressure.   Since the atmospheric pressure is the weight of all the air above the level at which it is measured, the pressure at higher levels will be less. Because the air at low elevations is compressed by the weight of the air above it, the decrease of pressure with height is most rapid in the lower atmosphere, amounting to about 1 mb for each 10 meters (m) increase in height. At higher elevations the rate of decrease is less.

Horizontal variation of pressure.   The horizontal variation in pressure is much smaller than the vertical variation. Sea-level pressures are almost always

[1] A mercury barometer is simply a U-shaped tube containing mercury, a very heavy liquid. One end of the tube is closed and free of all air. At sea level the weight of the atmosphere on the open end of the U-shaped tube pushes the mercury up into the closed end to an average height of 760 mm (29.92 in.).

between about 1050 and 960 mb, with the extreme values for the world ranging from 1084 to 877 mb. At higher levels within the atmosphere, there also exist horizontal variations of pressure. The ultimate cause of horizontal variations in pressure is the differential heating and cooling that the atmospheric system experiences. How the heating differences produce horizontal pressure differences is discussed later in this chapter.

An area which has lower pressure than surrounding areas at the same elevation is called a *low* or *cyclone*, while an area with higher pressure than its surroundings is known as a *high* or *anticyclone*. It should be emphasized that the terms "low" and "high" simply refer to the pressure relative to the surrounding pressure *at the same altitude*. It is not uncommon to find a high pressure at sea level while at greater elevations above it there may be a low, or vice versa. For example, a hurricane is an intense low-pressure system at sea level, yet directly above it at altitudes greater than about 12 km (7 mi) there exists a high-pressure area.

The horizontal distribution of pressure at a fixed level can be represented on a map by *isobars*, that is, by lines connecting places having the same pressure. Since weather stations are located at various elevations above sea level, the pressures measured by the station barometers are adjusted to equivalent sea-level values. If this were not done, the map would mainly reflect the different elevations of the stations. Maps portraying the isobars at fixed elevations above sea level can also be prepared; however, the pressure patterns at higher levels in the atmosphere are usually portrayed by *contours* showing the height of an isobaric surface. An *isobaric surface* is an invisible surface in the atmosphere on which the pressure is everywhere the same. Isobaric surfaces are not normally parallel to sea level; rather, they are gently sloping surfaces. Where an isobaric surface is at a low elevation, the pressure is low; where it is at a relatively high elevation, the pressure is relatively high. For example, in the cross section shown in

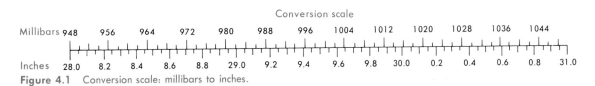

Conversion scale

Millibars 948   956   964   972   980   988   996   1004   1012   1020   1028   1036   1044

Inches 28.0   8.2   8.4   8.6   8.8   29.0   9.2   9.4   9.6   9.8   30.0   0.2   0.4   0.6   0.8   31.0

Figure 4.1   Conversion scale: millibars to inches.

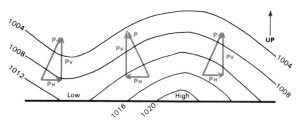

Figure 4.2   A vertical cross section showing several isobaric surfaces. The pressure gradient force (P) is perpendicular to the isobaric surfaces and is directed toward lower pressure. It can be partitioned into vertical (P_V) and horizontal (P_H) components. The slope of the isobaric surfaces is greatly exaggerated here. P_V is very much greater than P_H. Also note that the isobaric surfaces are at a higher elevation and have a dome shape in highs, while in lows they are lower and have a saucer shape.

Figure 4.2 the 1004-mb isobaric surface is at a higher elevation in the region of the high than in that of the low. In Figure 4.20 are portrayed the isobars of sea-level pressure and in Figure 4.21 are the contours of the 500-mb surface. These figures will be discussed in greater detail later in this chapter.

Forces Governing Atmospheric Motions

Perhaps the simplest route to understanding air motion is to study the forces acting on a single parcel of air. We shall first examine the nature of each of the four forces and then investigate how the forces act together to produce the wind. All motion, whether it be that of an automobile, a baseball, or an air parcel, can be described using the laws of motion set forth by Sir Isaac Newton in the seventeenth century. The laws of motion state that a force produces an acceleration; that is, a force causes a change in velocity. Since velocity has both a magnitude (size) and a direction, a change in velocity may be manifested in *either* a change in *speed* (slowing down or speeding up) or a change in the *direction* of motion. If there are no forces acting on a parcel of air, or if the forces acting on it cancel each other, a parcel of air which is at rest will remain stationary and one which is in motion will continue its motion in a straight line without any change in its speed.

Gravity.   The force of gravity (G) always acts downward on a parcel of air. Just as a pencil in a person's

hand will fall to the floor if it is released, so would a parcel of air fall if there were not other forces compensating for gravity. Not only would the pencil or air parcel fall, but they would fall at an increasing speed under the influence of gravity.

Pressure gradient force.   Atmospheric pressure in itself is not a force; however, differences in atmospheric pressure produce a force. The differences in pressure are expressed in terms of the *pressure gradient*, which is the rate of change of pressure with respect to distance. The *pressure gradient force* is a force which acts from higher toward lower pressure. It is perpendicular to the isobaric surfaces, and, like air motion, it can be divided into two components, one which points vertically upward (P_V) and one which is horizontal (P_H). Figure 4.2, which is a highly exaggerated vertical cross section through the atmosphere, shows the two components of the pressure gradient force. Because of the rapid decrease of pressure with elevation, the vertical component of the pressure gradient force is very large; however, this upward-directed force is nearly balanced by the large force of gravity, which acts downward. Since there is nearly a balance between these two large forces, the vertical acceleration of an air parcel (either upward or downward) is very small. When there is an exact balance between the upward-acting pressure gradient force and gravity, there is no vertical acceleration of the air. Such a balance is known as *hydrostatic* equilibrium. In most places most of the time, the atmosphere is nearly in hydrostatic balance; however, the small deviations which do occur are very important, for they can lead to clouds and precipitation if the air begins to move upward and to clearing skies if the air starts sinking.

The horizontal component of the pressure gradient force, although much smaller than the vertical component, can produce relatively large accelerations, since it is not as readily balanced. The horizontal pressure gradient force can be easily determined from a weather map. It points across the isobars at right angles toward lower pressure. Its size depends on the rate of change of pressure in the horizontal direction. Where the isobars are close together, the horizontal pressure gradient force is large; where the isobars are far apart, it is weak. On the weather map shown in Figure 4.20 the horizontal pressure gradient is large in western Kansas, where the isobars are close together, but quite weak in Florida, where they are widely spaced.

On upper-level charts, where contours are used to show the height of a constant-pressure surface (e.g., 500 mb), the horizontal pressure gradient force points across the contours from high heights toward lower heights. The force is largest and the wind strongest where the contours are close together.

Friction. Whenever air moves relative to the earth's surface, frictional drag tends to slow the air and alter its direction of movement. The force of friction (M) is greatest over rough surfaces, such as a forest or city. It is the relatively small obstacles that provide the greatest drag on the moving air. A tree-less mountain range may offer less frictional drag than a forested plain. It is common to experience strong winds over the sea or the prairie but much weaker winds in forested areas. The effect of friction is most pronounced near the surface; it becomes relatively insignificant at elevations greater than about 1 km (0.6 mi) above the surface.

Coriolis force. The laws of motion apply to motions which are measured with respect to nonrotating reference frames such as a point fixed in space. Because of the rotation of the earth about its axis, and because we prefer to measure the wind with respect to the earth's surface rather than to a point fixed in space, it is necessary to include the *apparent* force arising from the rotation of our frame of reference. This force, known as the *Coriolis* force, appears to an observer on the rotating earth to deflect a parcel of horizontally moving air 90° to the right of its direction of motion in the Northern Hemisphere and 90° to the left in the Southern Hemisphere.[2] Because the

---

[2]A simple way of demonstrating this force is to draw a line along a ruler held in a fixed position above a table while the paper on which the line is being drawn is turned. With respect to the fixed table (analogous to the fixed stars), the line drawn along the ruler is straight; however, on the turning paper, a curved line is sketched out. If the paper is turned counterclockwise (the same as the earth's rotation viewed from above the North Pole), the line on the paper turns to the right as viewed from the starting point of the line. Clockwise rotation (the earth's rotation seen from above the South Pole) produces a line which curves to the left. Thus to an observer on the earth (or turning paper), there appears to be a deflecting force acting to the right of the direction of motion in the Northern Hemisphere and to the left in the Southern Hemisphere.

Coriolis force acts at a right angle to the motion, it does not change the speed of the air motion; however the size of the Coriolis force is directly proportional to the speed of the motion relative to the earth. It also depends on the latitude at which the motion occurs. It is a maximum at the poles, where the full rotation of the earth about the zenith occurs. It decreases with latitude, becoming zero at the equator, where there is no rotation with respect to the local zenith.

In summary, there are four forces which can cause the velocity (speed or direction) of a parcel of air to change: the pressure gradient force (P)—which can be divided into its vertical (P_V) and horizontal (P_H) parts—gravity (G), friction (M), and the Coriolis force (C).

The Relation between Forces and the Wind

Winds (horizontal motions) are named according to the direction *from* which they come. Thus air moving from the south toward the north is called a *south* wind. On the weather maps of this text (e.g., Figure 4.20) arrows are used to describe the direction in which the air is moving. The arrows fly with the wind; for example, an arrow pointing *from* the south toward the north indicates a south wind. The relationship between the forces which control air motion and the wind they produce can be easily understood if care is taken to keep in mind the way in which wind direction is defined and also the direction in which each of the forces described in the previous section acts.

The wind at elevations above 1 km (0.6 mi). In examining how the various forces control the wind, it is convenient to first study the wind at elevations greater than 1 km (0.6 mi) above the surface, for at these heights the force of friction is very small and can be ignored. It was earlier noted that the horizontal motion of air, (i.e., the wind) is normally 100 to 1,000 times as great as its vertical motion. Thus, as a first step, it is reasonable to also assume that the air moves only horizontally; this implies that the vertical pressure gradient force (P_V) is exactly balanced by gravity (G). This leaves only two forces to be considered, the horizontal pressure gradient force (P_H) and the Coriolis force (C).

Figure 4.3 shows how a parcel of air in the Northern Hemisphere responds to these two forces. If

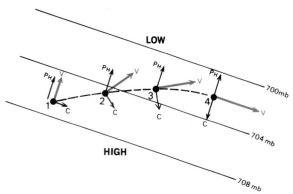

Figure 4.3 A small section of a Northern Hemisphere weather map at a height of 3 km where friction is negligible. The solid straight lines are isobars. Because of the horizontal pressure gradient force (P_H) an air parcel placed at (1) starts to move with velocity (V) across the isobars toward lower pressure. As it moves from (1) to (4) the Coriolis force (C) turns it toward the right until the geostrophic balance shown at (4) is reached.

the air is initially at rest, the Coriolis force is zero; however, in response to the horizontal pressure gradient force, the air parcel begins to move toward lower pressure, its speed increasing at it does. Once the motion starts, the Coriolis force begins to deflect the air to the right (Northern Hemisphere). Eventually the motion of the air parcel becomes parallel to the isobars, with the horizontal pressure gradient force just balanced by the Coriolis force. In regions where the horizontal pressure gradient force is large (i.e., where the isobars are close together), the wind will attain higher speeds than where the isobars are widely spaced. *One of the most prominent features of the wind at elevations greater than 1 km (0.6 mi) above the surface is that it blows nearly parallel to the isobars, with low pressure to the left of the wind in the Northern Hemisphere and to the right in the Southern Hemisphere.* In the ideal case where the Coriolis force *exactly* balances the horizontal pressure gradient force, the resulting wind is said to be *geostrophic.* (See Fig. 4.4.) Except within about 20° latitude of the equator, where the Coriolis force is usually too weak to balance the horizontal pressure gradient force, the actual wind at elevations above 1 km is approximately geostrophic.

In the above discussion and in Figures 4.3 and 4.4 only cases in which the isobars were straight lines were considered. In regions where the isobars (or

contours) are curved, the direction of the horizontal pressure gradient varies along the isobars, and as a result a balance between it and the Coriolis force is not achieved. This permits the air to move in a curved path, as shown in Figure 4.5. *In the Northern Hemisphere at heights above 1 km (0.6 mi) the wind tends to parallel the isobars, flowing counterclockwise about lows and clockwise about highs. Because of the different direction of the Coriolis force in the Southern Hemisphere, the flow is just reversed there: clockwise about lows and counterclockwise about highs. Regardless of the hemisphere, air motion about a low is known as "cyclonic flow," while air motion about a high is called "anticyclonic flow."* Usually the wind speeds in a cyclone are stronger than in an anticyclone; this is because the pressure gradients are greater in lows than in highs. Lows tend to be smaller in size but more intense than highs.

If one were to examine a great number of

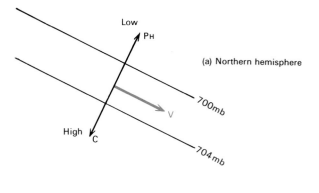

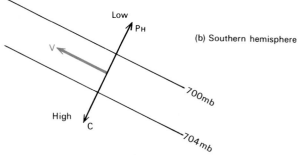

Figure 4.4 In both hemispheres the geostrophic wind (V) blows parallel to the isobars. However, the Northern Hemisphere low pressure is to the left of the wind, while in the Southern Hemisphere it is to the right.

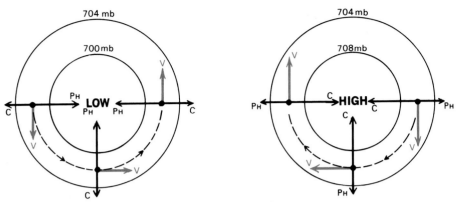

Figure 4.5   At elevations greater than 1 km above the surface, the wind (V) follows the curved isobars of lows and highs. Because the direction of the horizontal pressure gradient force (P_H) changes from place to place, a balance between it and the Coriolis force (C) is never reached. As a result air moves counterclockwise about lows and clockwise about highs in the Northern Hemisphere. In the Southern Hemisphere these wind directions are reversed.

weather maps for levels *greater than 1 km (0.6 mi) above the surface* and at latitudes more than about 20° away from the equator, the tendency for the wind to follow the isobars would be found so impressive that one would be hard pressed to find exceptions. However, the wind does often blow across the isobars, but the angle at which it crosses is usually so small that it is difficult to detect it by simply looking at a weather map. Nevertheless, the flow across the isobars is very important to the development and maintenance of lows and highs.

Wind in the friction layer.   In studying the wind in the first kilometer (0.6 mi) above the surface, the force of friction must be added to the horizontal pressure gradient force and the Coriolis force. As was shown in Figure 4.3, a parcel of air in response to a horizontal pressure gradient moves toward low pressure with the Coriolis force acting to deflect the air to the right (in the Northern Hemisphere). However, in the first kilometer of the atmosphere, friction with surface obstacles prevents the air parcel from reaching the speed that is necessary for a balance to be achieved between the horizontal pressure gradient force and the Coriolis force. As a result, the air parcel continues to move somewhat across the isobars toward lower pressure, as shown in Figure 4.6.

The angle at which the wind crosses the isobars depends on the roughness of the surface. Over

the relatively smooth oceans the angle may be 10°–20°, while over the continents it is more likely to be 20°–40°. In a dense forest the angle may approach 90°. These angles are typical for conditions at about 10 m

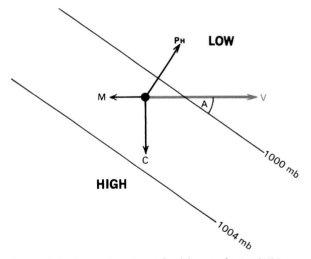

Figure 4.6   In the atmosphere's first kilometer friction (M) is an important force. Because it slows the wind speed, a geostrophic balance between the horizontal pressure gradient (P_H) and Coriolis (C) forces cannot be reached. As a result the wind (V) blows across the isobars at an angle (A) which is typically 10°–20° over the oceans and 20°–40° over land. A Northern Hemisphere example is shown.

(32 ft) above the surface. At higher elevations, but yet in the friction layer, the frictional drag on the air is less, so the wind speed is greater and the angle at which the wind crosses the isobars is smaller. At heights near 1 km, friction becomes negligible and the wind blows approximately parallel to the isobars.

In regions of low pressure, the air flow in the first kilometer above the surface is not only cyclonic but also somewhat inward toward the low center. In regions of high pressure, it is anticyclonic and somewhat outward from the high center. The top panel of Figure 4.7 illustrates this flow.

Convergence, divergence, and vertical air motion. Because the cyclonic flow of air in a low is accompanied by an inward motion near the surface due to friction, there is a *convergence* of air at low elevations. It might be expected that the accumulation of inward-spiraling air would cause the atmospheric pressure at the surface to rise and the low to disappear. This sometimes occurs; however, frequently lows do not disappear, and in fact the pressure at

their center sometimes decreases. Obviously, for a low to be maintained, there must be an outflow or *divergence* of air at higher elevations to compensate for the convergence at low levels (Fig. 4.7). *Thus lows are characterized by an inward spiraling of air at low elevations which rises and flows outward at high elevations.* The upward motion of the air allows it to expand and cool, with the cooling often leading to clouds and precipitation. This is the fundamental reason why lows (cyclones) are typically areas of clouds and precipitation.

In a high there is a divergence of air in the friction layer with the outward-spiraling air being replaced by air sinking from higher elevations. At these higher elevations there is a compensating convergence of air. The fair weather associated with highs (anticyclones) is the result of the sinking and warming of the air. Clouds do not form in sinking air.

The lower panel of Figure 4.7 illustrates the tendency for convergence at low levels to compensate for the divergence at higher levels, or vice versa. While the inflow or outflow of air in the lowest 1 km is quite evident on a weather map, the compensating outflow or inflow aloft is not readily apparent. However, because of the stronger wind speeds aloft, and also because the cross-isobar flow aloft occurs through a great depth of the atmosphere, compensation can occur. Finally, it should be noted that for a low to develop or deepen, the divergence at high elevations must exceed the convergence in the friction layer; and for a high to develop or strengthen, the upper level convergence must exceed the low-level divergence.

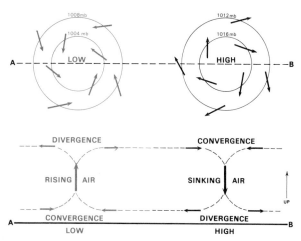

Figure 4.7 In the atmosphere's first kilometer the wind in the Northern Hemisphere blows counterclockwise and somewhat inward in lows and clockwise and somewhat outward in highs (top panel). The bottom panel is a vertical cross section along the line *AB* of the top panel. In lows there is convergence of air at low elevations, rising motion and divergence at higher elevations. In highs there is divergence near the surface, sinking motion and convergence aloft. In the Southern Hemisphere the rotation of air about lows and highs is reversed but the patterns of divergence and convergence are the same as in the Northern Hemisphere.

The Change in Wind with Height

In going upward through the first kilometer (0.6 mi) of the atmosphere, one finds that the wind speed and direction change because of the decreasing effectiveness of friction. Although this change is important, it is less prominent in the atmosphere as a whole than the changes in the wind with height that result from horizontal variations of temperature.

To understand how changes in wind with height are related to horizontal variations of temperature, it is necessary to recall that atmospheric pressure is the weight of the air above the level at which the pressure is measured, and that cold air is more dense than warm air. Thus, in a column of cold air the pressure decreases more rapidly with height than in a column of warm air. Figure 4.8 illustrates the rela-

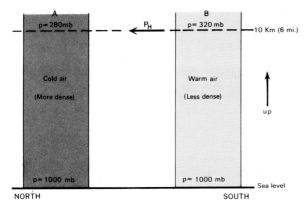

Figure 4.8 Because column A is colder than column B, there is a pressure gradient at an elevation of 10 km even though there is none at sea level. In column A the pressure (p) decreased from 1,000 mb to 280 mb between sea level and 10 km, while in column B the decrease is from 1,000 mb to 320 mb. In the Northern Hemisphere a pressure gradient force (P_H) directed toward the north implies that the geostrophic wind is from the west (i.e., into the page). (See Fig. 4.4.)

tionship. In this Northern Hemisphere example the pressure at the base of both warm and cold columns of air is 1000 mb; however, since the pressure decreases more rapidly in the cold, dense air, the pressure at an elevation of 10 km (6 mi) in the cold column is only 280 mb, compared with 320 mb at the same height in the warm, less dense column. Although there is no horizontal pressure gradient at sea level, there is a horizontal pressure gradient (P_H) directed toward the north at the 10-km level. Consequently, there would not be any wind at sea level; but at the 10-km level the geostrophic wind would blow from the west, that is, into the page of Figure 4.8. (Remember, at heights

greater than 1 km, the actual wind is very nearly geostrophic.) In this example the change in wind is from no wind at the surface to a wind blowing from the west at a height of 10 **km**.

Figure 4.9, an equator-to-North Pole vertical cross section showing the 1000- and 300-mb isobaric surfaces, illustrates the very important relationship between the northward decrease of temperature and the upward change in wind. In the cross section there are high-pressure areas near the earth's surface at about 80°N and 30°N and a low-pressure area near 60°N. In the lower atmosphere there would be anticyclonic air flow around the highs with a region of cyclonic flow around the low. However, because the polar air is colder and more dense than the tropical air, the distance between 1000- and 300-mb surfaces decreases from the tropics toward the pole. A taller column of warm, less dense air is needed to give a pressure difference of 700 mb (1,000 − 300) than a column of cold, dense air. As a result, the high near 80°N disappears at higher levels, while the high near 30°N is maintained even at great elevations. The resulting pressure pattern at the 10-km (6-mi) level is characterized by high pressure in the subtropics and a vast low-pressure area centered over the polar region. The surface low near 60°N leans toward the pole at higher elevations and becomes part of the large low aloft.

The cyclonic flow of air about the low-pressure area centered above the polar region explains the existence of the deep layer of westerly winds found in the middle- and high-latitude regions of the earth. A similar low-pressure area, with its encircling westerly winds, is found aloft over the south polar region. These huge circulation features are called the *polar vortices*. No other feature of the

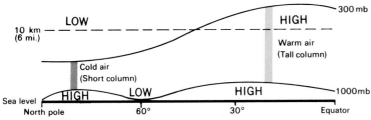

Figure 4.9 A schematic vertical cross section of the 1,000-mb and 300-mb isobaric surfaces. Near the surface there are two highs and one low along the cross section. However, because the distance between the 1,000-mb and 300-mb isobaric surfaces is greater in the warm air than in the cold air, the pressure pattern at 10 km shows a single high located over the subtropics and a vast low centered over the pole.

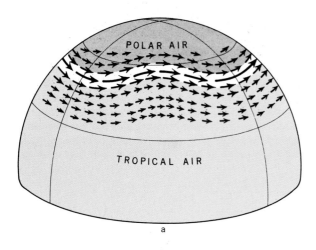

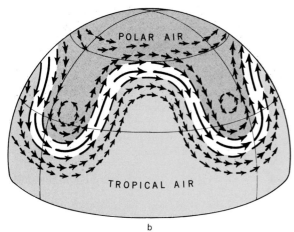

Figure 4.10 The jet stream and waves in the upper atmosphere. In stage *a* the jet is positioned well to the north, waves are weak, and weather is relatively quiet. In stage *b* the jet has developed great oscillations in the form of waves. These waves carry polar air into low latitudes and tropical air into middle and high latitudes, creating stormy periods.

atmosphere's circulation is more prominent. Within each polar vortex at elevations of 10 to 15 km (6 to 9 mi) are at least one and often two or three narrow zones of stronger winds—known as *jet streams*. Below the jet streams the poleward decrease of temperature is especially large. Figure 4.10 portrays the flow of air about the Northern Hemisphere polar vortex. The westerly winds associated with the polar vortices can be compared to the current in a deep river, while the lows and highs found near the earth's surface are relatively small cyclonic and anticyclonic eddies that

are carried along from west to east by the major river of air in which they are embedded. This is the reason why people who live in the middle- and higher-latitude regions of the earth look to the west for tomorrow's weather.

The polar vortices attain their greatest intensity at an elevation of about 12 km (7 mi). Below this height the air is generally colder in the polar regions and warmer in the tropics, so the strength of the westerly wind increases with height. However, above this height the air is usually warmer in polar regions and colder in the tropics; consequently, the vortices become weaker above about 12 km. The vortices are strongest and largest in the winter season when the south-to-north temperature contrast in the layer of air below 12 km is greatest. In summer, when the north-south temperature gradient is weak, the polar vortex is weaker and smaller.

Energy Transformations Which Produce the Wind

In Chapter 3 the workings of the atmospheric system were discussed in terms of the sources and transformations of its energy. Although air motion is fundamental to weather and climate, the kinetic energy (i.e., the energy of motion) of the atmosphere represents only about 1 percent of the energy supplied to the atmosphere by the sun. (See Fig. 3.2.) Thus if the wind is thought of as the output of a vast atmospheric engine, just as the motion of an automobile is the result of energy transformations within the car's engine, the atmospheric engine must be judged very inefficient. How is this small amount of kinetic energy achieved from the vast supply of internal and gravitational potential energy which resides in the atmosphere?

Consider the two columns of air shown in Figure 4.11. If the two columns originally had identical temperatures and pressures at each level, their total potential energies (i.e., the sum of their internal and gravitational potential energies) would be the same. Now, if the column at the right is heated, its temperature increases and the column of air expands upward. These changes reflect an increase in both the internal and the gravitational potential energies of the column. If the column at the left is neither heated nor cooled, its total potential energy remains unchanged. Originally the pressure at an elevation of 10 km was 300 mb in both columns; however, after the column at the right is heated, its pressure at 10 km

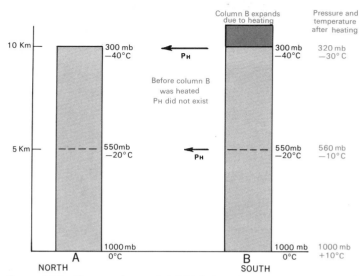

Figure 4.11   The two columns of air initially have the same temperatures and pressure at identical elevations, and thus their total potential energies are the same. After column B is heated its total potential energy is increased; it is warmer and has expanded upward. Before the differential heating there were no horizontal pressure gradients, but after B is heated there are. In response the air begins to move. A transformation of total potential energy to kinetic energy is underway.

increases to 320 mb (i.e., some of the air below 10 km moves to above 10 km during expansion). There is now a horizontal pressure gradient directed toward the north. In response to this pressure gradient, the air at the 10-km level begins to move toward the north. This represents a transformation of total potential energy to kinetic energy.

Once air is set in motion, it tends to pile up in some places and spread out in other places. In regions where the air piles up (converges), the pressure at lower levels rises; and in regions where the air spreads out (diverges), the pressure at lower levels decreases. This leads to new pressure differences and new motions. It is important to note that in this example the kinetic energy of the wind was not achieved until the column on the right was heated. It is equally important to note that the same effect could have been achieved if the left-hand column had been cooled while the right-hand column did not change. This is the reason for saying that *differential heating or cooling* of the atmosphere is the basic cause of the wind.

The kinetic energy that was produced by the differential heating described above will eventually be dissipated by friction with the earth's surface; and unless there is additional differential heating, the wind will cease. Its kinetic energy will have been transformed back into internal energy as the result of friction. As noted previously, the differences in heating and cooling in the atmosphere occur on many scales, the largest and most important being that which exists between polar and tropical latitudes. These differences are continually maintained because in the polar latitudes there is cooling due to a radiation deficit, while in tropical latitudes there is heating due to a radiation surplus. As a consequence the kinetic energy of the atmosphere (or wind) is maintained despite the effect of friction.

HOW ATMOSPHERIC MOTIONS PRODUCE WEATHER

Weather results from various motions of air within the atmospheric system. Winds carry cold air from the polar regions toward the tropics and warm air from the tropics toward higher latitudes. Likewise, they transport moisture-laden air from oceanic regions to the continents and drier air from the continents to oceanic areas. Although these motions are mainly horizontal, they frequently also have a slight downward or upward component. Whether the vertical motion is downward or upward determines whether the weather is clear or cloudy and wet.

Vertical Motions: Clouds and Precipitation

Vertical motion in the atmosphere can occur in a number of ways: (1) When horizontally moving air (wind) encounters a range of hills or mountains, some of the air first rises and then descends as it passes over the range. Such motion is called *orographic,* and any precipitation that forms because of it is known as *orographic precipitation.* (See Fig. 4.12.) (2) Small differences in the solar heating of the land surface often initiate local *convection currents.* Puffy cumulus clouds are likely to form in the rising current, while the sky between the individual cloud elements is clear, because here the air is descending. (3) But the most important cause of vertical motion is the large-

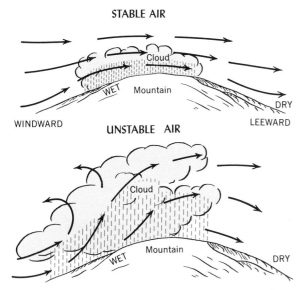

Figure 4.12 When air is forced to rise over a terrain obstacle, orographic precipitation is likely to occur. If the air is stable the clouds are stratified and have less vertical thickness, so the precipitation is light. But when the air is unstable the rising motion is greater, the clouds are thicker, and the precipitation is heavier.

scale horizontal convergence or divergence of air currents, such as those found in cyclones and anticyclones.

Hydrostatic Stability

The ease with which air can move upward or downward depends on how rapidly the temperature of the atmosphere decreases with height. Vertical motions (either up or down) are favored by a large (or steep) *lapse rate* (i.e., by a rapid fall-off or lapse of temperature with height). If the lapse rate is large enough, an air parcel which is pushed slightly upward will continue to rise. A lapse rate which permits this is said to be *hydrostatically unstable* or simply *unstable.* The air in such a region is also said to be *buoyant.* If the lapse rate is small or if the temperature actually increases with height (temperature inversion), the air will resist vertical displacement. Such a lapse rate is called *stable.* In the troposphere (the lower 7 to 17 km of the atmosphere) the average lapse rate is about 6.5°C/km. Of course, in some places and at some times the rate of temperature decrease with height is much greater or smaller than this.

If a parcel of air is lifted *through* the atmosphere, its volume expands because at higher elevations the atmospheric pressure surrounding it is less. The expansion of the rising air parcel causes its temperature to decrease, just as the air escaping from a tire expands and cools. If heat is neither added to nor removed from the rising parcel, its expansion alone causes its temperature to decrease 10°C for each kilometer it rises (or 1°C/100 m or 5.5°F/1,000 ft). Likewise, if this air sinks, it will warm 1°C/100 m. This rate of decrease of temperature with height is called the *dry adiabatic lapse rate.* Any process in which there is no loss or gain of heat is called *adiabatic.* The dry adiabatic lapse rate applies only to air which is rising or sinking adiabatically.

Whenever the lapse rate is greater than the dry adiabatic lapse rate, the air is unstable; when it is less, the air is stable if the air is unsaturated. In Figure 4.13 are examples of stable and unstable lapse rates for air which does not become saturated. If the rising parcel were to become saturated, some of its water vapor would condense to form clouds, and latent heat would be released. The addition of latent heat to the rising parcel reduces the rate at which it cools. The new rate of cooling, which would be closer

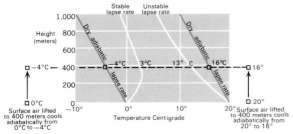

Figure 4.13 Examples of stable and unstable lapse rates for unsaturated air. The white line shows the actual air temperatures at different heights. When an air parcel is lifted, its temperature cools at the dry adiabatic lapse rate (brown line). In the stable case, surface air that is lifted to 400 m is cooler than its surroundings (−4°C versus +3°C). Thus it lacks buoyancy and sinks back. In the unstable case, the surface air lifted to 400 m is warmer than its surroundings (16°C versus 13°C) and is buoyant.

to 0.6°C/100 m, is called the *saturated adiabatic lapse rate.* This slower rate of cooling in effect makes the air more buoyant (i.e., less stable). The importance of hydrostatic stability is illustrated in the case of orographic lifting shown in Figure 4.12.

The hydrostatic stability of a *layer* of air is increased when it is cooled at the bottom or heated at the top, or when *subsidence* occurs, that is, when the layer sinks and spreads out laterally at a lower elevation. As the layer of air sinks, the top of the layer sinks farther and warms more than the bottom, thus producing a more stable lapse rate within the layer. On the other hand, a layer of air which is heated at the bottom or cooled at the top, or which experiences a general lifting and stretching, becomes less stable. Since anticyclones are regions in which there is subsidence, the air within them tends to be more stable than the air found in cyclones, where widespread rising motion is characteristic.

Formation of Clouds and Precipitation

Rising motion is essential to the formation of clouds and precipitation. All of the earth's precipitation and nearly all of its clouds occur in regions in which the air is rising. The way in which clouds form in rising air and the reasons for formation of precipitation in some clouds but not others are the central topics of this section.

Atmospheric water vapor. In Chapter 2 it was noted that the atmosphere is a mixture of dry air, water vapor, and various inorganic and organic impurities. While the proportions of the permanent gases are very uniform, the amount of water vapor is quite variable, ranging from practically nothing to as much as 4 percent of the total volume of air. Because the amount of atmospheric water vapor (an invisible gas) varies from place to place and from time to time, it is necessary that quantities be defined which describe the amount present. Although there are numerous such quantities, we shall use only three.

The *specific humidity* of a sample of air is simply the ratio of the mass of water vapor present to the total mass of the air. It is normally expressed in terms of the number of grams of water vapor present in 1,000 g of air. At the earth's surface the specific humidity in winter-time polar air may be only a small fraction of 1 g of water vapor for each 1,000 g of air, while in warm tropical air it may reach 40 g/1,000 g of air. The maximum amount of water vapor that can be present in the air depends on the temperature of the air; the warmer the air is, the more water vapor it can hold. The *saturation specific humidity* is the maximum value the specific humidity can attain for a given sample of air. The saturation specific humidity, which depends primarily on the temperature of the air but also slightly on its pressure, is *not* a measure of the actual water vapor content, but only of the amount that the air could contain. The curve in the graph of Figure 4.14 shows how the saturation specific humidity depends on temperature.

The *relative humidity* is the ratio of the specific humidity to the saturation specific humidity. It is normally expressed as a percentage. For example, if there are actually 6 g of water vapor present in 1,000 g of air but the air is warm enough to contain 12 g, the relative humidity is 50 percent (⁶/₁₂). The relative humidity does not provide a measure of the absolute amount of water vapor present but does indicate how near the air is to saturation. If the specific humidity in the 1,000-g parcel of air mentioned above remains at 6 g but the air is cooled to a temperature at which the saturation specific humidity is only 8 g/1,000 g of air, the relative humidity will then rise to 75 percent (i.e., ⁶/₈). If the air were cooled to a temperature where the saturation specific humidity is only 6 g/1,000 g of air, the parcel would be saturated (⁶/₆). (See Fig. 4.14). Normally, the relative humidity is high in the early morning hours when the

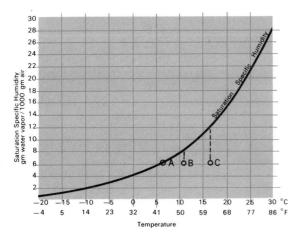

Figure 4.14 *The saturation specific ratio not only increases with temperature but increases at an increasing rate. For 1,000 gm of air containing 6 gm of water vapor, the relative humidity is 100 percent if the air temperature is 7°C (A); 75 percent if the air temperature is 11°C (B); and 50 percent if the air temperature is 17°C (C).*

temperature of the air is cool and the saturation specific humidity is low. In the afternoon when the air temperature (and also the saturation specific humidity) is higher, the relative humidity is lower, even though the actual specific humidity of the air has not changed.

A very useful indicator of the moisture present in the air is the *dew point temperature*, which is simply the temperature to which air must be cooled (at the same pressure) before it becomes saturated. The dew point temperature is always less than the air temperature except when the air is saturated, in which case the temperature and dew point are the same. Since the dew point temperature of a parcel of air does not change unless water vapor is evaporated into the air or condensed out, it provides an excellent measure of the actual amount of water vapor present in the air.

Condensation. As long as the temperature of a parcel of air is warmer than its dew point temperature, the air is unsaturated and condensation will not occur. However, if the air is cooled, its temperature approaches its dew point, or, viewed in terms of specific humidity, its saturation specific humidity decreases and approaches its specific humidity. When the dew point temperature is reached, a relative

humidity of 100 percent is achieved. The air is now saturated, and any further cooling will lead to condensation; that is, the invisible molecules of water vapor will cluster together to form the tiny droplets of liquid water of which clouds are composed.

In the atmosphere, cloud droplets will not form when the relative humidity of the air reaches 100 percent unless there are microscopic impurities present around which the water vapor molecules can cluster. In fact, in air which is completely cleansed of impurities, the relative humidity may reach 400 or 500 percent without condensation occurring. Fortunately, within the atmosphere there are enormous numbers of *condensation nuclei* present around which cloud droplets can form. For example, the breaking of ocean waves along shorelines results in a spray of sea water, some of which evaporates to leave tiny sea-salt particles. The particles, which are carried through much of the atmosphere by the wind, are excellent condensation nuclei. Certain combustion products also serve as condensation nuclei. The increased fogginess in industrial areas is attributed to the great abundance of condensation nuclei produced by combustion.

From the above description it is clear that condensation requires that (1) the atmosphere contain water vapor, (2) condensation nuclei be available, and (3) the air be cooled to its dew point. In the atmosphere away from the surface of the earth, the only way in which air is cooled sufficiently to produce clouds is through ascent and the accompanying adiabatic cooling.

Precipitation. The formation of a cloud does not ensure that precipitation will occur. It is not at all uncommon for a cloud layer to persist for a number of days without any precipitation developing. The tiny cloud droplets remain suspended in the rising air in which they form.

Most precipitation falls from clouds which are composed of a mixture of water droplets and ice crystals. Liquid water, particularly when it is in the form of tiny cloud droplets, does not always freeze when its temperature falls below freezing, 0°C (32°F). Some clouds may be as cold as −40°C (−40°F) yet contain unfrozen cloud droplets. However, if the cloud is colder than freezing—particularly if it is colder than about −10°C (14°F)—some of the cloud particles may form as tiny ice crystals rather than water droplets. It is not clearly understood why this occurs, although it may be that the type of condensation nuclei around which condensation occurs determines whether a water droplet or an ice crystal will form.

If both liquid droplets and ice crystals exist within a cloud, there is a strong tendency for the liquid droplets to evaporate and the ice crystals to grow. As an ice crystal becomes larger and heavier, it begins to fall through the clouds and grow still larger by colliding with cloud droplets and other ice crystals. If the cloud is thick, the falling ice crystal will leave the base of the cloud as a full-size snowflake. If the temperature in the lower part of the atmosphere is above freezing, the falling ice crystal melts and a raindrop results. In the middle- and high-latitude regions of the earth nearly all of the precipitation begins in this manner, and even in the tropics much of the precipitation starts in the form of ice.

Cloud forms.   Clouds provide a striking feature of the natural landscape. Although there are many varieties of clouds, ten basic cloud forms, or *genera*, are recognized by the weather analyst. Nine of the ten forms contain either the term *stratus* or *cumulus*. "Stratus" implies stratification; the clouds have a sheetlike appearance. The term *cumulus* indicates

that the clouds have some vertical development; the clouds consist of detached cloud elements appearing as individual heaps of clouds. Stratified clouds tend to occur in air which is ascending gently and rather uniformly, while cumuloform clouds occur in air which is rising more vigorously and less uniformly. The term *cirrus* is applied to clouds that have a streaky or wispy appearance.

The ten cloud genera are combined into four groups as illustrated in Table 4.1. Three of the four groups are established according to the height of the cloud base; a fourth group, vertically developed, is used for clouds which have relatively low bases but which may have high tops. For example, the cumulonimbus (or thunderstorm) cloud often has a base only 1 km (0.6 mi) above the ground, but its top may reach 20 km (12 mi). (See Fig. 4.15.) The high-cloud types occur at such high elevations that the cold temperatures permit only ice-crystal clouds to exist. The middle and low types are composed principally of water droplets; however, in the upper portions of some of these clouds (particularly the middle type), a mixture of ice crystals and water droplets may exist. While a small cumulus is composed entirely of water droplets, the towering cumulonimbus is composed of water droplets in its lower portion and ice crystals in

Figure 4.15 A cumulonimbus cloud, a type in which convective showers originate. Photographed from an airplane. *(Courtesy of T. Fujita.)*

its upper portion. Often the upper part appears in the shape of a blacksmith's anvil. (See Fig. 4.15.) It is at intermediate levels within the cumulonimbus, where there are both water droplets and ice crystals present, that the heavy precipitation of a typical thunderstorm forms.

Precipitation types.   Most of the earth's precipitation initially forms as snow or ice. If the air temperature from the cloud all the way to the ground is colder than freezing, the precipitation will reach the ground as snow. Typically, 25 cm (10 in.) of snow melts down to about 2.5 cm (1 in.) of water. If the temperature in the lower atmosphere is above freezing, the snow will melt and reach the surface as rain. Sometimes *drizzle*, a very fine mist, falls from low clouds. Occasionally a layer of air in which the temperature is warmer than freezing exists at intermediate elevations. In falling through this layer, the snow may melt and form rain; but if the rain then falls through a colder layer of air near the ground, the raindrops may freeze to form *sleet* or *ice pellets*. If the layer of cold air near the ground is very shallow, the rain may not freeze until it strikes the ground or objects such as trees or electric wires. This causes *glaze*, a layer of ice, to form on the objects. In thunderstorms the strong, turbulent motions may cause the falling precipitation to be repeatedly carried aloft where new layers of ice are added until large *hailstones* form.

In general, steady rain or snow falls from the rather thick stratiform clouds that form in stable air, while showery precipitation falls from the cumulo-form clouds, particularly the cumulonimbus, that form in unstable air.

Dew and fog.   On clear, calm nights the surface of the earth radiates some of its heat to space. If the temperature of the surface becomes cooler than the dew point temperature of the air which is in contact with the surface, dew (or frost) will form on the surface. At times, if there is just a slight stirring of air, a thin layer of air near the earth will be cooled by the cold surface to the point where a shallow layer of fog forms. Such fog is called *radiation* or *ground fog*. With ground fog present, the stars or moon may be seen but the horizontal visibility is greatly restricted.

Fog also forms when mild, humid air moves over a colder surface and is cooled to its dew point. Here the emphasis is on the horizontal movement of air over a colder surface. Such fogs are known as *advection fogs*. In winter when mild, moist air from the Gulf of Mexico moves northward over snow-covered regions of the midwestern United States, widespread advection fog develops. Similarly, dense and persistent advection fog forms over the Grand Banks, which are located south of Newfoundland, when air that has been over the warm Gulf Stream moves northward over the cold water of the Labrador Current.

Fog may also occur when rain falls through drier air near the surface. Evaporation of the falling rain not only cools the air but also adds water vapor to it. When the surface air becomes saturated, fog will

TABLE 4.1   THE TEN GENERA OF CLOUDS

	Typical heights of cloud bases	Genera
High	5–14 km (16,500–45,000 ft)	Cirrus Cirrostratus Cirrocumulus
Middle	2–7 km (6,500–23,000 ft)	Altostratus Altocumulus
Low	Below 2 km (6,500 ft)	Stratus Stratocumulus Nimbostratus
Vertical development		Cumulus Cumulonimbus

form. Such fogs are sometimes called *rain* or *frontal fogs*.

Air Masses and Fronts

In high latitudes the radiation deficit leads to the formation of extensive areas of cold polar air, particularly over the continents, while in low latitudes the radiation surplus produces warm tropical air. The winds of middle-latitude cyclones and anticyclones draw these contrasting air masses into the middle-latitude regions of the earth, where their interaction plays a crucial role in producing weather.

Air-Mass Characteristics and Origin

An *air mass* is an extensive portion of the atmosphere in which the characteristics of the air, particularly temperature and humidity, are relatively uniform in the horizontal direction. An air mass gains a distinctive character whenever it remains in contact with a large and relatively uniform surface long enough to take on the temperature and moisture characteristics of the surface. Those parts of the land or sea surface where air masses develop are called *source regions*. The uniform surfaces of the warm tropical oceans during any season and the snow-covered arctic plains of Canada or Siberia in winter are examples of source regions. For the air to fully gain the characteristics of such surfaces, it must remain over the source region for several days. The weak, divergent winds of anticyclones favor the formation of an air mass, particularly if the anticyclone is stagnant or very sluggish in its movement across the source region.

Since the atmosphere is mainly heated or cooled by the land or water surface over which it lies, the lower layers of the air mass first gain the characteristics of the source region. In the snow-covered regions of northern Eurasia and North America in winter or in Antarctica throughout most of the year, the air loses heat to the surface and becomes very cold in its lowest layers, resulting in the development of a surface temperature inversion. At times the temperature inversion may extend to an elevation of 3 km (1.8 mi) or more above the surface. Because the air is very cold, it cannot contain much water vapor; it is dry, cold, and hydrostatically stable. On the other hand, the warm tropical and subtropical oceans add both heat and moisture to the air above them. Since the air is heated from the bottom, the temperature of the air decreases rather rapidly with height and the lapse rate is relatively unstable.

Classification of Air Masses

Air masses are designated by the name of their source region. Source regions fall naturally into polar latitudes and tropical latitudes. The middle latitudes, by contrast, are the scene of frequent interaction between polar and tropical air masses, so they generally lack the uniform conditions essential to a source region.

The air-mass classification is further refined by dividing both the cold polar (P) and warm tropical (T) groups on the basis of whether the air gained its characteristics over the continents (c) or maritime areas (m). This division results in four major air-mass types: continental polar (cP), maritime polar (mP), continental tropical (cT), and maritime tropical (mT). The major classifications are summarized in Table 4.2 and their source regions in the North American region are shown in Figure 4.16.

Air masses are modified as they move away from their source regions. If the air mass moves over a warmer surface, it is heated from below and becomes less stable in its lower layers. When an air mass moves over a cooler surface, it is chilled from below and gains stability. In addition, if an air mass sinks either in its source region or as it moves out from the source region, it becomes more stable aloft. If it rises, as in a cyclonic circulation, it is stretched vertically and becomes less stable aloft.

Fronts

The converging winds of a cyclone carry contrasting air masses into its circulation, thus producing rather sharp air-mass contrasts. When two air masses with different temperatures (and, thus, different densities) come together, they do not freely mix. Rather, a pronounced transition zone, called a *front*, forms between them. On weather maps, a front is indicated as a line which marks the *warm edge of the transition zone* at the surface. Within the transition zone the *isotherms*, which are lines connecting points having the same temperature, are close together. Sometimes the transition zone may be as narrow as 50 km (30

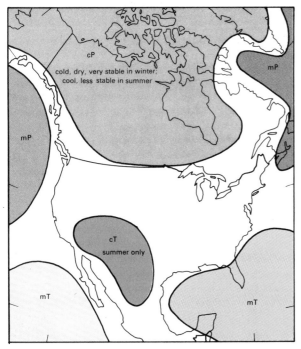

Figure 4.16   Four major North American air masses and their usual source regions.

mi), but more frequently it is 100 to 250 km (60 to 150 mi) wide. The passage of a front usually brings marked changes in temperature and humidity, since

its passage represents the transition from one air mass to another.

Fronts can exist only in cyclones or in troughs of low pressure where the converging winds keep the two contrasting air masses next to each other. The diverging winds of an anticyclone would destroy the frontal contrast. Anticyclones tend to be the sites of homogeneous air-mass formation, while cyclones are the places where contrasting air masses meet.

A front is a three-dimensional feature with the colder, more dense air mass forming a wedge of gentle slope under the warmer, less dense air. Since the colder air is beneath the warmer air, a frontal zone is typically characterized by a temperature inversion.

It is not common for a front to remain stationary for very long. Usually one of the contrasting air masses advances. If colder air advances, it underruns the warmer air, often resulting in ascent of the warm air. The portion of the front along which the cold air advances is called the *cold front*. When the warmer, less dense air advances, it tends to glide up over the wedge of colder air. This portion of the front is called the *warm front*. (See Fig. 4.17.) While a cyclone in general tends to be a region of rising air, the ascent is more pronounced in the frontal regions. Consequently, the clouds and precipitation of a cyclone are concentrated along the fronts.

TABLE 4.2   CLASSIFICATION OF AIR MASSES

Major group	Subgroup	Source region	Properties at source
Polar	Polar continental (*cP*)	Arctic Basin; northern Eurasia and northern North America; Antarctica	Cold, dry, very stable all year in Antarctica, but only in winter in Eurasia and North America; in summer cool, less dry, less stable
	Polar maritime (*mP*)	Oceans poleward of 40° or 50° latitude	Cool, moist, relatively unstable
Tropical	Tropical continental (*cT*)	Low-latitude deserts, especially Sahara and Australian Deserts	Hot, very dry, relatively unstable at low levels
	Tropical maritime (*mT*)	Oceans of tropics and subtropics	Warm, moist, greater instability toward west side of ocean

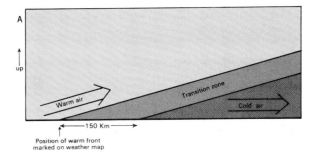

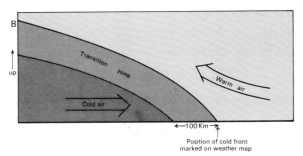

Figure 4.17 A cross section through an idealized (*a*) warm front and (*b*) cold front. On weather maps fronts are shown as lines marking the *warm edge* of the transition zone. In the diagram the vertical slopes of the frontal zones are greatly exaggerated. A typical slope of a cold front is about 1:100 and that of a warm front only about 1:200.

Atmospheric Disturbances

Nearly all of the precipitation the earth receives occurs in association with various atmospheric *disturbances*. A disturbance is simply a pattern of airflow (i.e., wind) which causes air within a major portion of the disturbance to rise. Even the orographic precipitation, which forms when air is forced to rise over highlands, occurs mainly when a disturbance is present in the highland region.

The cyclone, with its encircling winds and convergent air flow at low elevations, is a common type of atmospheric disturbance. In the middle- and high-latitude regions of the earth, cyclones normally contain fronts which separate the various air masses that are part of the cyclone's circulation. In the tropical regions, where there is very little air-mass contrast, cyclones lack fronts.

Middle-Latitude Disturbances

In the world's middle-latitude regions the daily weather changes are often large and erratic. A spell of fine, clear weather gives way to a stormy period during which a traveling disturbance brings precipitation. To appreciate the climate of the middle latitudes it is necessary to have some understanding of the disturbances which bring these day-to-day weather changes.

Structure and weather of a model cyclone.   The cyclones of the middle- and high-latitude portions of the earth are known as *extratropical cyclones*. Their existence has been recognized for more than a century; however, it was principally the work of a group of Norwegian meteorologists during World War I that led to the present concept of the extratropical cyclone. Although there are differences between individual extratropical cyclones, they are sufficiently alike to permit them to be described by an idealized model. The model cyclone shown in Figure 4.18 is essentially the same as that developed by the Norwegian J. Bjerknes in 1918. Within the cyclone's circulation are two different air masses, one cold and usually dry and the other warm and relatively moist. The transition zone separating the two air masses is called the *polar front* because it marks the southern border of the cold polar air. In Figure 4.18 the isotherms are close together in the transition zone. On a weather map the polar front is drawn along the warm edge of the transition zone. In the Northern Hemisphere counterclockwise flow of air about the low-pressure center carries the polar front southward on the west side of the cyclone as a cold front. On the east side the polar front is carried northward as a warm front.

As the warm air moves northward to the east of the low center, it tends to rise because of the general convergence of air within the cyclone. However, the main ascent of the warm air occurs when the northward-moving air reaches the warm front and tends to glide up over the colder air at the surface. Thus a broad area of clouds and precipitation typically develops to the north of the warm front.

The northwesterly winds to the west of the cyclone center carry cold air southward and eastward. As the cold front advances into the area previously occupied by the warm air, there is a tendency for the warm air to be displaced upward. Thus, along the cold front, in the region of increased ascent, a relatively

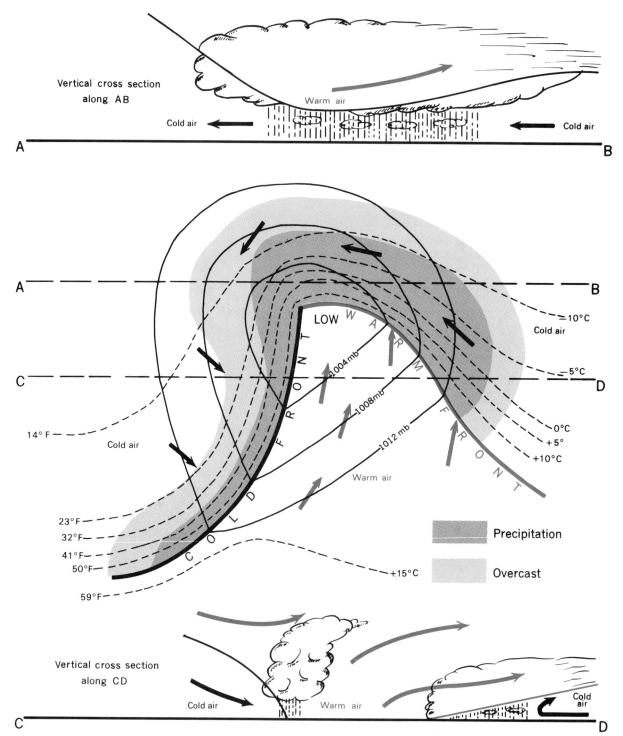

Figure 4.18 Norwegian model of an extratropical cyclone *middle panel*: weather map view; *top panel*: cross section along line *AB*; *bottom panel*: cross section along line *CD*.

narrow zone of cloudiness and precipitation often develops. The vertical cross sections shown at the bottom and top of Figure 4.18 illustrate the relative positions and movements of the warm and cold air in the regions south and north of the low-pressure center, respectively. Figure 4.19, a satellite photograph of a major cyclone centered near eastern Long Island, New York, clearly shows the clouds associated with the fronts.

No two cyclones are exactly alike. Nevertheless, as a cyclone approaches and passes a particular locality, a clearly recognizable sequence of weather events occurs. The type of sequence depends on whether the low-pressure center passes to the north

or south of the locality. First, consider the sequence associated with a passage of the center to the north. Assume that the cyclone center shown in Figure 4.18 moves directly eastward and that the locality for which we wish to describe the weather is located at points progressively further west along the line from D to C. With the approach of the cyclone (i.e., when the locality is near point D), the wind blows from the east or southeast, and high cirrus-type clouds move in from the west. As the warm front advances toward the locality, the clouds increase and thicken and steady precipitation begins. The temperature slowly rises until the warm front passes. With the passage of the warm front, the wind shifts to the south or

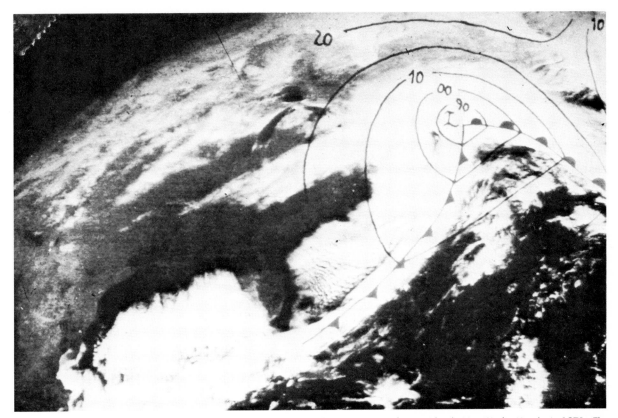

Figure 4.19 Satellite photo of a major cyclone centered near the eastern tip of Long Island, New York, March 4, 1971. The cold-front and warm-front positions and a few isobars have been superimposed. Note how the cloud pattern conforms to the frontal positions. The clouds behind the cold front formed because of the heating and moistening of the cold air as it flowed over the warm ocean. The broad white area extending from the middle Mississippi Valley northeastward toward the cyclone is snow that was produced by the cyclone as it moved northeastward. *(Courtesy NOAA and Space Science and Engineering Center, University of Wisconsin, Madison.)*

southwest, the precipitation ceases, and the sky partially clears. Within the warm-air sector of the cyclone there are variable amounts of middle-type clouds and warm temperatures. With the approach of the cold front, the cloudiness thickens and showery precipitation begins. As the cold front passes, the wind shifts from southerly to northwest and the temperature begins to fall. After the front has passed some distance to the east, the precipitation ceases, the clouds break, and the weather is colder.

To examine the weather events that occur as an eastward-moving cyclone center passes to the south of a locality, again refer to Figure 4.18, but in this case assume that the locality is progressively located at points along the line from B to A. Near point B the wind is from the east, the temperature is cold, and high clouds move in from the west. As the cyclone moves eastward, the clouds thicken, precipitation begins, and there is a slight rise in temperature. The wind changes from east to northeast and eventually to north. When the cyclone has moved well to the east (i.e., when the locality is near point A), the precipitation ends and the clouds break. With the low center passing to the south, the warm-air sector of the cyclone does not reach the locality; the warm air is found only aloft, where it glides up over the colder air near the surface. Major snowstorms or periods of cool, rainy weather are associated with cyclone centers passing to the south of a locality. Figures 4.20 and 4.21 are a surface and upper-level weather map of a major cyclone over the central United States. At the bottom of Figure 4.20 are time graphs showing how the weather changed at two localities as the cyclone moved eastward.

Origin and movement of extratropical cyclones.
The origin of an extratropical cyclone—a process called *cyclogenesis*—usually begins with the formation of a small low-pressure center along the polar front. As the surface low-pressure area develops, the air flow gradually becomes counterclockwise in the Northern Hemisphere (clockwise in the Southern Hemisphere). A wave (or bulge) forms on the polar

front; the cold polar air pushes equatorward to the west of the low center, and the warm tropical air flows poleward to the east of the center. The stages of a Northern Hemisphere cyclone are shown in Figure 4.22. As the cyclone matures, the wave on the front becomes larger. Typically, the cold front moves more rapidly than the warm front, eventually overtaking the warm front. In the region in which the cold front overtakes the warm front, the warm air is no longer found at the surface; rather, it is squeezed aloft. The transition zone which now separates the cold air that was to the west of the low center from that to the east is called the *occluded front*, and the cyclone is said to have undergone *occlusion*. If the temperature of the two air masses is about the same, the transition zone between the two can no longer be called a front. All that remains of the cyclone is, then, a counterclockwise flow of air or eddy within the cold air. (See panel F of Fig. 4.22.) The front separating the polar and tropical air is now located far to the south of the remaining eddy.

Extratropical cyclones develop in the broad current of westerly winds which is a part of the polar vortex. Within this broad westerly stream is the jet stream, a narrow zone usually only a few hundred kilometers wide, of much stronger winds. While the wind speed in the broad westerly flow is typically 50 to 100 km/hr (30 to 60 mi/hr), the wind speed in the jet stream is often 150 to 300 km/hr (90 to 180 mi/hr). The jet stream, which is usually strongest at altitudes between 10 and 15 km (6 to 9 mi), is located above the polar front. Recall that early in this chapter it was explained that the high-level westerly winds of middle latitudes are the result of the air at lower levels being cold in the polar regions and warm in the tropics. Since the temperature difference across the polar front is particularly large, there is an especially large increase in the speed of the west wind above it.

The formation of low-pressure areas along the polar front appears to be closely related to the jet stream. Along the jet stream itself, the speed of the wind varies from place to place. The regions of stronger winds tend to move along the jet stream, and

Figure 4.20 The surface weather map for March 18, 1971. Arrows show direction air is moving. The shaded area was having precipitation. Very strong winds and blizzard conditions occurred in western Nebraska. The dashed line shows the path followed by the cyclone's center: the numbers along the track are used to show what the weather was like at Madison, Wisconsin, and St. Louis, Missouri, when the low was centered at the numbered positions. As the low center passed south of Madison but north of St. Louis, the temperature at Madison remained near freezing (0°C) but at St. Louis rose to 11°C (52°F). In Madison 36 cm (14 in.) of snow fell. St. Louis had only some light rain.

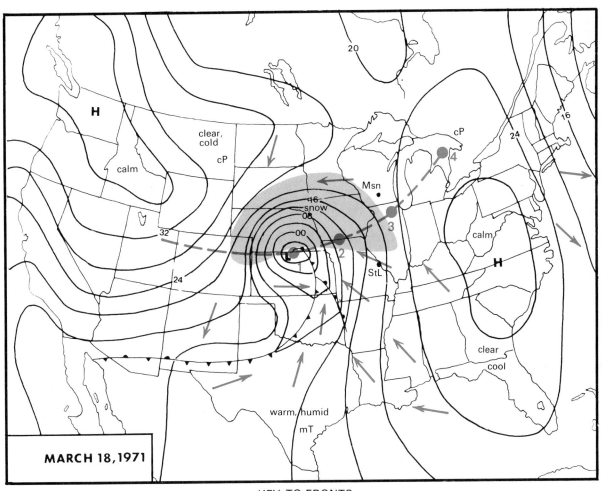

MARCH 18, 1971

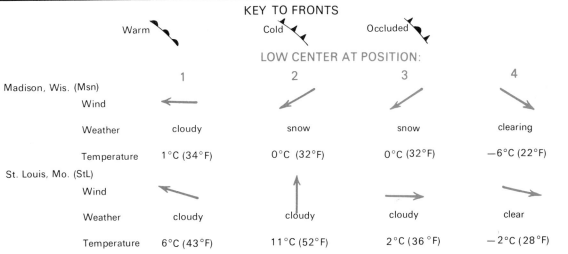

KEY TO FRONTS

Warm   Cold   Occluded

LOW CENTER AT POSITION:

	1	2	3	4
Madison, Wis. (Msn)				
Wind				
Weather	cloudy	snow	snow	clearing
Temperature	1°C (34°F)	0°C (32°F)	0°C (32°F)	−6°C (22°F)
St. Louis, Mo. (StL)				
Wind				
Weather	cloudy	cloudy	cloudy	clear
Temperature	6°C (43°F)	11°C (52°F)	2°C (36°F)	−2°C (28°F)

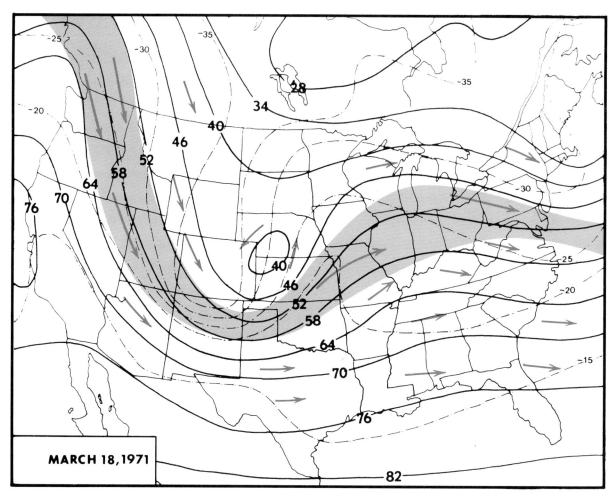

Figure 4.21 This March 18, 1971 map shows the air flow, temperatures, and elevations where the pressure is 500 mb (about 5,500 m or 18,000 ft). The solid lines are contours showing the height of the 500-mb isobaric surface; dashed lines are isotherms (°C). Arrows show the direction the air is moving. Shaded area shows the location of the jet stream. Note that on the surface map (Fig. 4.20) there is a definite low center. However, at higher levels, as shown in this figure, the low is replaced by a large wave in the westerly flow. Reading from the left, the contour values are 5760 m, 5700 m, etc.

as they do, areas of strong divergence develop aloft in certain regions. It is beneath these divergent regions that the atmospheric pressure near the surface decreases and a low-pressure system develops.

Aloft within the westerly flow large meanders, or waves, occur within the flow. In some areas the wind blows from the northwest and in others from the southwest. The development of these waves and surface cyclogenesis usually occur together. If the cyclone becomes a major storm, the wave in the westerly flow grows to a large size. The polar front

and jet stream then sweep far south in one area and north in another. (See Fig. 4.10b.) At these times there is an exceptionally large transport of heat from low latitudes to high latitudes. Thus the growth of a cyclone represents a vital step in the poleward transport of energy that is needed to offset the net loss of heat by radiation in high latitudes and its net gain in low latitudes.

Major extratropical cyclones grow to a size where their circulation may cover a somewhat circular area 2,000 km (1,200 mi) across. The surface

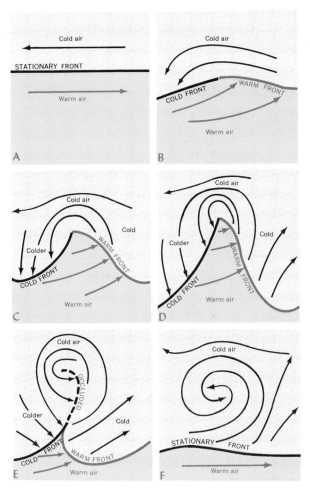

Figure 4.22 Six stages in the life of a frontal cyclone. *B* shows the beginning of a small horizontal wave along the front. In *C* there is a definite cyclonic circulation with well-developed warm and cold fronts. Because of the more rapid movement of the cold front, *D* shows a narrowed warm sector. In *E* the occlusion process is occurring; the cyclone has reached its maximum development, and the warm sector is being rapidly pinched off. In *F* the warm sector has been eliminated; the cyclone is in its dying stages and is represented by only a whirl of cold air. *(Courtesy of U.S. Weather Bureau.)*

cyclone tends to be carried along with the broad westerly flow in which it is embedded just as a shallow eddy in a river is carried along by the main current of the river. The speed of the cyclone's eastward movement depends on the average speed of the

westerly current. In the winter a typical speed is 1,200 km (720 mi) per day. In the summer, when the westerly current is weaker, a typical speed is 800 km (480 mi) per day. In the Northern Hemisphere, cyclogenesis most frequently occurs along the east coasts of North America and Asia and along the east slope of the Rocky Mountains. During the winter season the Mediterranean Sea region is also a favored location for cyclogenesis. Figure 4.23 shows the principal tracks followed by cyclones.

The weather of a locality is influenced not only by the track followed by an extratropical cyclone but also by its stage of development. During the early formative stage, a pattern of clouds and possibly some precipitation develops if moist air is drawn into the cyclone's circulation. As the cyclone grows, the cloud and precipitation areas increase in size, with the heaviest precipitation occurring as the storm approaches its full growth and the rising air motion is greatest. As the cyclone begins to weaken or occlude, the precipitation lessens even though the cloudiness is extensive. In its old age, the cyclone is characterized by only very weak rising motions and light precipitation; however, the cloudiness is widespread. Some cyclones develop, reach maturity, and occlude within a couple of days, while for others the life cycle may take a week or more.

Energy transformation during occlusion. In the early part of this chapter the way in which kinetic energy is achieved from the total potential energy of the atmosphere was discussed. The occlusion process of a cyclone represents a transformation of total potential energy to kinetic energy. As occlusion takes place, the cold, dense air sweeps completely around the cyclone's center near the surface, while the warmer (less dense) air is lifted to higher levels. As a result, the heaviest air is now at low elevations throughout the cyclone and the warmer air is at higher levels. This represents a lowering of the center of the mass of the air in the cyclone, and thus a transformation of total potential energy to the kinetic energy of the winds of the cyclone. The differential heating between high and low latitudes produces the cold and warm air masses, but it is their interaction during the cyclone occlusion process that transforms the total potential energy to kinetic energy.

Other middle-latitude disturbances. While extratropical cyclones are the major producers of precipita-

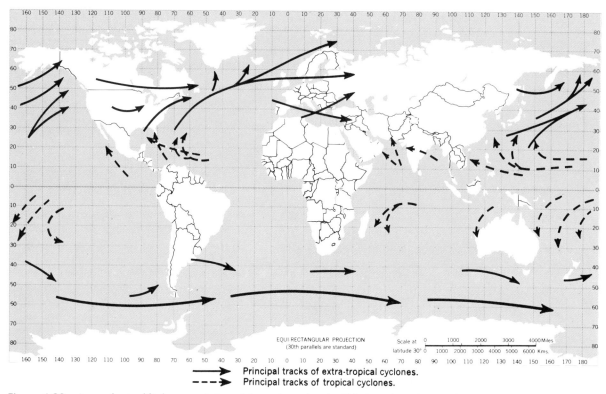

Figure 4.23 A greatly simplified representation of the main tracks of middle-latitude and tropical cyclones. *(After Petterssen.)*

tion, various weak disturbances that cannot properly be called cyclones also contribute to the precipitation of middle latitudes. Sometimes troughs—relatively narrow elongated regions of low pressure—are observed on the surface map. If the air is sufficiently moist, the convergence and rising air along the troughs may lead to precipitation.

At other times broad but poorly organized areas of low pressure appear on the weather map. Within these regions isolated areas of precipitation may develop, but generally they do not become organized as they do in frontal cyclones. At still other times areas of precipitation are noted on a surface weather map in regions where there is no indication of a disturbance. In these situations the cause is often found in the upper-level flow where some sort of weak disturbance exists.

Thunderstorms. Occasionally vigorous convection currents develop over an area of only a few square kilometers or less. Within this small area of strong

upward motion a towering cumulus-type cloud may develop. If the upper part of the cloud is composed entirely of ice crystals, the cloud is classified as a cumulonimbus, and very likely a thunderstorm will occur. (See Fig. 4.15.) Normally such a cloud top reaches a height of at least 10 km (6 mi) and occasionally it extends to 20 km (12 mi). Within portions of the cloud the updraft is so great that large amounts of liquid water and ice are carried far aloft. The strong vertical motions sweeping past the great mass of water and ice lead to a separation of electrical charge within the cloud. When the charge differences between various parts of the cloud or between the cloud and the ground become great, a lightning discharge occurs. The thunder results from the violent expansion of the air caused by the heat generated along the path of the lightning flash. Figure 4.24 is a simplified sketch of air motions in a thunderstorm.

When the amount of water in the cloud becomes so large that the rising air can no longer support the load, it falls as a heavy shower. The

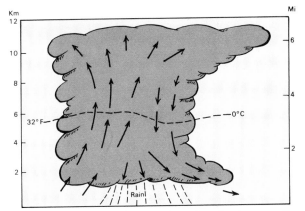

Figure 4.24 A vertical section through a thunderstorm. The cumulonimbus typically has an anvil-shaped top. Within the cloud there are both strong rising and strong sinking air currents.

falling rain drags down air from aloft. When this air reaches the ground, it spreads out laterally, producing the strong, gusty winds that often accompany thunderstorms. Although a single thundershower is usually of short duration and covers only a few square kilometers, the amount of rainfall it produces can be great. If new thundershowers develop next to the original storm, the area covered by the precipitation can be large. Sometimes a number of thunderstorms develop side by side along a line which may extend for distances of 500 km (300 mi) or more. Such lines of thunderstorms are called *squall lines*. They typically are found in the warm-air sector of a cyclone but fairly close to the cold front.

In particularly severe thunderstorms a rotating funnel-shaped cloud may protrude from the cumulonimbus. If the funnel cloud reaches the ground, a *tornado* occurs. The winds within the narrow funnel cloud, which is seldom wider than 1 km (0.6 mi), rotate at a great speed, at times greatly exceeding 400 km/hr (250 mi/hr). In severe squall lines, numerous tornadoes may develop, often resulting in a large loss of life and property.

Some thunderstorms develop in unstable air masses where just the daily heating of the surface by the sun may be sufficient to set off afternoon or evening thunderstorms. However, most thunderstorms occur when there is some convergence in the air flow at low levels. If the air is moist in its lower layers, even weakly convergent air flow, supported by solar heating, may be sufficient to cause the air to rise

to a level where it becomes saturated. The release of latent heat then adds to the buoyancy of the air, and the cloud may then develop rapidly into a cumulonimbus. Often less than an hour's time elapses between the beginning of cloud formation and the occurrence of a thunderstorm.

Thunderstorms are most numerous in the spring and summer, when the air near the earth's surface is strongly heated by the sun but the air at higher elevations is still relatively cold. During winter, thunderstorms are not uncommon in the region of the United States bordering the Gulf of Mexico. As the spring season advances, the frequency of thunderstorms increases and the area affected moves northward. Since thunderstorms occur mainly in maritime tropical air, the northward progression of thunderstorm activity marks the northward advance of the tropical air. Thus, Figure 4.25, which shows the average number of days with thunderstorms in the United States, also suggests the relative frequency of the occurrence of maritime tropical air. Two exceptions are the areas of relatively frequent thunderstorms shown in northeastern New Mexico and southwestern Montana. In these regions orographic factors contribute strongly to thunderstorm activity.

Anticyclones

Although much attention is rightly given to the atmospheric disturbances which are essential for the formation of precipitation, the anticyclone (or high-pressure area) also plays an important role in the

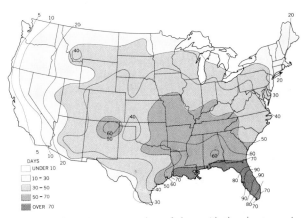

Figure 4.25 Average number of days with thunderstorms in the United States.

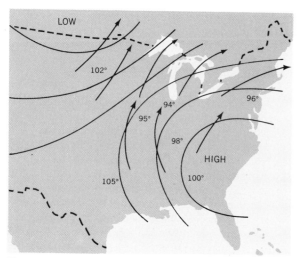

Figure 4.26 A warm anticyclone, relatively stagnant over the southeastern United States, produces unseasonably hot weather over the central and eastern parts of the country.

weather of the middle latitudes. The prolonged summer heat waves of the eastern and central United States occur when a high-pressure area becomes stationary over the southeastern part of the country. The clockwise flow around the anticyclone carries very warm, maritime tropical air northward from the Gulf of Mexico. (See Fig. 4.26.) Because the air motion in the lower atmosphere is divergent, there is a general subsidence of air over the region, which tends to inhibit the development of thunderstorms in the warm, moist air. Often these warm anticyclones are simply extensions of the vast subtropical highs which are centered over the subtropical oceans. These large circulation features reach from the earth's surface upward to very high elevations in the atmosphere. Since their circulation exists through most of the depth of the atmosphere, they move very little.

In winter strong high-pressure areas form over the very cold arctic plains of northeastern Asia (Siberia) and North America. These cold anticyclones, particularly the one over Siberia, persist for much of the winter. Occasionally the arctic high-pressure systems or parts of them move southeastward to the rear of an eastward-moving cyclone. These anticyclones contribute to major outbreaks of polar air and the bright, bitterly cold days of winter. Figure 4.27 shows such an anticyclone.

Between any two cyclones there is a region of relatively high pressure. Although these weak anticyclones are often poorly formed, their weakly divergent surface winds and subsiding air usually lead to a period of clearing weather between the cloudy, wet weather of the successive cyclones.

Pollution episodes. Occasionally a large high-pressure area becomes stationary over the heavily populated and extensively industrialized areas of the eastern United States or western Europe. Just as maritime tropical or continental polar air masses gain their characteristics from the surface over which they stagnate, so does the air associated with these stagnant highs acquire the characteristics of the surface. The industries, the great number of home-heating systems, and the vast number of motor vehicles in these urban areas pour great amounts of pollutants into the air. As long as the anticyclone remains stationary over the region, the pollution of the air steadily increases. The temperature inversions which develop in the subsiding air of the anticyclone act as a lid on the air over the industrialized area. Since the air near the surface cannot penetrate the inversion, the pollution is concentrated in a relatively shallow layer of air. (See Fig. 4.28.)

The pollution episodes can be especially critical in late fall and early winter when the sun is low in the sky and the use of heating systems and the release of pollutants are great. The sun's weak rays are insufficient to warm the surface air to a high enough temperature to cause convection, which would spread the pollutants over a deeper layer of air. In December, 1952, an anticyclone stagnated over southern England for several days. Before the high finally moved, it is estimated that 5,000 London residents died from breathing the highly polluted air. In recent years air-quality standards have been established which lessen the severity of such pollution episodes, yet the problem of air pollution remains as one of the major environmental problems of the late twentieth century.

Tropical Disturbances

Compared with the highly variable middle latitudes, weather in the tropics is more uniform. Day-to-day and seasonal changes in temperature are small. In fact, the diurnal temperature variation—that is, the difference between day and night—is usually greater

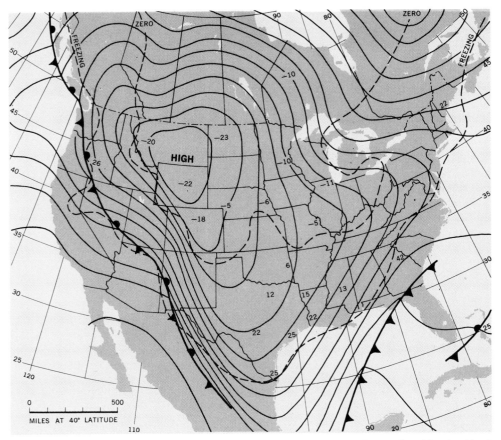

Figure 4.27 Polar-outbreak anticyclone advancing southward with a mass of unusually cold and stable *cP* air. Minot, North Dakota, experienced a temperature of −31°C (−23°F), Denver −28°C (−18°F), and Jackson, Mississippi, −11°C (13°F). Subfreezing temperatures extended to the Gulf of Mexico. *(From Weatherwise, June, 1962.)*

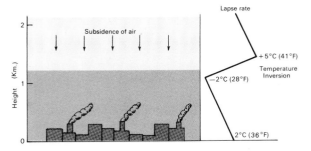

Figure 4.28 When an anticyclone stagnates over a large urban area, air pollution increases. The subsidence of air in the anticyclone produces a temperature inversion aloft. Because of the great stability of the air in the inversion, the pollutants remain trapped in the lower atmosphere.

than the seasonal temperature variation. There is, however, less uniformity in the occurrence of precipitation. Although the rhythm of daytime heating and nighttime cooling favors the development of afternoon showers and thunderstorms over land areas, there are a variety of tropical disturbances which bring nonperiodic variations of precipitation. Also, within most of the tropics there are marked seasonal differences in precipitation. Dry and wet seasons replace the four seasons of the higher latitudes.

For simplicity the tropical disturbances will be grouped into two classes—the weak and the severe. Although the intensity of the two classes differs, they share the common characteristic of moving generally from east to west. Within the tropics the wind, through a deep layer of the atmosphere, blows mainly from the east, and this deep easterly flow carries the disturbances with it. While the people of the middle and high latitudes look to the west for tomorrow's weather, residents of the tropics are more likely to look to the east.

Weak tropical disturbances. Weak disturbances are common throughout much of the moist tropics. Most of these disturbances have feebly developed pressure and wind systems. In fact, many of them are difficult to detect on a weather map. Often *stream-lines*, which are lines showing the air flow, are used rather than isobars to reveal the disturbances. Near the equator the Coriolis force is very weak, and as a consequence the wind often does not blow along the isobars, even above the friction layer. While extra-tropical cyclones share many characteristics and can be reasonably represented by a single model, there are a variety of weak tropical disturbances, which makes them difficult to describe. Only a few examples will be given here.

Often weak waves form within the general easterly air flow of the tropics. As these disturbances, known as *easterly waves*, move westward, an area of surface divergence and thus of fair weather occurs on the west side of the wave, while convergence and showery weather are found on the east side. Figure 4.29 shows the isobars and weather associated with

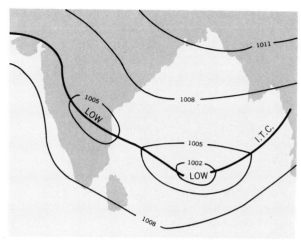

Figure 4.30 Weak tropical disturbances of the summer monsoon period over the Bay of Bengal and India. Some such monsoon lows appear to be associated with a fluctuating ITC.

an easterly wave moving westward in the Atlantic Ocean southeast of Florida.

During the summer monsoon season in the region of southern Asia, weak lows frequently develop along the *Intertropical Convergence Zone* (ITC), a region of major convergence between Northern and Southern Hemisphere air streams which will be described more fully in the next chapter. These weak lows, called *monsoon depressions*, move westward, bringing periods of especially heavy rainfall to regions such as India during the summer (high-sun) season. (See Fig. 4.30.)

Occasionally the cold front of a major extra-tropical cyclone sweeps into the fringes of the tropics. The cold air is warmed to temperatures not much different from those of the tropics. Although the front then ceases to exist, the convergence zone that had been associated with it may continue to move deeper into the tropics. As it does, clouds and precipitation occur along it.

Severe tropical disturbances. Occasionally a weak tropical disturbance, such as an easterly wave, may grow in intensity; a definite low-pressure center forms and strong cyclonic winds develop. If the winds attain a speed of at least 120 km/hr (75 mi/hr), the intense tropical cyclone is labeled a *hurricane* in the Atlantic Ocean or a *typhoon* in the Pacific. These

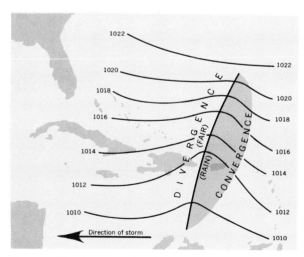

Figure 4.29 A tropical disturbance of a type known as an "easterly wave." *(After Riehl.)*

intense storms develop only over the tropical oceans where the water temperature is greater than about 27°C (81°F) and only at distances greater than about 5° of latitude away from the equator. Very close to the equator the Coriolis force is too weak to permit an intense cyclonic circulation to develop.

The intense tropical cyclone differs from the extratropical cyclones in a number of ways: (1) As Figure 4.31 shows, the isobars in a hurricane are more circular and the pressure gradient is much greater. (2) The size of the tropical cyclone is smaller, a diameter of 200 to 500 km (120 to 300 mi) being typical, which is roughly one-quarter the diameter of an extratropical cyclone. (3) While the energy of the extratropical cyclone is derived mainly from the contrasting densities of its cold and warm air masses, the energy of the tropical cyclone is chiefly furnished by the latent heat that is released during the formation of the torrential rains of the storm. (4) Tropical cyclones lack both the fronts and the patterns of precipitation that are found along the fronts of extratropical cyclones. Although the precipitation of a hurricane or typhoon is more evenly distributed than in an extratropical cyclone, there are numerous spiral bands extending outward from the low center along which the rainfall is especially heavy. Figure 4.32, a satellite photo of a hurricane, shows the spiral bands. (5) Well-developed tropical cyclones contain an *eye*, which is a region 10 to 50 km (6 to 30 mi) wide near the storm's center. In the eye there is actually sinking air motion, relatively clear skies, and light winds. (6) Tropical cyclones occur much less frequently than do extratropical cyclones.

In Figure 4.23 the dashed lines show the common tracks followed by intense tropical cyclones. The only tropical oceans free of these intense storms are the South Atlantic Ocean and the eastern part of the South Pacific. In both of these regions the water temperatures are colder than 27°C. Although the storms move generally westward across the tropical oceans, they frequently turn poleward as they reach the western parts of the oceans. They may then become caught up in the middle-latitude westerly flow and be carried toward the northeast in the Northern Hemisphere or the southeast in the Southern Hemisphere. As they move over the colder waters of the higher-latitude oceans, the storms weaken or die. They also weaken rapidly when they move over a land surface, since they then lose their favorable warm-water environment. Also, the increased friction between the strong winds and rougher land surface causes more air to flow across the isobars in toward the low center, thus reducing the pressure gradient.

Nearly all of the tropical cyclones develop in mid- and late summer and early fall, when the ocean temperatures in the summer hemisphere are at their warmest values of the year. An exception is the western part of the tropical North Pacific Ocean, where the water is warm enough to permit the occasional formation of a typhoon even in winter (low-sun season).

Because the hurricane and typhoon are oceanic storms, the land areas affected by them are mainly islands and the margins of some of the continents. The storm's winds, which may at times exceed 250 km/hr (150 mi/hr), cause much damage to buildings and vegetation. But more importantly, low-lying coastlines are often flooded by great waves or surges of ocean water generated by the storm's winds. The coastal flooding is especially severe when the storm occurs during a high-tide period. In November, 1970, a great storm surge drowned more than 200,000

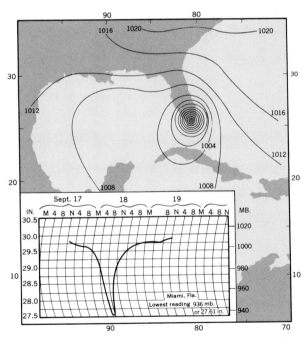

Figure 4.31 A Caribbean hurricane, together with a record of the pressure at Miami, Florida.

Figure 4.32 Hurricane Carmen approaching the Yucatan peninsula on September 1, 1974. Note the eye of the storm (small dark spot at the center) and the brighter spiral bands around the center. At this time winds just outside the eye of the storm exceeded 190 km/hr (120 mi/hr). The horizontal line across the center of the photo is due to some electronic noise during the transmission of the photo. (USAF Satellite Photo archived by NOAA at Space Science and Engineering Center, University of Wisconsin, Madison.)

persons along the densely populated Bay of Bengal coast of East Pakistan (now Bangladesh).

Although tropical cyclones weaken rapidly as they move inland, torrential rains may continue for several days, resulting in devastating floods. In June, 1972, hurricane Agnes moved inland and stagnated over Pennsylvania, setting off one of the greatest floods in American history. More than 100 lives were lost and property damage exceeded 3 billion dollars. However, the heavy rains of tropical cyclones are also beneficial. They are often responsible for filling the great reservoirs from which some of the large cities of the eastern seaboard of the United States draw their water supply.

REVIEW QUESTIONS

1. Why is the speed of vertical motion (rising or sinking) of air usually much less than the speed of the horizontal motion (the wind)?
2. In studying atmospheric motion, why is it necessary to include the Coriolis force?
3. Why does the wind at elevations above 1 km (0.6 mi) blow nearly parallel to the isobars?
4. Why is there convergence of air at low elevations in cyclones (lows) but divergence in anticyclones (highs)?
5. Why are cyclones usually regions of cloudy, wet weather and anticyclones regions of fair weather?
6. Why are there large low-pressure areas *aloft* over both polar regions?
7. Why is the relative humidity usually higher in early morning than in the afternoon?
8. Why is continental polar air more stable than maritime tropical air?
9. Why is there more likely to be precipitation on the side of a mountain range facing the wind (windward side) than on the opposite side (leeward side)?
10. Why does the cloudiness and precipitation of a cyclone tend to be concentrated in frontal zones?
11. Contrast the sequence of weather events that occur when the center of a major cyclone passes

somewhat to the north of your city with the sequence of those which occur when the center passes to the south.
12. How is the total potential energy of the atmosphere made available for transformation into the kinetic energy of the wind?
13. What are the principal differences between tropical and extratropical cyclones?
14. Why is a jet stream found above the polar front?
15. What atmospheric conditions lead to severe cases of air pollution?

SELECTED REFERENCES

Blanchard, D. *From Raindrops to Volcanoes*. Anchor Books, Doubleday & Company, Inc., Garden City, N.Y., 1967, 180 pp. This small book treats the problem of tracing the nuclei that are critical to the formation of clouds and precipitation.

Miller, A., and J. C. Thompson. *Elements of Meteorology*, 2d ed. Charles E. Merrill Books, Inc., Columbus, Ohio, 1975. Pp. 83–172. The causes of atmospheric motion are described in some detail, and then various scales of air motion, ranging from the large extratropical cyclones and anticyclones to the small but intense tornado, are examined.

Petterssen, S. *Introduction to Meteorology*, 3d ed. McGraw-Hill Book Company, New York, 1969. Chapter 4 provides descriptions of cloud types accompanied by color photos; chap. 5 describes the processes of cloud and precipitation formation; chap. 13 quite thoroughly treats fronts, cyclones, and anticyclones; and chap. 14 examines tropical weather systems.

Reiter, E. R. *Jet Streams*. Anchor Books, Doubleday & Company, Inc., Garden City, N.Y., 1967. 189 pp. The character of jet streams and their effect on weather are described.

Scorer, R., and H. Wexler. *A Colour Guide to Clouds*. The Macmillan Company, New York, 1964. 64 pp. This small atlas contains a wealth of cloud photos in color, with brief written descriptions of the features of each cloud type.

Climate: The Synthesis of Weather

Climate is a synthesis, or composite, of the day-to-day weather over a relatively long period of time. To fully appreciate the climate of a place, a person would have to live there for many years, experiencing the changing seasons and the variety of day-to-day weather events produced by the transient weather systems of the region.

In attempting to portray climate, the climatologist uses various methods to synthesize the weather events. The calculation of averages of the climatic elements, particularly temperature and precipitation, is a fundamental approach. The averages are usually based on 20 or 30 years of data. Maps are often used to portray the geographical distribution of the climatic averages. The use of monthly, rather than yearly, averages reveals seasonal differences. Because the mean temperature or precipitation total for an individual month is usually different from the long-term climatic mean, the statistical variance from the mean is also calculated. Furthermore, since averages fail to portray the day-to-day variations, the daily data are often used to obtain information such as the frequency of days on which the temperature falls below freezing or on which precipitation occurs.

Climatological data obtained using the approach described in the preceding paragraph reflect the influence of the climatic controls that were listed in Chapter 2: (1) latitude, (2) position on a continent, (3) ocean currents, (4) major terrain features, and (5) various atmospheric pressure and wind systems. The influence of the first four controls is entirely dependent on the geographical location of a place. However, the fifth involves the ever-changing patterns of air motion. The first four set the stage, but the pressure systems and their associated winds produce the day-to-day weather events of which climate is composed. Consequently, the climatologist is greatly interested both in the patterns of air flow associated with individual weather situations and in the composite pattern that is obtained by averaging the daily wind and pressure data.

Averages of the daily values of the wind at many locations reveal vast global wind systems which are collectively called the *general circulation* of the atmosphere. The composite motion of the atmosphere consists of the broad, more or less permanent global wind systems within which are embedded the smaller, mobile, and more transitory weather-producing systems.

The General Circulation

It was earlier emphasized that the basic cause of atmospheric motion is the unequal heating and cooling of various portions of the atmosphere. Since the general circulation represents the average motion, it reflects the average differences of heating and cooling. The net loss of energy due to radiation processes in high latitudes and the net gain in low latitudes are the dominant cause of the general circulation. The general circulation of the atmospheric and oceanic systems must somehow provide an average transport of energy from low to high latitudes.

It is estimated that about 75 percent of the poleward energy transport is accomplished by atmospheric motions and 25 percent by ocean currents. The current view of how the general circulation of the atmosphere accomplishes its portion of the transport is sketched in Figure 5.1. As the result of strong solar heating near the equator, the equatorial air is warmed, rises, and flows toward the poles at high elevations. Much of the warming is accomplished through evaporation of ocean water and its subsequent condensation and release of latent heat in the equatorial atmosphere. As the warm air flows poleward, it radiates some of its heat to space. By the time it reaches a latitude of about 30°N or 30°S, it has been cooled sufficiently to sink. Some of the sinking air then flows equatorward at low elevations to replace the rising air near the equator. Thus on either side of the equator there exist vast convection cells oriented north-south along the meridians. These

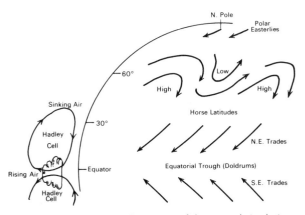

Figure 5.1 A schematic description of the general circulation. Between the equator and about 30°N and 30°S, large meridional convection cells (Hadley cells) transport energy toward polar regions. The trade winds have their origin in the descending branch of the Hadley cells. In middle and high latitudes cyclonic and anticyclonic eddies are mainly responsible for the poleward transport of energy.

mean meridional cells are called *Hadley cells*, after Hadley, who described some of their essential features in 1735. The Hadley cells provide the principal transport of energy from the equatorial region to about latitudes 30°N and 30°S.

Poleward of about 30°N and 30°S, the energy transport is mainly accomplished by cyclonic and anticyclonic eddies which are embedded in the Northern and Southern Hemisphere polar vortices. The southerly and northerly winds associated with these eddies carry warm, moist air toward the poles and cold, dry air toward the equator, thereby accomplishing a net poleward transport of energy. Although the poleward-moving air on the east side of a cyclonic eddy tends to rise and the equatorward-moving air on the east side of an anticyclonic eddy tends to sink, the average vertical displacement of this air is less than in the Hadley cells.

Global Wind Systems

Because of the earth's rotation, air currents which begin to move north or south are deflected by the Coriolis force, to the right in the Northern Hemisphere and to the left in the Southern Hemisphere. The effect of the earth's rotation is so great that the principal characteristic of the general circulation is not air motion along the meridians, but rather air motion along the parallels of latitude. Northerly or southerly flow is known as *meridional flow*, while easterly or westerly flow is called *zonal flow*. Although the zonal flow dominates, there is sufficient meridional flow to accomplish a poleward transport of energy.

Figure 5.2 is an idealized map sketch showing the mean global wind and pressure systems; in Figure 5.3 a vertical cross section extending from pole to pole is used to show the vertical extent of the various wind systems. The average flow consists of a shallow layer of weak easterly winds in polar latitudes, a deep layer of strong westerly winds in middle latitudes, and a deep layer of easterly winds in low latitudes. Between the middle-latitude westerlies and the low-latitude easterlies is a zone of subtropical high pressure, and between the tropical easterlies of the Northern and Southern Hemispheres is an equatorial trough of low pressure. The location and strength of these zonally oriented wind and pressure systems change with the season.

Except for the shallow polar easterlies,

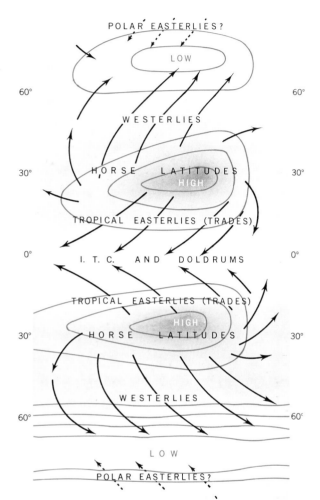

POLAR EASTERLIES?

LOW

60°   60°

W E S T E R L I E S

30°   H O R S E   L A T I T U D E S   30°
HIGH

TROPICAL EASTERLIES (TRADES)

0°   I. T. C.   A N D   D O L D R U M S   0°

TROPICAL EASTERLIES (TRADES)

HIGH
30°   H O R S E   L A T I T U D E S   30°

W E S T E R L I E S
60°   60°

L O W

POLAR EASTERLIES?

Figure 5.2 A much idealized representation of the earth's surface winds. Average airflow is predominantly from a westerly direction in middle latitudes and from an easterly direction in low latitudes.

Middle-latitude Westerlies

Upper-level westerly flow. In Chap. 4 the large polar vortices centered aloft near the North and South Poles were described. The westerly winds of these vortices are a major component of the general circulation. In winter the upper-level westerlies are strong and extensive; at an elevation of about 5 km (3 mi), for example, they occupy most of the area poleward from about latitude 20°–25°. In summer the westerlies at 5 km (3 mi) occupy a smaller area, roughly from latitude 30°–35° to the pole. (See Fig. 5.3.)

Within the broad, deep westerly flow are jet streams. Of particular significance is the polar jet, which has a mean position of about latitude 30°–35° in winter and latitude 45°–50° in summer. Its strongest winds are typically found at elevations of 10 to 12 km (6 to 7 mi) above the surface position of the polar front. The mean position of the polar jet is important to climate, since the impulses of stronger winds which propagate along the jet often cause the formation of extratropical cyclones on the polar front. The composite effect of these numerous cyclones provides a major contribution to the climate of the middle latitudes.

Although the mean flow aloft in the middle latitudes is from the west, there are variations in the flow from day to day as well as between seasons. At times the flow breaks down into great wavelike patterns, with the jet stream taking a sinuous course. At some longitudes the jet at times sweeps equatorward,

the major wind systems are usually best developed aloft, between 3 and 15 km (2 to 9 mi) above the earth. Near the earth's surface the zonal arrangements of the wind systems are less pronounced. Figures 5.4 and 5.5 show the mean sea-level pressure distribution and superimposed sketches of the average surface wind directions for the months of January and July.

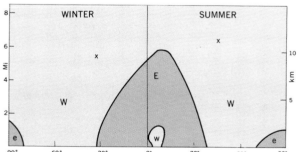

Figure 5.3 A pole-to-pole cross section of the earth's wind system. E = tropical easterlies or trades; W = westerlies; x = average location of the jet stream; w = the somewhat less certain belt of equatorial westerlies; e = polar easterlies. *(After Flohn.)*

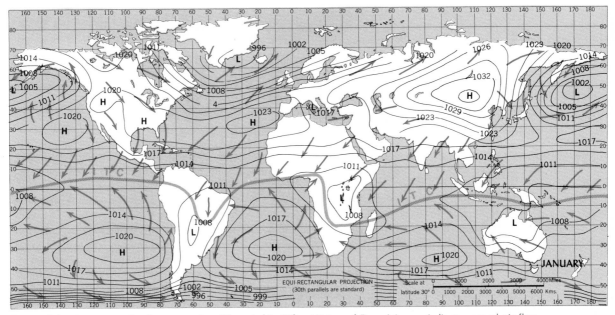

Figure 5.4   January sea-level pressure, in millibars (mb), *(After Mintz and Dean.)* Arrows indicate general air flow.

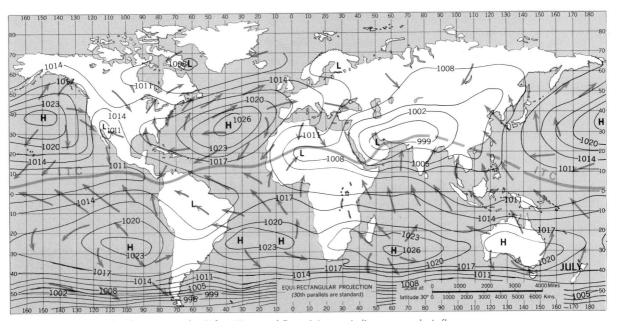

Figure 5.5   July sea-level pressure, mb. *(After Mintz and Dean.)* Arrows indicate general air flow.

accompanied by a major thrust of polar air, while at other longitudes it sometimes swings far poleward. (See Fig. 4.10.) These periods tend to be especially stormy times in portions of the middle latitudes. Because there are day-to-day changes in the position of the polar jet and the cyclones it causes, most of the middle latitudes benefit from the precipitation of the cyclones at one time or another.

Surface flow in middle latitudes.   At the surface, the wintertime westerlies are found from about latitude 30° poleward to 70°–75°, while in summer their extent is from about 40° to 65°–70°. Although in most of the middle latitudes the average surface winds show a strong preference for westerly direction, the circulation of air about traveling cyclones and anticyclones produces frequent day-to-day changes in wind direction.

The average wind at low levels deviates from true westerly flow mainly because of the large semipermanent pressure systems shown in Figures 5.4 and 5.5. During January, the subpolar low-pressure systems located near Iceland and the Aleutian Islands produce a mean cyclonic flow over the northern portions of the North Atlantic and North Pacific Oceans and the adjacent continents. Thus, in the western part of these regions, the winds tend to be northwest; in the eastern part, they favor southwest. In July the Icelandic low weakens and the Aleutian low disappears.

The strong semipermanent high-pressure area and its anticyclonic flow centered over Siberia in January also causes deviations from a mean westerly flow at the surface. This cold high-pressure system will be discussed more fully in the section on monsoon circulations.

Because of the more zonal arrangement of the land and ocean areas in the middle and high latitudes of the Southern Hemisphere, there is a more continous belt of low pressure and westerly winds extending around the earth. In the Northern Hemisphere the alternation of land and water along a parallel of latitude disrupts the simple north-south heating differences, leading to cells of higher and lower pressure within a zonal belt.

Polar easterlies.   At high latitudes, roughly poleward of 70°–75° in winter and 65°–70° in summer, the averages show a shallow layer of weak easterly winds, which do not extend above about 3 km. Above them are found the westerlies. Because of the shallowness of the polar easterly flow, most weather disturbances at these high latitudes are not carried from east to west. Rather, they tend to be carried along by the deep westerly flow found above the polar easterlies.

Subtropical highs.   Between latitudes 20° and 30° in winter and 30° and 40° in summer, the mean sea-level pressure is higher than in the regions to the north or south. These subtropical high-pressure systems are well developed over the oceans but only poorly developed and sometimes absent over the continents. Figure 5.6 shows the typical arrangement of isobars and air flow of an oceanic subtropical high-pressure cell. These anticyclones are composed of warm air and consequently extend to great altitudes. Near the center of the high-pressure cells, the surface winds are frequently calm or, at best, weak and variable. According to one story, these regions came to be known as the *horse latitudes* because of the large number of horses that were pushed overboard from becalmed sailing ships on their way to the New World in the sixteenth century.

The descending branch of the Hadley circulation coincides with the latitudes of the subtropical highs, which is consistent with the surface wind divergence and sinking air noted in anticyclones. Although there is a tendency for subsidence to exist throughout the subtropical highs, the strongest sinking motions occur in their eastern portions. Thus, while much of the latitudinal belt occupied by the subtropical highs is a zone with little precipitation, the aridity is much more pronounced in the eastern portions of the subtropical high cells.

Tropical easterlies or trade winds.   On the equatorward sides of the subtropical highs are the tropical easterlies or *trade winds*. Although these winds blow mainly from the east, surface friction causes them to also move outward from the high-pressure systems toward the equator, where the atmospheric pressure is lower. Thus in the Northern Hemisphere the winds blow somewhat from the northeast, while those in the Southern Hemisphere blow somewhat from the southeast. During the days of sailing ships, these

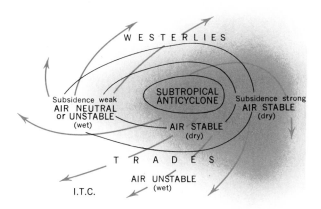

W E S T E R L I E S

SUBTROPICAL
ANTICYCLONE

Subsidence weak
AIR NEUTRAL
or UNSTABLE
(wet)

Subsidence strong
AIR STABLE
(dry)

AIR STABLE
(dry)

T R A D E S

AIR UNSTABLE
(wet)

I.T.C.

Figure 5.6 The airflow around a subtropical anticyclone, with general areas of stability and instability shown. The air on the eastern side of the anticyclone is much more stable than the air on the western side. The poleward part of the trades is more stable than their equatorward side. The intensity of shading suggests the degree of stability.

winds became renowned for their steadiness, and they were labeled "trade winds" because their reliability favored commerce.

Over the eastern portion of the oceans, where the subtropical highs and their subsidence are strong, disturbances are few, the winds are especially steady, and fair weather prevails. But in the western parts of the oceans where the anticyclones and their accompanying subsidence are weaker, the trades are less constant, disturbances are more numerous, and clouds and rains are more likely. There are likewise important contrasts within the trade-wind region in a north-south direction. As the trades move equatorward, evaporation from the warm oceans increases their moisture content. Also, as the air moves away from the region of strongest subsidence, its lapse rate becomes less stable, so disturbances are more apt to produce convective showers. Thus the trades are likely to be dry, fair-weather winds on their poleward and eastern sides while their equatorward and western sections are characterized by more clouds and precipitation.

Equatorial trough and ITC. Within the equatorial trough of low pressure, which has a mean location

near the equator, winds are much lighter and more variable than in the trade-wind region. This region is sometimes called the *doldrums*. Airflow from the west, known as the *equatorial westerlies*, is common over some longitudes of the doldrums. At other times and places the winds are easterly.

Within the equatorial trough lies the *Intertropical Convergence Zone* (ITC), along which the northeast trades of the Northern Hemisphere meet the southeast trades of the Southern Hemisphere. The low-level convergence of these two moist, relatively unstable air streams is accompanied by vertical motion which produces the heavy, showery rains for which the deep tropics are famous. Most of the convergence and precipitation occurs in the very weak disturbances that are found along the ITC. However, in some longitudes, such as portions of the eastern Pacific Ocean, the convergence and disturbances are weak or absent and the precipitation is meager. Although the precipitation varies from one longitude to another, satellite photos often clearly reveal bands of clouds associated with the ITC extending completely across the Atlantic or Pacific Oceans. (See Fig. 5.7.)

Latitudinal Shifting of the Zonal Wind Systems

Because the belt of maximum solar energy shifts north and south during the course of a year, the zonal wind systems also change their latitudinal positions. In the hemisphere that has winter there is a large north-south heating difference, and as a result the polar vortex is large and intense. With the coming of summer, the north-south heating difference decreases, and the polar vortex shrinks and weakens. The expansion and contraction of the polar vortex imply that the latitudinal zone occupied by the middle-latitude westerlies and their jets also varies with the changing seasons. Likewise, each of the other zonal wind systems shifts north and south. The displacements follow the sun, shifting northward in June and July and southward in December and January. The latitudinal shifting of the global wind system is usually greater over the continents, where the north-south temperature differences between seasons are greater than over the more temperate oceans.

Seasonal north-south shifting of the major wind and pressure systems is especially significant in

Figure 5.7 Photo made by the ATS-1 satellite positioned above the equatorial Pacific Ocean on February 20, 1972. North America (note peninsula of Baja California) is located in the upper right. The line of clouds extending east and west across the center of the picture is the Intertropical Convergence Zone. An extratropical cyclone is evident in the Gulf of Alaska (top middle). *(Courtesy NOAA and Space Science and Engineering Center, University of Wisconsin, Madison.)*

latitudes which lie near the northern or southern edge of a wind system. Such latitudes are under the influence of one wind system and its weather conditions in one season and the other wind system and its weather during the opposite season. The importance of this latitudinal shifting will become clearer when the major precipitation regimes of the earth are discussed later in this chapter.

Monsoon winds. The seasonal heating differences between continents and oceans also contribute to major seasonal reversals in the air flow which are

called the *monsoon* winds. The monsoon winds commonly blow from land to sea in winter and from sea to land in summer.

During winter a middle-latitude continent is colder than the surrounding sea surface. As a result there is a tendency for a cold high-pressure system to form over the continent, with the cold continental surface air tending to flow across the isobars outward over the sea. The strong high over Siberia in January provides an excellent example (Fig. 5.4). Because this winter monsoon originates over a cold land mass, it is dry, cold, and stable, and it therefore resists the upward movement of air which is needed for clouds and precipitation.

In summer, by contrast, the land air is warmer and less dense than the air over the sea. Atmospheric pressure is then lower over the land. As a consequence, surface air flows from sea to land. (See eastern and southern Asia in Fig. 5.5.) Because summer monsoon air originates over the sea, its humidity is high and precipitation is easily produced by atmospheric disturbances which move through these areas.

The climatic consequences of monsoons are often striking. In the middle latitudes, they tend to produce cold, relatively dry winters and hot, wet summers. Thus seasonal extremes in both temperature and rainfall are characteristic. In the tropics, the seasonal wind reversal obviously does not produce cold winters, but it does result in dry winters and wet summers. East Asia is by far the best example of a region of middle-latitude monsoons, although central and eastern North America also have some features of them. In the tropics, monsoons are especially characteristic of southern Asia, northern Australia, and Tropical West Africa.

Land and sea breezes. Like middle-latitude monsoons, land and sea breezes are wind reversals that originate from the unequal heating of land and water surfaces. But these wind reversals have a daily rather than a seasonal periodicity. At night the land's greater coolness results in a land breeze (that is, a wind from land to sea). During the day the land becomes warmer than the sea, and a sea breeze (a wind from sea to land) develops. Land and sea breezes seldom extend more than 25 km (15 mi) on either side of the shoreline.

Global Distribution of Temperature

The global distribution of temperature is mainly controlled by the latitudinal differences in solar heating. Temperatures are low in polar regions and high in the tropics. But there are east-west differences in temperature as well. These result from heating differences between continents and oceans and also from the presence of warm ocean currents moving poleward in some areas and cold currents flowing toward the equator in other areas. The major zonal wind systems not only play a major role in driving the

ocean currents but also carry the air that is warmed (or cooled) by the currents over the adjacent continent. Thus on the windward side of a continent the effect of the ocean currents is felt far inland, while on the leeward side the ocean currents have only a minor effect. In winter the prevailing westerlies carry the warmth of the North Atlantic Gulf Stream system far into Europe, while the eastern portion of the North American continent experiences very little of this warmth.

In examining the global temperature distribution, maps showing the average monthly temperatures for individual months are more useful than a map showing only the average annual temperature. Outside of the tropics the average annual temperature is generally an average containing some months which are much colder and some which are much warmer than the annual average. A map of the annual average temperatures would show values near 27°C (80°F) in low latitudes, where the solar radiation is greatest. Within a broad tropical belt extending from about 20°N to 20°S, the average annual temperatures are quite uniform: however, from these latitudes, the temperatures decrease markedly toward the poles.

January and July average temperatures. Figures 5.8 and 5.9 present the global temperature distribution during the extreme seasons of winter and summer. The temperatures shown on these maps have been adjusted to sea level by assuming that the temperature decreases an average of 6.5°C/km (3.6°F/1000 ft) increase in altitude. If this adjustment had not been made, the effects of elevation would have complicated the broad global pattern. In both seasons the isotherms are oriented generally east-west with colder temperatures toward the poles, reflecting the dominance of solar energy in determining temperature. There is a marked latitudinal shift in the isotherms during the course of a year, northward in July and southward in January. In other words, the isotherms tend to follow the sun. The gradient of temperature is greatest in the winter hemisphere, reflecting the large gradient of solar energy found there.

Because the continents warm and cool more rapidly than the oceans, the seasonal shift in the isotherms is greater over the continents than over the oceans. Thus in the winter season the isotherms bend

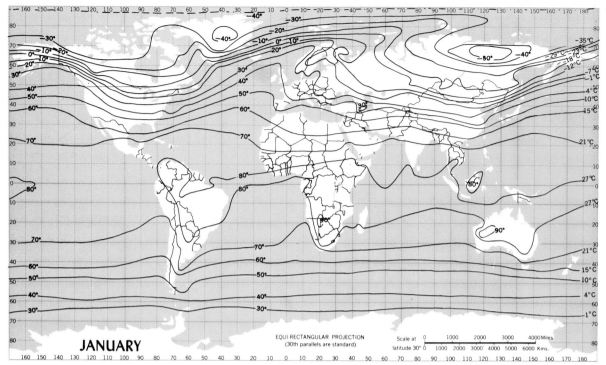

Figure 5.8 Average sea-level temperature for January.

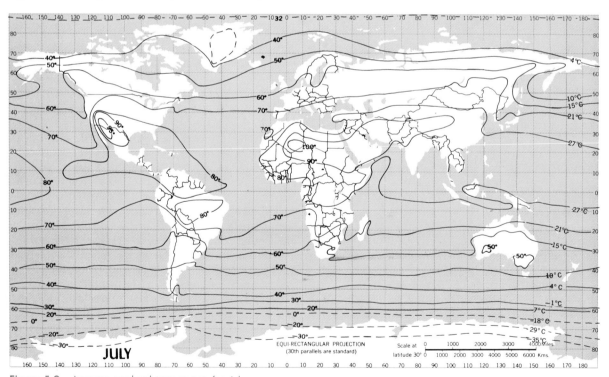

Figure 5.9 Average sea-level temperature for July.

equatorward over the continents, while in summer they bend poleward. Because of the great extent of the oceans in the Southern Hemisphere, there the continent-ocean contrasts are smaller than in the Northern Hemisphere.

The highest mean summer temperatures occur over the subtropical continents, for example, above 38°C (100°F) in central North Africa and above 32°C (90°F) in a large area of southwestern Asia and southwestern North America in July and above 32°C (90°F) in interior Australia and southern Africa in January. In winter the coldest mean temperatures are found over the high-latitude continents, particularly northeastern Asia, where a −46°C (−50°F) isotherm is noted in January, and Antarctica, where mean August temperatures as low as −68°C (−90°F) are recorded.

A closer inspection of Figures 5.8 and 5.9 reveals the presence of the cold and warm branches of the large ocean current systems. Please refer to Figure 7.9 for a map of the major ocean currents. The equatorward bending of the isotherms along the coast of southwestern North America, particularly in July, reflects the presence of cold, equatorward-flowing currents in these areas. On the other hand, the northward bending of the January isotherms over the Atlantic and Pacific Oceans is due to warm, poleward-flowing currents. The effect is particularly pronounced in the North Atlantic Ocean, where the isotherms bulge poleward beyond the northern tip of Scandinavia. It is ocean currents such as these that account for the 25 percent of poleward energy transport accomplished by the oceanic system.

Annual temperature range. The difference between the average temperatures of the warmest and coldest months is called the *annual range* of temperature. The largest annual range is over the great Northern Hemisphere continents, which become unusually hot in summer and cold in winter (Fig. 5.10). The range is never large near the equator, where solar energy varies little. Nor is it large over extensive water bodies, which explains why the range is small everywhere in the middle latitudes of the Southern Hemisphere. In summary, the range becomes larger toward higher latitudes, with the increase much more marked over the continents than over the oceans.

Global Distribution of Precipitation

The global distribution of precipitation is less regular than that of temperature. The mechanisms which produce precipitation within the atmospheric system are more complex and often act over smaller areas

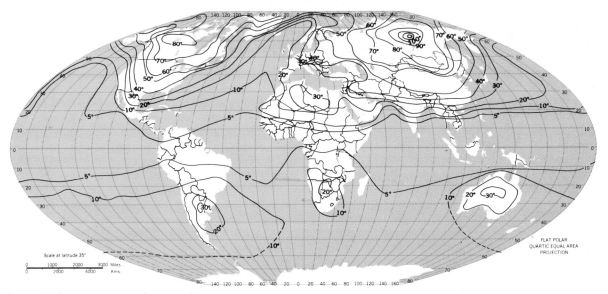

Figure 5.10 Average annual ranges of temperature.

than the mechanisms which control temperature. Nevertheless, global patterns of precipitation are clearly identifiable.

Most of the precipitation-producing disturbances are found in two of the zonal wind and pressure systems, the middle-latitude westerlies and the equatorial trough. Within the middle-latitude westerlies, extratropical cyclones are the major producers of precipitation. They most often form in the vicinity of the jet stream. However, since the jet stream frequently takes a meandering course within the broad zone of westerlies, all of the latitudes of the westerlies experience cyclonic storms at one time or another.

The tropical rains are concentrated in the equatorial trough, where various weak disturbances along the ITC are especially effective precipitation producers. The equatorward parts of the trade winds sometimes share in these rains, particularly the western portions of the trade-wind systems, where the air is relatively moist and unstable. Thus the equatorial trough and the adjacent portions of the trades can be considered as the major site of the tropical precipitation regime.

Separating the precipitation regime of the middle-latitude westerlies from that of the tropics is the broad zone of subtropical high pressure. The sinking air in the horse latitudes, particularly in the eastern portions of subtropical high-pressure cells, produces a latitudinal zone in which precipitation is meager. These are the latitudes of the world's great deserts. The world map of average annual precipitation (Fig. 5.11) reveals this zonal distribution of precipitation. For example, the region of heavy rainfall in equatorial west Africa is separated from the relatively wet region of western Europe by a broad dry zone extending east-west across northern Africa.

In Figure 5.12 the annual precipitation *averaged by latitude zones* is shown. The heaviest precipitation occurs near the equator, with secondary maxima near latitudes 50°N and 45°S. Because of the high temperatures in the tropics, evaporation of water from the tropical oceans is greater than in most middle-latitude oceanic regions. These moist maritime tropical air masses provide abundant precipitation in the region of the equatorial trough. Although evaporation is also great from the subtropical oceans, the climate of the subtropics is relatively dry because of the subsidence of air in the subtropical highs. The

northeast and southeast trades carry much of this moisture into the equatorial trough, where it contributes to the tropical rains. Likewise, some of the moisture gained from evaporation from the subtropical oceans is carried poleward in the circulation of individual middle-latitude cyclones, where it contributes to middle-latitude precipitation.

There are east-west differences in average annual precipitation as well as north-south differences. The east-west variations of average annual precipitation are produced by a number of factors: (1) mountain barriers, (2) the distance from the coastline of a continent, (3) the existence of individual semipermanent subtropical high cells, and (4) the occurrences of monsoon rains in some longitudes but not in others. In considering examples of these, please refer to the world map of average annual precipitation (Fig. 5.11). The influence of a middle-latitude mountain range can be seen in the northwestern United States, where the windward (west) side of the Cascade Mountains receives heavy precipitation while the leeward (east) side is dry. The effect of the distance from a middle-latitude coastline is illustrated by the west-to-east decrease of precipitation across Europe and western Asia. As cyclones move eastward across Europe, they move farther and farther away from a source of oceanic moisture. The influence of individual subtropical high-pressure cells can be seen by comparing the very light rainfall along the coast of northwestern Africa with the substantial rainfall of Florida, which is at the same latitude. Northwestern Africa experiences the strong subsidence of the eastern portion of the North Atlantic subtropical high-pressure cell, while Florida is under the western portion of the cell, where subsidence is weak. Finally, with respect to longitudinal variations of the monsoon winds, Arabia is arid, but much of India and southeastern Asia at the same latitude has heavy rainfall. The summer monsoon winds blow from the southwest, carrying moisture-laden Indian Ocean air into India, while Arabia fails to benefit from this flow of moist air.

Seasonal variations of precipitation. Because the zonal wind systems shift north and south with the seasons, latitudes which are near the boundary of a zonal wind belt are likely to experience marked seasonal differences in precipitation. With the changing seasons, they come under the influence of alternating wind systems. On the other hand, latitudes

AVERAGE ANNUAL PRECIPITATION

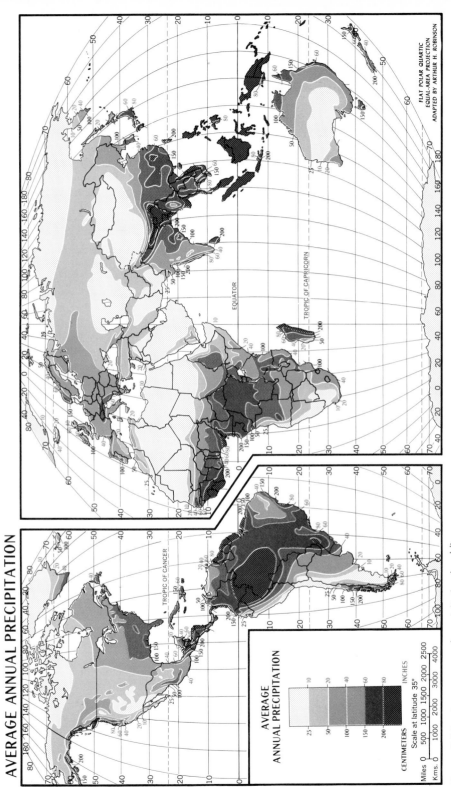

Figure 5.11 Average annual precipitation (world).

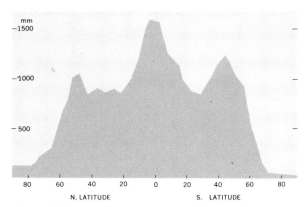

Figure 5.12 Distribution of annual precipitation amounts averaged by latitude zones. *(After Brooks and Hunt.)*

located near the middle of a zonal wind belt usually experience only small seasonal changes in precipitation. Please study Figure 5.13, which is a schematic illustration of this effect.

Near the equator, where the equatorial trough and ITC prevail in all seasons, rainfall not only is abundant but also falls throughout the year. One season may have more rainfall than another, but no season is dry. Farther from the equator, from roughly latitude 5°–10° to 15°–20°, rainfall decreases and becomes more seasonal. A marked dry period occurs in the low-sun, or winter, season when the dry trades prevail, while the high-sun, or summer, season is wet as the result of the ITC. This sequence of high-sun rainfall and low-sun drought is caused by the latitudinal shifting of the zonal wind systems. The low-sun drought is especially prominent over the western portion of a continent, where the trades have their origin in the region of strong subsidence on the eastern side of a subtropical high. Across the ocean, on the eastern side of a continent, the low-sun drought may be weak or absent because the trades reaching this area have blown across the ocean, gaining moisture and becoming less stable.

In the lower middle latitudes, at about 30°–40°, there are areas, usually restricted to the western

side of continents, where summer is the season of drought and winter is wet. Here, because of latitudinal migration of the pressure and wind systems, the stable eastern limb of a subtropical anticyclone controls the weather in summer and the cyclonic westerlies control it in winter.

In the middle latitudes poleward from about 40°, adequate precipitation falls at all times of the year. Yet this is not to say that all seasons have equal amounts. It is in the interiors of the great continents that the seasonal precipitation maximum and minimum are most emphatic. Here summer, with its warmer air of higher moisture content, is usually the wettest season. The drier winter is related to the lower temperatures and the prevalence of anticyclonic wind systems during that season.

Climatic Change

As noted earlier, climatic averages are based on relatively long weather records, typically 30 years. An examination of the records shows year-to-year variations; for example, some Januarys are much colder than the 30-year mean; others are warmer. These year-to-year variations are typical of all weather records. However, within a 30-year period there may be several consecutive years which are distinctly different from the long-term mean. Some of the fluctuations go relatively unnoticed, but others have a major impact on life. For example, some areas along the equatorward edge of the subtropical high-pressure systems barely receive sufficient summer rain from equatorial trough disturbances to permit marginal agriculture. If for several consecutive summers the global wind systems fail to shift as far poleward as they had previously, the rains of the equatorial trough will not reach the area and a series of drought years will occur. Beginning in the late 1960s and extending into the mid-1970s, this type of drought occurred in the Sahel, the semiarid region which lies just south of the Sahara Desert, producing great human suffering.

Not only are there fluctuations of climate

Figure 5.13 Schematic cross section through the atmosphere showing the main zones of horizontal convergence and ascent, and of divergence and subsidence, together with associated seasonal characteristics of precipitation: *A*, during the Northern Hemisphere summer; *B*, during the Northern Hemisphere winter; *C*, zones of seasonal precipitation. But remember that many nonzonal features of precipitation distribution cannot be adequately represented in this type of diagram. *(From Sverre Patterssen, Introduction to Meteorology, 2d ed., McGraw-Hill Book Company, New York, 1958.)*

A.

B.

C.

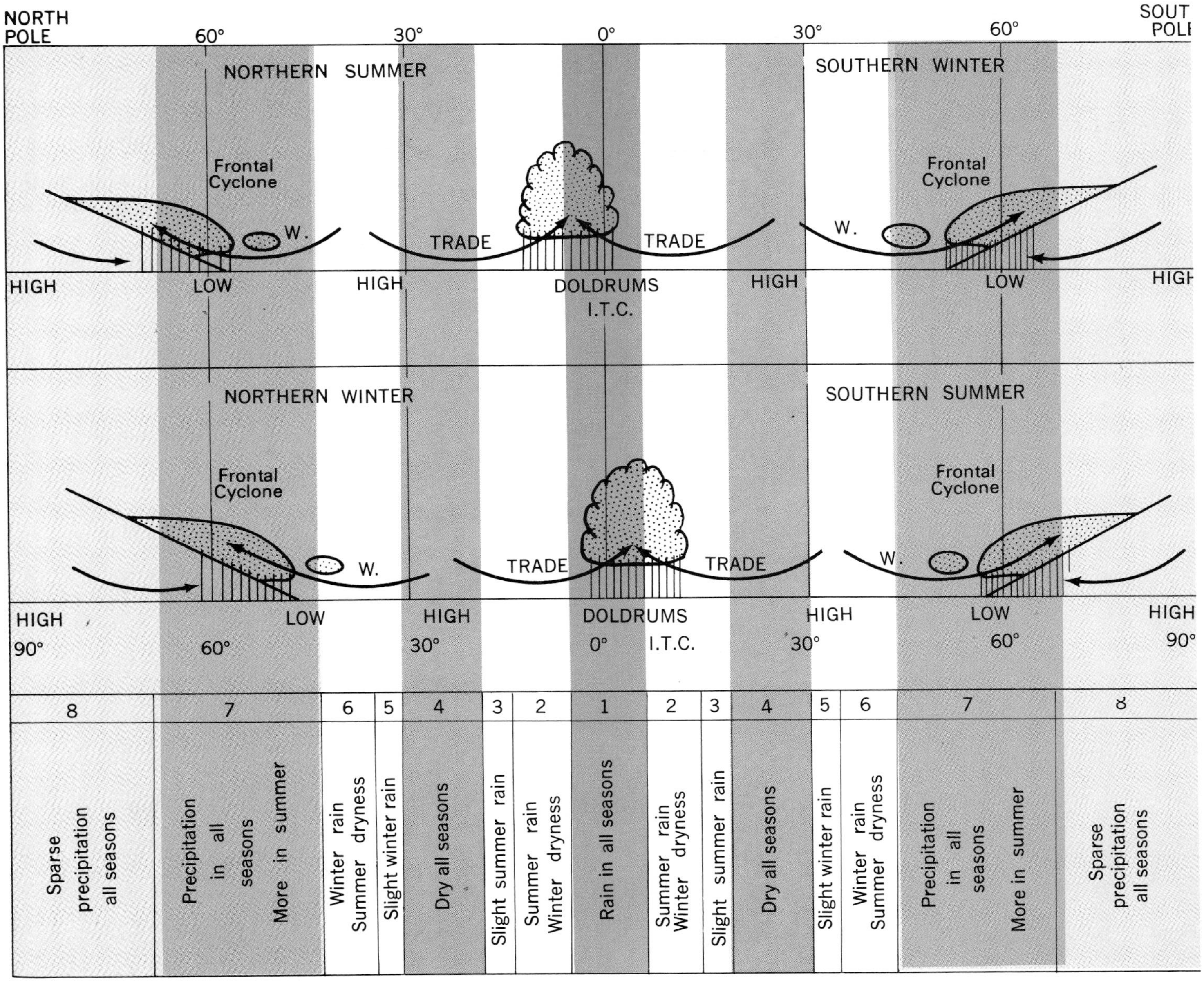
NORTH POLE
60°
30°
0°
30°
60°
SOUTH POLE
NORTHERN SUMMER
SOUTHERN WINTER
Frontal Cyclone
W.
TRADE
TRADE
W.
Frontal Cyclone
HIGH
LOW
HIGH
DOLDRUMS
I.T.C.
HIGH
LOW
HIGH
NORTHERN WINTER
SOUTHERN SUMMER
Frontal Cyclone
W.
TRADE
TRADE
W.
Frontal Cyclone
HIGH
LOW
HIGH
DOLDRUMS
HIGH
LOW
HIGH
90°
60°
30°
0°
I.T.C.
30°
60°
90°
8
Sparse precipitation all seasons
7
Precipitation in all seasons More in summer
6
Winter rain Summer dryness
5
Slight winter rain
4
Dry all seasons
3
Slight summer rain
2
Summer rain Winter dryness
1
Rain in all seasons
2
Summer rain Winter dryness
3
Slight summer rain
4
Dry all seasons
5
Slight winter rain
6
Winter rain Summer dryness
7
Precipitation in all seasons More in summer
8
Sparse precipitation all seasons

within a 30-year period, but weather records show that there are changes in the mean precipitation and temperatures between one 30-year period and another. For example, the temperature averages for the northeastern United States for the 1921–1950 period were warmer than those during the late nineteenth century, and the temperature averages since 1950 show a colder climate returning to the region. In fact, the first half of the twentieth century appears to have been one of the warmest periods in nearly 1,000 years.

Since records of actual temperature and precipitation go back only a century or two, the climatologist must also use other sources of evidence from recorded history, as well as past biological and geological events. The Viking explorations between about 900 and 1200 A.D. provide an example of historical evidence. The explorations occurred during a mild period when the ice of the far northern North Atlantic was less extensive than it is today. The Vikings succeeded in establishing colonies in Greenland, but after 1200 A.D. the climate turned colder and the ice became more extensive, causing the colonies to be abandoned.

Past climates can also be inferred from various biological events. A changing climate leaves its imprint on the vegetation of an area. Some species of trees become more abundant and others less abundant as the climate cools or warms. Scientists take cores of soil, including its organic matter, from lake bottoms and swamps and analyze them to determine the relative abundance of various types of pollen at different depths. This pollen evidence can then be used to reconstruct some aspects of the climate during the past several thousand years.

In Chapter 13 you will read of geological evidence which shows that during the past 2 million or 3 million years the climate changed so greatly that there were repeated major advances and retreats of great *continental* glaciers over large parts of North America and Eurasia. There is also geological evidence indicating that even within the past 300 years the *mountain* glaciers of the earth have advanced and then retreated in response to climatic changes.

Indeed, evidence from weather records, history, biology, and geology all point to a variety of periods of climatic change, some involving many thousands of years and others no more than several years. Some changes have affected the entire earth, others have been mainly confined to latitudinal belts, while still others have been felt only in limited areas of a latitudinal belt.

Possible causes of climatic change. Climate is greatly influenced by the general circulation of the atmospheric system. Consequently, changes in the controls of the general circulation can cause climatic change. These principally involve changes in the geographical distribution of the heating and cooling of the atmosphere. The actual cause of these changes is not yet understood, although a number of possibilities have been postulated: (1) Over periods involving tens of thousands of years there are small changes in the characteristics of the earth's orbit and in the inclination of its axis. These changes affect the north-south gradient of solar heating. (2) The output of solar energy by the sun itself, particularly its ultraviolet portion, may change with time. (3) A period of increased volcanic activity causes a large increase in the volcanic-dust content of the atmosphere. The increased dustiness of the atmosphere not only increases the earth's albedo but also increases the north-south heating differences because the sun's rays reaching the high latitudes have a longer path through the dusty atmosphere than do those reaching low latitudes. Air pollution due to human activity could likewise increase the albedo of the atmosphere. (4) The burning of large amounts of fossil fuel during the past century by our industrialized society has increased the carbon dioxide content of the atmosphere. This increases the greenhouse effect and could cause the earth's climate to warm unless compensated for by other factors such as a higher albedo due to increased dustiness. A larger greenhouse effect may also change the climate by causing a slight latitudinal shift in the zonal wind belts. (5) At times vast pools of ocean water warmer or colder than normal somehow develop. As a result, the frequency of occurrence and the paths followed by atmospheric disturbances in these regions may be altered. (6) The amount of sea ice present in the Arctic Ocean has also been suggested as a cause of the long-term periods of climatic change responsible for intervals of continental glaciation. If the Arctic Ocean, which is nearly surrounded by the North American and Eurasian continents, were mainly free of ice, there would be considerable evaporation from it. This would lead to greatly increased precipitation, mainly snow, on the far northern parts of these continents, causing the development of continental glaciers. As large amounts of glacial ice accumulated on the continents, sea level would decrease worldwide and the connection of the Arctic Ocean to the warmer North Atlantic between Greenland and Norway would be reduced. As a consequence, the Arctic Ocean would be deprived of the free flow of warmer water from the North Atlantic and would freeze. An ice-covered Arctic Ocean would provide little evaporation and thus little snow to feed the continental glaciers. Consequently, the glaciers, deprived of their snow source, would waste away, sea level would rise, the Arctic Ocean-North Atlantic connection would be better established, and the sea ice would melt. The process then would begin again, setting the stage for the next period of glaciation.

There are still other theories of climatic change, but none of the various possibilities has as yet been confirmed. The atmospheric system is very complex. How this complex system responds to various small changes in heating and the causes of the heating changes themselves remain as truly challenging scientific problems of our age.

Climatic Classification

In Chapter 2 it was noted that a principal goal of geography is to describe and explain the distribution of the earth's climates and their relationship to other important elements of the natural environment such as soils and vegetation. In order to accomplish this goal, it is necessary to reduce the great diversity of the earth's climates to reveal large classes which share common characteristics. The reduction is usually accomplished through classification, a process common to many sciences. Since climate is the output of the vast atmospheric system averaged over a period of time, a successful classification scheme should reflect the workings of the major components of the system.

Some approaches to climatic classification. One of the earliest and simplest classification schemes was done by the ancient Greeks, who divided the earth into five zones, one tropical, two polar, and two temperate. The tropical zone was bounded by the Tropics of Cancer and Capricorn ($23\frac{1}{2}°$N and $23\frac{1}{2}°$S), and the polar zones were bounded by the Arctic and

Antarctic circles ($66\frac{1}{2}°$N and $66\frac{1}{2}°$S). The temperate zones were between latitudes $23\frac{1}{2}°$ and $66\frac{1}{2}°$. This primitive scheme recognized the importance of the north-south variation of solar radiation and temperature. However, it failed to distinguish the major east-west variations of climate resulting from the arrangements of continents and oceans; the scheme would have been much more successful if the earth's surface were entirely land or entirely water.

During the nineteenth century, botanists devoted considerable effort to the study of the effect of the natural environment, particularly climate and soil, on plant growth. They recognized that native vegetation was greatly influenced by climate and that groups of plants were confined to various regions because of climatic factors. In the early part of the twentieth century the German botanist and climatologist Köppen devised a climatic classification based on the annual and monthly means of temperature and precipitation. He chose mean values of temperature and precipitation which corresponded with the geographical limits of various types of vegetation. Since the system was based on observations of temperature and precipitation, it represents an *empirical* approach to classification.

Other classification schemes have been developed that are purely *genetic*, that is, they are based entirely on the climatic controls, particularly the global wind systems. Although these schemes have considerable appeal, they fall short in that there are areas of the world which have climates that do not readily fit the expected major wind regimes. To develop subclassifications of the major wind regimes to handle these areas would produce an unwieldy classification scheme.

Classification Scheme Used in This Book

Although the climatic system used in this book has deep roots in the Köppen system and employs some of its basic boundaries, it is sufficiently different to make it inappropriate to label it a "modified Köppen system." The classification used here is essentially empirical, employing mean monthly values of temperature and precipitation to denote boundaries. The boundaries frequently coincide with the approximate limits of various forms of native vegetation. More importantly, the classification quite clearly reflects the influence of the major wind systems and the distribution of continents and oceans. Thus it is partially genetic in character.

The system employs six groups of climates. Five are differentiated on the basis of mean monthly temperatures. A sixth group, the dry climates, is based on annual precipitation; it includes those climates in which precipitation is less than *potential evaporation* (i.e., if surface water were available, more of it would evaporate than could be replaced by rainfall). In general, the five groups based on temperature are mainly zonal in arrangement, reflecting the importance of solar energy. The dry group often cuts through the others, occurring in all except polar latitudes.

The 6 major climatic groups are subdivided into a total of 11 main types. The 11 types reflect not only the major zonal arrangement but also the important factors of seasonal distribution of precipitation and the effects of oceans and continents. The 6 major groups and 11 types are shown in Table 5.1.

In the low latitudes is a winterless, frostless belt with rain adequate or more than adequate for agricultural purposes. This is the tropical humid or *A* group. It is subdivided into two types: *tropical wet* (*Ar*) and *tropical wet-and-dry* (*Aw*). On the low-latitude margins of the middle latitudes is the sub-tropical belt or (*C*) group where winters are mild and the growing season is long. Here two subdivisions are made: *subtropical dry-summer* (*Cs*) and *subtropical humid* (*Cf*). Poleward from the subtropics is the temperate belt or *D* group. Two types are recognized: *temperate oceanic* (*Do*) and *temperate continental* (*Dc*). Still farther poleward is the subarctic or boreal belt, the *E* group. It is not subdivided. In very high latitudes are the polar climates or *F* group, which are divided into the *tundra* (*Ft*) and *icecap* (*Fi*) climates. The dry climates or *B* group are divided into a *semiarid* or *steppe* type (*BS*) and an *arid* or *desert* type (*BW*).

The boundaries separating the climatic types described above, or, for that matter, boundaries used in any climatic classification system, should be treated with caution. Just as a front is a zone of transition separating two different air masses, so are climatic boundaries transition zones separating two different climates. In some areas, such as along the crest of certain mountain ranges, the transition zone may be quite sharp. In other areas, such as in the broad lowlands of a continent, the transition from one climate to another may be very gradual. The major

justification for climatic classification is that it reduces the diversity of climates to several large classes so that the world pattern can be more easily studied. *Classification is a tool, not a goal.*

An interpretive example. The world map of climate appears in Plate 1. In Figure 5.14 is a section of the world map. It will be used to illustrate the classification scheme and to relate the climatic types to the global wind systems.

In most of western Europe, shown in Figure 5.14, the climate north of the northern coast of Spain is temperate oceanic (*Do*). In this region of Europe, between four and eight months have mean temperatures above 10°C (50°F), while the coolest month has a mean temperature above 0°C (32°F). The region lies well within the zone of mid-latitude westerlies throughout the year, with extratropical cyclones providing a rather uniform seasonal distribution of precipitation. Since the area lies to the east of the relatively warm Atlantic Ocean, the prevailing westerly flow of these latitudes carries mild maritime polar air masses into the continent, producing unusually mild winters for these latitudes. Farther east in Europe the moderating effect of the Atlantic is not so strongly felt and the climate is classified as temperate continental (*Dc*).

In the Mediterranean Sea area shown in Figure 5.14, the climate is warmer than in western Europe, but there is at least one month cooler than 18°C (65°F); the climate is classified as subtropical dry-summer (*Cs*). During the winter these latitudes are within the westerlies, and traveling extratropical cyclones bring occasional rainy periods. With the northward shift of the zonal belts during the summer (July), the area comes under the influence of the eastern limb of the North Atlantic subtropical high-pressure system with its subsiding air, ensuring a warm, dry summer.

Not far south of the Mediterranean coast of North Africa, the winter precipitation becomes so light and the hot, dry summer becomes so long that potential evaporation exceeds precipitation. This marks the northern edge of the dry climates (*B*) of North Africa. Along the northern fringe of the dry climates is a narrow zone of steppe climate (*BS*), where an occasional *winter* (January) extratropical cyclone passing through the Mediterranean Sea produces some scant rainfall. The broad central portion of the dry climates is the Sahara Desert (*BW*), where

TABLE 5.1   CLIMATIC CLASSIFICATION

Group	Types
A. Tropical humid climates	Tropical wet (*Ar*) Tropical wet-and-dry (*Aw*)
B. Dry climates	Steppe, semiarid (*BS*) Desert, arid (*BW*)
C. Subtropical climates	Subtropical dry-summer (*Cs*) Subtropical humid (*Cf*)
D. Temperate climates	Temperate oceanic (*Do*) Temperate continental (*Dc*)
E. Boreal climate	Boreal (*E*)
F. Polar climates	Tundra (*Ft*) Icecap (*Fi*)
H. Highland climates	

Definitions and boundaries

A = Without frost. Average temperature of all months, over 18°C (65°F).
B = Evaporation exceeds precipitation.
    S = Steppe, or semiarid.
    W = (German Wüste) Desert or arid.
C = 8 or more months over 10°C (50°F); cool months under 18°C (65°F).
D = 4 to 8 months over 10°C (50°F).
E = Up to 3 months over 10°C (50°F).
F = All months below 10°C (50°F).
r = Rainy, not more than 2 months dry.
a = Average temperature of warmest month over 22°C (72°F).
b = Average temperature of warmest month under 22°C (72°F).
s = Summer (or high-sun period) is dry.
w = Winter (or low-sun period) is dry.
f = No dry season.
o = Oceanic.
c = Continental.
n = fog (German *nebel*), used only with B climates.
h = Hot, 8 or more months over 10°C (50°F), used only with *B* climates.
k = Cold, fewer than 8 months over 10°C (50°F), used only with *B* climates.
t = Warmest month below 10°C (50°F) but above 0°C (32°F).
i = All months below 0°C (32°F).
A/C boundary = Isotherm of 18°C (65°F) for coolest month.
C/D boundary = 8 months 10°C (50°F).
D/E boundary = 4 months 10°C (50°F).
E/F boundary = Isotherm of 10°C (50°F) for warmest month.
t/i boundary = Isotherm of 0°C (32°F) for warmest month.
B/A, B/C, B/D, B/E boundaries = Evaporation equals precipitation.
BS/BW boundary = One-half the precipitation that defines the *B/A, B/C, B/D, B/E* boundary.
h/k boundary in dry climates = Same as *C/D* boundary.
Do/Dc boundary = Isotherm of 0°C (32°F) for coolest month, up to 2°C (36°F) farther inland.

CLIMATES

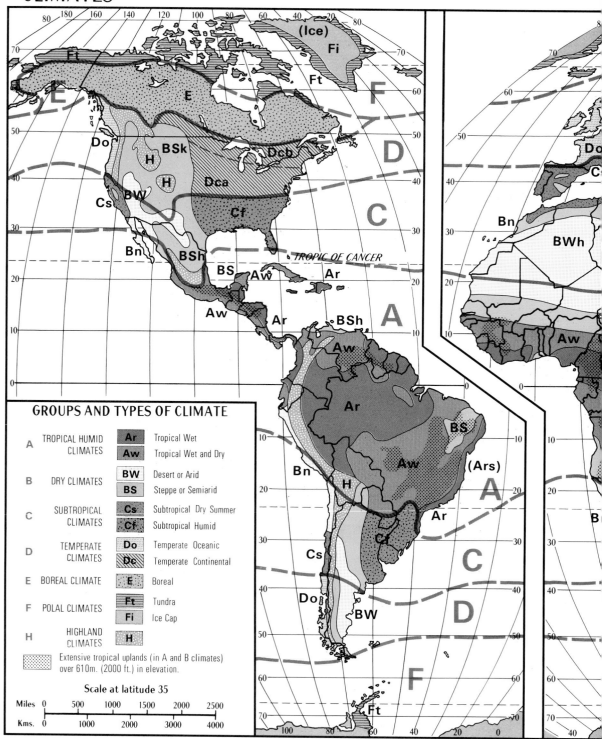

GROUPS AND TYPES OF CLIMATE

A	TROPICAL HUMID CLIMATES	Ar	Tropical Wet
		Aw	Tropical Wet and Dry
B	DRY CLIMATES	BW	Desert or Arid
		BS	Steppe or Semiarid
C	SUBTROPICAL CLIMATES	Cs	Subtropical Dry Summer
		Cf	Subtropical Humid
D	TEMPERATE CLIMATES	Do	Temperate Oceanic
		Dc	Temperate Continental
E	BOREAL CLIMATE	E	Boreal
F	POLAL CLIMATES	Ft	Tundra
		Fi	Ice Cap
H	HIGHLAND CLIMATES	H	

Extensive tropical uplands (in A and B climates) over 610m. (2000 ft.) in elevation.

Scale at latitude 35

Miles 0   500   1000   1500   2000   2500
Kms. 0   1000   2000   3000   4000

Plate 1 World map of climates.

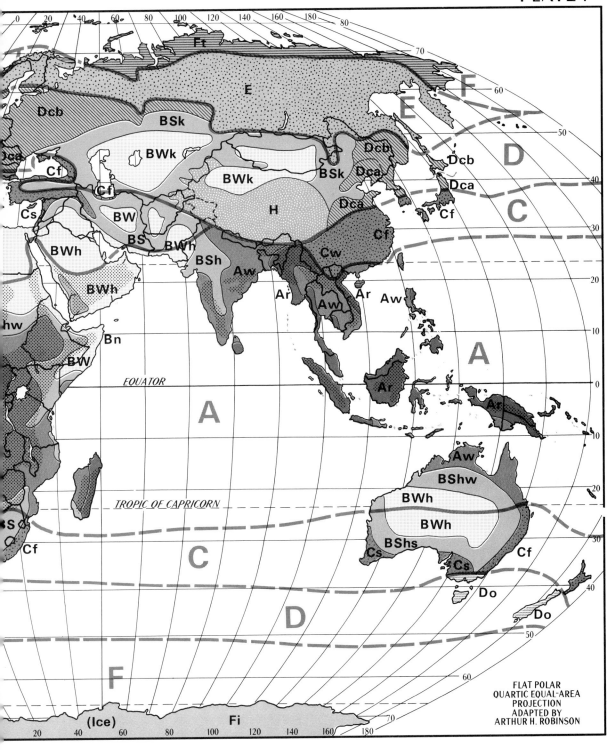

PLATE 1

FLAT POLAR
QUARTIC EQUAL-AREA
PROJECTION
ADAPTED BY
ARTHUR H. ROBINSON

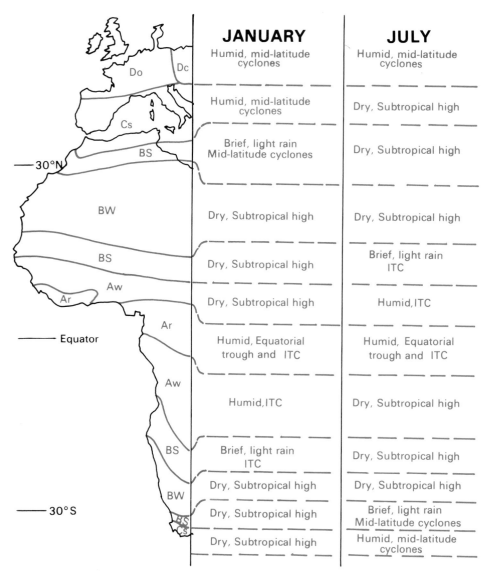

	JANUARY	JULY
Do / Dc	Humid, mid-latitude cyclones	Humid, mid-latitude cyclones
Cs	Humid, mid-latitude cyclones	Dry, Subtropical high
BS	Brief, light rain Mid-latitude cyclones	Dry, Subtropical high
BW	Dry, Subtropical high	Dry, Subtropical high
BS	Dry, Subtropical high	Brief, light rain ITC
Aw / Ar	Dry, Subtropical high	Humid, ITC
Ar	Humid, Equatorial trough and ITC	Humid, Equatorial trough and ITC
Aw	Humid, ITC	Dry, Subtropical high
BS	Brief, light rain ITC	Dry, Subtropical high
BW	Dry, Subtropical high	Dry, Subtropical high
BS / Cs	Dry, Subtropical high	Brief, light rain Mid-latitude cyclones
	Dry, Subtropical high	Humid, mid-latitude cyclones

Figure 5.14 The climatic classification related to the general circulation and its seasonal changes.

the subsidence of the subtropical high prevails regardless of season. Along the southern flank of the Sahara an area of steppe climate is found, but here an occasional disturbance associated with the doldrums and ITC may bring light *summer* rainfall.

South of the dry climates of North Africa are the tropical humid climates. Precipitation increases to the point where it exceeds potential evaporation, and warmth increases so that no month has a mean

temperature cooler than 18°C (65°F). Within this northern part of the *A* group is the tropical wet-and-dry type (*Aw*) of climate. During the high-sun season (July), the ITC and various equatorial-trough disturbances bring substantial rainfall. However, with the southward shift of the zonal wind belts in the low-sun season (January), the region comes under the influence of the dry trades, which have their source in the eastern limb of the subtropical high. A definite dry season occurs. Near the equator the equatorial trough prevails throughout the year, and no season is dry. This is the region of tropical wet (*Ar*) climate in Africa.

To the south of the *Ar* climate is the same sequence of climates that is found in northern Africa and the Mediterranean Sea area. But they are now in reverse order, since in the Southern Hemisphere January is the high-sun season. Because Africa does not extend deep into the Southern Hemisphere, the *D* climates are not encountered.

The areas examined in Figure 5.14 are all located in the western parts of continents. Over the eastern portion of continents the zonal arrangement of climates is not entirely the same. For example, note on the world map of climate that the *A* climates of Central America and the Caribbean Islands are terminated on their northern edge by the *C* group of climates rather than by dry climates. In this western part of the North Atlantic the subsidence of the subtropical high cell is weak, and dry climates do not occur. Rather, the *A* climates are terminated in southern Florida by the *C* climates, where at least one winter month is cooler than 18°C (65°F).

REVIEW QUESTIONS

1. If mean monthly temperature and precipitation data for individual months are available for your city, plot simple graphs showing the values for each January and each July for the past 30 years. Take note of how much the individual monthly means deviate from the 30-year mean. If your city is located near a coast, compare the year-to-year variations with those for an interior station, or vice versa. Discuss the reasons for the differences.
2. What major role does the general circulation play in the earth's energy balance?
3. Why is the position of the polar jet stream of particular significance to the weather and climate of a middle-latitude city?
4. How are Hadley cells related to the equatorial trough and subtropical highs?
5. What is the basic cause of the monsoon winds?
6. Contrast the climate of areas which are under the influence of the eastern part of a subtropical high with that of areas under its western portion.
7. Los Angeles, California, has relatively wet winters and nearly rainless summers, yet Acapulco,

Mexico, also located on the west coast of North America, has dry winters and wet summers. Explain these differences in terms of the general circulation and its seasonal change.
8. Why does northern Norway (north of the Arctic Circle) have a milder winter than northern Illinois?
9. What are possible causes for differences in the amount of precipitation within a latitudinal belt (i.e., east-west differences)?
10. What types of evidence are there indicating that the climate has changed?
11. What are some of the causes that have been postulated to explain climatic change?
12. What is the purpose of climatic classification?
13. What criteria are used to distinguish between the *C* and *D* climates? Between the *B* and all other climates?
14. Why does the tropical wet-and-dry climate (*Aw*) north of the Congo Basin have its rains in July while the *Aw* climate south of the Congo Basin experiences its rains in January?

SELECTED REFERENCES

Claiborne, R. *Climate, Man and History.* W. W. Norton & Company, Inc., New York, 1970. 444 pp. A lively account of climate and its role in history.

Miller, A., and J. C. Thompson. *Elements of Meteorology,* 2d ed. Charles E. Merrill Books, Inc., Columbus, Ohio, 1975. Pp. 173–204. A general description of climate is presented, along with data showing various world records of meteorological quantities. Also included is a brief history of climate.

Petterssen, S. *Introduction to Meteorology,* 3d ed. McGraw-Hill Book Company, New York, 1969. Pp. 176–197, 248–275. Chapter 11 describes the general circulation of the atmosphere, while Chapters 15 and 16 describe the global temperature and precipitation regimes.

Riley, P., and L. Spolton. *World Weather and Climate.* Cambridge University Press, London, 1974. Pp. 30–95. The second part of this small text treats the weather systems of various regions of the earth. Excellent specific examples are presented.

Trewartha, G. T. *An Introduction to Climate,* 4th ed. McGraw-Hill Book Company, New York, 1968. Pp. 237–253. The climatic classification scheme used here is described in greater detail.

The Earth's Climates

Chapters 2 through 5 have analyzed how the earth's weather and climate are produced by the energy of the atmospheric system. In this chapter the global pattern of climate, which can be thought of as the output of the atmospheric system averaged over time, will be studied. Each of the climatic types will be described and interpreted in terms of the climatic controls that produce its particular character. As each climatic type is discussed, it will be helpful to study the map of world climates (Plate 1).

TROPICAL HUMID CLIMATES—GROUP A: ALL MONTHS WARMER THAN 18°C (65°F)

The tropical humid climates (A) form a somewhat interrupted latitudinal belt 20° to 40° wide astride the equator. This belt is distinguished from all other humid regions of the earth by the fact that it lacks a winter. Frost is absent. On its poleward margins the group of tropical humid climates may be terminated either by diminishing rainfall or by decreasing temperature. Usually this belt merges with dry climates in the western parts of continents (Plate 1). On the more humid eastern sides, it extends poleward until a season of cold develops and occasional frosts occur in winter. Highlands, with their lower temperatures, are responsible for the principal interruptions in the

belt of tropical humid climates over the continents.

Normally the tropical humid climates occupy a wider belt, and thus extend farther poleward, along the eastern side of a continent. This is the side which is dominated by the relatively unstable and moist air in the western end of an oceanic subtropical anticyclone (refer back to Fig. 5.6). Narrowing of the belt of A climates toward the west side of a continent reflects the greater stability of the eastern end of a subtropical oceanic anticyclone.

Rainfall is relatively abundant, most of it being of the showery, convective type. Although temperatures in A climates are fairly uniform over the seasons and the years, rainfall is more variable, both in annual amounts and in seasonal distribution.

The two principal climatic types within the tropical humid group are distinguished from each other on the basis of their seasonal distribution of precipitation: tropical wet has ample rainfall for 10 or more months of the year; tropical wet-and-dry has a longer and more severe dry season (lasting more than two months).

Tropical Wet Climate (Ar)

Location. Uniformly high temperatures and heavy precipitation distributed throughout most of the year are the two basic characteristics of tropical wet (Ar) climate. *Ar* climate is typically found astride the equator and extending out 5° to 10° on either side. This latitudinal spread may be increased to 15° or even 25° along the eastern margin of a continent where the subtropical anticyclone is weak. The tropical wet climate is also called the *tropical rainforest* climate. It is closely associated with the equatorial trough and the intertropical convergence zone (ITC), where weak rain-generating disturbances are numerous and the air is relatively unstable. Characteristically, the tropical wet climate is bounded by the tropical wet-and-dry type on its poleward side over the central and western portions of a continent. Along the wetter eastern margins of continents, however, it usually extends farther poleward and makes contact with the subtropical, humid climate of middle latitudes.

The Amazon Basin in northern South America and the Congo Basin in Africa are the two largest continuous areas with tropical wet climate. A third, extensive, but not continuous, area includes much of insular and peninsular southeast Asia.

Temperature. Because areas with the tropical wet type of climate commonly lie near the equator in the belt of strong solar radiation throughout the year, temperatures are uniformly high. Yearly averages usually range between 25°C and 27°C (77°–80°F). Moreover, since the sun's noon rays are never far from a vertical position, and since the length of days and nights varies only slightly from one part of the year to another, there is little seasonal variation in temperature.

The annual temperature range, or *difference* between the *average* temperatures of the warmest and coolest months, is usually less than 3°C (5°F), but it may be somewhat greater farther from the equator. It is not because the average monthly temperatures are so high (indeed, average July temperatures in much of the subtropical southeastern United States are similar to the monthly averages of stations near the equator), but rather because the heat is so constant and monotonous, that tropical wet climates are sometimes considered forbidding.

The daily, or diurnal, range of temperature (the difference between the warmest and coolest hours of the day) is usually 6°–14°C (10°–25°F), which is several times greater than the annual range. For example, at Bolobo in the Congo Basin, the average daily range is 9°C (16°F), while the annual range is only 1°C (2°F). During the afternoons, the thermometer ordinarily rises to temperatures varying from 29° to 34°C (85° to 93°F) and at night sinks to 21°–24°C (70°–75°F). It is commonly said that night is the winter of the tropics.

During the day the heat combines with quiet air and high dew point temperatures to produce an atmospheric condition that is oppressive and sultry. Even the nights give little relief from the oppressive heat. Nocturnal cooling is weak because of the excessive humidity and the abundant cloudiness. The cooling is usually sufficient, however, to cause surface condensation in the near-saturated air, so that radiation fogs and heavy dew are common.

Figure 6.1 shows the daily march of temperature for the extreme months at a representative station within the tropical wet climate. It is a temperature regime in which the sun is almost completely in control. Temperatures rise each day and fall each night to about the same levels, so that one 24-hr period almost duplicates every other. Irregular invasions of cool air, a feature common in the middle latitudes, do not occur.

Precipitation. The tropical wet climates coincide fairly well with the earth's belt of heaviest annual precipitation (compare Figure 5.11 with the world climate map, Plate 1). Annual rainfall usually varies from 180 to 300 cm (70 to 120 in.). The air is warm, humid, and unstable, and the circulation in the equatorial trough is generally convergent, so that general ascent is prevalent. The result is an abundance of cumulus cloud and heavy showery rainfall, commonly accompanied by thunder and lightning.

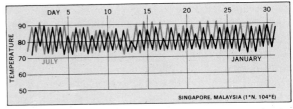

Figure 6.1 Daily maximum and minimum temperatures for the extreme months at a representative station with tropical wet climate (*Ar*). Diurnal solar control is almost complete, as shown by the regular rise and fall of temperature. The temperatures are in °F.

More rain usually comes during the warm afternoon and early evening hours, when solar heating makes the humid air increasingly unstable and buoyant; but night rains are frequent, too.

Days with rain are numerous, but certainly not all days have rain. The showery weather comes in spells of several days' duration, separated by brief periods of clearer skies. Thus rainfall does not have the daily regularity characteristic of the temperature. Weak atmospheric disturbances along the ITC within the equatorial trough account for the spells of wet weather. Therefore the shower activity is usually organized, being concentrated in disturbances and moving with them. Thus while irregular, nonperiodic weather changes are much weaker here than in the middle latitudes, they still occur, at least as far as rainfall is concerned.

Within the heart of *Ar* climates the abundant rainfall is distributed throughout the year, without even a single dry month (see data for Singapore). But more commonly, large areas have some seasonal variation, although their annual total is as great. (See Belem data.) The north-and-south migration of the equatorial trough places these areas alternately in its center and in its fringes (Fig. 6.2). A few places have one month, or at most two months, in which the rainfall is less than 63 mm (2.5 in.). Nevertheless, dense rainforest prevails throughout most of the region.

Resources of the tropical wet climates. Although approximately 10 percent of the earth's land surface has a tropical wet climate, this realm contains much less than 10 percent of the earth's population. The tropical wet areas show wide variations in population densities: the New World tropics are far emptier than those of the Old World.

Tropical wet regions have the most lavish and prolific vegetation of all climates. There is no dormant season imposed by either a season of cold or a long season of drought. Since plants grow more continuously and rapidly here than in any other climate, these regions would seem to offer the highest potential for food production. But while the climate provides a bountiful atmospheric environment for growing crops, this asset is seriously counterbalanced by soils made infertile by the abundant rains, which have leached out mineral plant foods and organic material. The topsoil of tropical wet areas is exhaust-

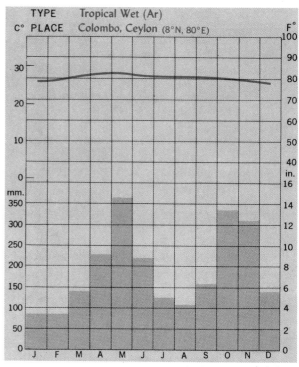

Figure 6.2   A representative station with tropical wet climate: average monthly temperatures (shown by the brown line) and average monthly precipitation (shown by the brown bars). Monthly temperatures are much more uniform than monthly amounts of precipitation. Colombo has no dry month, but the months near May and October are wettest because of the passage of ITC at those times.

ed by a few years of cropping, so the farmer is obliged to give each cultivated plot a long period of fallowing in which to recuperate.

Wild vegetation in these parts of the world is lush and evergreen. No other climate produces such a dense forest. For a farmer who must clear the land, this forest is a serious handicap. But at the same time it provides a great potential resource of wood, although logging this timber and transporting it involve both logistical and ecological problems.

Tropical Wet-and-Dry Climate (*Aw*)

This climate differs from the tropical wet type in two principal ways: first, it usually has less total annual precipitation; second, the rainfall is more seasonal in

CLIMATIC DATA FOR REPRESENTATIVE STATIONS WITH TROPICAL WET CLIMATE (*Ar*)

Belém, Amazon Valley (1°18′S, 48°W)

	J	F	M	A	M	J	J	A	S	O	N	D	Yr	Range
Temp., °C	25	25	25	25	26	26	26	26	26	26	26	26	26	1
°F	77	77	77	77	78	78	78	79	78	79	79	79	78	2
Precip., mm	340	406	437	343	287	175	145	127	120	91	86	175	2743	
in.	13.4	16.0	17.2	13.5	11.3	6.9	5.7	5.0	4.7	3.6	3.4	6.9	107.6	

Kisangani, Congo Basin (0°32′N, 25°E)

	J	F	M	A	M	J	J	A	S	O	N	D	Yr	Range
Temp., °C	25	25	25	25	25	24	23	23	24	24	24	24	24	2
°F	77	77	77	77	77	76	74	74	75	76	76	76	76	3
Precip., mm	84	104	175	142	155	89	112	226	191	249	170	71	1763	
in.	3.3	4.1	6.9	5.6	6.1	3.5	4.4	8.9	7.5	9.8	6.7	2.8	69.4	

Singapore (1°18′N, 104°E)

	J	F	M	A	M	J	J	A	S	O	N	D	Yr	Range
Temp., °C	26	27	27	27	28	27	27	27	27	27	27	27	27	2
°F	79	80	81	81	82	81	81	81	81	80	80	80	80	3
Precip., mm	252	172	193	188	172	172	170	196	178	208	254	257	2413	
in.	9.9	6.8	7.6	7.4	6.8	6.8	6.7	7.7	7.0	8.2	10.0	10.1	95.0	

character, for typically there is a dry season of over two months. These climatic differences result in replacement of the dense evergreen rainforest typical of *Ar* climate by lighter deciduous forest (i.e., trees that shed their leaves during the dormant season). There are also many areas of intermingled woodland and grass, so that the wet-and-dry type is sometimes called a *savanna* (grassland with scattered trees) climate.

Location. The tropical wet-and-dry regions are located on the poleward sides of the tropical wet climate, lying between it and the dry climates. Toward the rainier eastern part of the continent, the poleward side of wet-and-dry climate is adjacent to the subtropical humid regions of the middle latitudes. (See the world map of climates, Plate 1.)

Tropical wet-and-dry climate is typically found from about latitudes 5°–10° to 15°–20°, but it may extend farther poleward on the eastern side of a continent. This places the savanna in an intermediate position between the ITC and its unstable convergent air on the equatorial side and the subtropical anticyclones with their stable, subsiding, and diverging air on the poleward side. With the north-south shifting of the sun during the course of a year, there is a similar migration of pressure and wind systems. As a result,

latitudes from about 5° to 15° are alternately encroached upon by the wet equatorial trough and its rain-bringing disturbances at the time of high sun, and by the drier parts of the trades and the subtropical anticyclones at the time of low sun. This condition produces rainy summers and dry winters.

Temperature. Temperature conditions which were described for tropical wet climate largely apply to the wet-and-dry type as well. In tropical wet-and-dry the annual range of temperature, though still small, is somewhat greater: usually over 3°C (5°F), but seldom over 8° to 11°C (15° to 20°F) (see following table). The diurnal range, which continues to exceed the annual, is usually highest in the dry season, when the sky is clearer and humidity low. Diurnal temperature regularity is still strong (Fig. 6.3).

Often the hottest period precedes the time of highest sun (Fig. 6.4). This is because high sun is the time of rain and cloud, which somewhat reduce air temperatures (see the following table). Thus in the Northern Hemisphere savanna, the dry months of April and May are usually warmer than the rainier months of June and July.

Precipitation. Since the two tropical climates do not differ much in temperature, rainfall becomes the

CLIMATIC DATA FOR REPRESENTATIVE STATIONS WITH TROPICAL WET-AND-DRY CLIMATE (Aw)

Timbo, Guinea (11°N, 12°W)

	J	F	M	A	M	J	J	A	S	O	N	D	Yr	Range
Temp., °C	22	24	27	27	25	23	22	22	22	23	22	22	23	5
°F	72	76	81	80	77	73	72	72	72	73	72	71	74	10
Precip., mm	0	0	25	61	162	229	315	374	259	170	33	0	1628	
in.	0.0	0.0	1.0	2.4	6.4	9.0	12.4	14.7	10.2	6.7	1.3	0.0	64.1	

Calcutta, India (23°N, 88°E)

	J	F	M	A	M	J	J	A	S	O	N	D	Yr	Range
Temp., °C	18	21	26	29	30	29	28	28	28	27	22	18	26	12
°F	65	70	79	85	86	85	83	82	83	80	72	65	78	21
Precip., mm	10	28	35	51	127	284	308	292	229	110	13	5	1494	
in.	0.4	1.1	1.4	2.0	5.0	11.2	12.1	11.5	9.0	4.3	0.5	0.2	58.8	

Cuiabá, Brazil (15°S, 56°W)

	J	F	M	A	M	J	J	A	S	O	N	D	Yr	Range
Temp., °C	27	27	27	27	26	24	24	26	28	28	28	27	27	3
°F	81	81	81	80	78	75	76	78	82	82	82	81	80	7
Precip., mm	249	211	211	102	54	8	5	28	51	115	150	206	1387	
in.	9.8	8.3	8.3	4.0	2.1	0.3	0.2	1.1	2.0	4.5	5.9	8.1	54.6	

Normanton, Australia (18°S, 141°E)

	J	F	M	A	M	J	J	A	S	O	N	D	Yr	Range
Temp., °C	30	29	29	28	26	23	22	24	27	29	31	31	27	9
°F	86	85	85	82	78	73	72	75	80	85	88	87	81	15
Precip., mm	277	254	155	38	8	10	5	3	3	10	45	142	952	
in.	10.9	10.0	6.1	1.5	0.3	0.4	0.2	0.1	0.1	0.4	1.8	5.6	37.5	

critical element in distinguishing between them. Characteristically the wet-and-dry type has 1,000 to 1,500 mm (40–60 in.) of annual precipitation, which is somewhat less rain than that of the tropical wet climate. This reduction in rainfall reflects the transi-

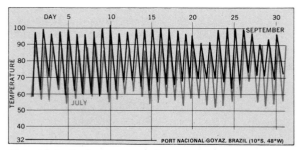

Figure 6.3 Daily maximum and minimum temperatures for the extreme months at a station with tropical wet-and-dry climate (Aw) in Brazil. Note the dominance of the periodic or solar control, also the large diurnal range of temperature at this interior station. September is hotter than July because it is less cloudy. Temperatures are in °F.

tional nature of the wet-and-dry climate. Within tropical wet-and-dry climates, rainfall usually decreases in a poleward direction (toward the subtropical highs). But it is the seasonality of precipitation, more than the smaller annual total, that mainly differentiates the two climates of the humid tropics. Aw climate has a marked dry season of more than 2 months' duration, characteristically at the time of low sun. In that season the drought is intense. The trees lose their leaves, the rivers shrink, the soil cracks, and the landscape is parched and brown. All nature appears dormant. Dust, as well as smoke from grass fires set by farmers, fill the air, so that visibility is often low. But during high sun, or summer, convective showers are numerous and the daily weather is like that of tropical wet regions (Fig. 6.4).

This marked seasonal rhythm of alternating drought and rains again shows the intermediate position of Aw between subtropical anticyclones poleward and ITC and equatorial trough equatorward. A poleward migration of pressure and wind belts with

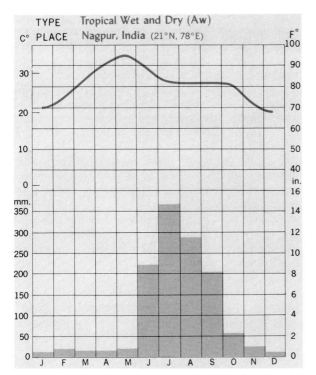

Figure 6.4 Average monthly temperatures and precipitation amounts for a representative station with tropical wet-and-dry climate (*Aw*) in India. Note that the highest temperatures are in May preceding the rains.

the sun brings to the wet-and-dry climate the rains of the ITC in summer and anticyclonic drought in winter. Note, however, that when the *Aw* climate in the Northern Hemisphere is having its wet season, its counterpart in the Southern Hemisphere is in the grip of drought. The relative lengths of the wet and dry seasons vary: the farther from the equator and the ITC, the shorter the wet season and the longer the dry.

Variability of rainfall.   Not only is rainfall in tropical wet-and-dry climate less in total amount and more seasonal in its distribution than in tropical wet, it also fluctuates more from year to year and hence is less reliable. One year may bring property damage and crop losses due to excessive rains; in the following one there may be even more severe losses from drought. This is an area that is especially susceptible to disastrous droughts produced by a small shifting of the global wind systems.

Upland tropical climate.   In tropical latitudes on several continents, especially Africa and South America, there are extensive upland areas with only moderate elevation. These have many of the usual features of tropical humid climates but differ chiefly in their somewhat lower temperatures, which of course are a result of higher altitude (Fig. 6.5). Parts are even sufficiently high for temperatures for one or more months to be below the minimum set for tropical climates. In the climate groupings used here, these extensive uplands of tropical Africa and South America are still classed as tropical humid, usually of the wet-and-dry type; but on the world map of climate they are set apart from the more standard lowland variety by a light stippling. Climatic modifications imposed by altitude are discussed more fully later in this chapter.

Resources of the tropical wet-and-dry climates.   Close to 15 percent of the earth's land area has tropical wet-and-dry climate. On a population map of the earth, many wet-and-dry regions, especially those in the New World and Australia, are conspicuous for their scarcity of people. Peninsular India is the most striking exception, for there the number of people is great. The savanna parts of Africa are intermediate in population density.

Although temperatures are constantly high in tropical wet-and-dry climate, the dormant season imposed by drought makes the productiveness of this climate considerably less than that of tropical wet climate. The smaller total amount of precipitation, and its variability as well, increase this disadvantage.

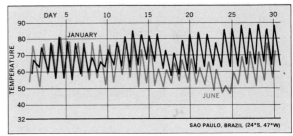

Figure 6.5 Daily maximum and minimum temperatures for São Paulo (elevation 770m, 2,545 ft), which is located on the Brazilian upland. Although the climate is tropical wet-and-dry, lower temperatures are imposed by altitude and also by the latitude. Solar control is dominant, but some nonperiodic air-mass changes are also evident here on the margins of the tropics. The temperatures are in °F.

Because of the dry season, vegetation cover is much less luxuriant. Trees are smaller, more widely spaced, and usually deciduous. Over large areas, grasslands made up of tall, coarse grasses are intermingled with woodland (the savanna). Much of the woodland is of little value commercially, and the mature natural grasses are too tall, coarse, and unnutritious to support an important commercial grazing industry.

The mature soils of the savanna climate appear to be leached and infertile like those that develop under the rainforest. As in most regions of infertile or difficult soils, the most attractive sites for cultivation are the fresh, young, unleached new alluvial surfaces (i.e., surfaces deposited by running water fairly recently in geologic time).

THE DRY CLIMATES—GROUP *B*: EVAPORATION EXCEEDS PRECIPITATION

Along much of its poleward side the tropical wet-and-dry climate merges into dry climates. Subtropical anticyclones or dry trades control the circulation for most of the year. The high-sun rains become lighter and last for a shorter period. The annual water loss by evaporation exceeds the annual water gain from precipitation.

Since the amount of water lost through evaporation increases with temperature, this loss is greater in warm climates than in cold ones. Thus the amount of annual rainfall which distinguishes between dry and humid climate varies: warm dry climates can have more annual rainfall and still be classified dry than would be allowed in cool dry ones under the same classification.

Based on annual rainfall amounts, two subdivisions of dry climate are commonly recognized: (1) the arid, or desert, type and (2) the semiarid, or steppe, type. In general the steppe is a transitional belt surrounding the desert and separating it from the humid climates beyond. The boundary between arid and semiarid climates is an arbitrary one, but commonly it is defined as one-half the amount of annual rainfall separating steppe from humid climates.

Location. Of all the climatic groups, dry climates are the most extensive, occupying more than one-quarter of the earth's land surface. As the world

climate map shows, they are a feature of tropical, subtropical, temperate, and boreal temperature zones.

In the tropics and subtropics, dry climates are concentrated between about latitudes 15° or 20° and 30° or 35°—zones which are influenced by the subtropical anticyclones. Here the dry climates characteristically are found away from the windward eastern side of a continent toward its western and central parts.

In the middle latitudes, drought conditions are most fully developed in the deep interiors of the great land masses. These regions are farthest removed from oceanic sources of moisture, and they are dominated by a cold anticyclone in winter. Dry climates are also found on the leeward side of major mountain ranges, particularly ranges oriented perpendicular to the prevailing winds.

Temperature. Since dry climates exist in a wide range of latitudes from tropical to boreal, it is impossible to make valid generalizations about their average annual temperatures. Some are hot, some are cold, some are intermediate.

As a class, however, continental dry climates have relatively large annual temperature variations compared with the average for their particular latitude. Summers in dry climates are likely to be abnormally warm or hot, and winters to be abnormally cool or cold, relative to the seasonal contrasts of the humid land climates at the same latitude. The large annual range is the result of the leeward and interior locations of most dry climates, as well as of the prevailing clear skies and dry atmosphere.

Even more striking, however, are the large daily extremes of temperature. Clear, cloudless skies and relatively low humidity permit an abundance of solar energy to reach the earth by day, but likewise they allow a rapid loss of heat at night. The meagerness of the vegetation cover in deserts also contributes to the large diurnal ranges, for it is too sparse to prevent the surface from becoming intensely heated by day and rapidly chilled at night.

Precipitation and humidity. Rainfall in the dry climates is always scanty. In addition, it is so variable from year to year that even the low average cannot be depended upon. It is also significant that there are more years when rainfall is below the average than when it is above, for it is the occasional humid year which tends to lift the average. A general rule is that dependability of precipitation commonly decreases with decreasing amount. Therefore two handicaps—meagerness and unreliability of rainfall—go together.

With a few exceptions, relative humidity is low in the dry climates—10 to 30 percent being usual for midday hours—and potential evaporation is characteristically high. Specific humidity, on the other hand, is not always low. Desert air in warm and hot climates usually contains a considerable quantity of water vapor, even when the air is far from saturated. There is little cloudiness. The direct sunlight, as well as that reflected from the earth, is blinding in intensity.

Winds. Dry regions are often windy places, since the sparse, stunted vegetation exerts very little frictional drag upon air movement. Moreover, the rapid daytime heating of the lower air over deserts leads to strong convectional overturning. This interchange of lower and upper air tends to accelerate the horizontal surface winds during warm hours when convection is at a maximum.

When strong winds occur, desert air is often murky with fine dust, which fills the eyes, nose, and throat, causing serious discomfort. Some of this dust is carried beyond the desert margins to form the loess (deposit by wind) of bordering regions. Heavier, wind-driven coarse sand, traveling close to the surface, is the principal tool of the wind in sculpturing desert landforms.

In the classification of climates employed here, dry climates, including both steppe and desert, are divided into two great subgroups based upon temperature contrasts. One is the dry climates of the tropics-subtropics, or hot steppes and deserts. The other is the dry climates of middle latitudes, or the cold-winter steppes and deserts.

Tropical-Subtropical Dry Climates (*BWh* and *BSh*)

Location. As noted previously, hot steppes and deserts coincide fairly well with the subtropical anticyclones and their dry trades. But because subsidence is weaker in the western part of an oceanic cell, dry climates do not ordinarily extend to the adjacent eastern side of a continent, which because of the low-latitude easterlies is also the windward side. The drought-making effect of strong subsidence along the eastern flanks of an oceanic anticyclone (west side of the continent) is strengthened by the stabilizing influence of the cool ocean currents which are found along several of the western coasts. Both controls act to intensify the aridity and to extend it farther equatorward along the western sides of continents (see especially Peru and southwestern Africa in Figure 5.11).

Precipitation. In their driest parts, tropical-subtropical deserts are the most rainless regions of the earth. The majority of these areas receives less than 250 mm (10 in.) of precipitation annually and large parts less than 120 mm (5 in.). Cairo, Egypt, averages only 25 mm (1 in.), and in sections of the Chilean desert no rain may fall for several years in

CLIMATIC DATA FOR REPRESENTATIVE STATIONS IN TROPICAL-SUBTROPICAL DESERTS (*BWh*)

	J	F	M	A	M	J	J	A	S	O	N	D	Yr	Range
Jacobabad, Pakistan (28°N, 68°E)														
Temp., °C	14	17	24	30	33	37	35	33	32	26	20	15	26	23
°F	57	62	75	86	92	98	95	92	89	79	68	59	79	41
Precip., mm	5	8	5	5	3	8	23	23	5	3	3	5	89	
in.	0.2	0.3	0.2	0.2	0.1	0.3	0.9	0.9	0.2	0.1	0.1	0.2	3.5	
Alice Springs, Australia (24°S, 134°E)														
Temp., °C	29	28	25	20	16	12	12	14	18	23	26	28	21	17
°F	84	82	77	68	60	54	53	58	65	73	79	82	69	31
Precip., mm	43	33	28	10	15	13	8	8	8	18	30	38	252	
in.	1.7	1.3	1.1	0.4	0.6	0.5	0.3	0.3	0.3	0.7	1.2	1.5	9.9	

CLIMATIC DATA FOR A REPRESENTATIVE STATION IN TROPICAL-SUBTROPICAL STEPPE WITH HIGH-SUN RAINFALL (*BSh*)

		J	F	M	A	M	J	J	A	S	O	N	D	Yr	Range
					Kayes, Mali (14°N, 12°W)									
Temp.,	°C	25	27	32	34	36	33	29	28	28	29	28	25	29	11
	°F	77	81	89	94	96	91	84	82	82	85	83	77	85	19
Precip.,	mm	0	0	0	0	15	99	211	211	142	48	8	5	739	
	in.	0.0	0.0	0.0	0.0	0.6	3.9	8.3	8.3	5.6	1.9	0.3	0.2	29.1	

succession. Average figures are not particularly useful in describing the scanty rainfall of deserts, since it is so erratic. What little rain does fall is largely of the shower type.

The steppes, while somewhat less arid than the deserts, also have undependable rainfall. Steppe areas lie more on the margins of the subtropical highs, so that during the course of a year they are encroached upon briefly by atmospheric disturbances and their rainfall. (See Fig. 5.14.) Thus total annual rainfall may amount to 350–650 mm (14–26 in.).

Those tropical steppes which are located on the equatorward margins of the deserts are likely to have a brief period of relatively heavy rains at the time of high sun, for then the ITC and its disturbances are farthest poleward. Rainfall periodicity in these steppes is like that of the adjacent tropical wet-and-dry climate except that the dry season is longer and the total precipitation less (see the data for Kayes in the above table).

Belts of steppe climate which lie on the poleward side of tropical deserts, and usually in fairly close proximity to the subtropical dry-summer type, have nearly all their rainfall in the cool season. Like the nearby Mediterranean climates, they receive rain from middle-latitude cyclones, which follow more equatorward routes in winter than in summer. (See the data for Benghazi.)

Temperature. In the low-latitude dry climates scorching, desiccating heat prevails during the period of high sun. Average hot-month temperatures are usually between 30° and 35°C (86° and 95°F), and those of the winter season between 10° and 15°C (50° and 59°F) (Fig. 6.6). Thus annual ranges are of 14°–17°C (25°–30°F) or even more. Such relatively large seasonal differences are not found in any other tropical climates.

The temperature difference between day and night may equal or even exceed that between winter and summer. Midday readings of 38° to 43°C (100° to 110°F) are common in summer (Fig. 6.7), and over 55°C (131°F) has been recorded. At a station in Death Valley, California, the daily maxima in 1960 reached or exceeded 38°C (100°F) for 136 consecutive days. On summer nights the temperature may drop to 25°–30°C (77°–86°F), which is a welcome relief after the parching daytime heat but is still relatively warm.

During winter, midday temperatures are

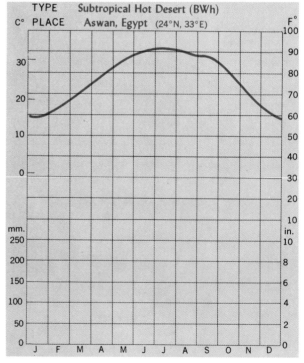

Figure 6.6 A hot-desert station in subtropical latitudes. Note the relatively large annual range for the latitude. Precipitation amounts are too low to plot on the graph.

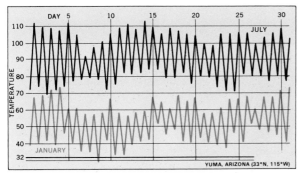

Figure 6.7 Daily maximum and minimum temperature for a hot-desert station located on the northern margins of the subtropics in Arizona. Although solar control is dominant, nonperiodic air-mass effects associated with passing cyclones and anticyclones are fairly conspicuous at this latitude in winter. The temperatures are in °F.

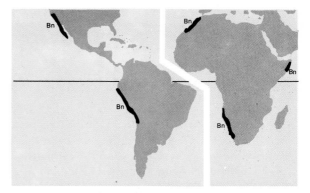

Figure 6.8 Distribution of cool coastal dry climates (*Bn*) in tropical and subtropical latitudes. Characteristically this subtype of tropical-subtropical dry climate is located along coasts paralleled by cool ocean currents fed by upwelling. Temperature inversions are common, and fog is frequent.

pleasantly warm, averaging 18° to 24°C (65° to 75°F), while nights are distinctly chilly, with minimum temperatures dropping to 7° to 13°C (45° to 55°F).

Daily weather. Solar control dominates daily weather in the tropical dry climates. One day is like another, with temperatures rising to about the same level during the period of afternoon heat and falling to nearly the same minimum every night. Some nonperiodic variety in weather is found in the more marginal parts, where disturbances bring spells of showery or rainy weather on the low-latitude frontier in summer and the poleward frontier in winter. On the poleward margins, some nondiurnal temperature variations are likewise derived from passing middle-latitude cyclones accompanied by weak invasions of polar air in winter (Fig. 6.7).

Cool marine dry climates (*Bn*). The normal features of tropical-subtropical dry climates—hot sum-

mers, large annual and diurnal temperature ranges, low humidity, and little cloudiness—are considerably modified along the coastlines of several deserts, where cool ocean currents, fed by upwelling, flow parallel to the coast (Fig. 6.8). Cool currents have a marked influence on weather along the desert coasts of Peru and northern Chile and the Kalahari in southwestern Africa. They also affect the Atlantic coasts of the Moroccan Sahara, northwestern Mexico, and Somalia in eastern Africa. Note that most of these regions are found along tropical west coasts, and that they center in latitudes 20°–30°, although in some instances they may extend equatorward to nearly 5°. The Somali coast in eastern Africa is the principal exception to west-coast location.

In most such coastal dry climates, three features of temperature contrast strikingly with those of the usual tropical dry climates: (1) summer temperatures are markedly lower, (2) the annual range is less, and (3) the daily range of temperature is

CLIMATIC DATA FOR A REPRESENTATIVE STATION IN TROPICAL-SUBTROPICAL STEPPE WITH LOW-SUN RAINFALL (*BSh*)

		J	F	M	A	M	J	J	A	S	O	N	D	Yr	Range
						Benghazi, Libya (32°N, 20°E)									
Temp., °C		13	14	17	19	22	24	26	26	26	24	19	15	21	13
	°F	55	57	63	66	72	75	78	79	78	75	66	59	69	24
Precip., mm		94	45	18	3	3	0	0	0	3	8	54	79	302	
	in.	3.7	1.8	0.7	0.1	0.1	0.0	0.0	0.0	0.1	0.3	2.1	3.1	11.9	

CLIMATIC DATA FOR A REPRESENTATIVE DESERT STATION ON A COOL-WATER COAST (*Bn*)

		J	F	M	A	M	J	J	A	S	O	N	D	Yr	Range
							Lima, Peru (12°S, 77°W)								
Temp.,	°C	22	23	23	21	19	17	16	16	16	17	19	21	19	7
	°F	71	73	73	70	66	62	61	61	61	62	66	70	66	12
Precip., mm		0	0	0	0	0	5	8	13	13	3	0	0	45	
	in.	0.0	0.0	0.0	0.0	0.0	0.2	0.3	0.5	0.5	0.1	0.0	0.0	1.8	

greatly reduced (compare Figure 6.9 with Figure 6.7; also see climatic data for Lima).

Rainfall along these cool tropical desert coasts is exceedingly low—even lower than in much of the interior desert—because these areas are most directly under the influence of the stable eastern end of an oceanic subtropical anticyclone and also of stabilizing effects of cool coastal water. The cool water so effectively chills the surface air that convection due to solar heating is rare. For a distance of nearly 3,300 km (2,000 mi.) along the desert coasts of Peru and northern Chile, annual rainfall is only about 25 mm (1 in.).

But although precipitation is meager, fog and low stratus clouds are abundant, so that the bright sunshine common to most deserts is greatly reduced, especially in winter. The fog and stratus clouds owe their origin to the cool water and the prevalent low-level temperature inversion. The special classification *Bn* is given these coastal deserts, the letter *n* representing *nebel*, the German for "fog."

Middle-Latitude (Temperate and Boreal) Dry Climates (*BWk* and *BSk*)

Location. As mentioned earlier, dry climates in middle latitudes usually are found in the deep interiors of the great continents, far from the oceans, which are the principal sources of the atmosphere's water vapor. Further intensifying the aridity of these deep interiors is the fact that parts are largely surrounded by mountain or plateau barriers which block the entrance of humid maritime air masses. (See Plate 1.) Where high mountains closely parallel a coast, as in western North America, dry climates approach relatively close to the sea. Many of the very driest parts are low in altitude and have basinlike configurations.

In Patagonia (Argentina) dry climates actu-

ally reach the east coast. There the land mass is so narrow that all of it lies in the *rain shadow* of the Andes. "Rain shadow" is a term used to describe those areas in the lee of mountain ranges where descending air produces a dry climate. These same mountains disrupt the cyclonic storms that cross the continent from the west.

Temperature. Dry climates of middle latitudes differ from their counterparts in the tropics mainly in that they undergo a season of severe cold. Otherwise they have many features in common with the tropical-subtropical dry climates. Because of their interior locations on large continents, their annual temperature ranges are large. Their wide latitudinal spread of 15° or 20°, however, makes it impossible to give representative overall temperature figures (see Figure 6.10 and the following tables). Diurnal ranges are also large (Fig. 6.10).

Patagonia in Argentina is again somewhat the exception. There the narrow land mass and the cool waters offshore result in temperatures that are more marine than continental, so that summers are unusually cool and winters relatively mild.

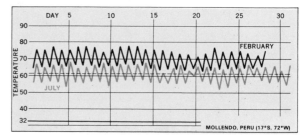

Figure 6.9 Daily maximum and minimum temperatures for a low-latitude desert station located on a coast paralleled by a cool ocean current. Note the abnormally low average temperatures and the small daily ranges. Compare with Fig. 6.7. The temperatures are in °F.

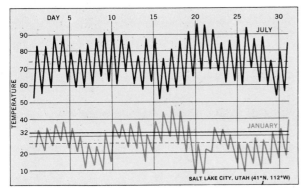

Figure 6.10   Daily maximum and minimum temperatures for a middle-latitude steppe station (*BS*). Note the strong nonperiodic air-mass control, especially in winter. A large diurnal temperature range is typical of summer. The temperatures are in °F.

Precipitation.   Probably no middle-latitude deserts are so rainless as the most arid tropical deserts. In all likelihood, some precipitation falls every year. Unlike the dry climates of the low latitudes, those of middle latitudes receive a part of their total precipitation in the form of snow, although the amount is small. The snow cover varies in depth and duration depending chiefly on latitude.

Most middle-latitude dry climates receive the greater part of their precipitation in the warmer months. As previous chapters have shown, this is a characteristic of continental climates in general, humid as well as dry. Chiefly it is the parts which lie closest to subtropical latitudes, and therefore to the subtropical dry-summer type, that may have more precipitation in winter than in summer.

Middle-latitude steppes, like their counterparts in the tropics, occupy transitional, or intermediate, positions between deserts and the humid climates. Since they have more precipitation than deserts, the steppes are somewhat better utilized and populated. But just because of this, and because the rainfall is unreliable, they are also regions of greater economic catastrophe (Fig. 6.11). A succession of humid years may tempt settlers to push the agricultural frontier toward the desert. Then drought years come, crops fail, and disaster follows.

Resources of the dry realm.   The dry climates cover over one-quarter of the earth's land surface. It

is unfortunate that such an unproductive climate should be so extensive. For the most part, dry lands coincide with great blank spaces on the world population map, as do parts of the wet tropics and nearly all of the cold polar and subarctic lands. Indeed, these three climates—the dry, the cold, and the constantly hot—offer the greatest obstacles to a large-scale redistribution of population on the earth.

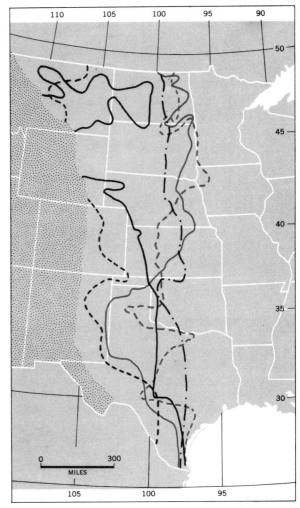

Figure 6.11   Wide fluctuations in the location of the annual boundary separating dry from humid climates over a period of five successive years in the semiarid-subhumid region east of the Rocky Mountains. Black dots indicate the mountain-plateau area. *(After Kendall.)*

CLIMATIC DATA FOR REPRESENTATIVE STATIONS IN MIDDLE-LATITUDE DESERTS (*BWk*)

Santa Cruz, Argentina (50°S, 69°W)	J	F	M	A	M	J	J	A	S	O	N	D	Yr	Range
Temp., °C	15	14	13	9	5	2	2	3	7	9	12	13	8	13
°F	59	58	55	48	41	35	35	38	44	49	53	56	47	24
Precip., mm	15	10	8	15	15	13	18	10	5	10	13	23	155	
in.	0.6	0.4	0.3	0.6	0.6	0.5	0.7	0.4	0.2	0.4	0.5	0.9	6.1	

Kuche, Sinkiang, China (970 m, 3,182 ft) (44°N, 89°E)	J	F	M	A	M	J	J	A	S	O	N	D	Yr	Range
Temp., °C	−12	−3	7	13	18	22	24	23	18	12	2	−7	9	36
°F	10	26	45	56	65	71	76	73	65	54	35	19	49	66
Precip., mm	3	3	5	3	3	33	18	8	5	0	3	8	86	
in.	0.1	0.1	0.2	0.1	0.1	1.3	0.7	0.3	0.2	0.0	0.1	0.3	3.4	

CLIMATIC DATA FOR REPRESENTATIVE STATIONS IN MIDDLE-LATITUDE STEPPES (*BSk*)

Williston, North Dakota (48°N, 104°W)	J	F	M	A	M	J	J	A	S	O	N	D	Yr	Range
Temp., °C	−14	−13	−6	6	12	17	21	19	13	7	−3	−10	4	35
°F	6	8	22	43	53	63	69	67	56	44	27	14	39	63
Precip., mm	13	10	23	28	54	81	43	43	25	18	15	13	366	
in.	0.5	0.4	0.9	1.1	2.1	3.2	1.7	1.7	1.0	0.7	0.6	0.5	14.4	

Ulan Bator (Urga), Mongolia (1160 m, 3,800 ft.) (48°N, 107°E)	J	F	M	A	M	J	J	A	S	O	N	D	Yr	Range
Temp., °C	−27	−20	−11	1	9	14	17	15	9	−1	−13	−27	−2	44
°F	−16	−4	13	34	48	58	63	59	48	30	8	−17	28	79
Precip., mm	0	3	0	0	8	43	66	54	13	3	3	3	193	
in.	0.0	0.1	0.0	0.0	0.3	1.7	2.6	2.1	0.5	0.1	0.1	0.1	7.6	

Because of the shortage of rainfall and extreme year-to-year variability, it appears that the earth's dry climates are doomed to remain relatively unproductive. Neither artificial rainmaking by cloud seeding nor methods for converting sea water into fresh water seem likely to create any large increase in dry-land agriculture in the near future. In a few places agriculture can be expanded by an increased use of irrigation and of drought-resistant plants cultivated by dry-farming methods. But, again, it is unlikely that either of these techniques will open up extensive new areas of dry land to agricultural settlement.

The desert climate is responsible for a sparse vegetation cover which has relatively low resource value. Some deserts are almost completely barren wastes; in others there is a thin mantle of widely spaced woody shrubs with some short desert bunch-grass, but even the grazing value of this vegetation is very low. Semiarid regions have short, shallow-rooted, widely spaced grasses with a considerably higher grazing value than that of the desert shrub; i.e., they are capable of supporting more livestock per unit area. This grass is a great natural asset of the steppes.

Soils are not important in deserts, largely because the rainfall deficiency makes it impossible to farm them. In the middle-latitude steppes the very modest amount of leaching and the organic material derived from the root mat of the grasses make for excellent dark, fertile soils. Unfortunately this admirable soil resource of middle-latitude semiarid lands cannot be fully exploited because of the precipitation handicap.

THE SUBTROPICAL CLIMATES—GROUP *C:* 8 OR MORE MONTHS ABOVE 10°C (50°F), AT LEAST 1 MONTH BELOW 18°C (65°F)

Within the subtropical group of climates (*C*) annual precipitation exceeds potential evaporation; consequently, the group is classified on the basis of temperature rather than precipitation. The subtropical climates lack the constant heat of the tropics; a definite seasonal rhythm in temperature occurs. Although the wet and dry seasons of the tropics are replaced by winter and summer, portions of the subtropical group of climates have marked seasonal contrasts in precipitation.

Over the western parts of the continents the equatorward fringes of the subtropical climates merge into the steppe climates (*BS*), while over the eastern parts of the continents they adjoin the tropical wet-and-dry climates (*Aw*). These differences across the equatorward boundary of the *C* group emphasize the contrast that exists between the eastern and western limbs of the great oceanic subtropical anticyclones. The strong subsidence in the eastern portion of these subtropical high-pressure areas leads to great dryness over the adjacent western portions of the continents and thus to a *B/C* boundary. However, the greater moisture and weaker stability that exist in the western part of the subtropical high permits the subtropical climates (*C*) to adjoin the humid *A* group. (See Plate 1).

The *C* group of climates is divided into two types which reflect the major east-west contrast in precipitation that exists across the subtropical oceans. On the west side of continents are found the subtropical dry-summer climates (*Cs*), while on the east side are found the subtropical humid (*Cf*) climates.

Subtropical Dry-Summer Climate (*Cs*) (Mediterranean)

This climate is characterized by a concentration of the year's modest amount of precipitation in the winter season, while summers are nearly or completely dry. The winters are mild, and the summers are from warm to hot with abundant sunshine. The climate is unique in being the only one of the earth's humid climates with drought in summer and a strong rainfall maximum in winter.

The subtropical dry-summer type has strongly marked climatic characteristics which are fairly well duplicated in five regions: the borderlands of the Mediterranean Sea, central and coastal southern California, central Chile, the southern tip of South Africa, and parts of southern Australia.

Location. Subtropical dry-summer areas typically are found on the tropical margins of the middle latitudes (30°–40°) along the western sides of continents. (See Plate 1.) Their location on the poleward side of a subtropical high places them between the subsiding air of an oceanic anticyclone's stable eastern end on the one hand and the rain-bringing cyclones of the westerlies on the other. With the north-south shifting of wind belts during the course of a year, these west-side subtropical latitudes are joined to the dry tropics at the time of high sun and to the humid middle latitudes at low sun. Tropical constancy therefore characterizes them in summer and middle-latitude changeability in winter. The subtropical dry-summer type is a transitional climate situated between low-latitude dry climates equatorward and cool, temperate marine climates farther poleward.

In both central Chile and California, mountains terminate this type abruptly on the land side. As for southern Africa and southwestern Australia, the poleward tips of the continents barely reach into the middle latitudes. Thus on these continents the subtropical dry-summer climate occupies the southern and southwestern extremities. Only in the region of the Mediterranean Sea Basin, which is a major route of winter cyclones, does the *Cs* climate extend far inland, penetrating for 3,300 km (2,000 mi) or more and affecting extensive areas. It is for this reason that the subtropical dry-summer type is often called *Mediterranean* climate.

Temperature. Two subdivisions of the *Cs* type may be recognized, based mainly on the degree of summer heat. A warm-summer subtype (*Csa*) is situated either inland from the coast or on a coast bordered by warm water, while a cool-summer subtype (*Csb*) occupies limited areas where coasts are washed by cool ocean currents—mainly in coastal California and Chile.

Except along cool-water coasts, average summer-month temperatures are hot, 24°–27°C (75°–80°F) being common (Fig. 6.12). The heat is dry, like

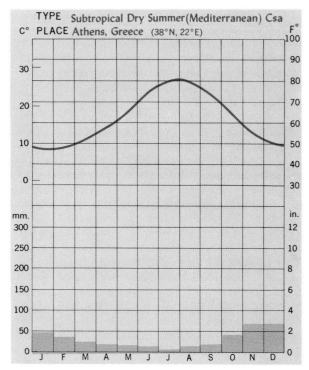

Figure 6.12 A subtropical dry-summer station, hot-summer subtype (*Csa*).

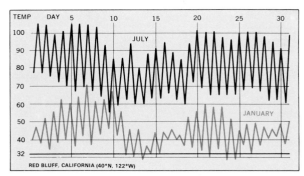

Figure 6.13 An interior subtropical dry-summer station in California (*Csa*). Note the hot summer and the large diurnal range of temperature. Solar control is dominant in summer, but irregular, nonperiodic air-mass control is conspicuous in winter. The temperatures are in °F.

that of the semiarid climates. Afternoon July temperatures in the Great Valley of California are likely to reach 32°C (90°F) or above, and 38°C (100°F) is not uncommon. The land blazes under a pitiless sky. Because the air is dry and there are few or no clouds, night cooling is rapid and daily ranges are large, resembling those of dry climates (Fig. 6.13).

Summer temperatures along the cool-water coasts of subtropical Chile and California are significantly cooler than inland. Santa Monica on the California coast has an average warmest-month temperature of only 19°C (66°F). So does Valparaiso, Chile, in sharp contrast to the hot interior (Fig. 6.14). In such locations summer fog and low stratus clouds are frequent. Because winter temperatures are somewhat milder than those inland, the annual temperature range is abnormally small—only 5°C (9°F) at San Francisco and 6°C (11°F) at Valparaiso. Diurnal ranges also are small (Fig. 6.15).

It is for the mild winters that dry-summer climate is justly famed. People of the colder, higher

latitudes seek it out for comfortable winter living. The absence of severe winter cold is due both to the subtropical location and to the region's position on the windward (western) sides of continents. Usually

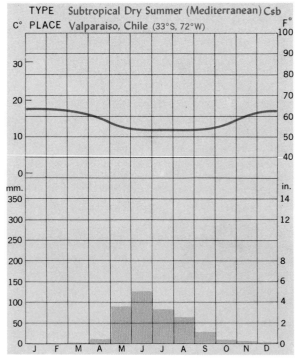

Figure 6.14 A Southern Hemisphere subtropical dry-summer station, coastal cool-summer subtype (*Csb*).

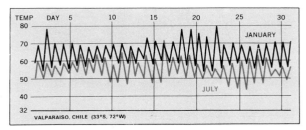

Figure 6.15 The same cool-summer subtype (*Csb*) as in Figure 6.14. Note the small diurnal range of temperature and the low summer (i.e., January) temperatures. The temperatures are in °F.

the winter months have average temperatures between 7° and 13°C (45° and 55°F), with coastal locations being somewhat milder than those inland (Figs. 6.12 and 6.14).

Frosts in subtropical dry-summer regions are mainly the result of radiation cooling following the advection of polar air by winds in advance of a cold anticyclone. Subfreezing temperatures are usually confined to a shallow layer of surface air, especially in low spots where air drainage concentrates the chilled air. For this reason such sensitive crops as citrus are customarily located on slopes.

It is not because of their frequency and severity that frosts are so much dreaded in these regions of sensitive fruit and vegetable crops. Rather, it is their infrequency that tempts farmers to take a chance on the frost hazard. Ordinarily the growing season does not quite extend over the whole year, for frosts do occasionally come during the three winter months. They usually occur on only a few nights, however, and only rarely are they severe.

Temperature inversions and air pollution. Many of the large urban areas of the *Cs* climates suffer from chronic air pollution, particularly during summer. Strong and persistent temperature inversions are common in the subsiding air on the east side of the subtropical highs. The inversions act as a lid, keeping the pollutants emitted by industries and vehicular traffic trapped in the lower atmosphere (Fig. 4.28). In coastal regions, such as the Los Angeles metropolitan area, where mountains are found a short distance inland, the pollution problem is accentuated, since the mountains impede the horizontal transport of the polluted air. It was in the Los Angeles area that the word *smog* was first used to describe the mixture of smoke and fog that often occurs over the city. Because the subtropical anticyclones are such a fixed feature of the atmospheric system's circulation, the *Cs* cities which suffer from air pollution are less likely to experience periods of relief, especially in

CLIMATIC DATA FOR REPRESENTATIVE SUBTROPICAL DRY-SUMMER STATIONS (*Cs*)

	J	F	M	A	M	J	J	A	S	O	N	D	Yr	Range
Red Bluff, California (Interior) (40°N, 122°W)														
Temp., °C	7	10	12	15	19	24	28	27	23	18	12	8	17	21
°F	45	50	54	59	67	75	82	80	73	64	54	46	62	37
Precip., mm	117	99	81	43	28	13	0	3	20	33	74	110	618	
in.	4.6	3.9	3.2	1.7	1.1	0.5	0.0	0.1	0.8	1.3	2.9	4.3	24.3	
Santa Monica, California (Coast with Cool Water) (34°N, 118°W)														
Temp., °C	12	12	13	14	16	17	19	19	18	17	14	13	15	7
°F	53	53	55	58	60	63	66	66	65	62	58	55	59	13
Precip., mm	89	76	74	13	13	0	0	0	3	15	35	59	376	
in.	3.5	3.0	2.9	0.5	0.5	0.0	0.0	0.0	0.1	0.6	1.4	2.3	14.8	
Perth, Australia (Coast) (32°S, 116°E)														
Temp., °C	23	23	22	19	16	14	13	13	14	16	18	22	18	10
°F	74	74	71	67	61	57	55	56	58	61	66	71	64	19
Precip., mm	8	13	18	40	125	175	165	145	84	54	20	15	861	
in.	0.3	0.5	0.7	1.6	4.9	6.9	6.5	5.7	3.3	2.1	0.8	0.6	33.9	

summer, than do the cities in the eastern United States.

Precipitation. As a general rule the dry-summer climates have too little rather than too much annual rainfall. Normal precipitation is 400–600 mm (16–24 in.). The *Cs* region is usually bordered by steppe climate along its equatorward margin, so that it is driest along this frontier and rainfall amounts increase poleward. Thus San Diego in southernmost California receives only 250 mm (10 in.) of rain; Los Angeles, less than 100 miles farther north, 380 mm (15 in.); and San Francisco, about 250 mi still farther north, 500 mm (20 in.). Rainfall mounts with increasing distance from the influence of the subtropical anticyclone. The general deficit of water and the variation in rainfall amounts from year to year are reflected in the large-scale use of irrigation water.

Most of the modest rainfall on lowlands originates in cyclones of the middle-latitude westerly winds. To an unusual degree the rainfall is concentrated in the cooler half of the year. At Los Angeles, over three-quarters of the year's rain comes during the four months from December to March, and only 2 percent from June to September. The rainfall regime, therefore, is that of the deserts in summer and that of the westerlies in winter.

This seasonal alternation of drought and rain is, as previously indicated, a consequence of the north-south migration of wind and rainfall belts following the course of the sun. A poleward shifting of the sun in summer brings these subtropical latitudes along west coasts under the influence of the stable eastern margin of a subtropical anticyclone. Subsiding air, temperature inversions, a near absence of atmospheric disturbances, and, in some locations, cool ocean water along the coast, all join to produce aridity (Fig. 6.16). But in winter, when the wind and rainfall belts move to their equatorward limits, these same latitudes come under the influence of the westerlies with their cyclonic storms and frontal systems. Although winter is distinctly less sunny than summer, it is by no means a season of prevailing overcast.

Lowlands in dry-summer climates rarely have snow. In central and southern California, annual snowfall averages less than 25 mm (1 in.), and there is none at all along the coast south of San Francisco. But highlands adjacent to dry-summer climates may have a moderate-to-heavy snowfall and

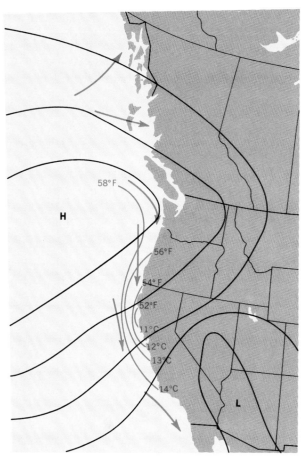

Figure 6.16 Pressure, winds, and temperatures of the ocean water along the Pacific Coast of the United States in midsummer. Cool-summer coastal climates and drought are a consequence of these controls. *(After Patton.)*

a deep snow cover, whose meltwater is an invaluable source of irrigation for the drier lowlands during the spring and summer.

Seasonal weather. Daily weather is less changeable in the subtropical climates than it is farther poleward, where traveling cyclones and anticyclones are more numerous and better developed. A typical summer day in noncoastal California resembles one in a low-latitude desert. Moreover, one day is much like another, with drought, brilliant sunshine, low relative humidity, high daytime temperatures, and marked nocturnal cooling. Along seacoasts there is often a daily sea breeze, which greatly moderates the desert heat.

In autumn, as the westerlies creep equatorward following the course of the sun, an occasional cyclone arrives, accompanied by its cloud cover and rain. The dry and dusty land begins to assume new life under the greening effect of the precipitation. Winter brings an increase in the frequency and strength of cyclones, and it is then that irregular, nonperiodic weather changes are most marked. Rainy days are sandwiched between sunny ones when the daytime hours are comfortably mild, even though the nights may be chilly with occasional frosts. Spring is a delightful season in the Mediterranean year: fresh and yet warm. This is the harvesting period for many grains. Passing cyclones gradually become fewer as summer approaches.

Resources of the dry-summer climates. Although this is the most restricted of all the climatic realms, embracing less than 2 percent of the earth's land surface, it is one of the most attractive. The near absence of snow and cold, the plentiful fair weather and sunshine, the abundance of fruit and flowers—all have given this dry-summer realm a reputation far out of proportion to its size.

The subtropics approach the bountiful temperature regime of the tropics more nearly than any other part of the middle latitudes. Their almost tropical temperature conditions, combined with their proximity to the great markets of the middle latitudes, give the two subtropical realms a unique commercial advantage. In them farmers can grow certain warmth-loving or frost-sensitive crops—citrus, figs, viniferous grapes, rice, sugar cane, cotton—which thrive in few other parts of the middle latitudes. The subtropical climates likewise enable farmers to produce out-of-season vegetables and flowers for the markets of regions farther poleward, where a season of severe cold imposes a long dormant period.

On the other hand, the dry-summer realm's relatively meager total precipitation and long summer drought place definite climatic limitations upon agricultural production. These factors also tend to limit the kinds of crops grown, causing emphasis on drought-resistant perennials, such as the olive and the vine, and on annuals which mature quickly, such as barley and wheat. The large-scale development of

irrigation represents an attempt to overcome the handicap of summer drought.

It is fortunate that the usual 400–600 mm (16–24 in.) of rain is concentrated in the cooler months of the year, when evaporation is at a minimum. If the same modest amount fell mainly during the hot summer, when evaporation is greater, much less of it would be effective for plant growth, and the climate would be semiarid.

Modest precipitation and summer drought produce a vegetation cover of woody shrubs and widely spaced, stunted trees; some dry-summer regions also have scattered patches of desert bunchgrass. This plant cover is of some value for grazing, particularly of sheep and goats. Only on the wetter mountain slopes do forests have genuine commercial value; the stunted trees and the bushes of the valleys and lower slopes are useful chiefly as checks to erosion.

On mountain and hill slopes, the soils of dry-summer regions are inclined to be thin and stony, and a large part of them remains uncultivated. It is the young alluvial soils of the valleys which are the attractive sites for farming.

The very attractiveness of the dry-summer subtropical climate has led to its deterioration in some areas. The great influx of population and industry into southern California has brought critical levels of air pollution. In some respects, the atmospheric circulation over southern California is simply incapable of supporting a sprawling urban community. Also, the clearing of hillsides for housing tracts has removed the brush which kept erosion in check. In recent years the news stories of early autumn brush fires sweeping to the edges of communities and of winter rainstorms accompanied by mudslides point to the strain that the large population has placed on this area.

Subtropical Humid Climate (*Cf*)

Subtropical humid areas differ from subtropical dry-summer areas in three ways: (1) Characteristically, they are located on the eastern rather than the western side of a continent; (2) ordinarily they have more annual precipitation; and (3) this precipitation is distributed throughout the year or else is concentrated in the warmer months—either way, summer is a humid season.

Location. The two subtropical climates have similar latitudinal positions from about 25° or 30° to 35° or 40°. (See Plate 1.) But since the humid subtropical type is characteristically situated on the eastern side of a land mass, it is under the influence of the weaker subsidence and less stable air in the western limb of the semipermanent subtropical anticyclone. In this location there is also some tendency for a monsoon system of winds, which favors summer precipitation. In addition, warm ocean currents parallel these east coasts.

Although both subtropical types of climate lie on the tropical margins of the middle latitudes, they are usually flanked by unlike climates to north and south. While the subtropical dry-summer type characteristically changes into dry climate on its equatorward side, the subtropical humid type is bounded by tropical humid climates. Similarly, the dry-summer climate usually merges into a mild, rainy marine climate on its poleward side, while (in Asia and North America, at least) subtropical humid adjoins severe continental climates. Because of these differences in the neighboring climates, the alternating southerly and northerly winds associated with traveling cyclones and anticyclones advect air masses with markedly different temperatures and humidities into the humid subtropics.

Temperature. The two subtropical climates are fairly similar in temperature. (Compare Figure 6.12 with Figure 6.17.) Since there are no cool ocean currents along subtropical east coasts, the humid type has no cool-summer subtype. Summer is normally hot, with monthly averages around 25°–28°C (77°–82°F). In contrast to the dry heat of California, high humidity in conjunction with high temperature produces sultry, oppressive weather resembling that of the humid tropics. Not only are the days hot and sultry: nights are oppressive as well. July daily maxima in the United States Gulf Coast usually reach 32° to 38°C (90° to 100°F). Summer temperatures are slightly less high in the Southern Hemisphere as the result of its more extensive oceans.

Winters are relatively mild in these subtropical latitudes, average cool-month temperatures usually varying between 5° and 10°C (41° and 50°F). But there are important regional variations depending on the size of the continent. During the coldest month, Shanghai, China averages 3°C (38°F); Buenos Aires,

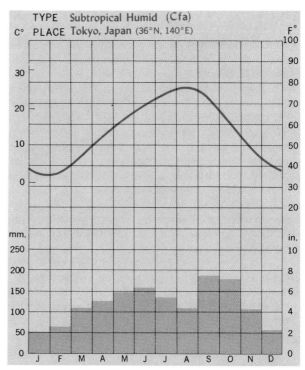

Figure 6.17 Compare with Figures 6.12 and 6.14. Seasonal rainfall distribution here is quite different from that in the dry-summer climate.

Argentina, 10°C (50°F); and Dallas, Texas, 7°C (45°F). Midday winter temperatures are pleasantly mild, around 10° to 15°C (50° to 59°F), and on winter nights minimum temperatures of 2° to 6°C (35° to 43°F) are usual. However, passing cyclones and anticyclones result in irregular spells of warmer and colder weather (Fig. 6.18).

Nighttime freezing temperatures may be expected occasionally during the winter months, but the number of freezes is not large. The growing season is long—from 7 or 8 months up to almost the entire year. Daytime temperatures normally rise above freezing. In the humid subtropics of both Asia and North America, freezes are more frequent and more severe than in their Southern Hemisphere counterparts. In the United States very cold polar air sometimes penetrates to the Gulf of Mexico coast. Both North America and Asia extend far northward into the source regions of continental polar air, but there are only broad lowlands between the Gulf of Mexico

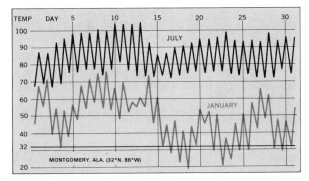

Figure 6.18 Daily maximum and minimum temperatures for the extreme months at a subtropical humid station in the United States. Note the strong periodic, or solar, control in summer. By contrast, winter shows strong nonperiodic or air-mass control. The temperatures are in °F.

and the Arctic in North America, while in Asia mountain ranges impede the southward penetration of polar air. Consequently, the low-temperature records in the subtropical United States are lower than in subtropical Asia.

Precipitation. The circulation around oceanic subtropical anticyclones usually carries humid, relatively unstable air into the eastern subtropics of the continents, providing an environment favor-

able to abundant rainfall. However, there are considerable variations in rainfall in the humid subtropics. Chiefly it is the interior western margins that are driest.

As a rule there is no marked dry season. More often than not, summer is the wettest and winter has the least rain. But in parts of east Asia, where the winter monsoon is strong, winter may be genuinely dry.

In the summer, sunshine is relatively abundant, although less so than in the dry-summer subtropical climates. Much of the summer precipitation is of the showery, convective type, developing in warm, humid maritime tropical air which has been made unstable by a heated land surface. Most of the showers occur in conjunction with the passage of weak disturbances, in which convergence acts to lift the unstable air. The North American humid subtropics have the highest frequency of thunderstorms in the United States. Tropical cyclones (hurricanes and typhoons) contribute to the summer and fall precipitation of the humid subtropics, mainly the North American and Asian sections.

Winter precipitation is chiefly cyclonic in origin. Gray, overcast days with rain are unpleasantly chilly. Snow falls occasionally when a vigorous winter cyclone follows a southerly track, but it seldom stays on the ground for more than a few days.

CLIMATIC DATA FOR REPRESENTATIVE SUBTROPICAL HUMID STATIONS (Cf)

	J	F	M	A	M	J	J	A	S	O	N	D	Yr	Range
Charleston, South Carolina (33°N, 80°W)														
Temp., °C	10	11	14	18	23	26	28	27	25	20	14	11	19	18
°F	50	52	58	65	73	79	82	81	77	68	58	51	66	32
Precip., mm	76	79	84	61	84	130	157	165	132	94	64	81	1202	
in.	3.0	3.1	3.3	2.4	3.3	5.1	6.2	6.5	5.2	3.7	2.5	3.2	47.3	
Shanghai, China (32°N, 122°E)														
Temp., °C	3	4	8	13	19	23	27	27	23	17	11	6	15	24
°F	38	39	46	56	66	73	80	80	73	63	52	42	59	42
Precip., mm	71	51	99	112	84	167	188	110	99	94	43	33	1163	
in.	2.8	2.0	3.9	4.4	3.3	6.6	7.4	4.7	3.9	3.7	1.7	1.3	45.8	
Sydney, Australia (33°S, 151°E)														
Temp., °C	22	22	21	18	15	12	11	13	15	17	19	21	17	11
°F	72	71	69	65	59	54	52	55	59	62	67	70	63	20
Precip., mm	91	112	125	137	130	122	127	76	74	74	71	71	1212	
in.	3.6	4.4	4.9	5.4	5.1	4.8	5.0	3.0	2.9	2.9	2.8	2.8	47.7	

Seasonal weather. Irregular, nonperiodic weather changes are usually less noticeable in the humid subtropics than they are farther poleward, where the conflict between air masses is more marked and cyclonic storms are more numerous.

In summer, when the storm belt is farthest poleward, weather changes are at a minimum (Fig. 6.18). Because the sun largely controls the weather, diurnal regularity of temperature is characteristic; humid, sultry days are the rule. Frequent spells of showery weather accompanying weak disturbances alternate with periods of several days in which no rain falls. The weather resembles that of the wet tropics.

In North America and Asia, late summer and fall are the hurricane season. Although these storms are not numerous, their severity more than makes up for their infrequency. Sunny autumn days furnish delightful balmy weather. With the approach of winter the equatorward-advancing cyclonic belt produces a gradually increasing number of gray, cloudy days and begins to import periods of cooler weather.

In winter the middle-latitude westerlies and their cyclones are farthest equatorward, so that irregular weather changes are more frequent and extreme. Tropical air masses may arrive and push daytime temperatures to well above 20°C (68°F), only to be followed by northerly winds of polar origin which reduce temperatures by as much as 20°C (36°F) within 24 hr, resulting occasionally in severe freezes. There are many bright, sunny winter days, distinctly pleasant and exhilarating out of doors. As spring comes, the cyclonic belt retreats and regular diurnal sun control is gradually reestablished.

Resources of the humid subtropics. The more abundant precipitation of the humid subtropics, together with the lack of a genuinely dry season, make this climate potentially more productive than its west-coast counterpart. Although its sultry tropical summers are not ideal for human comfort, they are excellent for luxuriant plant growth.

The abundant rainfall and warm temperatures produce lush wild vegetation. This usually consists of forests, although grasses may replace trees in regions of more modest precipitation. The character of the forests varies so much among humid subtropical regions that generalizations are difficult to make. Trees grow more rapidly in the humid subtrop-

ics than they do in other climates of the middle latitudes, so that natural or artificial reforestation is a quicker process than it is farther poleward.

Usually the mature forest soils of the humid subtropics are low in fertility, a factor which diminishes the effects of the bountiful climate. This inferiority of the soil is not surprising, however, considering the high leaching power of the many rains and the low humus-producing character of forest vegetation. Where grasses replace forests, as they do in the subhumid portions of the subtropics, the soils are darker in color and much more productive. The lower rainfall results in less leaching, and the grasses provide a greater abundance of organic matter.

THE TEMPERATE CLIMATES—GROUP *D*: 4 TO 8 MONTHS ABOVE 10°C (50°F)

The early Greeks labeled the climates of the middle latitudes as "temperate," which in the Greek means "mixed." Today the term "temperate" is usually interpreted as "moderate." The *D* group of climates is moderate in that these regions have mean annual temperatures that are between those of the cold polar and hot tropical climates. However, the moderate mean *annual* temperatures in large portions of the middle latitudes are obtained from mean *monthly* values that range from very cold in winter to very warm in summer. Likewise, large *day-to-day* temperature changes are likely to occur as eastward-traveling disturbances alternately draw tropical and polar air masses into middle latitudes. In this respect the Greek interpretation "mixed" appropriately describes the temperate climates.

Two main types comprise the temperate group: a mild one designated as *oceanic* (*Do*), and a more severe one called *continental* (*Dc*). The boundary used to separate the two is the 0°C (32°F), isotherm for the coldest month of the year. In a few locations the 2°C (36°F) isotherm has been used. An annual temperature *range* of 20°C (36°F) has also been suggested to separate the large temperature ranges of the *Dc* climate from the smaller ranges of the *Do* climate.

Temperate Oceanic Climate (*Do*)

Location. This mild marine climate typically lies on the western or windward side of middle-latitude continents, poleward from about 40°, where onshore westerly winds carry marine air inland. Warm ocean currents add significantly to the character of the climate. It is not found on the eastern or leeward side of the continents.

On its equatorward side, temperate oceanic climate normally adjoins the subtropical dry-summer type. It extends far into the higher middle latitudes, where it is eventually terminated by the boreal or tundra type. The depth to which the oceanic climate penetrates inland from the west coast depends largely on the presence (as in North America and Chile) or absence (as in Europe) of mountain barriers. (See Plate 1.)

Temperature.   Since this is an ocean-controlled climate, it does not have large seasonal extremes of temperature. The annual temperature curve is relatively flat, for summers are on the cool side and winters are mild for the latitude. Thus the annual range is small (Fig. 6.19). The pleasantly cool summers are excellent for human comfort, although they are too cool for the best growth of some cereal crops. Average summer-month temperatures of 16°–18°C (60°–65°F) are 3° to 6°C (5° to 10°F) lower than those of the continental interior in similar latitudes.

Winters are exceptionally mild for the latitude. The coastal lands of western Europe are 10° to 18°C (18° to 32°F) warmer than the mean temperature for their latitude in January. And while Seattle is only 3°C (5°F) cooler than Montreal (in the interior) in July, it is 15°C (27°F) milder in January. Winter isotherms tend to roughly parallel the coastline, with the temperatures decreasing more rapidly inland than poleward. This is evidence that land-water control is stronger than latitude. Average January temperatures range from somewhat below 4°C (40°F) to slightly over 7°C (45°F). Annual ranges vary from about 8° to 14°C (15° to 25°F) (Fig. 6.19).

Freezing temperatures are more frequent and more severe than in the subtropical dry-summer climate to the south. Still, the growing season is long, considering the latitude. In the American north Pacific Coast region, 6 to 8 months are characteristic. At Paris, France, frost normally occurs only on about half the nights during the three winter months. However, winter is severe enough to produce a dormant season for plant life. During occasional cold spells, temperatures may remain constantly below

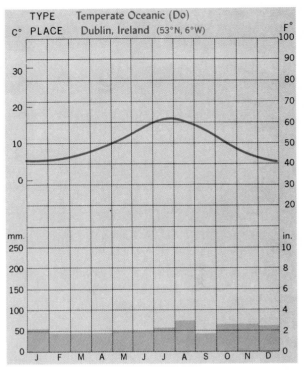

Figure 6.19   *Monthly temperature and rainfall for a temperate oceanic station in western Europe. Note the small annual range of temperature and the modest amount of precipitation well distributed throughout the year.*

freezing for several days in succession (Fig. 6.20). Such cold spells occur when there is a westward and southward thrust of anticyclonic polar air from the interior of the continent such as that illustrated by the weather map shown in Figure 6.21.

Although the magnitude of the irregular temperature fluctuations is not as striking in these marine climates as it is in the continental interiors, the passage of cyclones and anticyclones causes some degree of temperature variability (Fig. 6.20).

Precipitation.   Temperate oceanic climates are humid, with adequate precipitation in all seasons (Fig. 6.19). The total varies greatly from region to region, partially depending upon the amount of surface relief. Where lowlands prevail, as they do in western Europe, rainfall is only moderate, usually 50 to 90 cm (20 to 36 in.) per year, but the humid marine climate extends well inland. The evaporation rate is relative-

CLIMATIC DATA FOR REPRESENTATIVE TEMPERATE OCEANIC STATIONS (*Do*)

	J	F	M	A	M	J	J	A	S	O	N	D	Yr	Range
Paris, France (49°N, 2°E)														
Temp., °C	3	4	6	11	13	17	19	18	15	11	6	3	10	16
°F	37	39	43	51	56	62	66	64	59	51	43	37	50	29
Precip., mm	38	30	40	43	54	59	56	56	51	59	45	43	574	
in.	1.5	1.2	1.6	1.7	2.1	2.3	2.2	2.2	2.0	2.3	1.8	1.7	22.6	
Hokitika, New Zealand (42°S, 171°E)														
Temp., °C	16	16	15	13	10	8	7	8	10	12	13	14	12	9
°F	60	61	59	55	50	47	45	46	50	53	55	58	53	16
Precip., mm	249	186	247	234	249	247	229	239	234	299	269	269	2949	
in.	9.8	7.3	9.7	9.2	9.8	9.7	9.0	9.4	9.2	11.8	10.6	10.6	116.1	
Portland, Oregon (45°N, 123°W)														
Temp., °C	4	6	8	11	14	16	19	19	16	12	8	5	12	15
°F	39	42	46	51	57	61	67	66	61	54	46	41	53	28
Precip., mm	170	140	122	79	59	40	15	15	48	84	165	175	1112	
in.	6.7	5.5	4.8	3.1	2.3	1.6	0.6	0.6	1.9	3.3	6.5	6.9	43.8	

ly low, so that small totals of precipitation are highly effective. Where there are highland barriers, as in Chile and western North America, precipitation is heavy on the windward slopes but dry climates prevail to the east of the mountains. Snow is more common than in the subtropical climates, but in lowlands it ordinarily lies on the ground for only 10 to 15 days during the year. In highlands, however, snowfall is heavy and a deep snow cover persists for several months.

Normally there is no dormant season imposed upon vegetation because of a rainfall deficien-

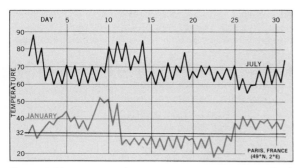

Figure 6.20   A marine-climate station in western Europe inland from the coast. Nonperiodic air-mass control of temperature is conspicuous. The temperatures are in °F.

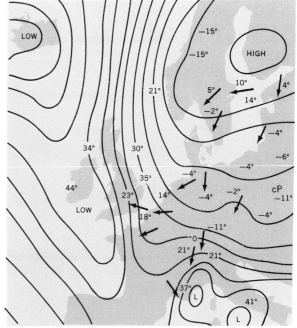

Figure 6.21   Weather controls favoring unseasonably low winter temperatures in western Europe. A cold anticyclone to the north and east is delivering cold *cP* air to the regions west and south of its center. Temperatures shown are the night minima. (*After Kendrew.*) The temperatures are in °F.

cy; the winter period of dormancy is due entirely to low temperature. Winters tend to be somewhat rainier than summers in locations closest to the ocean and in the areas lying nearest to the dry-summer type. There are only a few places—parts of Washington and Oregon, for example—that have one or more summer months which are really dry.

Over lowlands, where orographic effects are absent, the precipitation is chiefly frontal, or cyclonic, in origin. While much of it falls as steady light rain from a gray overcast (Fig. 6.22), some is in the form of showers which originate in fresh maritime polar air which may become unstable over the land. Temperate oceanic regions have few thunderstorms.

Although the total amount of precipitation on lowlands is modest, the number of rain-days is unusually high. Thus the frequent rains are light to moderate ones. For example, while Paris receives only about 574 mm (23 in.) of precipitation a year, this amount is spread over 188 days.

This oceanic climate is one of the earth's most cloudy types. Dark, gloomy, overcast weather is very common. Over extensive areas in western Europe, average cloudiness is greater than 70 percent, the sun sometimes remaining hidden for several weeks in succession, especially in winter and fall.

Seasonal weather.   Cyclonic storms are numerous, so that the nonperiodic weather element dominates temperate oceanic climate (Fig. 6.20). Fall and winter, in spite of mild temperatures, are stormy seasons with frequent periods of cyclonic weather. Spells of bright, crisp anticyclonic weather associated with continental polar air masses are the exception; but when they do occur, this climate is likely to have its most severe freezes.

As spring advances, cyclones become fewer and sunshine more abundant. The air is still cool, but the sun is strong; thus in western Europe, late spring is acclaimed the most delightful season. Summer temperatures bring a sense of physical well-being, and where sunny days are numerous, as in the American Pacific Northwest, a more pleasant summer climate would be hard to find. When cloudy, rainy days do occur in summer, however, they may be unpleasantly chilly.

Resources of the temperate oceanic climate. The frost-free period of 6 to 8 months and the rela-

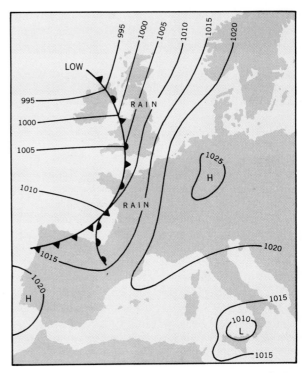

Figure 6.22   An occluded storm in western Europe, producing light but steady and widespread rainfall, a low cloud ceiling, and low visibility. Most of the cyclones that affect western Europe are in an advanced stage of occlusion. Over lowlands, such storms tend to produce much cloud but only a modest amount of precipitation.

tively mild winters permit fall sowing of many cereal crops, and animals can graze out-of-doors nearly all year. Storage of animal feed for winter use is therefore not a large-scale operation, as it is in the more severe continental climates. Another asset is the dependability of the precipitation year in and year out, a feature which is reflected in uniformly high crop yields.

Somewhat offsetting the advantages of the mild winters and the long frost-free season in this oceanic climate is the deficiency of summer heat. While warm-month temperatures of 16° to 18°C (60° to 65°F) are ideal for human comfort, they are not the best conditions for a crop such as corn. On the other hand, the climate is almost perfect for grass, so that pastures are usually excellent and hay and forage crops thrive.

In these mild west-coast regions the original vegetation cover was chiefly forest, both deciduous and evergreen. These forests have largely been removed from the lowlands, but they still cover extensive areas in some highlands. The earth's finest coniferous forest is located in the North American sector. While the podzolic soils of this humid climate are leached and only moderately fertile, they are suitable for a wide variety of crops. However, under constant cultivation they deteriorate rapidly unless given proper care.

This is the first of the climatic realms discussed here where surface and drainage features resulting from glaciation are at all prominent. Except on the European lowlands, the glacial features affecting temperate oceanic regions were produced chiefly by mountain or valley glaciers. Where highlands closely approach the sea (as they do in the higher latitudes of Pacific North America, Norway, Scotland, southern Chile, and the southern island of New Zealand), the heavy snowfall has been conducive to the development of valley glaciers. These have created fiorded coastlines, ragged in outline, with many long, narrow, and steep-walled arms of the sea as well as innumerable islands.

In western Europe, extensive continental glaciers once covered most of the area north of the Elbe River in Germany. On the highlands, commonly composed of resistant crystalline rock, ice scouring removed the weathered rock and soil, grooved and polished the bedrock, and gouged out many lake basins. On the lowlands, composed of less resistant rocks, features associated with ice deposition are conspicuous. Among these are numerous lakes and swamps. (See Chapter 13 for a discussion of glaciation.)

Temperate Continental Climate (Dc)

Location. Although fairly severe in its seasonal extremes, this climate is nevertheless found in some of the earth's most prosperous and well-developed regions in both North America and Eurasia. Since the temperate continental type is a product of broad continents in middle latitudes, it does not occur in the Southern Hemisphere.

In North America and Asia the latitudinal spread of the Dc climate is some 10° to 20°, extending from about 35° or 40° on the south to 50° or 60° on the north (Plate 1). But there are differences in location on the two continents. In Eurasia one area of Dc climate is found in eastern Europe and western Asia and another in the far eastern part of Asia. Separating these two areas of Dc climate are the B climates of central Asia. The lack of a mountain barrier in western Europe permits mild Atlantic Ocean air to penetrate well inland, so that only when central Europe is reached are winter temperatures low enough to permit a Dc classification. Farther east, in central Asia, the absence of a moisture source leads to the dry climates found there. Along the eastern edge of Asia, moisture from the Pacific is sufficient to again permit a Dc climate. In western North America mountain barriers prevent mild, moist Pacific air from reaching far inland. As a consequence, there is a large region of dry climate to the east of the mountains, in their rainshadow. However, farther east, from the central Great Plains states to the Atlantic Coast, moisture carried northward from the Gulf of Mexico provides adequate precipitation to produce an extensive region of Dc climate. In both eastern Asia and eastern North America, temperate continental climate is bordered by boreal climates on the north and by subtropical humid ones on the south. But in Europe and western Asia, it meets Mediterranean and dry climates on its southern margins.

Temperature. Seasonal temperatures are relatively severe; winters are cold and summers warm to hot (Figs. 6.23 to 6.26). Depending largely on latitudinal location, the average July temperature may vary from 24°C (75°F) or even more in the south to 18°C (65°F) in the north. The January average shows a much greater variation: from about −20°C (−4°F) in the north to −4°C (25°F) or above in the south. As a consequence, the annual range of temperature is large everywhere, and it increases both from south to north and from the coast toward the interior. At Peoria, Illinois (41°N), for example, the January and July averages are −4° and 24°C (24° and 75°F), giving an annual range of about 28°C (51°F). But at Winnipeg, Canada (about 50°N), the comparable figures are −20° and 19°C (−4° and 66°F) and the range is 39°C (70°F).

The length of the frost-free season likewise changes from south to north, approaching 200 days on the southern margins and declining to about 100 days

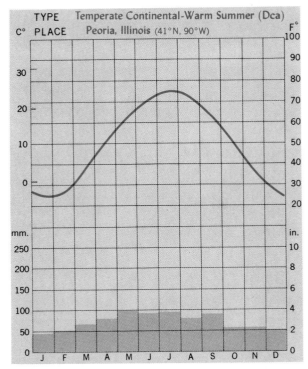

Figure 6.23 A station representing the warm-summer subtype of temperate continental climate. The large annual range of temperature and the rainfall maximum in the warm season are characteristic.

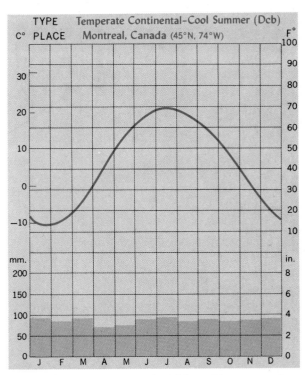

Figure 6.25 Temperature and rainfall conditions at a station with temperate continental climate, cool-summer. Note the large annual range of temperature. At this station there is no seasonal concentration of precipitation, a feature characteristic of the northeastern United States and adjacent parts of Canada, where winter cyclones are numerous.

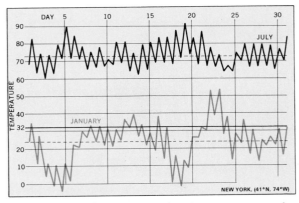

Figure 6.24 Daily maximum and minimum temperatures for the extreme months at a station with a temperate continental climate, warm-summer. Nonperiodic air-mass control is conspicuous, especially in winter. The temperatures are in °F.

on the subarctic side. This feature creates large latitudinal contrasts in agricultural land use.

Average temperatures in winter and summer are not only extreme but also variable from one year to another. In marine climates one winter is apt to be much like another, but continental climates show wide departures from their normal seasonal temperatures. Average winter temperatures are distinctly lowered by the snow cover in the temperate continental, boreal, polar, and highland climates. Only in these climates does the snow cover last long enough to have a marked influence upon winter temperature.

Seasonal gradients. In continental climates there are great differences between summer and winter in the rate of change in temperature in a north-south

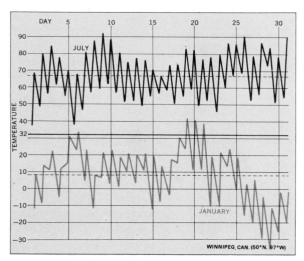

Figure 6.26 Temperate continental climate, cool-summer. Note the very large and irregular temperature changes, evidence of strong air-mass control associated with cyclones and anticyclones. The temperatures are in °F.

direction (Fig. 6.27). This reflects the similar seasonal gradients in solar radiation (Fig. 3.5). In winter the isotherms are much more closely spaced than in summer; in the central and eastern United States, for instance, the temperature gradient is two to three times as steep in January as in July. Thus sudden and marked temperature changes associated with cyclone passages and the accompanying shifts in wind direction are much more likely in winter than in summer (Figs. 6.24 and 6.26).

Temperature subtypes. Temperate continental climates are divided into two subtypes: a more moderate one with warm-to-hot summers and cool winters (*Dca*), and a more severe one (*Dcb*) located poleward, which has less hot summers and more rigorous winters (compare Figure 6.23 with Figure 6.25). A suggested boundary separating the two is the isotherm of 22°C (72°F) for the warmest month. In the warmer subdivision the frost-free, or growing, season is about 5 or 6 months, and in the colder one only 3 to 5 months. The snow cover is deeper and lasts longer in

Figure 6.27 Isotherms for the extreme months. Surface temperature gradients in the temperate continental climates of the central and eastern United States are much steeper in winter than in summer.

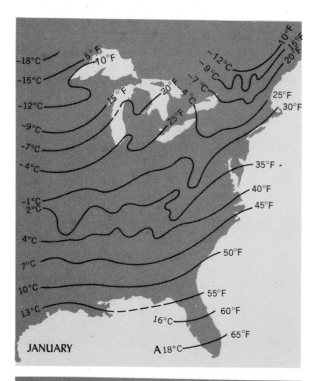

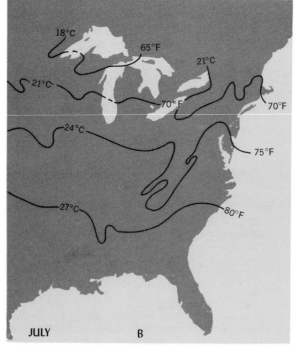

the more northerly subtype. (See climatic data for stations representing each subtype.)

Precipitation. Moderate amounts of annual rainfall, 500 to 1,000 mm (20 to 40 in.), concentrated in summer are the rule. Although this is a humid climate, there are large areas where annual precipitation is rather scant. Still it is enough for the climate to be classified as subhumid rather than semiarid. Rainfall decreases from the seaward margins toward the interiors and usually toward higher latitudes as well.

Summer is normally the season of maximum rainfall, which is typical of continental climates (Fig. 6.23). It is the result of several conditions: (1) Low temperatures make the specific humidity, or reservoir of water vapor in the atmosphere, much lower during the winter than it is in the summer. (2) Convection is at a minimum during the winter months, for at that season the weak sunlight and cold snow surface tend to increase the stability of air masses. In summer, on the other hand, the warm land surface has a tendency to make the air masses moving over it unstable. (3) Because of the seasonal extremes of temperatures and hence of pressure, a tendency toward a monsoon wind system develops. This leads to an outflow of dry,

cold cP air in winter and to an inflow of tropical maritime (mT) air with high rainfall potentialities in summer.

But in spite of a prevalent summer rainfall maximum, there are extensive areas in which evaporation exceeds precipitation during the warmest months. As a result, a deficiency of water commonly occurs at the peak of the growing season. This may be reflected in seared pastures and lawns and occasionally in stunted crops.

Winter precipitation is largely frontal or cyclonic in origin. In North America, mT Gulf of Mexico air masses move poleward up the Mississippi River valley with no mountains to interfere. These air masses are drawn into frequent passing cyclonic storms, so that they come into conflict with cold polar air masses and are forced to ascend over them. Widespread frontal precipitation results. Thus the North American continental climate has a moderate amount of winter precipitation. This amount increases eastward, until along the Atlantic seaboard winter is as wet as summer (Fig. 6.25). In northeastern Asia, where the outward-flowing winter monsoon is stronger, mT air is unable to advance far poleward, so that winter precipitation in northern China and Manchuria is very meager. For example, Peking, which

CLIMATIC DATA FOR REPRESENTATIVE STATIONS IN THE TEMPERATE-CONTINENTAL WARM-SUMMER SUBTYPE (*Dca*)

		J	F	M	A	M	J	J	A	S	O	N	D	Yr	Range
New York City (41°N, 74°W)															
Temp., °C		−1	−1	4	9	16	21	23	22	19	13	7	1	11	24
	°F	31	31	39	49	60	69	74	72	67	56	44	34	52	43
Precip., mm		84	84	86	84	86	86	105	110	86	86	86	84	1067	
	in.	3.3	3.3	3.4	3.3	3.4	3.4	4.1	4.3	3.4	3.4	3.4	3.3	42.0	
Bucharest, Rumania (44°N, 26°E)															
Temp., °C		−3	−2	4	11	16	20	23	22	18	12	5	−1	11	26
	°F	26	29	40	52	61	68	73	71	64	54	41	30	51	48
Precip., mm		30	28	43	51	64	84	71	48	38	38	48	43	584	
	in.	1.2	1.1	1.7	2.0	2.5	3.3	2.8	1.9	1.5	1.5	1.9	1.7	23.0	
Mukden, China (42°N, 123°E)															
Temp., °C		−13	−10	−1	8	16	22	25	24	16	9	−2	−10	7	38
	°F	8	14	30	47	60	71	77	75	61	48	29	14	44	69
Precip., mm		5	8	20	28	56	86	160	155	84	40	25	5	673	
	in.	0.2	0.3	0.8	1.1	2.2	3.4	6.3	6.1	3.3	1.6	1.0	0.2	26.5	

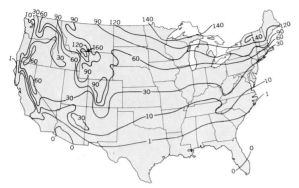

Figure 6.28 Number of days with snow cover in the United States.

receives 630 mm (25 in.) a year, has 240 mm (9.4 in.) in July and only 2.5 mm (0.1 in.) in January. Also see the climatic data for Mukden.

A portion of the *Dc* climate's winter precipitation is in the form of snow, and a permanent snow cover, varying from a few weeks to several months in duration, is typical (Fig. 6.28). In those parts of the northeastern United States and southeastern Canada where winter cyclones are particularly numerous and well developed—the Great Lakes region, the St. Lawrence River Valley, northern New England, and the Canadian Maritime Provinces—snow becomes very deep. Northern New England, northern New York, and portions of the Great Lakes region have more than 2 m (7 ft) of snowfall during an average winter,

and snow remains on the ground for more than 4 months.

Much of the summer rainfall is in the form of convective showers and thunderstorms. This is because the warm, humid summer air is made unstable by heating from below as it travels over a warm land surface. Of the summer rainfall at Madison, Wisconsin, 75 to 90 percent occurs in thunderstorms. These showers are almost always connected with some form of larger atmospheric disturbance.

Seasonal weather. In no other type of climate are rapid nonperiodic weather changes so pronounced as in the temperate continental, for it is in these regions that the contrast between polar and tropical air masses reaches a maximum. The cold season, when the polar vortex is large and intense, is the time when the continental climates have the largest day-to-day weather changes. At that season diurnal sun control is usually subordinate. Weather conditions are dominated by moving cyclones and anticyclones embedded within the westerly flow of the polar vortex. Many times the daily rise and fall of temperature with the sun is obscured by the larger nonperiodic oscillations caused by invasions of polar and tropical air masses (Figs. 6.24, 6.26, and 3.9). The central and eastern United States, since it is freely open to the movements of air masses from both north and south, is a region of unusual storminess. Storminess is less marked in continental eastern Asia. In summer, major cyclones are fewer, fronts are weaker, and the

CLIMATIC DATA FOR REPRESENTATIVE STATIONS IN THE TEMPERATE CONTINENTAL COOL-SUMMER SUBTYPE (*Dcb*)

		J	F	M	A	M	J	J	A	S	O	N	D	Yr	Range
						Madison, Wisconsin (43°N, 89°W)									
Temp.,	°C	−8	−7	−1	7	13	19	21	21	16	10	2	−6	7	29
	°F	17	20	30	45	56	66	70	69	60	50	35	22	45	53
Precip., mm		33	25	48	69	86	110	96	79	86	56	48	38	770	
in.		1.3	1.0	1.9	2.7	3.4	4.3	3.8	3.1	3.4	2.2	1.9	1.5	30.3	
						Moscow, U.S.S.R. (56°N, 37°E)									
Temp.,	°C	−11	−9	−5	3	12	17	19	17	11	4	−2	−8	4	30
	°F	12	15	23	38	53	62	66	63	52	40	28	17	39	54
Precip., mm		28	25	30	38	48	51	71	74	56	35	40	38	536	
in.		1.1	1.0	1.2	1.5	1.9	2.0	2.8	2.9	2.2	1.4	1.6	1.5	21.1	

weather is more regular and sun-controlled in both Asia and North America.

Special seasonal weather types. The normal cycle of weather changes which take place with the passage of a well-developed cyclone, followed by an anticyclone, was described in Chapter 4. In reality, however, there is a great variety of possible weather changes, depending upon the season, the size and intensity of the atmospheric disturbance, the nature of the air masses involved in the storm, the track it follows, and the patterns of air flow aloft. As a consequence, no satisfactory classification of weather types has ever been developed. Nevertheless, everyone is familiar with some weather types which are sufficiently distinctive, and so frequently repeated, that they have been given names: *heat wave, cold wave, Indian summer, blizzard,* and *January thaw* are illustrations. But the less distinctive unnamed ones are more numerous. A real comprehension of temperate continental climates is not possible without an appreciation of this variety of weather types which in combination produce the seasons. It requires a study of the daily weather map, together with a firsthand observation of weather conditions.

Winter, the season of maximum temperature gradients and strongest air-mass contrasts, is the period of greatest weather variety. A well-developed anticylone arriving from arctic Canada with its mass of fresh *cP* air may produce bitterly cold weather with subzero temperatures (Fig. 4.27). The northwest winds found between the arctic anticyclone and the preceding cyclone bring a sharp drop in temperature—the well-known *cold wave.* If there is an unusually steep pressure gradient between the cyclone and anticyclone, blizzardlike conditions with violent winds may usher in the cold wave. But if an anticyclone moves eastward from the North Pacific, it brings with it maritime polar air which becomes modified in crossing the Rocky Mountains. This kind of anticyclone usually produces mild, bright winter weather to the east of the mountains.

A deep cyclonic storm, especially if it originates in the Colorado area and takes a route northeastward across the country, produces widespread heavy snowfall to the north of its center (Fig. 4.20). Occasionally, intense cyclones develop along the east coast of the United States and move northeastward just offshore. These are the storms that bring *nor'easters* and heavy snow to the northeastern United States and southeastern Canada. Figure 4.19 is a satellite photograph of such a storm. These are only a few of the huge number of weather types which combine to produce the winters of humid continental climates.

In summer, while sun control and diurnal regularity are relatively stronger than during other seasons, nonperiodic weather irregularities do occur. A somewhat stagnant warm anticyclone to the south and east may envelop the temperate continental area of the United States in a prolonged *heat wave,* bringing a succession of days when the daily maximum temperature is between 32° and 38°C (90° and 100°F) (Fig. 4.26). Such a heat wave may be suddenly ended by the arrival of a cyclonic storm with a well-developed cold front and severe thunderstorms. Following the passage of the cold front there may be several days of delightfully cool weather associated with an anticyclone and polar air.

In spring and fall, the transition seasons, there is a more even struggle between storm and sun control. One and then the other takes over, so that summer and winter conditions tend to alternate. Mild, warm days in April and early May, with a regular diurnal rise and fall of the thermometer resembling summer, may be followed by more winterlike conditions as a passing cyclone lays down a snow cover and the following *cP* invasion produces a severe freeze.

Autumn brings some of the loveliest days of the year, but likewise some wet and gloomy days. Bright, clear weather, with warm midday temperatures and crisp, frosty nights, comes with anticyclonic control. In October and November, after a severe frost and perhaps even a snowfall, a warm anticyclone may become established over the southeastern United States, leading to a temporary return of near-summer conditions. The result is those much-cherished spells of warm, hazy weather known as *Indian summer.* However, in large urban areas Indian summer has increasingly become a period of severe air pollution. But at this season well-developed cyclonic storms may clear the air of pollution and bring raw, gray days with chilly rain. Occasionally a temporary snowy winter landscape may be seen as early as October.

Resources of the temperate continental realm. The temperate continental climates include some of the most agriculturally productive areas of the world. Climatically, however, they are less bountiful than the humid subtropics, chiefly because of the shorter growing season, but also because of a greater overall deficiency of heat. This tends to exclude many of the more sensitive crops, as well as those requiring a long period between frosts. As a result, farmers in this climate place greater dependence upon quick-maturing annuals. Compared with the subtropics, there is also a shorter period during which livestock can forage for their food, and a much longer one during which they must be protected against cold and given feeds that have been stored in barns and granaries.

A further climatic handicap is that extensive areas have rainfall which is only modest in amount and which tends to be undependable. Relatively wide fluctuations in crop yields from year to year reflect these disadvantages. A factor which compensates for the modest and variable precipitation is that it is concentrated in the warm growing season.

Forests in the more humid portions and tall-grass prairie in the subhumid interiors—this is the pattern of native vegetation within temperate continental climates. In their virgin state, the prairies provided some of the finest natural grazing land on earth. Almost all the prairie has long since come under cultivation, however, for it constitutes some of the world's best agricultural land. The original forests of the more humid regions were characterized by conifers predominating toward the northern margins of the realm, with mixed forests and purer stands of deciduous broadleaf trees farther south. The virgin forests of the temperate continental realm were among the finest and most extensive of the earth.

Soils in the humid continental realm vary widely, depending upon the nature of the climate, the original vegetation, and the recency of glaciation. Moderately fertile soils (podzolic types), which are characteristic of areas with mixed or deciduous forests, represent the best of the forest soils. On the cooler poleward margins of the humid continental realm, where needle trees tend to replace the broadleaf varieties, the soils are inferior, for here they are more strongly leached of mineral plant foods and have a much lower humus content. On the other hand, some of the earth's superior soils are found in the subhumid sections of the realm where prairie grasses used to predominate. The lower rainfall results in less leaching, and the grasses provide an abundance of organic matter, so that the soils are high in soluble minerals and dark in color. Such excellent soils partly compensate for the less abundant and less reliable rainfall.

Considerable areas in both the North American and European sectors of the temperate continental realm have been subjected to recent glaciation by continental ice sheets. Where the irregularities of the land surface are relatively great or the bedrock is resistant—as, for example, in New England, northern New York State, and parts of Sweden and Finland—erosion by the glaciers has carried much of the topsoil away. The soils are often thin and stony, and lakes are numerous. In other regions, where deposition by glaciers prevailed, the drainage systems have been disrupted, creating many lakes and swamps and a rolling and somewhat patternless terrain of rounded hills and associated depressions. There the soils are usually deep, but they vary greatly in composition and quality.

BOREAL CLIMATE—GROUP *E:* UP TO 3 MONTHS ABOVE 10°C (50°F)

Location. This group of climates has much in common with the temperate continental, except that it is located farther poleward and is distinctly more severe. In fact, it is so severe that over most of the very large area which has a boreal climate, general cereal agriculture is impossible, and population is sparse or even absent.

Boreal, or subarctic, climate is to be found only in the higher middle latitudes (50° to 55° or 65°) of the great Northern Hemisphere continents (Plate 1). On its poleward side it usually borders on tundra, one of the polar climates. This northern boundary is approximately the northern limit of forests. On its southern margin, boreal climate usually adjoins continental climates or, in some locations, dry climates. It lies within the realm of the middle-latitude westerlies throughout the year.

Temperature. Long and bitterly cold winters, very short summers, brief falls and springs, and unusually large annual temperature ranges are the main temperature characteristics of boreal climate (Fig. 6.29). Thus the boreal group represents land-

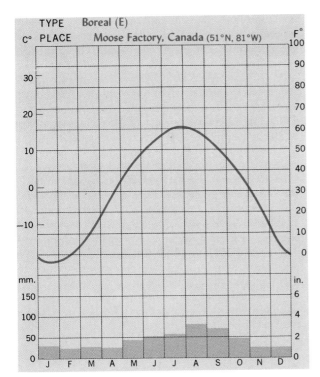

Figure 6.29 Cool summers, severe winters, large annual ranges of temperature, and modest precipitation, usually concentrated in summer, are characteristic of boreal (subarctic) climate.

controlled climate at its maximum development (Fig. 6.30).

By reason of both its length and its severity, winter dominates the climatic calendar. Frosts may arrive in late August, and ice begins to form on ponds in September. At Yakutsk, Siberia, the average monthly temperature drops 21°C (37°F) between October and November. Within an extensive area in northeastern Siberia, near the center of the great winter anticyclone, the *average* January temperature is below −46°C (−50°F), and at Oimyakon, Siberia, the thermometer has fallen as low as −65°C (−95°F). However, over most of the North American and European sectors, average January temperatures of −18° to −26°C (0° to −15°F) are the rule. It is common, however, for the average temperatures of 6 or 7 months to be below freezing and for averages of 2 to 3 months to be below −20°C (−4°F). Because of the excessive and long-continued cold, large areas of the boreal realm are permanently frozen down to great depths (Fig. 6.31). Spring, like autumn, is very short. At Yakutsk the mean temperature rises 14°C (25°F) between April and May, and 10°C (18°F) between May and June.

The most striking characteristic of summer in the subarctic is not so much coolness but brevity. Typically, the warmest month, July, has an average temperature near 17°C (62°F), which is no lower than that of many stations in temperate oceanic climates farther south. Moreover, it is not uncommon for midday temperatures to reach 27°C (80°F) and above (Fig. 6.30). But July's modest warmth is fleeting, for June and August averages are between 10° and 16°C (50° and 60°F). As a rule the average period between killing frosts is only 50 to 80 days, and many stations occasionally have freezing temperatures even in July and August. Average temperatures of 10°C (50°F) or above occur only during a period ranging from 1 to 3 months. Somewhat compensating for the briefness and coolness of summer is the unusually long period of daylight in these higher latitudes. Thus at 60°N, June days have an average of 18.8 hours of possible sunshine.

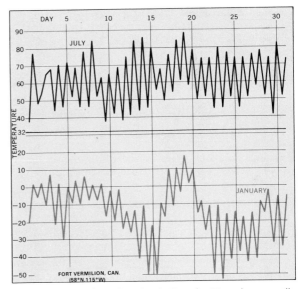

Figure 6.30 A boreal station in Canada. Note the unusually strong nonperiodic air-mass control of temperature changes in winter. Summer shows greater diurnal regularity. The temperatures are in °F.

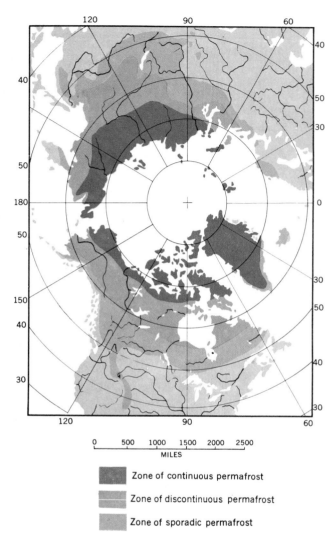

Figure 6.31   Distrubition of permafrost in the Northern Hemisphere *(After Black.)*

Precipitation. Precipitation in the boreal realm is meager—most of it under 500 mm (20 in.) and large parts under 380 mm (15 in.). These low figures are related to cold temperatures and associated low specific humidity, the well-developed winter anticyclone with its settling air and diverging wind systems, and the great breadth of the land masses in the subarctic latitudes. In lower latitudes, areas with less than 500 mm (20 in.) of precipitation would be classed as semiarid. But where there are such low temperatures,

and therefore low evaporation rates, and where the ground is frozen so much of the year, this amount of precipitation is sufficient for a humid climate and for forest growth.

The year's precipitation is concentrated in the warmer months, when the specific humidity of the air is highest and atmospheric stability is least (Fig. 6.29). The especially low winter temperatures and the strong anticyclone both operate to inhibit winter precipitation. Winters are especially dry over east-central Siberia: the three midwinter months have less than 10 percent of the annual precipitation while the three summer months account for about 60 percent. The meager winter precipitation in boreal regions is in the form of dry snow, which produces a snow cover of variable depth that persists for as long as 7 months.

Almost all boreal precipitation on lowlands originates in cyclonic storms. Thunderstorms are uncommon. There are enough disturbances at all seasons to cause marked nonperiodic weather changes, although winter may have much settled anticyclonic weather (Fig. 6.30).

Resources of the boreal realm. This is one of the most extensive of the earth's geographic realms, but it is also one of the least productive and least populated. In subarctic regions the extractive industries—those based on extracting natural resources, such as hunting, fishing, mining, and logging—are unusually important, but these are capable of supporting only a meager population. The landscape therefore is composed predominantly of natural features: humans have left only a faint imprint.

The boreal realm is fundamentally handicapped by a climate whose brief, cool summers set very definite and very low limits upon agriculture. At present commercially successful farming is not likely in regions where the frost-free season is less than 80 or 90 days, as it is in all except the most southerly portions of the subarctic.

Subarctic Eurasia and North America are covered by what is largely a virgin coniferous forest. Conifers usually occupy about 75 percent of the forest area; such deciduous trees as birch, poplar, willow, and alder take up most of the rest. The forest is not impressive, either in the size of the trees or in the density of the stand, so that it does not represent nearly so great a potential supply of forest products as its area might seem to indicate. Most subarctic timber

CLIMATIC DATA FOR REPRESENTATIVE BOREAL STATIONS (*E*)

Fort Vermilion, Alberta, Canada (58°N, 116°W)

	J	F	M	A	M	J	J	A	S	O	N	D	Yr	Range
Temp., °C	−26	−21	−13	−1	8	13	16	14	8	0	−12	−20	−3	42
°F	−14	−6	8	30	47	55	60	57	46	32	10	−4	27	74
Precip., mm	15	8	13	18	25	48	54	54	35	18	13	10	313	
in.	0.6	0.3	0.5	0.7	1.0	1.9	2.1	2.1	1.4	0.7	0.5	0.4	12.3	

Yakutsk, Siberia, U.S.S.R. (62°N, 130°E)

	J	F	M	A	M	J	J	A	S	O	N	D	Yr	Range
Temp., °C	−43	−37	−23	−9	5	15	19	16	6	−9	−29	−41	−11	62
°F	−46	−35	−10	16	41	59	66	60	42	16	−21	−41	12	112
Precip., mm	23	5	10	15	28	54	43	66	30	35	15	23	348	
in.	0.9	0.2	0.4	0.6	1.1	2.1	1.7	2.6	1.2	1.4	0.6	0.9	13.7	

is probably more valuable for pulpwood and firewood than for good lumber. Moreover, the inaccessibility of these northern forests and their great distance away from world markets considerably reduce their resource value.

In addition to the rigorous climate, the soils of boreal regions are impoverished—a combination which presents almost insurmountable difficulties to the farmer. The needles from the coniferous forest provide little organic material for the soil, while the groundwater, which is high in organic acids derived from the carpet of half-decayed needles, causes an excessive leaching of soil minerals.

After climate and soils, the third handicap to agricultural settlement within the subarctic realm is deficient drainage. Most of subarctic North America and Scandinavia, Finland, and western Soviet Russia have an abundance of lakes and swamps—a consequence of continental glaciation. In addition much of the boreal and tundra areas of North America and eastern and northern Siberia have poorly drained land because of the permanently frozen subsoil and rock, a condition called *permafrost* (Fig. 6.31). Summer thaw penetrates only 0.5 to 4.0 m (1.5–13 ft).

Polar Climates—Group *F:* All Months below 10°C (50°F)

Just as the tropics lack a cool season, so the polar regions lack a significant period of warmth. It is the prevalence of monotonous heat that typifies the low latitudes. In the high latitudes, monotonous cold is the distinctive feature.

The polar climates occupy such a high latitude position that through much of the year they are within the polar easterlies. But, as was noted in Chapter 5, the polar easterlies are shallow, and above them are found the westerlies. However, at these high latitudes the westerly flow is considerably weaker than in middle latitudes, where greater north-south temperature contrasts exist.

Location.   Polar climates are confined to the high latitudes of the earth, largely poleward of latitude 60°. The poleward limit of forest growth is commonly accepted as the boundary of polar climates. Over the great continents, this vegetation boundary coincides approximately with the 10°C (50°F) isotherm for the warmest month. Here during much of the winter the sun is constantly below the horizon, so that darkness prevails and cold is intense. Moreover, while in summer the sun may never set, it is never far above the horizon, and its oblique rays deliver relatively little energy to the earth's surface.

In the Southern Hemisphere, the only extensive nonoceanic area with polar climates is the Antarctic continent, the approximate center of which is at the South Pole. Since the Arctic is almost a landlocked sea, except for the frozen ocean, the polar climates there are confined to the northern borders of Eurasia and North America and to the island continent of Greenland.

Polar climates may be subdivided into two types, with the warmest-month isotherm of 0°C (32°F) serving as the boundary between them. (1) Where the average temperatures of all months are below freezing, the growth of vegetation is impossible, and a permanent snow-and-ice cover prevails. These are the icecap climates. (2) Where one or more of the warm-season months has an average temperature above 0°C (32°F), but not over 10°C (50°F), the ground is free from snow for a short period. A meager and primitive vegetation cover known as *tundra* is present.

Tundra Climate (*Ft*)

Tundra climate on land areas is almost exclusively limited to the Northern Hemisphere; in the Southern Hemisphere, oceans prevail in latitudes where this climate normally would develop. The most extensive tundra areas include most of North America's Arctic archipelago, the coastal borders of Greenland, and the parts of both Eurasia and North America which rim the Arctic Ocean.

Temperature. A long, cold winter and a very short, cool summer are the rule in tundra climate (Fig. 6.32). Since the average temperature of the warmest month by definition is between 0° and 10°C (32° and 50°F), even midsummer is raw and chilly, like March and April in southern Wisconsin, or January in Alabama. Usually only 2 to 4 months have average temperatures above freezing. At Pond's Inlet, a tundra station at about 73°N in Canada, the average July temperature is 6°C (42°F), with the thermometer rising to about 10°C (50°F) at midday and sinking to about 2°C (35°F) at night. Daily ranges in tundra areas are small in both summer and winter. Killing frosts may occur at any time, although it does not freeze on most July nights. The continuous but weak summer sun frees the land of its snow cover for a few

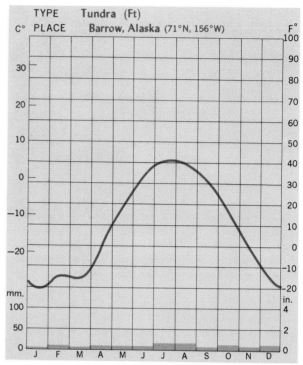

Figure 6.32 A tundra station on the north coast of Alaska. Note the large annual range of temperature, the cool summer, and the meager precipitation.

months, but the subsoil remains frozen, so that the surface is wet and poorly drained. Tundra vegetation consists of lichens, mosses, sedges, and bushes.

In Chapter 5, it was noted that although climatic classification schemes are either basically

CLIMATIC DATA FOR REPRESENTATIVE TUNDRA STATIONS (*Ft*)

		J	F	M	A	M	J	J	A	S	O	N	D	Yr	Range
					Sagastyr, Siberia, U.S.S.R. (73°N, 124°E)										
Temp., °C		−37	−38	−34	−22	−9	0	5	3	1	−14	−27	−33	−17	43
°F		−34	−36	−30	−7	15	32	41	38	33	6	−16	−28	1	77
Precip., mm		3	3	0	0	5	10	8	35	10	3	3	5	84	
in.		0.1	0.1	0.0	0.0	0.2	0.4	0.3	1.4	0.4	0.1	0.1	0.2	3.3	
					Upernivik, Western Greenland (73°N, 56°W)										
Temp., °C		−22	−23	−21	−14	−4	2	5	5	1	−4	−10	−17	−9	28
°F		−7	−10	−6	6	25	35	41	41	33	25	14	1	16	51
Precip., mm		10	10	15	15	15	15	25	28	25	28	28	13	234	
in.		0.4	0.4	0.6	0.6	0.6	0.6	1.0	1.1	1.0	1.1	1.1	0.5	9.2	

empirical or genetic, they often lead to approximately the same climatic boundaries. In the original Köppen system, the 10°C (50°F) isotherm for the warmest month was chosen as a boundary because it marked the approximate border between boreal forest and tundra. Recent studies have shown that this boundary is also a genetic boundary. During the summer the Canadian tundra is predominantly under the influence of air masses which originate over the cold, largely ice-covered Arctic Ocean, while the boreal forest mainly experiences air masses which originate over the milder Pacific Ocean or warmer North American continent. Consequently, the border between boreal forest and tundra is also the mean location of a frontal zone separating these different air masses. Figure 6.33 shows the mean position of the frontal zone in summer, and Figure 6.34 shows the mean July streamlines (lines parallel to the average air flow at the surface).

Precipitation.   Given the low temperatures of these high latitudes, the modest annual precipitation— usually less than 25–30 cm (10–12 in.)—is not surprising. In continental locations the year's precipitation, nearly all of it cyclonic in origin, is concentrated in the warmer months of the year when the specific humidity of the air is highest (Fig. 6.32). This is less the rule in marine-controlled areas. The meager winter snowfall is dry and powdery, so that the strong

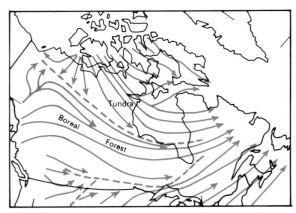

Figure 6.34   Streamlines of the mean July surface winds show that the air over the tundra originates over the Arctic Ocean, but the air over the boreal forest has its source over the continent or mild North Pacific Ocean. *(From Bryson [Fig. 28], "Air Masses, Streamlines and the Boreal Forest," Geographical Bulletin, vol. 8, pp. 228–269 [1966].)*

winds sweep the level surfaces bare. It has been estimated that 75 to 90 percent of the surface of Arctic tundra lands is nearly free of snow at all seasons.

Icecap Climate (*Fi*)

This least known of the world's climatic types extends over the great permanent continental ice sheets of Antarctica and Greenland and over the perpetually frozen ocean in the vicinity of the North Pole. Only since the mid-1950s has a reasonable amount of weather data been obtained from these ice-covered regions where no month's average temperature rises above freezing.

Temperature.   Since both Antarctica and Greenland are ice plateaus whose higher interior parts have average elevations of near 3,000 m (10,000 ft), any recorded surface-air temperatures for the interiors would be higher if reduced to sea level. Very strong surface temperature inversions prevail on 80 to 90 percent of the days.

At Eismitte in high interior Greenland, the average coldest-month temperature is about −47°C (−53°F) and that of July is −11°C (12°F), providing a range of 36°C (65°F). At Vostok at an elevation of 3,500 m (11,000 ft) in interior Antarctica, the aver-

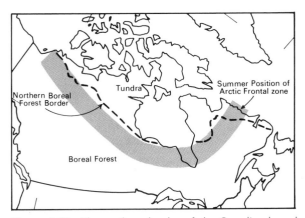

Figure 6.33   The northern border of the Canadian boreal forest lies near the mean summer position of an Arctic front and also the 50°F (10°C) isotherm for July. *(From Bryson [Fig. 33], "Air Masses, Streamlines and the Boreal Forest," Geographical Bulletin, vol. 8, pp. 228–269 [1966].)*

CLIMATIC DATA FOR REPRESENTATIVE ICE-CAP STATIONS (*Fi*)

	J	F	M	A	M	J	J	A	S	O	N	D	Yr	Range
	South Pole, Antarctica (90°S) (2,800 m, 9,200 ft)													
Temp., °C	−29	−40	−54	−58	−57	−57	−59	−59	−59	−51	−39	−28	−49	31
°F	−20	−40	−65	−72	−71	−71	−74	−74	−74	−60	−38	−18	−57	56

Precip. No reliable data.

	J	F	M	A	M	J	J	A	S	O	N	D	Yr	Range
	Eismitte, Interior Greenland (70°54′N, 40°42′W) (3,030 m, 9,941 ft)													
Temp., °C	−41	−47	−40	−31	−20	−16	−11	−17	−22	−36	−43	−38	−30	36
°F	−42	−53	−40	−24	−4	4	12	1	−8	−32	−46	−37	−22	65

Precip. No data.

age August temperature is −68°C (−90°F), and on August 24, 1960, the temperature fell to −88°C (−127°F). Certainly these are the lowest temperatures on earth. Because of the high elevation of the South Polar region, temperatures fall rapidly once the sun sets in March. In fact, the cooling is so rapid that the 4 or 5 months between April and August are equally cold. (See Fig. 6.35.)

These data for both Greenland and Antarctica reflect conditions in the higher interiors; weather in the lower marginal areas is not so severe. In icecap climates, short-time temperature fluctuations do occur. These variations, which reach a maximum in winter, are associated with invasions of low-pressure systems whose clouds reduce the rate of heat loss and whose winds sometimes advect warmer air from the oceans.

Precipitation. The icecap climates have only meager precipitation, practically all of it falling as snow. Because the snow is badly drifted by the wind, measurements are all but impossible. It is likely that most of the inland snow originates in the cyclonic storms

that move along the margins or occasionally penetrate the interior regions of the ice plateaus.

At Eismitte in interior Greenland, 300 mm (12 in.) of snow fell in 204 days in one year. At the South Pole station on the ice plateau of Antarctica, a recent year had only 17 days with measurable precipitation, but there were 248 days with some precipitation, even though the amounts were usually too small to measure. The annual fall totaled only 12 mm (0.48 in.) of water equivalent. There were 100 overcast days and 165 that were clear. It is believed that on the average the whole Antarctic continent receives less than 100 mm (4 in.) of water equivalent annually. The intensely cold atmosphere and consequent low specific humidity, the extreme stability of the air, and the rarity of upslope winds all act to inhibit precipitation.

HIGHLAND CLIMATES

There is no such thing as a highland *type* of climate. Mountain country has an almost endless variety of climates, depending on altitude and on exposure to sun and winds. Thus different altitudes have different climates; valley weather contrasts with that of the exposed peak; windward slopes differ from leeward slopes; and southern exposures are unlike those facing north. And these many kinds of highland climates are multiplied again by differences in latitude and continental location.

Because this great complexity of climates within highlands would be impossible to illustrate on a small-scale map, they have been grouped together under a single designation on the world map of

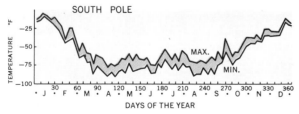

Figure 6.35 Five-day means of maximum and minimum air temperatures at the surface, 1958, South Pole, Antarctica. *(After Sabbagh.)* The temperatures are in °F.

CLIMATIC DATA FOR A HIGHLAND STATION IN THE TROPICS

	Quito, Ecuador (2,800 m, 9,300 ft) 0°10′S, 79°W													
	J	F	M	A	M	J	J	A	S	O	N	D	Yr	Range
Temp., °C	12.5	12.8	12.5	12.5	12.6	12.8	12.7	12.7	12.8	12.6	12.4	12.6	12.6	0.4
°F	54.5	55.0	54.5	54.5	54.7	55.0	54.9	54.9	55.0	54.7	54.3	54.7	54.7	0.7
Precip., mm	81	99	122	178	117	38	28	56	66	99	102	91	1072	
in.	3.2	3.9	4.8	7.0	4.6	1.5	1.1	2.2	2.6	3.9	4.0	3.6	42.2	

climate. Generally, regions with an elevation below 1,300–1,600 m (4,000–5,000 ft) are not included.

Solar energy. Intensity of sunlight increases with elevation in the cleaner, drier, thinner air of mountains. Dust, clouds, and water vapor, which reflect or absorb solar radiation, are concentrated at lower elevations. On a clear day, probably three-fourths of the solar energy penetrates to 2,000 m (6,400 ft) but only one-half to sea level. This greater intensity of sunlight at high altitudes has an important effect upon soil temperature and, both directly and indirectly, upon plant growth.

Temperature. The most important effect of increased elevation is the decrease in air temperature (on the average, about 6.5°C/km, 3.6°F/1,000 ft), which occurs in spite of the increased intensity of solar energy. Quito, Ecuador, situated on the equator at an elevation of 2,800 m (9,300 ft) (see preceding table), has an average annual temperature of only 13°C (55°F), which is about 16°C (25°F) lower than that of the adjacent Amazon lowlands. Because the dry and more dust-free air at Quito is incapable of absorbing much solar or terrestrial radiation, the air remains chilly. Yet for the same reason the sunlight itself is strong, so that the climate is one of cool shade and hot sun. One is never warm except in the sun.

Importance of vertical change. The vertical rate of temperature change along mountain slopes is a few hundred times greater than the north-south horizontal gradient over continental lowlands. Consequently in the tropics, where lowlands are continuously and oppressively hot, the cooler highlands may become the centers of population concentration. Such is the case in much of tropical Latin America. There is a striking vertical zonation, not only of contrasting climates but also of agricultural and vegetation belts,

in tropical highlands. Thus in tropical valleys where there is a luxuriant rainforest such heat-requiring crops as rubber, bananas, and cacao thrive. Somewhat higher, they may give way to an economy based on coffee, tea, maize, and a variety of food crops. On the still higher and cooler slopes, middle-latitude cereals and potatoes become more important, as do pastures for animal grazing which are terminated along the highlands' upper margins by the permanent snowfields.

By contrast, highlands in middle latitudes are less attractive climatically and have fewer vertical zones of contrasting vegetation and agriculture. Here even the lowlands are none too warm, so that any reduction in temperature with altitude, resulting in a cooler summer and a shorter growing season, materially reduces the opportunities for agricultural production.

Diurnal and seasonal temperatures. The thin, dry air of mountains and high plateaus permits not only the entry of strong solar radiation by day but also the rapid loss of earth radiation at night. This results in rapid daytime heating and rapid night cooling. Thus large diurnal ranges of temperature are characteristic of highland climates (Fig. 6.36).

At high altitudes in tropical highlands, this results in many days with night freezing and daytime thawing. Such frequent and rapid oscillation between the two has marked effects upon vegetation and soil. The great temperature difference between day and night in tropical highlands stands in contrast to the very small difference between the average temperatures of the warmest and coldest months, or the annual range. This combination of a large daily and a small annual range of temperature is one of the distinctive features of high-plateau and mountain climates in the tropics.

Although the temperature is lower on a

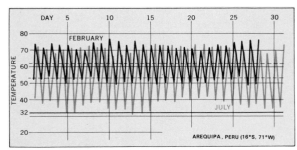

Figure 6.36   Daily maximum and minimum temperatures of the extreme months at a tropical mountain station located at moderate altitudes. Note the diurnal regularity of temperature change, indicating sun control. Diurnal range is greater in July, the drier season, when there are the fewest clouds. The temperatures are in °F.

tropical mountain than on an adjacent lowland, the two locations have similar temperature patterns. Monotonous repetition of seasonal and daily weather belongs alike to tropical highlands and plains (Figs. 6.36 and 6.37). For instance, at Quito the temperature difference of less than 0.5°C (1°F) between the warmest and coolest months is very similar to that in the Amazon lowland in the same latitude. Mexico City at 2,300 m (7,500 ft) has an average annual temperature 10°C (18°F) below that of Veracruz in the same latitude but on the coast; yet their annual ranges are both about 6°C (11°F).

Precipitation.   Highlands have heavier precipitation than the surrounding lowlands. This is a fact of great importance, especially in dry climates. Not only

ANNUAL MARCH OF TEMPERATURE

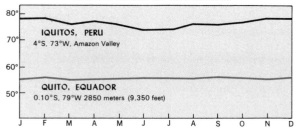

Figure 6.37   A comparison of the annual march of temperature at Iquitos, a lowland station, and Quito, a highland station, both in equatorial latitudes. Note the generally lower temperature at Quito. On the other hand, a small annual range of temperature is characteristic of both stations. The temperatures are in °F.

are settlements attracted to the humid slopes and to the well-watered mountain valleys, but streams descending from the rainier highlands carry the influence of highland climate far out on the dry lowlands. There the mountain waters (including meltwater from snowfields) are put to multiple uses—irrigation, power development, and, in some places, transportation.

In addition, because mountains in regions of drought are "islands" of heavier precipitation as well as lower evapotranspiration, they are likewise islands of heavier vegetation cover, and sometimes of more abundant agricultural production. In dry lands, highlands are likely to bear a cover of forest, in contrast to the meager grass and shrub vegetation of the surrounding lowlands.

Winds and weather.   On exposed mountain slopes and summits, winds are strong and persistent. By contrast, protected mountain valleys may be relatively quiet areas. Highland regions are particularly subject to numerous local winds and their accompanying weather, occasioned by the great variety of relief and exposure present. It is common in valleys and along heated slopes to have an upslope wind by day, when convection is at a maximum, and a downslope wind at night. Where well-developed cyclonic storms are present, as in the middle latitudes, the passing low-pressure system may induce a downslope wind, known as the *foehn* or *chinook*. Such winds are characterized by great dryness and unseasonable warmth.

In highlands the weather shifts within a 24-hr period are likely to be greater than on adjacent lowlands. Extreme changes from hot sun to cool shade, from chill wind to calm, from showers and thunderstorms of rain or possibly snow to intense sunlight—these give the daily weather an erratic quality. Even in the tropics, the complex sequence of weather within a day is in marked contrast to the uniformity of the average daily and monthly temperatures.

REVIEW QUESTIONS

1. What features of the general circulation are responsible for the major differences between the tropical wet (*Ar*) and tropical wet-and-dry (*Aw*) climates?

2. Why is nighttime sometimes called the winter of the tropical wet (*Ar*) climate?

3. Contrast the dominant characteristics of the vegetation found in the tropical wet (*Ar*) climate with those of the tropical wet-and-dry (*Aw*) climate.

4. The world map of climate (Plate 1) shows that the east side of the island of Madagascar has a tropical wet (*Ar*) climate but the west side is classified as either tropical wet-and-dry (*Aw*) or steppe (*BS*). What causes the climate to be drier on the west side?

5. At latitude 28°N the climate on the Atlantic coast of Africa is desert (*BW*), yet across the ocean the climate at the same latitude in Florida is subtropical humid (*Cf*). What is the cause of this climatic difference?

6. The Sahara Desert is bounded on the north and south by steppe climates. Contrast the seasonal occurrence of the precipitation in the northern steppe with that in the southern steppe and explain the cause of the seasonal differences.

7. What factors contribute to the very intense desert climate found along the coast of northern Chile and Peru?

8. Why is the subtropical dry-summer (*Cs*) climate confined to coastal California while in the Mediterranean area the climate extends eastward from Portugal to the Middle East countries?

9. Contrast the typical weather of the Mediterranean climate (*Cs*) during winter with that in summer.

10. Why is air pollution a particularly severe problem in the subtropical dry-summer (*Cs*) climatic region of California?

11. Although northern Asia provides a better source region for continental polar air than does northern North America, the humid subtropics (*Cf*) of North America experience more severe freezes than do the humid subtropics of Asia. Why?

12. What empirical criterion is used to differentiate between the temperate oceanic (*Do*) and temperate continental (*Dc*) climates?

13. Why is the temperate oceanic climate (*Do*) found on the western sides of Eurasia and North America but not on the eastern sides?

14. Why is western Oregon humid (*Do* climate) but eastern Oregon dry (*BS* climate)?

15. Why do areas having a temperate continental (*Dc*) climate receive more precipitation in summer than in winter?

16. Why are there no boreal climates (*E*) in the Southern Hemisphere?

17. Why is the South Pole colder than the North Pole?

SELECTED REFERENCES

Riley, D., and L. Spolton. *World Weather and Climate.* Cambridge University Press, London, 1974. Pp. 96–118. While following the same classification system used in this text, this reference provides additional sets of climatic data and discussion.

Trewartha, Glenn T. *An Introduction to Climate*, 4th ed. McGraw-Hill Book Company, New York, 1968. Pp. 254–391. The classification scheme is the same as used here, but the various climatic regions are discussed in greater detail.

———. *The Earth's Problem Climates.* University of Wisconsin Press, Madison, 1961. 334 pp. The causes of the earth's climates, particularly those which do not readily fit the gross global pattern, are treated in depth.

Van Riper, J. E. *Man's Physical World*, 2d ed. McGraw-Hill Book Company, New York, 1971. Pp. 240–320, 627–659. The world's climatic regions are classified using the Köppen-Geiger classification criteria. A large number of sets of climatic data are included in the appendix.

Water and the Sea

The Waters of the Earth

Dwellers of the land are not likely to realize the enormous significance of water in the study of the earth systems. In the first place, there is a surprising amount of it. More than 70 percent of the earth's surface is sea (Fig. 1.1), and the ocean basins contain an almost incomprehensible volume of water (Table 7.1). Water is present in large quantities in the "solid" crustal zone, and the continents are literally saturated with it. Most of the sculpturing of the land surface is accomplished by water, and, as we have seen, it is a normal and important constituent of the atmosphere. Furthermore, it is indispensable to life on the earth, since the living cells of plants and animals are largely water, and it is as essential as light to the life-maintaining action of photosynthesis.

People, of course, need water to keep themselves alive and to produce the plants and animals they use for food. But, in addition, a modern industrial and commercial society must have a huge, continuous supply of it—far beyond that needed for drinking and raising food crops. Because in a technological society water is so readily polluted, its management has become critical. Certainly no other economic resource is so important in modern life.

Amounts of water. Besides the water being held in chemical bond in the materials of the deep interior of the earth, there is an enormous amount of water near the surface. The outermost 3 miles of the solid-liquid earth contain three times as much water as all other substances put together, and six times as much as the next most abundant compound, the mineral feldspar. Table 7.1 provides an estimate of the distribution of this vast supply.

As the table shows, more than 97 percent of the water near the earth's surface is in the ocean basins. Most of the remainder is locked up, so to speak, in icecaps and glaciers (mostly Antarctica and Greenland), leaving only a very small proportion as the supply in lakes and streams, in the soil, in living tissues, and in the atmosphere.

Properties of water. Water has many characteristics that make it unique among the common inorganic substances. Two of these qualities which are unusually important in producing major environmental contrasts are its dissolving power and its commonplace occurrence in solid, liquid, and vapor forms.

Pure water is scarcely ever found in nature, for as soon as liquid water forms in the atmosphere, it dissolves carbon dioxide and becomes weak carbonic

TABLE 7.1   APPROXIMATE DISTRIBUTION OF WATER NEAR THE SURFACE OF THE EARTH (IN CUBIC KILOMETERS OF LIQUID EQUIVALENT)

	km³	Percent of total
In the solid earth		
Within 1,000 m of the surface	7,000,000*	0.5
On the earth		
In the ocean basins	1,350,400,000	97.6
In icecaps and glaciers	26,000,000	1.9
In lakes, streams, and rivers	230,000	†
In the surface soil, plants, and animals	17,000	†
In the atmosphere		
In solid, liquid, and vapor	13,000	†
Total	1,383,660,000	100.0%

*Approximately 4.17 cu km equals 1.0 cu mi.

†Negligible.

From U.S. Geological Survey and other sources.

acid (H_2CO_3). When this acid reaches the solid earth, it begins to react with the other compounds there. Although the reactions are ordinarily not rapid, the fact that there is so much water causes the total amount of activity to be large. Water is able to dissolve almost every constituent of the earth's crust, and as a consequence it serves as the great carrier of food for the organic life which subsists on the minerals of the crust. Furthermore, because of this unique high solvent power, billions of tons of dissolved materials are constantly being moved across the land, ultimately finding their way to the sea. Sea water is a complex solution of organic and inorganic solids and gases which has been well defined as a dilute solution of almost everything.[1]

Water is unique in that it is the only natural substance that can occur in the solid, liquid, and vapor states within the range of temperatures that occur near the surface of the earth. Because the temperatures vary from place to place and from time to time, large amounts of water (1) are temporarily locked in storage as ice, a solid, (2) are evaporated from the sea and transported through the atmosphere as water vapor, a gas, only to be condensed again as liquid or solid precipitation, and (3) exist as varying volumes of liquid in rivers, lakes, and oceans.

[1]Harris B. Stewart, Jr. *The Global Sea.* D. Van Nostrand Co., Inc., Princeton, N.J., 1963.

Other properties of water are important to humanity or help to create differences in the environment. Only a few can be mentioned, such as water's expansion upon freezing. This causes ice to form on the surface of oceans, lakes, and rivers rather than the bottom, and it also contributes to the breakdown of rocks. Other important properties of water are its capacity for absorbing energy and transporting it; its high surface tension, essential to the formation of raindrops and waves; its low viscosity and high density, which make the sea surface an efficient medium on which to travel and make its waves so destructive; and the capillary attraction which holds within the soil the water on which the roots of plants feed and which allows that water to serve as a lubricant or an overload that furthers mass movements of the regolith.[2]

The Hydrologic Cycle

Practically all of the water (liquid and vapor) near the surface of the earth is in constant circulation. The waters of the oceans and the water vapor in the

[2]The greater adhesion of a liquid to a solid than to itself is termed *capillary attraction* and allows the liquid to spread in thin films over the surface of the solid and even to move upward, as in a wick or in the very fine interstices and pores of the soil.

atmosphere are moved about by the winds, and the waters of the land return to the sea under the pull of gravity. This never-ending movement of the waters of the earth, powered by energy from the sun and the gravitational force of the earth's mass, is often called in total the *hydrologic cycle*. The atmospheric part of the system can be likened to a huge distilling process, drawing primarily upon water from the sea. Some of the complexity of the hydrologic cycle is illustrated in Figure 8.1 in the next chapter, which treats waters of the land.

A vast amount of solar energy reaches the sea.[3] A little over half is used to evaporate water from its surface. Sea water has a high *specific heat*, which is defined as the amount of energy required to raise 1 gram 1°C, and very large amounts of energy are required for evaporation. Although the amount needed to vaporize water depends on the temperature of the water, it approaches 600 calories per gram. The vapor circulates as part of the atmosphere, and it is continually being subjected to the forces, considered earlier, which cause much of it to condense (releasing the heat of vaporization to the air) and fall back to the sea and land surfaces as a liquid or solid. Naturally, evapotranspiration from the land (which includes evaporation from wet surfaces and the emission of water vapor by plants, called *transpiration*) contributes water vapor to the atmosphere, but as a source of moisture it is far less significant than the sea.

The global water balance. The approximate annual water balance of the hydrologic cycle for the earth as a whole is shown in Figure 7.1 in absolute amounts of water (cubic kilometers) as divided between the land area and the sea area. Expressed as average equivalent depths of water, about 120 cm/yr are evaporated from the total sea surface (3.62×10^8 km²), with about 110 cm/yr being returned as precipitation. The difference is supplied by runoff from the land area. The land areas (1.49×10^8 km²) contribute an average of only about 47 cm/yr in evapotranspiration, but they receive precipitation totaling nearly 71 cm/yr, the excess being the discharge of rivers to the oceans. As pointed out earlier in the book, most precipitation over the land is derived from maritime air masses.

It is obvious that the average figures conceal

[3]About 3.9×10^{23} gram calories per year.

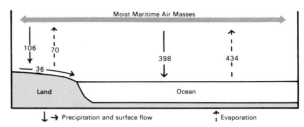

Figure 7.1 The global water balance between oceanic and land evaporation and precipitation in approximate cu km of liquid equivalent.

important variations. Much of the land surface, perhaps half, is desert, icecap, cold tundra, or other cold or dry areas that contribute little in the way of evaporation; similarly, the colder waters of the high-latitude oceans provide relatively little moisture. On the other hand, the tropical oceans and the lush and moist tropical forests, with their high receipts of energy, provide much more than the average. This is shown in Figure 7.2, which maps the variation of the relation between evaporation and precipitation. It will be noted that although the equatorial areas provide large quantities of moisture to the atmosphere, this supply is more than balanced by the greater amounts of precipitation there. The major areas that supply more water to the atmosphere than they receive from it are the sea surfaces under the great subtropical anticyclonic cells.

The timing of the hydrologic cycle is also complex. There are significant variations in the total amount of water involved in the cycle from time to time as well as in the proportions existing in each part of it. Furthermore, there is in each region of the earth a definite annual regime, i.e., the timing of the functioning of the cycle during a year. Just as there are significant spatial variations of the climatic elements, so there are general spatial patterns in the functioning of the hydrologic cycle. Our knowledge of some of these is as yet much scantier than our knowledge of the variations in the climatic elements.

Variations in the amounts of evaporation and precipitation in different parts of the earth, together with variations in energy receipt, give rise to circulatory systems of water both in the oceans and on the land. Those of the sea will be considered in the balance of this chapter and those of the land in the next.

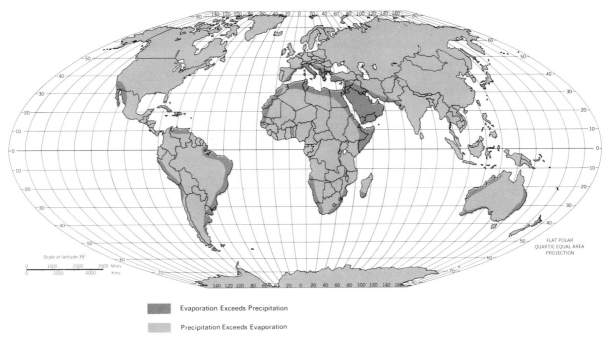

Evaporation Exceeds Precipitation

Precipitation Exceeds Evaporation

Figure 7.2 Areas where the mean annual evaporation exceeds the mean annual precipitation. Note that the areas of greatest evaporation occur in subtropical oceans. *(After Dietrich.)*

THE SEA

Of all the contrasts on the planet earth, none is so great as that between the land and the sea. For humans, the oceans are a foreign environment within which they can exist only with the help of complex engineering technology. Yet the sea, not the land, is the predominant earth environment, since most of the surface of the solid earth is submerged. Although people do not live in the sea, they have much to do with it, for it serves them as a modifier of their climate, a route of transport, a partitioner of their lands, and a source of food and of minerals.

Other than its seemingly limitless expanse, probably the most impressive attribute of the sea is that it is never still. The constant motion of the sea surface varies from the small wavelets that lap the shore to the great rollers that crash as surf and the tides which rise and fall with predictable regularity. Beneath this mobile surface there are much larger, slower, horizontal and vertical flows of water. The sea, like the atmosphere, is a great circulatory system.

The energy balance of the sea. The world ocean is constantly receiving and losing energy; but considered as a whole, over time it remains in a steady state. On the average, then, it is neither warming nor cooling, and the various horizontal and vertical temperature changes that are observed remain in essential balance.

The only important source of heat for the sea is the sun. It has been estimated that the amount of solar energy received at the sea surface is about 295 cal./cm² per day. To this can be added from several sources: (1) very small amounts of heat supplied to the ocean bottom by the flux of heat from the interior of the earth, (2) heat obtained from friction (transformation of kinetic energy to heat), (3) heat supplied from biological and chemical processes, (4) conduction and precipitation from the atmosphere, and (5) condensation on the sea surface. None of these five supplies even 0.1 percent as much energy as is provided by direct and diffuse solar radiation.

The sea loses all the heat it absorbs. More than half is lost through evaporation of water, a lesser amount by radiation from the sea surface, and a smaller amount yet by the conduction of heat from a warmer sea surface to cooler air in contact with it. That the energy received is balanced by the energy lost is true only for the whole sea, not for particular parts. Some areas receive more heat than they lose to the atmosphere and to space, while in other areas the relationship is reversed. Consequently, the only way the entire mass can retain its essential steady state is through the transfer of heat from one place to another by means of circulatory movements within the sea itself. These will be considered in more detail later. The major elements of the heat budget are shown in Figure 7.3.

It is worth observing here that although the restless sea surface contains a seemingly large amount of kinetic energy obtained from wind stress and some from tidal energy, the transformation of this adds very little heat to the ocean. Most of this energy is transported shoreward at a slow rate, to be concentrated and dissipated at the margins of the land. In some shallow or very turbulent areas this energy can, of course, become locally significant. Nevertheless, the amount of heat obtained from this source is even less than that supplied by flux from the interior of the earth.

Properties of Sea Waters

Surface temperatures. Surface temperatures of the seas range from about −2°C (28.4°F), which is the approximate freezing point of sea water, to about 30°C (86°F)—a much smaller range than temperatures have on the land. Seasonal changes in surface

temperature at a given place are remarkably small, amounting to no more than 1° to 3°C in tropical waters and 4° to 8°C in the upper middle latitudes. Between day and night, sea-surface temperatures vary no more than a fraction of a degree. This extreme conservatism of ocean temperatures is highly important to the earth's climates, as has been noted.

Although the seasonal changes of surface temperatures are small, they are not so slight as to be unimportant, particularly in the middle and high latitudes. Many thousands of square miles of the ocean surface in the Arctic and Antarctic freeze during the winters and thaw again during the summers, and additional areas are invaded seasonally by icebergs. In middle-latitude waters, where winter cooling of the surface is especially great, an "overturning" commonly occurs. The chilled surface waters become cold enough and therefore dense enough to sink, while slightly warmer waters from below come to the top.

As we have seen, the sea is heated chiefly by absorption of radiation from the sun and the atmosphere and cooled largely by outward radiation and by the evaporation of water from the surface. Since solar radiation is relatively evenly distributed through the low latitudes and decreases significantly from tropics to poles, it is not surprising to find that ocean temperatures follow essentially a latitudinal pattern (Fig. 7.4). The tropical seas are warm, and variations from place to place are small. Poleward of the tropics, temperatures fall off rapidly with increasing latitude.

However, the fact that sea-surface isotherms do not strictly follow the parallels of latitude indicates that solar radiation is not the only control. Air temperatures also have an effect, particularly in lowering sea temperatures near the eastern coasts of continents in the middle latitudes during the winter. Much more important, however, is the circulation of ocean water in the great surface current systems, largely as a result of atmospheric circulations, of which the swirls of the subtropical highs are the most important. These bring warm water into the middle latitudes on the western sides of the oceans and move it across to the eastern sides, while they bring cool water equatorward on the eastern sides of the subtropical oceans and on the western sides in the high latitudes (Fig. 7.9).

The effects of these movements of the ocean

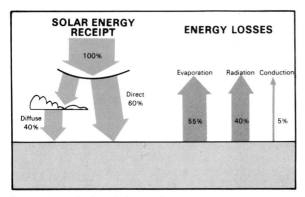

Figure 7.3 The heat balance of the seas.

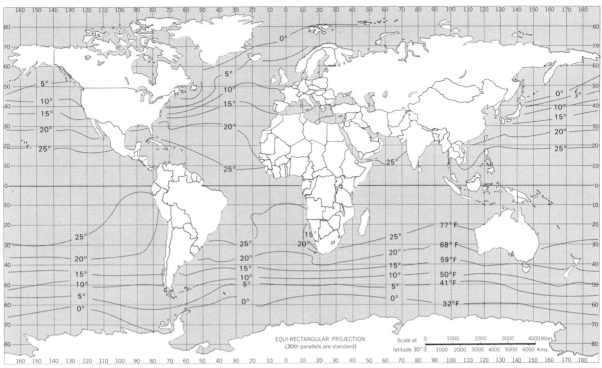

Figure 7.4   Surface temperatures of the oceans show a basic latitudinal pattern. The variations in this pattern are caused mainly by the great surface current systems. *(After Schott, et al.)*

waters may be seen in Figure 7.4. The average sea temperature on the coast of southern Japan, washed by a warm current, is nearly 6°C (10°F) warmer than that in southern California, in the same latitude but washed by a cool current reinforced by upwelling. Between Labrador, flanked by a cold Arctic current, and northern Ireland, in the path of the warm west-wind drift, the difference is more than 8°C (15°F) in August, and during the winter it is nearly twice that.

The importance of sea-surface temperatures in affecting air-mass characteristics, moderating the air temperatures of coastal areas dominated by sea air, causing coastal fogs, etc., has already been emphasized in preceding chapters.

Salinity.   Sea water is a very complex dilute solution of a great many things. In addition to gases such as CO_2, the other materials dissolved in sea water average about 35 parts per 1,000 parts of water. This proportion of other materials is made up of close to

19 parts of chlorine and 11 parts of sodium, the constituents of common salt. The most abundant other elements are magnesium, sulfur, calcium, and potassium, with only magnesium consisting of as much as 1 part per 1,000. There are also minute quantities of an immense number of other substances. Most of these "impurities" probably result from the chemical decomposition of rock materials on the lands being taken into solution and carried into the seas by streams. Some have been derived from volcanic gases and dust in the atmosphere. In any case, it is important to remember that the ocean basins are the lowest parts of the earth's surface and therefore receive various wastes, some of human origin, carried in by water.

The degree of concentration of dissolved salts is called the *salinity* of the water. It is a remarkable fact that although the salinity varies significantly from place to place, the relative proportion of the several dissolved salts does not. The variation in salinity is affected principally by the relative rates of precipitation and evaporation. Heavy rainfall lowers the surface salinity by dilution; strong evaporation raises the salinity by removal of water and concentration of salts. Variations from the average surface salinity of about 35 parts per 1,000 are small, and values greater than 38 or less than 32 are rare in the open seas (Fig. 7.5).

The highest salinities in the open sea are found in the dry, hot subtropics, where evaporation is great. Nearer the equator salinities decrease because of heavier rainfall. In the cooler middle latitudes salinities are relatively low because of the decrease in evaporation and the considerable rainfall. Surface salinities are also generally low in Arctic and Antarctic waters, chiefly because of the effect of melting land ice, which releases quantities of fresh water.

In coastal waters and nearly enclosed seas, on the other hand, the salinity often departs greatly from the mean. In hot, dry, nearly enclosed seas, such as the Red Sea and the Persian Gulf, the salinities

reach 38 to 40 parts per 1,000, because the water is subject to strong evaporation but cannot mix freely with less saline waters from the depths of the open sea. On the other hand, near the mouths of large rivers, or in confined seas into which large rivers flow, such as the Black Sea and the Baltic Sea, dilution by fresh water reduces the salinity below 20 parts per 1,000.

The mean density of sea water becomes greater with increasing salinity. Thus where evaporation is rapid, the surface water becomes excessively saline and dense and tends to sink, being replaced by water from below.

Movements of Sea Waters

The wind blowing across the sea surface transfers some of its momentum to the water. Some of this produces waves and some drives the water in the same general direction but with modification by the

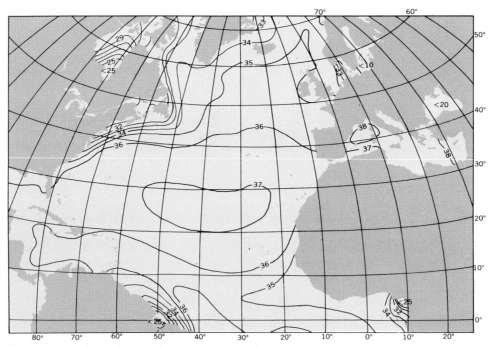

Figure 7.5 Surface salinities in the North Atlantic and adjacent waters. (Values in parts per thousand.) *(Modified from Dietrich,* General Oceanography: An Introduction. *Interscience Publishers, John Wiley & Sons, Inc., New York, 1963.)*

Coriolis effect. The sea surface therefore exhibits a strong correspondence in its horizontal movements to the atmospheric circulations above it. In addition, differences in energy receipt cause variations in temperature and evaporation, which in turn affect salinities and densities. Changes in these then promote vertical exchanges of water. These movements are tremendously modified and complicated by several factors, a notable one being that the water is confined in a variety of connected basins of varying size and irregular shape which greatly upset simple flows.

The movements of the sea have important effects upon many marine phenomena, such as the distribution of temperatures of the sea water, the existence and concentration of marine organisms, coastal erosion, and navigation. As we have already seen, the temperature of the sea surface also has an important effect on the atmosphere and thus on weather and climate.

Waves

Waves are the smallest and most localized of the movements of ocean waters. They are an important factor in the operation of oceangoing ships, and an even more important one in shaping the coastline by erosion and redistribution of the eroded material.

Most waves are generated by the wind, although they may continue far beyond the area stirred by the wind and persist long after it has ceased to blow. Where waters are deep and wind velocities are low or moderate, wave movements are smoothly progressive, with each water molecule describing essentially a circle as the wave impulse passes. The water rises on the front of the wave, moves forward as the crest passes, drops down the rear slope, and moves

backward in the succeeding trough (Fig. 7.6). With high wind velocities, the crest of the wave is tipped forward and breaks, forming a whitecap.

Near the shore, where the depth of water decreases, an approaching wave is slowed by friction from below. The crest rises, steepens, and finally crashes forward in the form of a breaker. It is here that the erosional effect of waves is greatest.

The height of waves in the open sea and the length between their crests depend upon the velocity of the wind, the length of time it has blown, and the distance it has driven the waves across the surface (called the *fetch*). Up to a certain point, wave height and length become greater with increasing values of wind velocity, duration, and fetch.

There are significant variations among the oceans in the frequency of occurrence and the direction of movement of high waves. In latitudes equatorward of 30°, winds of gale force are relatively rare except in hurricanes and local squalls. High waves are correspondingly rare, a fact that is recognized in the heavier loading permitted to ships operating in tropical waters.

On the other hand, the North Atlantic and North Pacific Oceans, along with the corresponding latitudes in the southern seas—the "roaring 40s" and 50s—are notorious for the long, high waves that may be encountered during winter blows. Wind velocities of 20 to 35 m/sec (45 to 80 mi/hr) with long duration and long fetch generate waves as great as those in the smaller but more intense hurricanes of lower latitudes. Such storm waves have on occasion caused minor damage to even the largest ocean vessels and have forced them to reduce speed and change course to prevent further battering and to lessen the violence of their rolling.

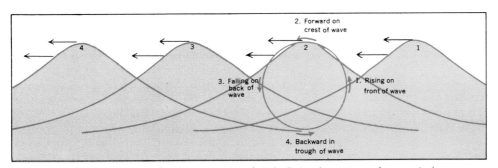

Figure 7.6   How a water particle moves in a vertical circle during the passage of a wave in the open sea.

Currents and Drifts

The ocean waters are constantly moving in a great circulatory system that involves both horizontal and vertical transfers. These movements are initiated by the transfer of kinetic energy from the winds to the surface waters and by variations in the densities of waters resulting from differences in their temperatures and salinities. The resulting flows, involving huge volumes of water, help to transport heat from the tropical and subtropical zone of excess receipt of solar radiation to the poleward zones where there is more energy radiated to space than is received from the sun.

Were it not for the continents interrupting or breaking up the movements of the water of the seas, the overall pattern of water circulation would be the same as that in the atmosphere: toward the east in the middle latitudes and toward the west in the low latitudes. The waters being driven by the wind are, as already noted, subject to the Coriolis effect and move at an angle to the wind direction: to the right in the Northern Hemisphere and to the left in the Southern. Consequently, the directions of the atmospheric movements, the Coriolis force, and the blocking effect of the continents combine to produce a circular flow about the subtropical high-pressure centers in each major ocean basin, clockwise in the Northern Hemisphere and counterclockwise in the Southern.

Much the larger part of the surface movement is a slow, relatively inconspicuous transfer, at an average rate of about 1 m/sec (approximately 2 mi/hr), that affects only shallow depths. These slow movements are more correctly spoken of as *drifts*, in contrast to the deeper, narrower, and more rapidly flowing *currents*. The swiftest currents occur where discharge takes place through narrow channels. An example is the Florida Current, which achieves velocities of nearly 3 m/sec in making its exit from the Gulf of Mexico through the narrow strait between Florida and Cuba.

Deep circulations.

The waters of the seas can be thought of as being composed of a rather thin, warm surface layer overlying a much thicker, colder lower layer. The warm water is slightly less dense, so it remains on top until it becomes dense enough, largely through cooling, to sink. A considerable amount of very cold water is produced by radiation of heat in the

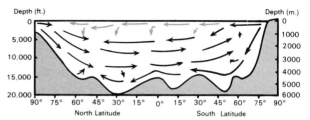

Figure 7.7   The general flow characteristics of a section through the Atlantic Ocean. Brown arrows represent warm waters, and black arrows represent cold waters. *(After Wust, et al.)*

polar areas. In general, the cold water from the polar areas sinks and moves equatorward at depth. Radiation and freezing along the edge of the antarctic ice supplies most of what is called *bottom water* for the world's oceans.

The general character of the deep circulations is indicated very diagrammatically for the Atlantic Ocean in Figure 7.7. It must be emphasized, however, that our observational knowledge of these circulations is quite fragmentary, and much of what is thought to occur is based upon inference. Each ocean basin has unique characteristics, and our understanding is very uneven. For example, much more is known about the Atlantic than about the Pacific.

Wind-driven surface pattern.   Except for the polar seas, all the great oceans exhibit broadly similar patterns of surface currents and drifts. This is a natural outcome of the general similarity of the prevailing wind patterns described in Chapter 4.

The most conspicuous elements of the circulation are great elliptical swirls about the subtropical oceanic high-pressure cells (Fig. 7.8). On the equatorward sides of the anticyclones in both hemispheres, the surface waters are driven steadily westward in the trade-wind zones. These are the Equatorial Currents. In the Pacific and Indian Oceans, and much less markedly and consistently in the Atlantic Ocean, the Equatorial Currents are separated by an eastward-moving Equatorial Countercurrent, which coincides approximately with the position of the intertropical convergence zone (ITC). Upon reaching the western sides of the ocean basins, the Equatorial Currents swing poleward around the ends of the high-pressure cells, bathing the eastern shores of the continents with waters warmed by their long journey through the tropics.

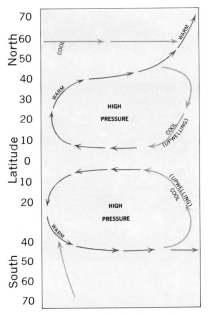

Figure 7.8 Generalized scheme of ocean currents.

At about latitude 40°, westerly winds and deflection cause the waters to turn slowly eastward across the ocean in the form of a west-wind drift. In the eastern part of the sea the drift divides, a part of it being driven by the winds equatorward along the coast as a relatively cool current until it again joins the Equatorial Current and thus completes the low-latitude circuit. In the Northern Hemisphere, however, a considerable portion of the west-wind drift is carried poleward by the stormy southwesterlies, its relatively warm waters washing the west coasts of the continents and eventually entering the Arctic Ocean. The Arctic, compensating for this receipt of warm water, produces an outward flow of cold water that passes down the western side of the ocean into the middle latitudes. In the Southern Hemisphere much of the west-wind drift continues clear around the earth in the unbroken belt of ocean that occupies the southern middle latitudes. If this idealized pattern is compared with a somewhat generalized map of actual currents (Fig. 7.9), it will be seen that the concept is basically valid.

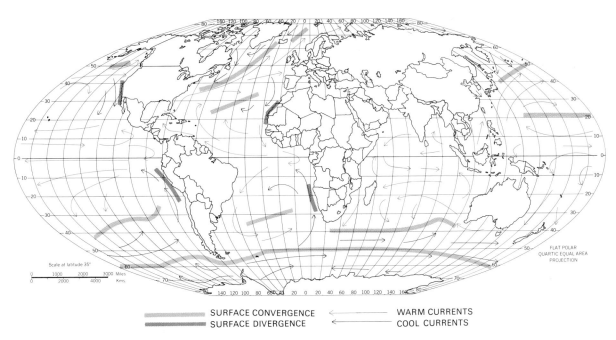

SURFACE CONVERGENCE   WARM CURRENTS
SURFACE DIVERGENCE   COOL CURRENTS

Figure 7.9 Surface currents of the oceans in Northern Hemisphere winter, showing zones of convergence and divergence and, accordingly, of sinking and upwelling of sea waters.

Surface convergence and divergence. The locations of the major zones of lateral convergence and divergence have been indicated on Figure 7.8. Divergence occurs at the western portions of the Equatorial Currents and in the eastern parts of the middle-latitude west-wind drifts. Convergence takes place at the eastern ends of the Equatorial Currents and in western parts of the middle-latitude oceans, where the poleward-moving warm surface currents meet the equatorward-flowing cold surface currents from the polar seas. Slow convergence also occurs in the generally circular motion of the waters in the subtropical areas.

Where lateral convergence occurs, surface waters must sink. If there are no significant density differences involved, the sinking takes place throughout the area of convergence. But if the convergence involves distinct currents which differ in density, the denser waters sink beneath the less dense, in a manner comparable to the behavior of converging air masses at a front. At the important zones of convergence in the middle latitudes, the cold polar waters plunge deeply below the warm waters that have come from the tropics. The polar waters then continue their direction of flow for thousands of miles at great depth. Although the convergence zone is likely to be relatively turbulent, there is remarkably little mixing of the contrasting waters.

Surface divergence is accompanied by the rising of water from below. In many areas of divergence the upward movement is sluggish and diffuse. In contrast, along the subtropical west edges of the continents where there are equatorward-blowing winds, the Coriolis force causes the upper layer of water to move away from the coasts, and large volumes of cold water to rise to the surface near the shore from depths of 100 to 300 m. This vigorous upwelling brings with it a large supply of nutrients, resulting in an extraordinary development of small plant and animal life. The upwelling also reinforces the low temperatures of the equatorward-moving currents. For example, during the summer the water temperature along the coast of central California, where the upwelling is strongest, is actually lower than that much farther north along the coast of Oregon and Washington. Upwelling in these areas has profound effects upon the climate of the coastal strip and upon sea life in these coastal waters.

Tides

Nearly all shores of the open seas experience the distinct periodic rises and falls of sea level known as the *tides*. Like most familiar natural phenomena, they have been known and studied from very early times, and along the way they have become a symbol of the certainty and inflexibility of natural processes. But an understanding of how and why the tides vary from place to place has been slow in coming, and even now it is not securely grasped. The basic factors that produce the tides are not especially obscure, but the actual mechanism of tidal activity on the earth is exceedingly complex and can be no more than briefly summarized here.

Forces causing the tides. In a system such as that of the earth and the moon, one body does not revolve about the other; instead, both bodies revolve about the center of gravity in the pair. Since the earth has much greater mass than the moon, the center of gravity of the earth-moon pair lies just within the earth and always on the side nearest the moon. Around that point the center of the moon moves in a large circle, while the center of the earth travels in a much smaller circle. It should be noted that this movement of the earth is a *revolution* about the center of gravity, not a *rotation*.

Of the forces involved in such a system, two are important to the tides: (1) the gravitational pull of the moon upon the earth, and (2) the centrifugal reaction which necessarily accompanies the small revolution of the earth. The gravitational attraction decreases rapidly with increasing distance from the moon, and hence it is significantly greater on the side of the earth nearest the moon than on the side opposite. The centrifugal reaction, on the other hand, is the same everywhere on the earth, for as the center of the earth revolves in a circle around the center of gravity of the pair, all points on the earth follow circular paths of the same size and move at the same speed.

At the center of the earth, the gravitational attraction and centrifugal reaction must be equal in strength. This means, however, that on the side toward the moon the greater gravitational strength will cause a net moonward pull, and on the opposite side the lesser gravitational strength will result in a

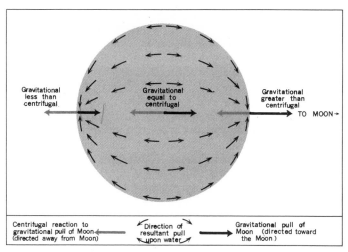

Centrifugal reaction to
gravitational pull of Moon
(directed away from Moon)   Direction of
                                 resultant pull
                                 upon water   Gravitational pull of
                                                    Moon (directed toward
                                                    the Moon)

Figure 7.10   The principal forces involved in the production of the tides.

net pull away from the moon (Fig. 7.10). The effect upon the fluid oceans will be to draw a flow of water toward both the point nearest the moon and the point farthest from the moon, raising the water levels at those two places and consequently depressing them elsewhere. As the earth rotates on its axis, each point in the ocean, therefore, will receive two outward pulls per day, one reaching a maximum when the point is on the side toward the moon and the other when the point is on the side away from the moon. Because the moon rises about 50 min later each day, the successive periods of high water at a given point come at intervals of about 12 hr, 25 min.

The moon, like the sun, changes its latitude seasonally, reaching maxima of slightly more than $28\frac{1}{2}°$ N and S. Hence, except when the moon is overhead at the equator, one of the two points of maximum tidal force will be located north of the equator and the other will be precisely opposite, at the same distance south of the equator. Therefore any place not on the equator will experience one stronger and one weaker tidal pull during the course of a single rotation.

The sun also generates tidal forces, in precisely the same manner as the moon. However, the distance between the sun and earth is so many times greater than that between the earth and moon that the tide-producing forces of the sun are much smaller. In fact, the effects of the sun do not appear as separate tides, but simply as modifications of the lunar tides.

At times of new moon and of full moon, the earth, moon, and sun are nearly in line, so that the lunar tides and the solar tides occur in the same places, and the height of the solar tides is added to that of the lunar tides. This causes the high tides of those periods to be unusually high and the intervening low water to be unusually low. These are the periods of *spring tide*, which occur every two weeks. When the moon is at its first and third quarters, the earth-sun line is nearly at right angles to the earth-moon line. The solar tides then fall between, and detract from, the lunar tides, causing the difference between low and high tide to be less pronounced than usual. These are the periods of *neap tide*, which also recur every two weeks.

Variations over the earth.   The seas are not continuous, but form a series of interconnected basins of many shapes and sizes. Therefore the tides do not actually behave as simple progressive bulges which appear to move westward about the earth. Instead, each major ocean basin and bordering sea tends to respond separately to the rhythmic pulls of the tidal forces. In each basin the water develops an oscillatory or swashing movement of the sort that may be produced by tilting or swinging a basin of water. Because of the Coriolis effect most of the oscillatory movements become circular. The wave of high tide swings about a central pivot, counterclockwise in the Northern Hemisphere, clockwise in the Southern.

Most basins respond most actively to the twice-daily pull of successive maxima of tidal forces, so that they have two high and two low tides per day. A few, however, because of their particular size and depth, respond more actively to the once-daily pull exerted by the stronger of the two tidal maxima, and thus yield only one high and one low tide per day. Most of the Gulf of Mexico, parts of the eastern Caribbean, and several basins around the margin of the western Pacific have only one daily tide. Elsewhere two is the rule, although often one is higher than the other. In Figure 7.11 the graph for New York shows the common pattern, while that for Honolulu shows a pronounced alternation of tidal heights.

The average difference in water level between low and high tide at any place is called its *mean tidal range.* The range is determined by several factors. In the open seas, ranges are least at the points or areas around which the tidal movements swing and increase outward from those centers. Common tidal ranges on exposed coasts are between 1 and 3 m. In nearly enclosed bodies of water, such as the Mediterranean and Baltic Seas and the Gulf of Mexico,

ranges are commonly less than ½ m. However, if the connection with the open ocean is broader and the range in the adjacent ocean is large, even a semienclosed sea may experience substantial tides. For example, ranges exceeding 2 m occur in the North Sea, the Persian Gulf, and the Sea of Okhotsk. Even inland lakes and ponds have their tides, but the ranges are so small as to be negligible.

Most places of great tidal range are situated on funnel-shaped bays or estuaries, where the range increases from the bay mouth toward its head. Thus Liverpool has a range of 9 m, while the head of the Bay of Fundy, Nova Scotia, has 13 m (43 ft) and, at time of spring tide, sometimes as much as 15 m (50 ft) of extreme tidal range.

Some important harbors, notably those of the British Isles and the adjacent coasts of Europe, are seriously inconvenienced by their large tidal ranges. In the ports of London, Rotterdam, Hamburg, and Bremen, among others, it has been necessary to construct docking basins with lock gates to maintain water levels high enough to keep moored vessels afloat at low tide and to decrease the inconvenience of change of level while loading and unloading.

Tidal currents. In order to raise or lower the water level in a semienclosed bay, sound, or lagoon, water must flow in or out through the opening. If the tidal range is large and the bay is large, the volume of water pouring through a narrow entrance will also be great. The resulting velocities of the current through the opening may become high enough, not infrequently 2 to 4 m per sec (5 to 10 m/hr), to carry out erosion that deepens the channel and maintains the opening against bar development.

Such strong tidal currents may also make it difficult to handle ships in the entrance channels and to dock large vessels. In the days of sail, ships were often compelled to await a favorable direction of tidal current before they could enter or leave a harbor.

Life in Sea Waters

All life in the sea, like that on the land, is ultimately dependent upon solar energy which enters into the process called *photosynthesis.* Plants which possess chlorophyll utilize water and dissolved carbon dioxide to form more complex organic hydrocarbons, and in

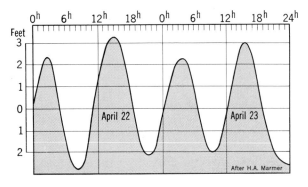

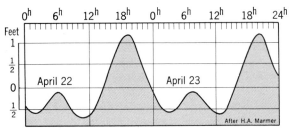

Figure 7.11 The intervals and amounts of tidal rise and fall during a 48-hr period at New York (top) and Honolulu (bottom). *(After Marmer.)*

doing so they give off oxygen. These plants form the primary element in food chains in that they are consumed by animals, which in turn serve as food for other animals. Life in the sea is abundant only in those limited areas where conditions are suitable. It rapidly thins out in less favorable areas and also as the energy moves from one level in the food chain to the next. The conversion of energy from one level to the next is only about 10 percent efficient, so that the abundance of life falls off rapidly with higher forms of life.

Only a tiny fraction of the energy reaching the sea is utilized to sustain plant growth there; much that is available is not used because of other environmental conditions which set a limit on how much plant life can be sustained. For example, the availability of nutrients is severely limited in most parts of the sea, making them like deserts insofar as life is concerned. Furthermore, the continuous circulations of ocean waters tend to remove the growing plants from the environment to which they are best adapted.

Major classes of marine organisms. The many forms of life that exist in the sea may be grouped into three categories according to their mobility. (1) The *plankton* are small, sometimes microscopic forms of life consisting of plants (phytoplankton) and animals (zooplankton) which are incapable of much self-determined movement, either because they have no means of locomotion or because they are so small as to be at the mercy of drifts and currents. The animal plankton and some other forms of sea creatures feed directly upon the phytoplankton. Other animals eat zooplankton or higher forms of life. It is apparent that if the phytoplankton were removed from the sea, most sea life would soon perish. (2) The sessile or generally immobile forms of life are those plants, shellfish, corals, etc., that are more or less permanently attached to the sea bottom, largely in shallow waters. (3) The free-swimming forms, which include the larger fish, Crustacea, and sea mammals, are those that are capable of moving about over considerable distances in search of food.

Nutrients in the sea. Like other plants, the phytoplankton need not only carbon dioxide and light, but also a large number of nutrient elements (chiefly phosphorus, nitrogen, and silicon) which enter into

their structures and regulate their life functions. Abundant life in the sea can be expected only within about 100 m of the surface where solar radiation is sufficient, and then only where abundant nutrients are present.

In general, nutrient substances tend to be depleted in the upper layer because they are consumed by the plant life that exists there, and to be ample in deeper waters because they are released there by the decomposition of dead organisms that have sunk down from the surface layers. Maintenance of life in the surface waters thus depends on mechanisms that replenish the depleted supply of nutrients, both by bringing nutrient-rich deeper waters upward and by carrying in nutrients from the organically rich continents. Coastal waters in general, and areas near the mouths of major rivers in particular, tend to be relatively high in nutrients brought from the land. As for the processes that carry deeper waters toward the surface, several have been discussed previously: winter overturning in the upper middle latitudes, upwelling along the subtropical west coasts, rising of water with the divergence of surface currents, and various forms of turbulence, either along the margins of well-defined currents and boundaries between water masses of contrasting density or associated with storm wave action in shallow waters.

One measure of the primary productivity of the oceans is given by the amount of carbon that is extracted and fixed in the plant life by the photosynthetic process. In the most productive areas this can approach 300 g of carbon per square meter of ocean surface per year, while in the more "barren" areas the fixation rate may be as little as 30 g of carbon. The primary productivity of the ocean waters has been estimated and it is mapped in Figure 7.12.

The greatest concentrations of nutrients in the surface layers are found (1) in the upper middle latitudes, especially toward the eastern sides of the oceans where divergence occurs; (2) along the subtropical west coasts of continents; (3) in diverging western equatorial waters; (4) along the margins of such well-defined currents as the Gulf Stream and the Kuroshio; and (5) in shallow coastal waters. Perhaps the poorest surface waters in terms of nutrient supply are in the tropical regions and the central areas under the great subtropical anticyclonic whirls, where continuous slow convergence and sinking of saline wa-

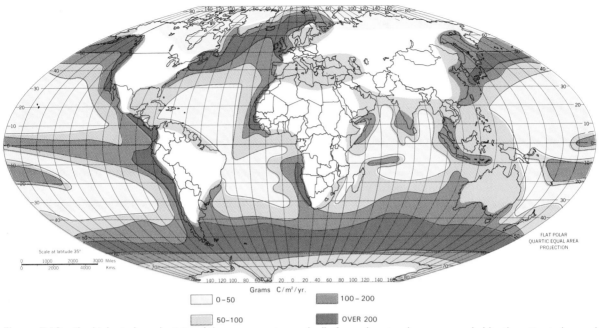

Grams C/m²/yr.

☐ 0–50	▨ 100–200
▨ 50–100	▦ OVER 200

Figure 7.12   The biological productivity of the oceans varies markedly from place to place, as revealed by the estimated annual amount of carbon fixed per square meter. *(After Lieth.)*

ters occur without a compensating rise of water from below in the same area. As a consequence, these regions are notably poor in sea life.

Fish and sea mammals.   Fish can be grouped according to their very different habits of swimming, spawning, and feeding. Some fish, including such important commercial varieties as cod, haddock, hake, halibut, flounder, and sole, live and feed far below the surface, commonly at depths of 70 m (214 ft) or more. As a class these are referred to as *demersal* fish. The first three named are highly mobile and, as adults, feed chiefly upon other fish and invertebrates. Halibut, flounder, and sole, on the other hand, belong to the flatfish group and are adapted to living directly upon the sea bottom, where they feed chiefly on mollusks, worms, and other bottom-dwelling organisms. The young of both groups feed on plankton.

A second major class are the *pelagic* fish—those that spend most of their time in the open ocean near the surface. Many of these, including the anchovy, herring, mackerel, and sardine, characteristically travel in large groups or schools. Others, such as

tuna, eels, and sharks, do not congregate to the same degree. Most pelagic fish are strong swimmers and move about over long distances. Many are plankton feeders.

A few saltwater fish, notably salmon, spawn in freshwater streams rather than in the bordering seas. This characteristic leads to large concentrations of the fish near the mouths of major rivers during the spawning season—a factor which, like the schooling habits of herring, has affected the techniques of fishing.

In addition to fish and shellfish, the living resources of the sea include numerous sea mammals, some of which are valuable for their skins, oil, bone, or flesh. Seals and sea lions spend much time on shore, where they breed and bear their young. Whales and porpoises, also great travelers, are strictly water dwellers. Many of the largest whales subsist chiefly on plankton, while most of the smaller whales, as well as porpoises, seals, and walruses, are largely fish eaters.

Since they gather in places which are rich in plankton, fish and sea mammals are concentrated on the continental shelves, in areas of upwelling or turbulence, and in the seasonally overturning waters of the higher latitudes. The bottom-dwelling forms of sea life—including oysters and other shellfish, crabs, lobsters, and sponges, many of which are valuable to man—are most abundant in the shallow waters of the same areas.

The waters of the North Atlantic and the North Pacific, especially the continental shelf areas poleward of about latitude 30°, are noteworthy for their immense populations of fish. The corresponding waters of the Southern Hemisphere also appear to be rich in sea life, though they are less well known. Certain of the most abundant fish of the Northern Hemisphere, including herring, do not occur naturally in southern waters.

It is commonly believed that the warm tropical seas are generally less densely populated by fish than the cooler waters of the globe. Yet, while this may be true, fish are abundant enough in the warm oceans to permit many peoples of the tropical coasts to derive a large part of their food from the sea. It seems clear that in the warm waters of the low latitudes there is a greater variety of species than in the higher latitudes, but that the number of individuals in any single species is likely to be much smaller. For example, there are no known tropical counterparts of the tremendous schools of herring and sardines that are found in cooler waters.

Food from the sea. The sea nurtures a prodigious amount of life. Much of it, such as plankton, is at the lower end of the food chain and is generally not used by humans. In recent years people have taken annually in the order of 60 to 70 million metric tons of food materials from the sea, nearly all being fish, about half of which is made into fish meal for livestock feed. The harvest has increased dramatically in the last 50 years. There are, of course, both absolute productivity limits and economic controls which will prevent an unlimited increase, but it seems entirely possible that the total may rise in the future. Although these amounts seem large, it should be noted that fish supply less than 5 percent of the protein in the average human diet the world over.

Fisheries. Other than the waters off western South America, from which Peru annually has taken from 5 to 10 million tons of anchovies in recent years, most of which is made into fish meal, the great commercial fisheries line the margins of the North Atlantic and North Pacific Oceans, where fish exist in unparalleled abundance and where there are high concentrations of human population in the adjacent lands (Fig. 7.13).

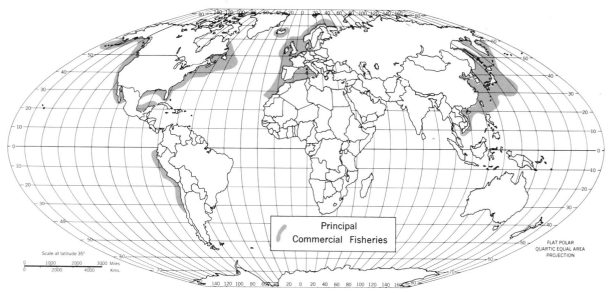

Figure 7.13 The largest harvests from the sea are in the coastal waters off western South America and in the North Atlantic and the North Pacific Oceans.

The great area of the shallower waters off China, Japan, and eastern Siberia is the world's most productive fishing ground. Although from time to time Peru has been the world's leader, Japan has been for many years a leading nation in total catch, her annual production in recent years amounting to nearly one-sixth of the world total. China and the Soviet Union also rank high. Primary products of the cold waters in this area are herring and the great king crabs; sardines, tuna, and mackerel come from the warm waters.

The stormy waters of the eastern North Atlantic and the North Sea rank just behind the western North Pacific in their yield of fish. All the countries fronting on these rich waters, from Iceland to Portugal, are important fishing nations and have a long tradition of maritime activity. Cod, haddock, mackerel, and especially herring are the chief products of the commercial fishery here. Northwestern Europe and Iceland are the leading regions of the world in export of fish for human consumption.

The coastal waters and, more significantly, the offshore banks (relatively broad, shallow submarine platforms) of New England, Newfoundland, and maritime Canada also rank high in annual productivity. The North Atlantic Banks, extending from Nantucket to the eastern coast of Newfoundland, are among the world's great producing regions for cod, herring, mackerel, haddock, and halibut.

The fishery of the Pacific Coast of North America has tended generally to decline and to shift its centers of activity. The salmon fishery was once important in northern California, Oregon, and Washington, but now it is confined largely to Alaskan waters. Overfishing, together with unknown biological factors, have also reduced the California sardine fishery. Tuna fishing is important in the upwelling waters from southern California southward along the coast of northern Mexico.

Because of their value, many of the large sea mammals have been ruthlessly hunted and their numbers greatly reduced, especially in the Northern Hemisphere. The whale fishery is now largely in antarctic waters. Even there, several of the most valuable species are in imminent danger of extinction, as are the fur seals of the Bering Sea.

REVIEW QUESTIONS

1. Predict the seasonal differences in the relationship between the water-balance elements (evaporation and precipitation) and the salinity of the surface water in (a) the Mediterranean Sea and (b) the Gulf of Mexico.
2. Describe the deviations which together would make up the average annual water temperature along the 50° N parallel over the oceans.
3. What happens to the energy required to evaporate water from the sea surface?
4. Describe some characteristics of water which make it unusual among inorganic substances.
5. All other things being equal, how much smaller would the oceans have to be and how much larger would the land areas have to be for the land to contribute as much water as the sea to the atmospheric portion of the water balance?
6. Why are the subtropical anticyclonic areas the areas of greatest net contribution of water to the atmosphere?
7. What effect would there be on the earth's tides if the moon orbited the earth in an elliptical path rather than a circle?
8. Waters flowing into the sea have always contained a great variety of substances in solution and suspension. Are these "pollutants," and what is the difference between what was being carried to the sea 100 years ago and today?
9. Follow a parallel across the sea and describe and account for the salinity variations that might be expected along it.
10. Abundant fish life is commonly found in cold waters. Why?

SELECTED REFERENCES

Carson, Rachel. *The Sea Around Us.* Oxford University Press, Fair Lawn, N.J., 1951. A best seller for many years, and with good reason. A fascinating account of the still mysterious sea.

Dietrich, Gunter. *General Oceanography: An Introduction.* English translation by Feodor Ostapoff. Interscience Publishers, John Wiley & Sons, Inc., New York, 1963. A liberally illustrated broad introduction to the subject. It covers a wide range of topics.

Sverdrup, H. U., M. W. Johnson, and R. H. Fleming. *The Oceans: Their Physics, Chemistry and General Biology*. Prentice-Hall, Inc., Englewood Cliffs, N.J., 1942.

The Ocean: A "Scientific American" Book. W. H. Freeman and Company, San Francisco, 1969. A selection of 10 articles from *Scientific American*, ranging from the origin of the seas to their resources.

von Arx, W. S. *An Introduction to Physical Oceanography*. Addison-Wesley Publishing Company, Inc., Reading, Mass., 1962. A first-class, relatively advanced treatment of the subject, with emphasis on physical principles and processes.

Williams, Jerome. *Oceanography*. Little, Brown and Company, Boston and Toronto, 1962. A clearly written, basic introduction.

Waters of the Land

Only 2 to 3 percent of the waters on the earth are found on or near the surface of the land, but that water is a fundamental element of the physical environment. It is unlike the saline water in the oceans in one vital respect, being what is called *fresh water*. Naturally, there are various degrees of "freshness"; but most land-based life, from man to the tiniest plants and insects, has evolved to depend upon this kind of water. Fresh water is therefore an essential mineral in the biosphere.

The waters of the land are unevenly distributed, a fact of primary significance in the understanding of the variations of land-based life on the earth. The uneven distribution of water is a consequence of the interaction of a variety of factors, ranging from the initial supply to the nature of the land surface. The geographical study of water on the land appropriately begins with the mechanism which supplies this critical resource to the land.

The Hydrologic Cycle

In the previous chapter we learned that one of the great circulatory systems of the earth involves its water. Some of the water condensed in this vast, continuously operating distilling process falls on the land. This is the only source of fresh water. The functioning of the hydrologic cycle with respect to waters on the land is very complex, and some of its major characteristics are illustrated in Figure 8.1.

Over the land areas of the earth, precipitation generally exceeds evaporation; consequently, much of the water that falls on the land is ultimately destined to return, as liquid, to the ocean reservoir. Its movement in that direction is not likely to be very direct, however. Although some falls upon lake or stream surfaces and thus starts back immediately, most is shed on the ground and must find its way to a stream. Once in a stream, this surface water, responding to the pull of gravity, may flow either directly toward the ocean or into some enclosed basin on the land. In such a basin it may evaporate or sink beneath the land surface. Where there is no such topographic interruption to its return to the ocean, the stream of surface water continues on its course, sometimes being delayed in a wide place, such as a freshwater lake or swamp, but always moving toward the sea. On the way, some of it may leave the stream by sinking into the stream bed.

Perhaps two-thirds of the average 71 cm (28 in.) of water which falls on the land area of the earth each year returns seaward in the form of vapor, the remainder returning as discharge from rivers. Some

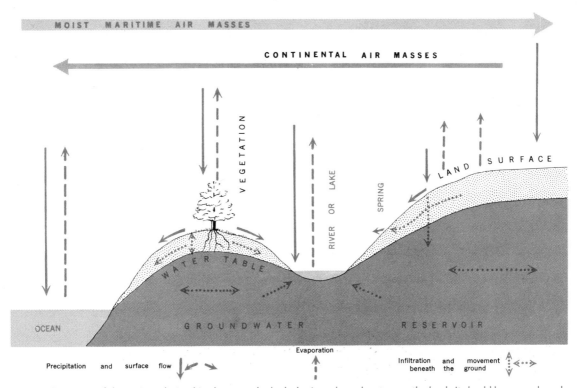

Figure 8.1   Some of the major relationships between the hydrologic cycle and waters on the land. It should be remembered that only a small proportion of the water involved in the hydrologic cycle falls on the land.

of the vapor is supplied by direct evaporation from the surface water, but a significant amount, perhaps a third, results from vegetative transpiration. Some of the vapor supplied by evapotranspiration on the land is returned through precipitation, but most of it is carried away from the land by the relatively dry continental air masses which move from the land to the sea.

A portion of the water that falls on the land neither evaporates again nor enters a stream, but instead sinks downward into the loose soil. Some of this is taken up by plants, whence it is again evaporated through the leaf pores. A fraction of the water in the soil may move upward by capillary force, but some continues downward to become part of the groundwater, the water that fills the cracks and pore spaces of the rocks in the outer zone of the solid earth, as well as that which occurs in the looser soil that commonly covers the rocks. Within the groundwater reservoir the water may move laterally as well as

vertically. Some of it discharges directly into the ocean, below sea level. But by far the larger part drains by seepage and springs into streams and rivers, thus again becoming surface water.

The history of a specific mass of water would normally include many interruptions and complications which are not evident from a general summary of the hydrologic cycle. For example, some water may become locked up in ice masses in polar or high-altitude regions, or may be held in plant or animal tissues for years, or may even be locked up in chemical combination with other minerals. However, these kinds of complications do not greatly affect the geographically significant fact about the hydrologic cycle on the land, namely, that water from the sea is precipitated as fresh water on the land and moves back to the sea via drainage and evaporation.

Variations over the earth.   There are great differences over land areas in the operation of the hydrologic cycle. This results from variations in weather and climate, plus the complications caused by differences in vegetative cover, soil and rock character, and many other factors, including man's activities.

Regions that have a great deal of open surface water, a damp soil, and a dense vegetative cover will probably furnish a proportionately large amount of water to the atmosphere. Likewise, the clearer, windier, and warmer an area, the greater will be the possibility of transferring water from the land to the air. Thus the climatically or seasonally dry lands, generally being clear, windy, and warm, have a high *potential* evapotranspiration; but because there is little surface or soil water and meager vegetation in these areas, the actual amount is relatively low.

The timing of the hydrologic cycle is also a complex matter. From time to time there are significant variations in the total amount of water involved in the cycle and the proportions existing in each part of it. There is also a definite pattern to the annual regime, that is, the timing of the functioning of the cycle during a year. And just as the spatial variations of the climatic elements result in significant geographical patterns, so there are general spatial patterns in the functioning of this cycle. Our knowledge of these is much scantier than our knowledge of the variations in climatic elements.

Water as a Resource

Water is indispensable to biologic processes, but fresh water has also become a primary commodity in man's advanced technological society. Where it is scarce, as in desert areas, water has always been carefully used. Even today, in areas where the supply is relatively abundant, water is the object of a surprising amount of management effort, and a vast number of physical structures, large and small, have been created, such as dams, aqueducts, canals, reservoirs, piping systems, and sewers to collect it, purify it, distribute it, cleanse it, and carry it away. Equally significant are the social systems that have been developed to deal with such complex problems as its allocation and the control of pollution.

Until recently a relatively small amount of water was required to supply the immediate needs of humanity. Beginning with the Industrial Revolution, however, water steadily increased in significance,

until today it is certainly the most used material in our complex modern life. Quite apart from its uses in place, that is, for such things as outdoor recreation and surface transportation, it is required for a large variety of purposes. It is our major industrial and home solvent, coolant, and waste carrier; virtually all manufactured electricity requires water; and most all industrial production requires amazing amounts of it. For example, 1 gal of gasoline requires some ten times that volume of water for its preparation; a steel mill uses perhaps 240,000 liters (64,000 gal) of water for each ton of steel it produces; and vast amounts are used for irrigation.

The rapidly growing population of the earth naturally requires ever-increasing amounts of fresh water, but the demand is rising even faster than the population in all technologically developed areas. For example, in the United States the population grew from 150 million in 1950 to over 200 million in 1970, an increase of about 35 percent. By contrast, during that 20-year period the amount of water used for the four principal uses—urban supply, rural supply, irrigation, and industrial utilization—showed about an 85 percent increase. It is estimated that in 1970 an average of about 1,400 billion liters (370 billion gal) per day was used.[1] This amounts to more than 6,800 liters (1,800 gal) per capita per day. Although much of this is returned to the water supply, often polluted, perhaps to be used again, nearly a quarter is "consumed" by such processes as being evaporated or incorporated in crops, livestock, and manufactured products.

The continuing rapid increase in the use of water (Fig. 8.2) is a disquieting fact of modern life. It appears unlikely that there will ever be a drop in per capita use; consequently, a wise use policy involving reuse and minimum waste is imperative.

Withdrawal and nonwithdrawal uses.   Water diverted for some use from its natural place is termed a *withdrawal* use. All water conveyed for the purpose of industrial processes, domestic use in the home, the generation of thermoelectric power, and livestock and crop production is classed as withdrawal. *Nonwithdrawal* uses include navigation, fishing, and other activities which do not require removing the water.

[1]C. Richard Murray and E. Bodette Reeves. *Estimated Use of Water in the United States in 1970.* U.S. Geological Survey Circular 676, Washington, D.C., 1972.

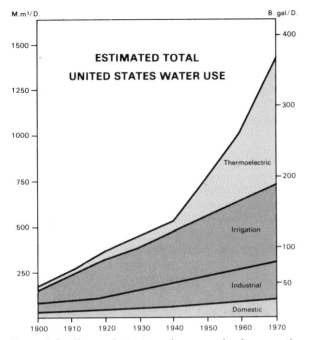

Figure 8.2 The steady rise in total water use has been greatly increased in recent years by a burgeoning demand for electricity, more than 80 percent of which is provided by thermoelectric plants. Scales are millions of cubic meters per day (M. m³/D.) and billions of gallons per day (B. gal/D.). *(Based upon various sources, including Murray and Reeves.)*

Water for withdrawal use must meet stringent purity requirements; for most purposes it must be fresh. Regions of abundant precipitation usually, although not always, have ample sources of fresh water close at hand. In dry regions, on the other hand, the supply of fresh water is restricted and it must be used with great care. These differences are of critical significance in human geography.

Since the amount of water for withdrawal uses varies so much from place to place, the total amount consumed in the world is a meaningless figure. Some idea of the magnitude may be gained from knowing that the domestic use of water in the United States averages around 300 liters (80 gal) per person per day, and that even under the most primitive living conditions anywhere on earth, a person probably requires 8 to 15 liters (2 to 4 gal) per day. Although domestic use has the highest priority, it accounts for only a minor portion of the total amount consumed. The quantities withdrawn for irrigation, industry, and steam power production are incomparably larger.

Withdrawal supplies are obtained both from the surface water in streams and lakes and from the groundwater reservoir. Surface is by far the more important, since it is usually easier to obtain. The proportion of the United States supply which comes from each source is illustrated in Figure 8.3.

Pollution. Pure water scarcely exists, for all natural water contains various other substances. The list of dissolved and suspended materials found in fresh water in significant amounts is very long and includes such things as oxygen, carbon dioxide, salts, acids, and sediments, and various life forms ranging from bacteria to algae to fish, to say nothing of human refuse. *Pollution* is an entirely relative term and is not easy to define.

The water on the land is part of a natural ecological system in which constant change is taking place tending toward a balance. For example, if some dead organic material gets into some surface water, it is attacked by bacteria. The bacteria break it down into materials such as nitrates and carbon dioxide. These are in turn converted to new organic material by algae. Small fish eat the algae, bigger fish eat them, and so on, and they all ultimately die. The cycle may continue with no basic change taking place. If, however, there is too little oxygen or too much nutrient nitrate, then the bacteria die or the algae grow too abundantly, and in either case the cycle slows down or stops, with consequent unpleasant odors and appearance. The water thus may become unfit for many uses. Because people are part of the ecological system, one can argue that water pollution is that change or condition which renders it unfit for the intended use. The difficulty arises in determining the appropriate use, because there are innumerable competing demands.

Streams form natural drains by which material from the land is carried away. This is a proper use, for the bacterial and other processes in the water break down the material. But streams are also scenic recreational areas, sources of water supply, and places for fish to live. The variety of possible uses requires water of different characteristics; but so long as the amount of added material is in balance with the ability of the other natural factors to cycle it, then no

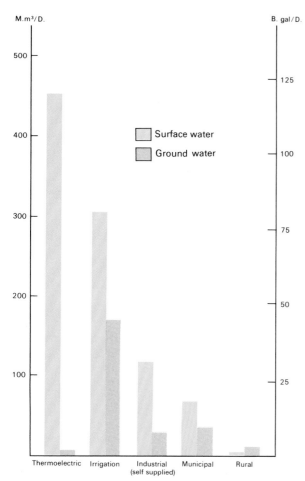

Figure 8.3 Estimated withdrawal uses of surface and ground-water in the United States in millions of cubic meters and billions of gallons per day. Perhaps a third of the municipal supply is used for commercial and industrial purposes. *(From Murray and Reeves.)*

logical balances are often upset. In the natural state, an ecological system, such as the soil, has a given rate of productivity, but people are often not satisfied with that. Instead they may overload it by adding artificial fertilizers in order to obtain larger crop yields or greener lawns. The water that runs off carries a significant portion of the fertilizer into lakes and streams, where it stimulates excessive growth of algae. Waste chemicals from manufacturing processes, acids from mining, radioactive materials from industry, and pesticides from all sorts of husbandry activities are other forms of water pollution.

Because pollution causes changes which many find undesirable and which may in fact be irreversible, it has become a matter of great concern to government. Much more study is needed, however, to understand the complications that result from people changing the character of the waters of the land. As yet it is not possible to map with any certainty the geographical distribution of the various kinds of pollution. About all that can be said is that the greater the industrial demands in an area, the greater the pollution of its waters is likely to be.

SURFACE WATER

Not only is surface water the major source for withdrawal uses, but the most important nonwithdrawal uses—such as navigation, waste disposal, recreation, and the sustaining of wild life—depend almost entirely upon surface water supplies. Surface water can be divided into two major parts: the water held in more or less temporary storage, and the water known as *surface runoff*, which is in the process of draining off the land.

Water Storage

Surface water temporarily held in storage on and in the upper portion of the land includes the water in the loose materials and rock above the saturated ground-water reservoir, the water in ice and snow on the surface, and the water in the tissues of plants and animals. For shorter or longer periods and in larger or smaller amounts, some portion of the total supply of surface water is always in storage.

Figure 8.4 gives a generalized picture of the average distribution of storage water by latitudinal

major change occurs. On the other hand, if the drain becomes overloaded, then the cycle changes and we say the stream has become *polluted*. In this sense modern technology is causing the pollution of much of the waters on the land.

The major forms of pollution of the surface water are already evident. One is the overloading of streams with human and industrial wastes so that they are turned into sewers. One of the major industrial uses of water is simply to cool things, and when the temperature of the water is raised, delicate eco-

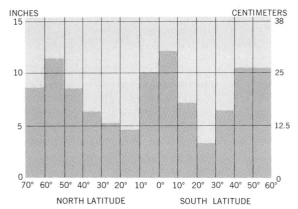

Figure 8.4 General distribution of the water detained in temporary storage on and near the surface of the land at various latitudes, expressed as a depth per unit area. Values are the averages of computed monthly totals. Since the storage water of one month may be carried over to the next, the graph does not reveal the total amount of water involved. (Data from van Hylckama.)

zones. This graph might be said to show the latitudinal variation of "average wetness." The general symmetry of the two hemispheres is, of course, to be expected. In addition, the latitudinal variations within a hemisphere clearly reflect the heavy precipitation in the tropics and the lower precipitation and higher evaporation in the subtropics. The large values shown for the cooler regions in the higher middle latitudes are results of the winter storage of snow and ice, as well as the lessened evaporation at all seasons.

The annual variations in the amount of water in storage at the various latitudes also exhibit some symmetry; i.e., similar latitudes have similar regimes. Figure 8.5 shows schematically for each latitude the season of the year when the most water is likely to be detained. In the higher latitudes, late winter and spring are usually the seasons of maximum storage. This is because low winter temperatures have allowed very little winter evaporation and have locked up a large volume of water in snow and ice. In the lower latitudes, the maximum storage occurs during and shortly after the wet season.

Surface Runoff

The drainage in streams, called *surface runoff*, comes from three immediate sources: (1) the water that

emerges from the underground (groundwater) reservoir, (2) the water from rainfall that remains after losses due to evapotranspiration, and (3) the water released from storage. The total amount of water which drains off the land and back into the sea is very large, the annual total approaching 30,000 cu km. Although many hundreds of streams and rivers flow to the sea, only a few contribute a large proportion of the total. By far the largest is the Amazon River in South America, which accounts for nearly a fifth of the total discharge of all rivers; it discharges more than four times the volume of the Congo River in Africa, the second largest.

Measurement of runoff. The runoff or discharge of a drainage basin or watershed (a landform drainage region) is determined from the amount of water its streams discharge, expressed as a depth per unit of time. This figure is obtained by dividing the total annual volume of discharge by the area of the drainage region to obtain a quotient of an average depth of water; means of these values for a number of years may then be mapped. Although this is the same method by which precipitation is expressed, maps of average annual runoff provide a somewhat more generalized picture of variations from place to place.

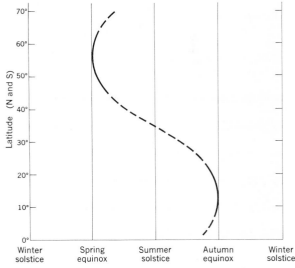

Figure 8.5 Highly schematic diagram showing the season of maximum water detention on the land at the various latitudes in both hemispheres. Where the relationship is less clear, the curve is shown as a broken line.

This is so because the volume of runoff for a region can be obtained from only one point, a stream-gaging station, and consequently, the total runoff is equally apportioned to all parts of the watershed. A map of runoff thus shows only the generalized pattern of variation over a series of drainage basins, not the actual amount that drains at every point.

Figure 8.6 is a map of the average annual runoff of the United States. If it is compared with the map of average annual precipitation, a general correlation between the two can be seen.

Stream flow.   Most of the time, surface runoff is fed by emerging groundwater. However, when water accumulates on the land surface, as it often does during a shower, for example, most of it quickly collects in channels. One recognized classification of stream channels distinguishes between those that contain flowing water all of the time and those that do so only part of the time. The first kind are called *permanent* streams, the second *intermittent*.

Direct surface runoff occurs when the accumulation of water on a sloping surface exceeds the water-infiltering capacity of the surface forms and materials. Heavy rains and snowmelt, and a surface material with a slow infiltration capacity, such as a "tight" clay or frozen soil, all promote direct surface runoff. Where there is not enough slope to draw off the water, it simply collects as temporary "standing water" in swamps, marshes, and shallow lakes.

Marked variation from place to place and from time to time is a characteristic of both total amounts of runoff and the proportions supplied from various sources. Yearly variations are characteristic of those areas where variability in precipitation from one year to the next is common. The short-term minor variations result from differences in individual storms, while seasonal variations result from differences in the amounts of precipitation and in the release of storage water. The proportion of runoff supplied from the groundwater reservoir is subject to the least fluctuation.

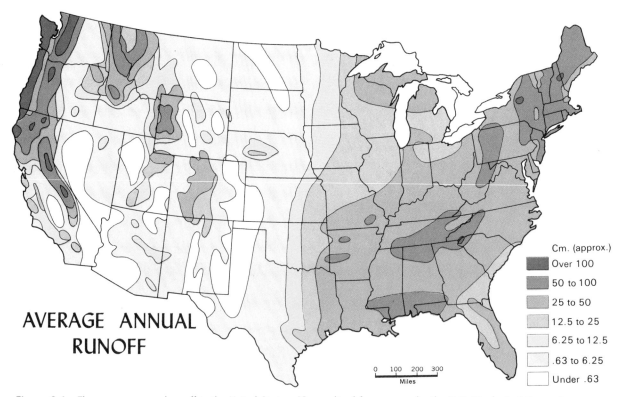

AVERAGE ANNUAL RUNOFF

Cm. (approx.)
Over 100
50 to 100
25 to 50
12.5 to 25
6.25 to 12.5
.63 to 6.25
Under .63

0   100   200   300
Miles

Figure 8.6   The average annual runoff in the United States. *(Generalized from a map by the U.S. Geological Survey.)*

Peak discharges called *floods* are normal phenomena and occur with varying frequency—the greater the magnitude, the lower the frequency. Floods can be very destructive to people's use of areas subject to inundation. Flooding rivers commonly shift their channels in lowland plains; they cause great destruction to structures, and they often delay or prevent the use of large areas of agricultural land. Because areas subject to inundation are desirable in some other respects, people tend to encroach on them, and disaster often results at great social cost. It has been estimated that some 12 percent of the population of the United States lives in such areas. Considerable research and investigation of the possible adjustments to floods are necessary to lessen the misery and cost caused by these recurring natural phenomena.

Regimes of runoff. As everyone knows, creeks and rivers fill up after a heavy rain. There is, however, a lag between the time of rainfall and the rise of stream levels. Not only does it take time for the surface flow of water to reach the streams, but a share of the rain water filters downward through the soil and then moves laterally to seep out again where runoff channels have cut below the temporarily water-filled upper soil layers. This water moves more slowly because of friction.

One might expect that the annual runoff regime would reflect seasonal variations in precipitation amounts. In large areas, however, the annual variation in runoff is more closely regulated by the release of storage water, and peak runoff generally is associated with the period of peak storage. In the tropics the peak runoff comes after high sun, but for a large part of the middle- and higher-latitude areas in the Northern Hemisphere it occurs after the spring equinox (Fig. 8.7).

Figure 8.8 is a composite graph illustrating the average regime of runoff for two areas in Ohio. As winter wanes and spring advances, temperatures (and consequently evaporation) are still relatively low, and the top layer of soil is likely to be frozen. Rainfall and storage water from melting snow and ice contribute considerable direct surface runoff. As temperatures rise farther and plants begin to grow, an increasing proportion of the precipitation and storage

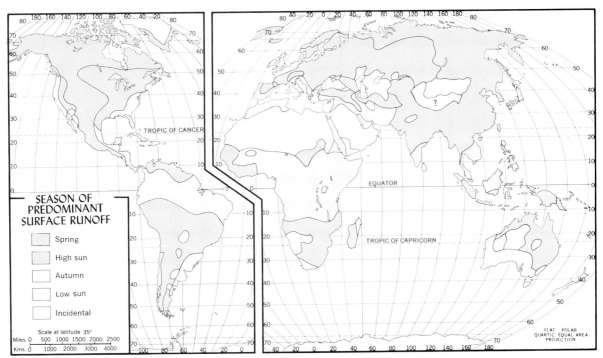

Figure 8.7 Generalized map of the season of predominant surface runoff. *(After L'vovich and others.)*

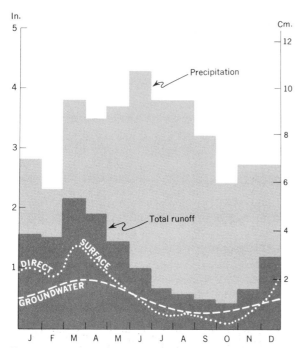

Figure 8.8 Twenty-five-year combined averages of precipitation and total runoff as recorded at the Hocking and Mad Rivers, near Athens and Springfield, Ohio. The dotted and dashed white lines show the proportions of the total runoff supplied from direct surface runoff and from groundwater. *(From U.S. Geological Survey.)*

water is subtracted through evapotranspiration. Thus, even though the precipitation reaches a maximum in the summer, surface runoff decreases, and groundwater, an equalizing influence, provides an increasing proportion of runoff water. In the autumn the decreases in both plant growth and air temperatures allow an increase in direct surface runoff as well as a steady replenishment of the groundwater reservoir.

The concentration of surface runoff in the early part of the warm season tends to increase poleward. Soggy ground and flooding are common springtime phenomena in areas with humid climates in the middle and higher latitudes.

World map of annual runoff. The world map of average annual runoff (Fig. 8.9) suggests some general correlations with world climate and precipitation patterns. For example, the areas of copious precipita-

tion generally have the greatest runoff. There are two such major areas: the regions of abundant tropical rainfall, where runoff is high despite the extremely high evapotranspiration; and the areas with oceanic climates, where relatively large amounts of precipitation are combined with cool temperatures and consequent low evaporation rates. But Figure 8.9 also shows that low-runoff zones can extend into humid climatic areas well beyond the dry-land boundaries, for in many of these humid regions a great part of the precipitation comes in the high-sun season and is quickly lost to evapotranspiration.

The distribution of surface runoff illustrated in Figure 8.9 is a result of many variables. By far the most important are the climatic factors, which tend to operate over extensive areas, in contrast to the more local effect of factors associated with the land surface.

Climatic factors. As already observed, runoff tends to vary directly with precipitation; but differences in the nature of the precipitation are also important. Where heavy or very frequent showers occur, a greater proportion of the fall will immediately become runoff because other factors come into play. For example, the rate of ground infiltration will decrease as a consequence of saturation or compaction of the soil.

Figure 8.10 shows that actual runoff is heavy in the tropics in spite of the high evapotranspiration there, because rainfall is proportionately even heavier.[2] The subtropical areas, owing to their generally high temperatures and low precipitation, are the zones of lowest annual runoff. The middle and higher latitudes, where evaporation rates are relatively low, have the highest ratios of annual runoff to annual precipitation.

Land-surface factors. Primarily as a result of variations in permeability, the land surface adds complexity to the general distribution of annual runoff that is basically determined by the climatic pattern. Large areas are covered with surface materials that permit rainfall to percolate quickly to consider-

[2]Water held in storage near the surface, as well as that which percolates down to the groundwater reservoir, is merely delayed, not lost, as a potential source of runoff. On the other hand, any water that is evaporated is lost. Consequently, the total runoff is the amount of precipitation minus the loss due to evapotranspiration.

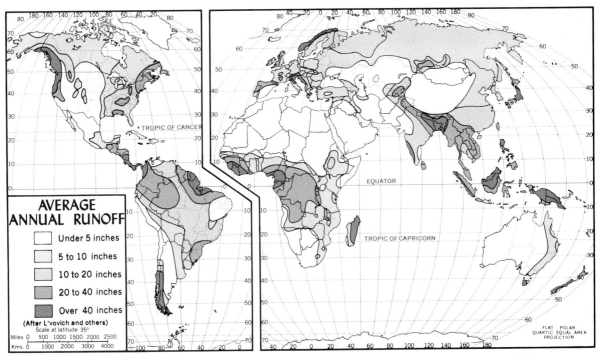

Figure 8.9   Highly generalized world map of average annual runoff. For some large areas few data are available.

able depths, where the water is beyond the reach of plant roots and the evaporation process. Thus surfaces underlain by pervious lavas and limestones are capable of absorbing vast quantities of water rapidly. Commonly these areas are notoriously low in direct surface runoff amounts. Also, sandy and gravelly areas are likely to have permeable surface materials and thus low direct runoff. Such areas, both small and large, fringe many mountainous regions, particularly in dry-climate lands. On the other hand, in areas with very low permeability in marginal sections of dry climates, rainfall collects in surface depressions, so that a large proportion of it evaporates. In general, there is likely to be more variability in annual runoff from place to place in the dry areas of the earth than elsewhere.

Lakes

Surface runoff sometimes accumulates in lakes or ponds. If a water area is shallow enough to allow vegetation to grow through the thin covering of water, it is called a *swamp, marsh, muskeg,* or *bogland.* By definition, all such bodies of water, as distinguished from streams, must lie in basinlike depressions of the land surface.

The existence of basins in a surface runoff system markedly affects the character of both the water and the runoff process. Water leaving a lake tends to be clear and to have a relatively uniform temperature, and it has been considerably modified by the biological processes at work in the lake. Another significant effect of a lake on the runoff process is its regulation of the rate of flow.

A lake acts as a reservoir, detaining water during times of heavy surface runoff and releasing it later at a more uniform rate. This has great utility to humanity in at least two ways: It reduces both the incidence and severity of downstream flooding; and at the time of minimum flow, it raises the volume of the stream above what it would otherwise be. The maintenance of a higher minimum volume is advantageous in many ways. For example, two non-withdrawal uses, navigation and the production of

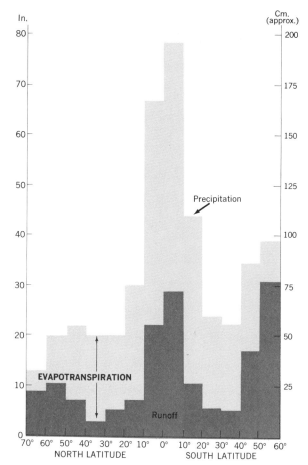

Figure 8.10 Comparison of the average annual total runoff with average annual total precipitation on the land per unit area according to latitude. The vertical difference between the two colored areas represents the loss through evapotranspiration. *(From L'vovich and Drozdov.)*

hydroelectric power, are generally limited by the minimum flow—the former by its depth, the latter by its volume.

The occurrence of lakes. Basins containing lakes, swamps, or marshes occur for many reasons. In some parts of northern North America and Europe, there are literally tens of thousands of major and minor basins resulting from glaciation. Lakes and swampy areas are also common on the flat lowlands adjacent to many stream channels and near their mouths, as

well as on coastal areas of unusually gentle pitch. In all these types of areas, the drainage of the land is poor; that is to say, the rate of precipitation is high enough and the rates of runoff and evaporation are low enough so that the balance among them results in "standing" water. Great structural deformations of the earth's crust have created numerous lake basins, including some of the world's most outstanding lakes. Lakes Tanganyika and Nyasa in Africa, as well as the Dead Sea, are examples of lakes that have developed in huge down-dropped trenches.

A surprising amount of fresh water is contained in the lakes of the earth. The total has been estimated at 125,000 cu km, and 80 percent of that is thought to be in the 40 largest.[3] Lake Baikal in central Asia has the largest volume, nearly equal to the combined total of the Great Lakes in North America. The lakes of Asia, North America, and Africa contain nearly three-quarters of the fresh water on the land.

In dry regions, most basins are not filled to overflowing by the meager surface runoff; hence they are not quickly integrated into stream drainage. These basins of interior drainage may contain temporary lakes, most of which have saline rather than fresh water. This is because the surface streams feeding into them are charged with minerals in solution, which gradually become concentrated by evaporation.

Where natural lake basins are absent, humans may make artificial basins (Fig. 8.11). More and more of these reservoirs are being constructed in areas where the regime of surface runoff has a large range between maximum and minimum flow. Man-made lake basins are subject to the same forces as natural basins. Thus, although people can easily prevent the outlets from eroding deeper and draining the reservoir, they find it very difficult to control the silt content of the inflow in order to keep the basin from filling with sediment. This requires careful planning and regulation of the land use in an entire drainage basin, and such a long-range program is not easy to carry out because many competing interests are involved.

[3]R. L. Nace. "World Water Inventory and Control," chap. 2 in *Water, Earth, and Man,* edited by Richard J. Chorley. Methuen & Co., Ltd., London, 1969.

Figure 8.11   The Hiwassee Dam of the TVA impounds a lake 22 mi long with a shoreline of 180 mi. Note the contour that extends up the "drowned" tributary valleys. *(Tennessee Valley Authority.)*

Lakes as ecosystems. All freshwater lakes form a complex ecosystem diagramed in Figure 8.12. Through photosynthesis, using solar energy, carbon dioxide, and water, plants (algae) produce glucose and give off oxygen. The glucose is combined with other nutrient material in the water, and the plants serve as food for the herbivores, which use the oxygen for respiration and in turn give off carbon dioxide. The food chain extends through carnivores and, of course, ultimately to the decomposers, consisting of bacteria and fungi, which break down the dead organic material to nutrients which again enter the chain. A lake is said to be *eutrophic* when richly supplied with nutrients.

Although the ecosystem of a lake tends toward a balance, a lake cannot remain unchanged forever. Lakes age by such processes as filling with sediment from the watershed, filling up with accumulations of organic matter, and lowering of the outlet. For most "permanent" lakes, such changes are rela-

tively slow, but in many areas people have hastened the processes. One way has been by increasing the rate of erosion in the watershed. More serious in many places is the excessive eutrophication of lakes (and streams) caused by (*a*) nitrogen-rich runoff waters from fertilized soils, (*b*) discharge of organic wastes, and (*c*) discharge of the nitrate- and phosphate-rich products of sewage treatment plants. These all stimulate the rapid growth of the algae, the decomposition of which places an excessive demand on the oxygen. Thus, eutrophication causes additional death of the life in a lake.

Withdrawal Surface Water as a Resource

Withdrawal surface water has several important characteristics as a resource. Because surface waters are partly derived from the immediate runoff of rain water, they usually range considerably in temperature, are colored and turbid, and are classed as *soft* (less mineralized than the ground waters of the same region). Surface waters generally contain significant quantities of sediment and organic matter, including bacteria. Consequently, users of withdrawal surface water must as a rule treat it in several ways: (1) for the destruction of bacteria—by chlorination or other means of disinfection, (2) for the coagulation of very fine sediment and colloidal matter, and (3) for the removal of sediment—by filtration. Water used for irrigation must not have too high a mineral content, and water for many industrial uses, ranging from boilers to canning, must have various mineral specifications.

The large industrial and municipal withdrawal uses of water also commonly are associated with serious problems of pollution when the effluent (the used water) is returned to surface drainage.

In many areas of the world, cities have grown up without an adequate, easily obtainable supply of surface (or ground) water, and water must be transported great distances by aqueduct. For example, Los Angeles brings water from the Owens River–Mono County area on the eastern side of the Sierra Nevada, nearly 300 miles away, and from the Colorado River on the California-Arizona border. Denver and Colorado Springs now bring water, by way of tunnels, from the western slope of the Rocky Mountains as far as 100 miles away.

The provision of water for the rapidly increasing urban areas in industrial societies is an exceedingly difficult problem. As the cost of providing fresh water steadily increases, man is turning to the great sources of saline water, primarily the oceans. The basic problem is simply the monetary and energy cost of converting saline to fresh water. However, with the price of fresh water rising and the cost of converting saline water decreasing as a result of power and engineering economies and developments, within a generation the two may be equal for significant areas of the earth. A second significant problem will be that of disposing of the removed salt.

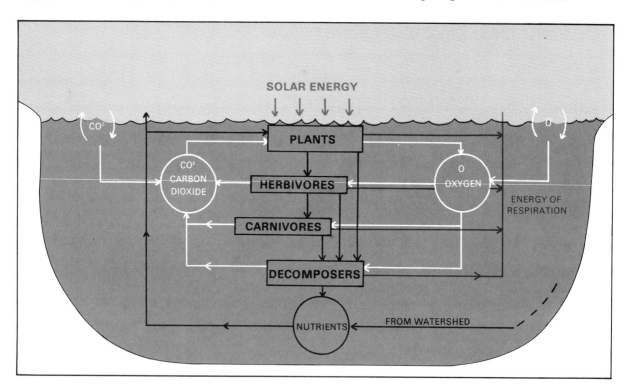

Figure 8.12   A diagram of the ecosystem of a lake.

GROUNDWATER

A proportion of the precipitation that falls on the land sinks into the porous soil and on down into the more consolidated bedrock beneath. Some is held only temporarily in the soil and is lost through evapotranspiration; some may soon emerge to join the surface water; and some percolates slowly downward to join the vast reservoir of fresh water which saturates all the continental areas of the earth at greater or lesser depth. Although the small proportion that at any time is held in the upper part of the land surface is in a kind of transition state between surface water, atmospheric water, and groundwater, it is generally classed as part of the groundwater.

Groundwater Zones

Basically, liquid water responds to two great forces: that of gravity and that of molecular attraction. The force of gravity pulls water directly downward. On the other hand, molecular attraction, through surface tension and capillarity, tends to cause water to adhere to surfaces in a thin film or to creep into crevices and tiny channels and to remain suspended there in spite of gravity. As water moves downward from the surface of the ground, a portion is left behind as a consequence of molecular attraction. The upper portion of the ground is therefore commonly damp, although by no means saturated.

Several zones or layers of groundwater are recognized (Fig. 8.13). Water derived from immediate precipitation, from melting snow, or from the surface runoff of some other area first passes into the *zone of soil water*. This upper section of the soil, usually consisting of fine materials with a large admixture of organic substances, can absorb and retain a considerable quantity of water until some of it passes into another stage of the hydrologic cycle by evapotranspiration, leaving the soil either by direct evaporation or through the roots and transpiring surfaces of plants.

Some of the water that enters the zone of soil water will be quickly lost through evapotranspiration. The remainder will gravitate into an *intermediate zone* below the reach of most plant roots. There it will adhere to the surfaces of rock particles, the sides of cracks, and other openings. Although these voids may be temporarily filled during a time of copious

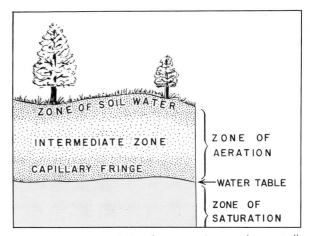

Figure 8.13 Zones of subsurface water. In many places not all the zones occur.

groundwater, usually they are not. Air also circulates among these spaces.

The intermediate zone and the zone of soil water above it are collectively called the *zone of aeration*. The amount of water in this zone fluctuates as a consequence of losses from evapotranspiration.

The downward-moving water that does not pause in the zone of aeration ultimately enters the *zone of saturation*, where all the pore spaces, cracks, and other openings among the earth particles and the bedrock itself are filled with water.

Immediately above the zone of saturation, and thus at the bottom of the zone of aeration, is a region called the *capillary fringe*. Here surface tension holds the water which is above the saturated zone in interconnected voids or "tubes" so small that water cannot drain out of them. These extend some distance into the zone of aeration. Water may creep upward a short way from the saturated zone into the capillary fringe, but the fringe is primarily supplied from above. The thickness of the capillary fringe depends upon the sizes of the voids; the smaller they are, the thicker it will be. Thus in sandy areas, the thickness may be 30 cm (1 ft) or less, while in clay areas, where the soil particles are much smaller, it may be 1 m or more. The capillary fringe is important because in areas where the availability of groundwater is critical to plant growth, the capillary fringe may provide a source of water for deep-growing plant roots.

The water table. The top of the saturated zone, or the contact surface (interface) between the zones of aeration and saturation, is called the *water table*. By definition it is a continuous surface, and it has much the same sort of configuration that the land surface does, except that its undulations are somewhat more subdued. The water table intersects the land surface in low places in the valleys of flowing streams and in lake basins; and although it rises beneath hills, it is proportionately farther below the land surface at their summits.

The basic law of groundwater movement, which accounts for much of the configuration of the water table, is known as *Darcy's law.* This law states that, other things being equal, flow through a permeable medium is proportional to the flow potential or difference in head between points. In uncomplicated situations the head or hydraulic gradient is the ratio of the difference in elevation between the intake and discharge points to the horizontal distance between them (Fig. 8.14). Therefore, if one postulates a constant rate of flow, the greater the distance between the place where the water enters the saturated zone and where it discharges, the higher the head must be. Water in the saturated zone near a discharge point can escape with little head, while that farther away will pile up higher until the rate of addition to the saturated zone balances the rate of flow.

Since the additions to the saturated zone change from time to time, the elevation of the groundwater table will change, rising higher during

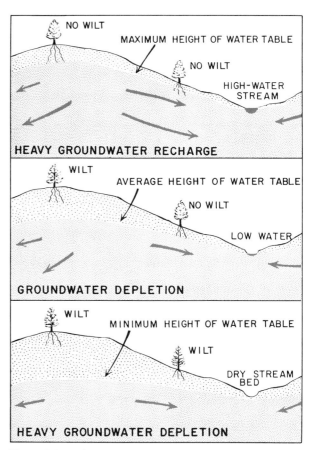

Figure 8.15 Fluctuations in the level of the groundwater table have important effects upon streams and vegetation.

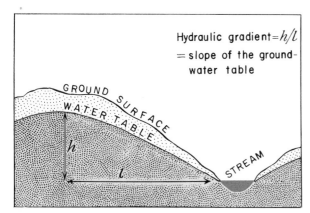

Figure 8.14 In a medium of uniform permeability, the slope of the water table will be proportional to the hydraulic gradient or head.

periods of net groundwater recharge and falling during periods of net discharge. This will have significant effects on vegetation and stream levels (Fig. 8.15). Similarly, the level of water in ordinary wells, being at the elevation of the water table, will tend to fluctuate with precipitation both seasonally and over the long term (Fig. 8.16).

Groundwater Discharge

Water added to the groundwater reservoir must ultimately leave it either by emergence into the surface water supply (outflow to streams) or by evapotranspiration. Streams may be classed as gaining or losing in their relationship to groundwater. Gaining

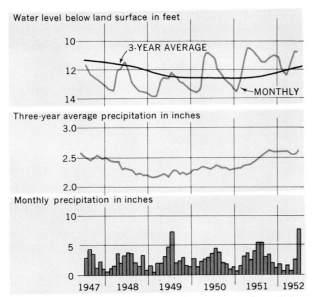

Water level below land surface in feet

Three-year average precipitation in inches

Monthly precipitation in inches

Figure 8.16 Monthly and 3-yr averages of the levels of the water in a well an Antigo, Wisconsin, in relation to monthly and 3-yr averages of precipitation for a period of 5 yr. A 3-yr average for any month is the average of it and the preceding 35 mo. *(After U.S. Geological Survey, Water Supply Paper 1234.)*

streams are those which are fed where the stream channel intersects the water table, so that water drains into the stream from the groundwater reservoir. Losing streams are those from which water feeds into the ground; here the water table lies beneath the bottom of the stream channel (Fig. 8.17).

The streams of humid climatic regions tend to be gaining streams, and because of the progressive addition of outflowing groundwater, they generally increase in volume downstream. On the other hand, dry-land streams tend to have the opposite characteristics, not infrequently "drying up" entirely in their lower courses.

Where groundwater discharges onto the land surface instead of into a flowing stream, a spring exists. Springs result from a variety of conditions involving the position of the water table, the configuration of the land surface, and the nature and arrangement of the bedrock and its covering. Figure 8.18*A* shows where springs would develop on the sides of a valley which has eroded below the usual level of the water table. Springs of this type are common; often they are the main water sources for small brooks at the headwaters of rivers. The spring site in

Figure 8.18*B*, on the other hand, would result from the movement of water downward through the porous formations (colored in the diagram) and then horizontally along the top of an impervious layer of shale. Such subsurface conditions tend to produce many such springs, so that water may issue at about the same elevation throughout a region.

Occurrence of Groundwater

The depths and thicknesses of the groundwater zones have great influence on the characteristics of other elements in physical geography, such as soils and vegetation. The number of variables involved is large, but the most important factors that affect the character of the groundwater reservoir in any place are, first, the precipitation and evaporation of the area and second, the porosity and permeability of the water-bearing materials.

Precipitation and evaporation. The greater the precipitation and the less the evaporation, the more water is available to percolate downward to the saturated zone, and consequently the higher the groundwater table is likely to be. In some areas the balance of these two factors maintains a level of the ground-

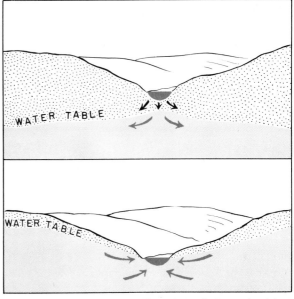

Figure 8.17 Cross sections illustrating a losing and gaining stream.

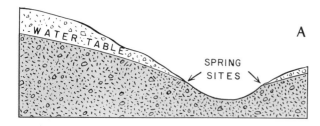

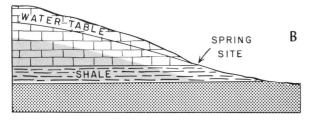

Figure 8.18 Two of the many possible conditions of surface, material, and structure that are related to the occurrence of springs.

water table that commonly intersects the undulations of the land surface, giving rise to numerous lakes, swamps, and streams. By contrast, in dry climates and in areas where meager precipitation occurs at the time of high temperatures, the water table is likely to be deeply buried everywhere except in the lowest valleys.

Porosity and permeability. *Porosity* is the ratio (percentage) of the volume of the interstices in a mass of material to the total volume. This ratio depends upon many factors, but primarily upon the shape, arrangement, and assortment of the particles in the material. Unconsolidated or loosely cemented sands and gravels, some kinds of rocks such as sandstone, and greatly fractured bedrock are porous because the sum of the spaces is large. The range can be very great: silts, glacial tills, sands, and gravels characteristically have a porosity of from 20 to 40 percent, while consolidated sedimentary rocks, such as sandstone, limestones, and shales, can range from less than 5 percent to 25 percent. Massive igneous rocks usually have very low porosities, but greatly weathered forms and some volcanic materials, such as basalt and tuff, can have porosities as great as 50 percent or more. Some structured clays—the fine particles which make up a large fraction of many soils—have porosities of 50 to 60 percent.

Permeability refers to the ease with which water can move within a porous material. Permeability—or, conversely, impermeability—depends primarily on molecular attraction, which tends to retard the movement of water.

The amount of surface area in a mass is inversely related to the average size of the particles. That is, the smaller the particles, the larger the total surface area. The larger the surface area, the greater the volume of water that can be retained by molecular attraction (surface tension). Hence fine-textured (finely divided) materials tend to be relatively impermeable.

The permeability of the soil is strongly affected by the amount of organic material it contains. In general, the more organic material there is, the more water the zone of soil water can absorb and transmit—i.e., the more permeable it is.

Infiltration. The movement of water into the soil is known as *infiltration*. The rate at which infiltration takes place varies with porosity and permeability, and with time as well. In general, assuming that the zone of soil water is only normally damp at the beginning of a rainfall, the rate of infiltration will be high. Thereafter it will rapidly decline in most kinds of soil, for the soil spaces become clogged because of the movement of soil particles and the swelling of the components from being moistened.

This general relationship is illustrated by the *shapes* of the idealized curves in Figure 8.19. The *positions* of the curves show that the more permeable and porous the soil is, the greater will be the ultimate infiltration capacity after the initial decline.

Aquifers. Beneath the ground surface, some rock formations and accumulations of certain materials hold large supplies of water and allow it to move easily. Called *aquifers*, these formations are relatively widespread, since they are normal products of the gradational processes. Sandstones and some limestones, as well as beds of gravel and sand, are well-known aquifers.

The pattern of aquifers in any place is likely to be very complex, for few areas are underlain by undisturbed materials. The general pattern in the United States is shown in Figure 8.20. National and state agencies are continuously making detailed studies of the occurrence of aquifers, since their depth,

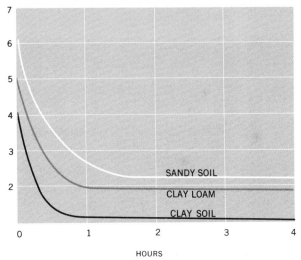

Figure 8.19 Diagrammatic curves showing the relative infiltration rates in soils of different textures.

their extent, and the quality of their waters are matters of great concern in most areas.

The Water Budget

The amount of moisture in the soil, the additions by precipitation, the downward losses by gravity, and the upward losses by evapotranspiration change in their relationship with one another from time to time and, of course, from place to place. The annual pattern of the changes at a place is known as the *water budget.* This functioning of the hydrologic cycle as it affects the variations in groundwater is an important topic in the study of physical geography. It involves the interaction of many variables, such as temperature, precipitation, and winds, as well as the pattern of vegetation growth, which is both a consequence and a contributing factor.

The manner in which water is made available to the soil and taken from the soil by plants during the course of a year can be represented graphically as in Figure 8.21.[4] This shows the water budget at

[4]The measurement of evapotranspiration is difficult, and so far it has been more practicable to compute a close estimate by means of a variety of empirical equations. Since there is no net loss of water in the hydrologic cycle, the sum of actual

Rockford, Illinois, a station representative of the middle western United States. During the winter months, there is a surplus of water as a consequence of low temperatures. In spring, as temperatures rise, plants begin to utilize the soil moisture. But even though the withdrawal by evapotranspiration now exceeds the amount added by precipitation, soil moisture is still available.

Early in summer, the combination of high evaporation and the great withdrawal because of the transpiration of rapidly growing plants depletes the soil moisture to the point where even the increased warm-season rainfall cannot maintain the supply. A period of water deficiency follows, lasting until September. As autumn progresses, plant requirements decrease rapidly, lower temperatures reduce evaporation rates, and precipitation is again available for the recharge of the soil. By midwinter the soil has been recharged, and the cycle begins to repeat itself.

Regional differences in the water budget. Other things being equal, potential evapotranspiration varies directly with temperature, and water deficit varies inversely with precipitation. Clearly, because the magnitudes and annual marches of temperature and precipitation differ from place to place, innumerable combinations of the elements of the water budget can occur. Micro differences will also result from variations in the character of the soil, its vegetative covering, and its management. Figure 8.22 gives the water budget of Berkeley, California, showing the large water deficit that results from the meager total precipitation and the high-sun minimum. Students can superimpose their own mental curves of potential evapotranspiration on the temperature and precipitation graphs included in Chapter 6.

Since precipitation is the ultimate supplier of soil water, it might be surmised that recharge of the soil would ordinarily occur at the time of maximum precipitation. The situation is more complicated than that, however. In those humid areas where the rainy season occurs during high sun, recharge usually produces a marked surplus in the early part of the rainy season. Subsequently, the increasing temperatures soon turn the tide in favor of losses by evap-

evapotranspiration and runoff must equal precipitation. But since neither evapotranspiration nor runoff is as simple to measure as precipitation, maps of these two factors are at present not nearly so reliable as maps of precipitation.

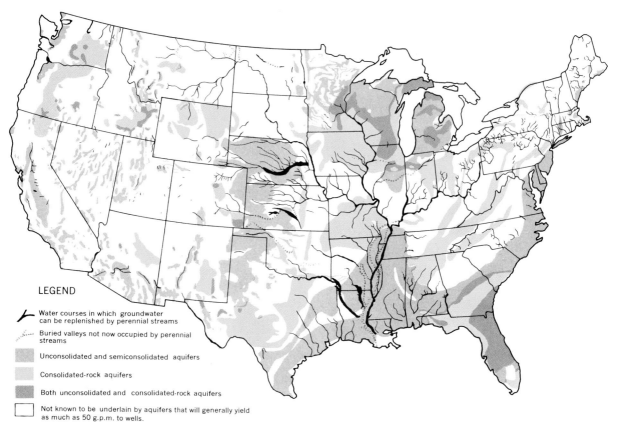

Figure 8.20 Major aquifers of the United States capable of yielding to individual wells 190 liters (50 gal) per min or more and containing not more than 2,000 parts per million of dissolved solids. *(Based upon a map by H. E. Thomas, U.S. Geological Survey.)*

otranspiration, so that even though amounts of rainfall continue to increase, the recharge of the groundwater tends to decrease (Fig. 8.21). Only in the humid tropics, where potential evapotranspiration rates are relatively constant, and in those subtropical areas having a maximum of precipitation during low sun, does maximum recharge ordinarily occur during the period of maximum precipitation (Fig. 8.22). The recharge of soil moisture in arid regions follows a similar regime, closely tied to the annual variations in precipitation amounts.

Groundwater as a Resource

Throughout the world, groundwaters are not as important a source of water supply as surface waters. Nevertheless, the groundwater reservoir is extensive-

ly utilized, especially in places where surface supplies are limited or have undesirable qualities and in smaller cities and villages, in suburban areas, and on farms.

Mineralization. Almost no water is free from dissolved or suspended material. Since groundwater ordinarily has been filtered through the earth, sometimes for many years, before it again comes or is brought to the surface, it is relatively free from suspended materials. On the other hand, it commonly contains dissolved minerals. Some of these, such as sulphur or iron, may give it a disagreeable taste or make it unfit for certain industrial processes; while some minerals may have tonic, laxative, or other medicinal qualities.

Among the most abundant of the dissolved

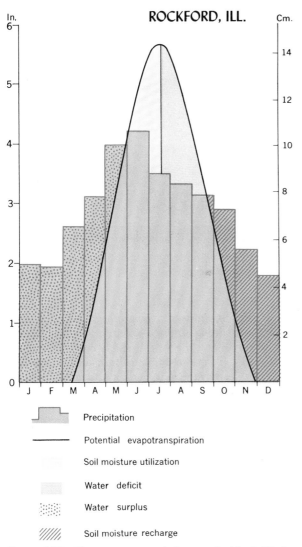

give it a quality called "hardness," which does have an influence on its domestic and industrial utility.

Hardness usually is stated as the number of parts of dissolved mineral (expressed as $CaCO_3$ equivalent) per million parts of water (ppm). Groundwater is usually harder than surface water (Fig. 8.23). Some very soft water may contain as little as 5 to 10 ppm, and water containing as much as 60 ppm still is

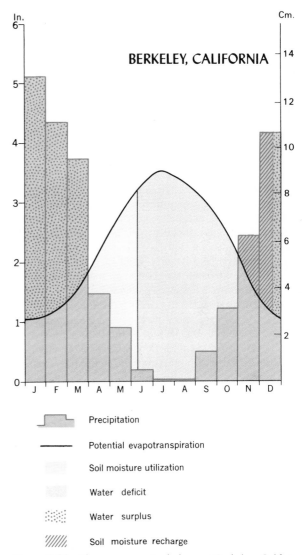

Figure 8.21 The average water balance at Rockford, Illinois, based on mean monthly values. *(Data from Thornthwaite, Mather, and Carter.)*

minerals or salts often found in groundwater are compounds of calcium, sodium, and magnesium. In humid regions, most of the readily soluble sodium compounds have long since been removed from the upper portion of the ground. However, limestones and other limey rocks furnish calcium and magnesium carbonates (CO_3) and bicarbonates (HCO_3) which, although they do not much affect the taste of water,

Figure 8.22 The average water balance at Berkeley, California, based on mean monthly values. *(Data from Thornwaite and Mather.)*

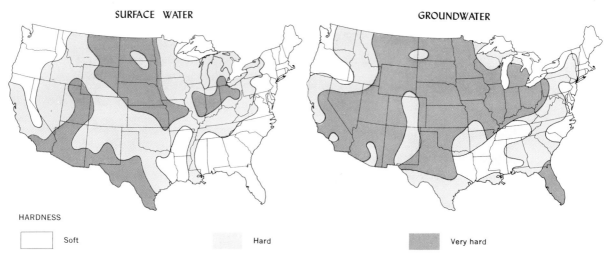

Figure 8.23 Approximate hardness of surface and groundwaters in the United States. Note that only limited sections of the northeast, northwest, and south central regions have both soft groundwater and soft surface water, and that hard groundwater occurs more widely than hard surface water. *(Generalized from various sources.)*

considered soft; but if it contains more than 120 to 180 ppm, it is considered hard water. In regions of lime-containing sedimentary rocks, well waters in common use contain 300 to 500 ppm and in a few places as much as 700 to 800 ppm. Generally, the groundwaters that supply some 10 percent of the urban population in the United States are twice as hard as the surface waters used for that purpose (160 ppm compared with 80 ppm, approximately). Hard waters, if not "softened" by chemical treatment, may cause serious problems in the home and in certain industrial processes. This is because of their chemical reactions, especially reactions which produce precipitates that coat utensils and tanks and reduce the effective diameters of pipes.

Springs and wells. Large numbers of springs, most of them on valley slopes, provide a water supply for rural families. More important, there are many springs that are noted for the purity or the medicinal quality of their waters, and in some localities the bottling and shipping of these waters is a considerable industry. Sometimes thermal and medicinal springs with special properties have served as reasons for population concentration: around them health and recreational resorts of considerable size have grown up.

Wells are simply holes that extend below the

water table so that groundwater may be brought to the surface through them. Formerly, many wells were dug by hand, and they were seldom deep. Millions of such wells still are in daily use in nearly all parts of the world, although their shallow and open construction makes them particularly subject to surface pollution.

Most wells today are either driven or drilled. In unconsolidated materials a point (a pointed length of pipe with screened holes in it) can be forced into the ground and into an aquifer. As the point goes down, successive sections of pipe are added, and this forms a casing, lessening the likelihood of pollution from surface waters. A drilled well results from boring a hole into the solid bedrock until a rock aquifer is pierced. The hole is then cased (lined with metal), at least in its upper portion. Of all wells, ordinarily only drilled ones extend very far beneath the surface, tap large supplies of water, and merit the term *deep wells*.

Artesian wells. Any well in which water rises of its own accord above the level of the tapped aquifer is an *artesian well*. Artesian wells are possible with several types of underground structure, two of which are illustrated in Figure 8.24. The favorable situation must include the following conditions: The aquifer must be exposed in a region of sufficient precipitation to fill it with water; it must dip beneath a capping

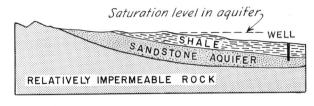

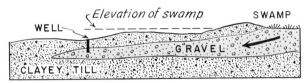

Figure 8.24 *Above:* A structural artesian condition like that which occurs in the northern Great Plains of the United States. The shale forms an impervious cap to the aquifer. *Below:* A local artesian condition that might be found in an area of glacial deposition. In this case the impervious material is finely divided glacial material (clayey till).

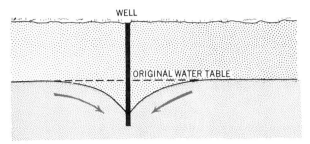

Figure 8.25 The development of a cone of depression around a well. If withdrawal continues to exceed the rate of lateral movement, the cone will ultimately reach the bottom of the well.

layer of some impermeable material; it must extend into a region where the land surface is lower than it is at the exposed end; and there must be enough partial constriction (or total blockage) of the aquifer so that the water which collects in its lower portion comes under pressure. Groundwater will then rise in a well, or even flow from the opening, as long as the rate of recharge exceeds the rate of loss through natural seepage and through withdrawal from the well.

Notable artesian structures underlie some truly large areas—for example, the northern Great Plains region of the United States. Likewise, parts of the east central dry lands of interior Australia are blessed with artesian structures which supply water for farming and sheep raising. Artesian structures also occur over large areas in northern Africa and central Argentina.

Effects of withdrawal on the groundwater reservoir. The total volume of water in the hydrologic cycle does not appreciably change, and the groundwater reservoir at any place is in cyclic equilibrium with respect to its discharge and recharge. The reservoir rises and falls in response to the fluctuations (short-term and long-term) of the climatic components of the cycle, but nevertheless it is in overall balance between inflow and outflow. This can be termed the *hydrologic equation.* It follows that any tapping of the groundwater reservoir by wells must result in a lessening of the available water in the

reservoir, simply because this tapping causes an increase in outflow. Groundwater, then, is not renewable in the same sense that surface water is; serious problems of depletion have already occurred in many areas because of "overuse."

When water is withdrawn from a well at a rate greater than lateral movement of groundwater can supply it, a cone of depression forms around the well. As long as the withdrawal exceeds the rate that water can be supplied, the cone steadily deepens and widens (Fig. 8.25). Obviously, if withdrawal continues to exceed the water's rate of lateral movement, the cone will continue to deepen until it reaches the bottom of the well.

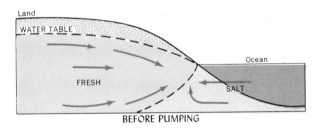

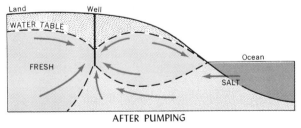

Figure 8.26 Pumping from the groundwater reservoir near the ocean may result in salt water mixing with the fresh water in the well.

In numerous places where wells are located near the sea, the depletion of the fresh groundwater supply has caused salt water to move toward the well (Fig. 8.26). This is, of course, a form of contamination, and the remedies are expensive. One method is to force fresh water into the aquifer at strategic places, both in order to "hold back" the salt water mechanically and in order to reduce the net outflow from the reservoir by recharge.

REVIEW QUESTIONS

1. Follow a drop of water as it might move in the hydrologic cycle from the ocean to a particular part of the land and back to the ocean.
2. Compare and account for the relative amount of activity in the functioning of the hydrologic cycle in (a) the equatorial areas and (b) the higher latitudes.
3. What part of the oceans supplies the largest proportion of water to the atmosphere in the functioning of the hydrologic cycle? Why?
4. Suggest reasons why the withdrawal use of water in the United States has increased more rapidly than has its population.
5. In what ways can water be held in storage?
6. In many areas of the middle latitudes the period of peak precipitation is not the period of maximum runoff. Why?
7. Describe notable sources of pollution for the surface water in streams and lakes from (a) natural and (b) human-caused or enhanced causes.
8. Why does the addition of nutrients "overload" a lake?
9. What are the consequences of withdrawing water from the groundwater reservoir by means of deep wells?
10. Compare the likely chemical characteristics of groundwater and surface water.
11. Develop the probable water budget for any place.

SELECTED REFERENCES

Carter, Douglas B., T. H. Schmudde, and D. M. Sharpe, *The Interface as a Working Environment: A Purpose for Physical Geography*, Tech. Paper No. 7, Commission on College Geography, Association of American Geographers, Washington D. C., 1972. An approach to environmental dynamics with an emphasis on the role of water.

Chorley, Richard J. (ed.). *Water, Earth and Man.* Methuen & Co., Ltd., London, 1969. A basic book for study and reference with chapters by experts. Selections from the larger book are incorporated in *Introduction to Geographical Hydrology*, a University Paperback, Methuen & Co., Ltd., 1971.

Hubschman, Jerry H. "Lake Erie: Pollution Abatement, Then What?" *Science*, Vol. 171 (Feb. 12, 1971), pp. 536–540. A detailed consideration of the problems associated with the most polluted of the Great Lakes.

Leopold, Luna B. *Water: A Primer.* W. H. Freeman and Company, San Francisco, Calif., 1971. A first-rate introduction to basic aspects of hydrology, water supply, and water use. Written in nontechnical language.

Murray, C. Richard, and E. Bodette Reeves. *Estimated Water Use in the United States in 1970.* U. S. Geological Survey Circular 676, Washington, D. C., 1972. A thorough compilation by regions as well as in total. Free on application to the Geological Survey.

Olson, Ralph E. *A Geography of Water.* Wm. C. Brown Company, Dubuque, Iowa, 1970. A brief treatment with emphasis upon the waters of the land.

Todd, David Keith (ed.). *The Water Encyclopedia* Water Information Center, Port Washington, N. Y., 1970. A compendium of an amazing amount of information on all aspects of water.

Van Hylckama, T. E. A. "The Water Balance of the Earth," *Publications in Climatology*, No. 9. Drexel Institute of Technology, Laboratory of Climatology, 1956. Pp. 58–117. A basic study.

Water. Yearbook of Agriculture, 1955. U. S. Government Printing Office, Washington, D. C. Still a good basic source.

Wolman, M. Gordon. "The Nation's Rivers," *Science*, Vol. 174 (Nov. 26, 1971), pp. 905–918. A careful consideration of trends and magnitudes of changes in water and river quality.

Land-Surface Form

Introduction: The Surface Form of the Land

Although human beings may be said to live "in" the atmosphere, and although the planet which they inhabit is clad largely in water, their true home is the surface of the land. Only there can they move about freely without artificial aid, found their dwellings and workshops, and grow the plants that are the basis of their food system. This land surface that is our home is extremely complex. It is distributed in oddly shaped masses of all sizes, placed relative to one another with little apparent system. Its surface form varies from nearly flat to indescribably rugged, the pattern of variation being irregular and intricate and the transitions often abrupt. The material exposed to view is most commonly rather fine-particled soil, but in places it is sand, boulders, saturated mud, any of dozens of kinds of naked bedrock, or even ice.

Not only is the land surface complex; it is also dynamic. Over the long span of geologic time, whole mountain systems have been raised up and worn away, icecaps of subcontinental size have formed and disappeared, and islands have been thrust up from the sea and submerged again. Even the continents themselves have changed in size and shape and, most surprisingly, have apparently moved long distances relative to each other and to the poles. Even

in the far shorter span of recorded human history, coastlines have changed, sand dunes have shifted, mountainsides have been stripped of their soil, networks of deep gullies and ravines have been cut, and imposing volcanic cones have been built up or blasted away. In some of these changes human beings themselves have played a significant although often unintentional role. For others they have been only spectators.

Striking and fascinating as these changes may be, they are probably less important to our everyday lives than some other processes that are more commonplace. It is largely through these slow, unobtrusive processes that the land surface functions as part of an immense mechanism for short-term movements and transformations of energy and matter. In that mechanical system, water moving across the surface or down through the soil and weathered rock is the principal dynamic agent, while gravity provides much of the motive power. Among the functions of the system are the surface and near-surface operations of the hydrologic cycle, much of the slow modification of the surface form, the development and alteration of the soil, the growth of plants, and the nourishment and many of the activities of all forms of animal life. Some aspects of this land-surface system have already been treated in the chapters on water;

others will be discussed in this and succeeding chapters on land-surface form; still others will be emphasized in the chapters dealing with vegetation and soils.

How the land surface may be studied.   Because the land surface is so varied in form, has had so long and complex a history of development, and is functionally connected to so many other phenomena, it can be studied from many points of view. Some studies, for example, focus upon the physical processes that shape the forms of the land; others consider the forms and materials of the surface largely as clues to the unraveling of earth history. This book will emphasize the existing land surface: the nature and pattern of its variation, the processes that have produced that specific character and pattern, and the ways in which it currently functions as part of the environmental system in different regions. Unavoidably these chapters will introduce considerable material from the systematic earth sciences in order that the origin and dynamics of the existing surface may be understood as well as described. Throughout, however, the goal is geographical—an improved understanding of how and why the various sections of the land surface differ in form and function, and how these differences relate to the pattern of other phenomena, including the activities of human beings.

The diversity of surface forms is so great and their pattern so complex that the task of assembling a coherent description of the continental surfaces has proved to be slow and difficult. Large areas of the earth are still poorly mapped, and few sections have been systematically and analytically described. Knowledge of the origin of the varied landscapes is even less advanced, and investigation of how the solid land surface functions as part of an environmental system is still in its infancy. Most present surface features were formed by events that happened long before the period of recorded human history. The nature and sequence of these events can only be inferred from the study of features and processes that exist and occur now. The processes that shape the surface or carry on its environmental functions are difficult to observe and, as a rule, work so slowly that their cumulative effects are hard to evaluate.

Although the study of land-surface form is moving ahead faster than ever before as masses of new data are brought to bear, the gaps in observational data, the incomplete understanding of processes, and the conflicts in interpretation of evidence are still so striking that they cannot help but appear even in an introductory treatment such as this one.

Time and process in surface-form development. The shortness of the human life span led ancient people to develop a false idea of the permanence of the natural features of the earth's surface. Since they could see little change in surface forms, even over several generations, it was natural for them to think of the landscape as essentially unchanging. Only along certain rivers and seacoasts and near unusually active volcanoes could significant changes be noticed, and these could be regarded as exceptions—perhaps as willful acts of the gods.

Now that something is known of both the vast reaches of geologic time and the extreme changeability of land surfaces, we realize that a human being's short life is a poor yardstick with which to measure the rates of earth-shaping events and not the best point of view from which to try to understand them. It is like trying to conceive the distance from the earth to the moon in inches. It is difficult to realize how much can be accomplished over millions of years by the almost imperceptibly slow processes that can be seen at work today. A stream that is eroding its bed at the modest rate of 3 cm (1.2 in.) per century can cut a canyon 300 m (1,000 ft) deep in a million years, which is not a long period of geologic time. In the history of the earth's surface development, there has been ample time for slow processes to change the surface drastically and repeatedly. The lands in their present form are in no way permanent but represent only a momentary stage in a long and complex history of change.

The natural processes responsible for these changes may conveniently be grouped into two major sets: (1) those that deform the rocky crust of the earth or locally alter its composition (*tectonic processes*), and (2) those that move earth materials about from place to place over the surface, picking up here and depositing there (*gradational processes*). These two sets of processes are active at the same time, and, as will be seen, they commonly work in opposition to each other. At any moment in earth history the land surface reflects the existing state in the never-ending war between tectonics and gradation.

The Land Surface as a Functioning System

It has been suggested that the land surfaces and the processes at work upon them or immediately beneath them can usefully be considered as a major segment of the immense interconnected mechanism that is the earth's environmental system. Individual aspects of the land-surface system are treated in greater detail elsewhere, but a general overview will be valuable at this point.

The operations of the land-surface system, like those of all other parts of the total earth system, involve movements and transformations of mass and energy. Mass, in the land-surface system, consists of liquid or frozen water, the mineral matter of rock and soil, and organic matter, living or in various stages of decomposition. Most water enters the land-surface zone as precipitation, having been derived chiefly from the sea by evaporation. The mineral matter of the continental crust appears to have come originally from the earth's interior, with considerable change occurring during and after its emergence. All organic matter is derived ultimately from the basic process of photosynthesis, whereby carbohydrates are synthesized from water and carbon dioxide in green plants by the application of energy in the form of sunlight. Other substances, such as nitrogen, calcium, and iron, are taken into the plants by the uptake of soil water carrying them in solution and are incorporated into the plant structures. In the operations of the surface system, these various elements of mass are transported broadly about over the surface, up or down through the soil or rocks, and may in part be swept laterally off the continents into the sea or upward into the atmosphere. All such transfers require energy.

Energy enters the land-surface system (1) as radiant energy or sensible heat transferred from the sun or the atmosphere, (2) as heat conducted upward from the earth's interior, (3) as energy of motion transferred to surface particles by the frictional drag of moving air, (4) as potential energy imparted to masses of earth material upraised by tectonic activity, or (5) as potential energy imparted to water by evaporation, upward diffusion in the atmosphere, and precipitation on the uneven surface of the land. Of these sources of energy, the second is probably the least important. Energy absorbed at the surface raises the temperature of exposed materials, evaporates quantities of water from the soil and from plants,

and, in relatively small amounts, accomplishes photosynthesis, hence indirectly accounting for all energy expended in animal activity. The potential energy possessed by precipitation water is converted, under the urging of gravity, into energy of flow, either downslope across the surface or downward through the pores of the soil or rock materials. Potential energy of high-standing earth may be similarly converted into energy of motion if particles or masses break loose under the urging of gravity and roll or slide downhill. Commonly, however, movement of solid matter is initiated or aided by the flow of water or sometimes by the frictional drag of the wind. The energy of movement of water or earth is eventually dissipated as heat through friction.

It is these continual movements of energy and matter that make the earth's surface shell a dynamic rather than an inert realm. Even over the shortest periods of time the land surfaces are active with ongoing processes, and our lives are intimately involved with those processes: the flow of streams, the percolation of water through the soil, the take-up and evaporation of water and the associated intake of nutrients by growing plants, and the washing, blowing, or sliding of earth down slopes. Without these processes, and especially without those involving water, the face of the earth would be as lifeless and, were it not for more active tectonics, as unchanging as that of the moon. For it is these same processes that have, over long periods of time, caused profound changes in the forms, materials, and organisms on the continental surfaces and produced the complex mosaic of distinctive natural environments that we know.

It cannot be overemphasized that all of the processes and all of the areas of the land-surface system are interlinked and interdependent. A major change in one may well produce changes in all the rest. Precipitation and runoff help to shape the land form, but it has already been noted that land form affects precipitation and runoff. Gradual destruction of a great mountain system by erosion may alter the climatic pattern of a whole continent or even a hemisphere. Erosion affects the character of the soil and hence the vegetation growth, but soil and vegetation cover also affect erosion, not to mention runoff and evapotranspiration. Rapid clearing of the forest from a broad area will certainly change the runoff regime, erosion rate, and ecological balance of that area, and it would be surprising if it did not induce reciprocal changes in the ecology, stream regimen, and sedimentation rates in the regions adjacent.

Characteristics and Classes of Land-Surface Form

Characteristics of Land Surfaces

Because there are so many types of land surfaces distributed over the earth without apparent order, it is by no means easy to understand their nature and arrangement or even to describe them systematically. Nevertheless, even a complex land surface can be characterized usefully if one considers it in terms of specific properties rather than as a complicated whole. Certain characteristics can be described quantitatively; others are difficult to quantify but can be characterized by words or diagrams. A complete and systematic description of a given land surface will employ all available techniques—verbal, numerical, and graphic—in order to be as objective, precise, and clear as possible. Only with such specific and systematic information can one compare, characteristic by characteristic, any particular part of the surface with any other part in the same manner that we habitually use in comparing climates.

If one does carefully compare many small areas in order to determine precisely how each differs from the others in land-surface form, one soon accumulates a long list of specific characteristics. If one then analyzes this list, one finds that it is possible to group the many characteristics under four headings: (1) slope (or inclination), (2) surface material, (3) arrangements, and (4) dimensions. In other words, the difference between any two sections of the land surface can be expressed in terms of these four major sets of properties.

Slope. *Slope* refers simply to the inclination of the land surface at a particular spot. Normally any section of the surface measuring a few kilometers across is made up of many small bits of sloping land, each one differing from its neighbors in steepness. Steep slopes, gentle slopes, and slopes of intermediate steepness may all be present in a single area. One area may differ greatly from another, however, in the predominance of each of these major slope classes. For example, a section of the Texas coastal plain near Corpus Christi is 95 percent occupied by very gentle slopes (Fig. 9.1*A*), while in a section of hilly southwestern Wisconsin only 30 percent of the area is gently sloping, with intermediate and steep slopes occupying the greater part of the area (Fig. 9.1*B*). It is doubtful that any other single bit of information could tell as much about the fundamental contrast between these two regions. The figures not only suggest the contrasting appearance of the areas, but also hint at important differences in the usefulness of the land.

Surface material. Most of the earth's land surface is covered with relatively fine-particled mineral matter with some partially decomposed organic debris mixed in (Fig. 9.2*A*). Wherever such soil (using the term in a very broad sense) does not make up the surface layer, that fact is worth knowing. Surfaces of bare bedrock, loose sand, cobbles and boulders, permanent ice, and standing water are fundamentally different from soil surfaces in appearance and feel as well as in origin and function (Fig. 9.2*B* and *C*).

The character of the bedrock many feet below the surface and the chemical and detailed physical properties of even the surface layers do not as a rule belong in a list of terrain elements. But the gross physical nature of the surficial materials cannot be omitted from a terrain description without running the risk of serious misrepresentation. It would, for example, be futile to attempt a characterization of much of Finland or of northern and eastern Canada without mentioning that standing water and exposed bedrock together probably occupy as much or more of the area than soil does. The icecap of Antarctica, the sand-dune seas of the Libyan Sahara, and the wide coastal marshes of South Carolina and Georgia are all distinctive because of their unusual surface materials.

Arrangements. *Arrangements* are the relative positions of features within an area. Streams, ridge crests, peaks, areas of gentle slope, steep bluffs, and exposures of bare rock are all set upon the land surface in distinctive horizontal arrangements or patterns that are best seen from an airplane or on a map. In some regions pattern is one of the most striking of all characteristics, especially where it departs from the usual treelike arrangement of valleys or streams and of the ridges between them that is illustrated in Figure 9.3*A*. The remarkably parallel

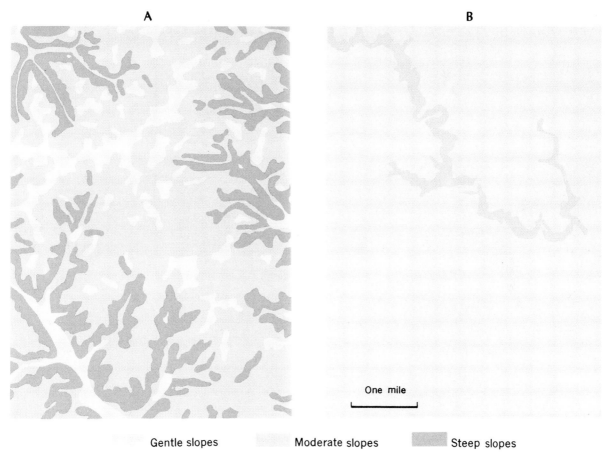

Figure 9.1 An example of contrast in slope. *A* is from the coastal plain near Corpus Christi, Texas; *B,* from the hill land of southwestern Wisconsin. *(From U.S. Geological Survey topographic sheets: Petronilla, Texas, and Boaz, Wisconsin.)*

arrangement of ridges in the middle belt of the Appalachians between central Pennsylvania and northern Alabama (Fig. 9.3*B*), the random dotting of small, isolated volcanic hills on the plains of south central Oregon (Fig. 9.3*C*), and the aimless maze of lakes, swamps, and streams in northeastern Minnesota (Fig. 9.2*B*) are indispensable ingredients in any meaningful description of those regions. The patterns establish the character of the terrain, they are highly significant clues to the geologic history of the region, and they are clearly reflected in the patterns of other phenomena such as soils, native vegetation, and agricultural utilization of the land.

Vertical arrangements are also significant, especially vertical distribution of surface area and profiles—a "profile" in this sense being the change of slope or gradient along a given line. Profiles can illustrate such characteristics as the cross-section forms of valleys; the evenness, jaggedness, or presence of deep clefts in major mountain crests (Fig. 9.4); and the various changes in gradients of streams from their headwaters down to their mouths. Regional contrasts in these and in vertical distribution of surface area are sometimes striking and important (Fig. 9.5). The student of earth history often finds these characteristics especially valuable, for they may sometimes be used to determine or infer previous uplifts of the crust, earlier variations of stream

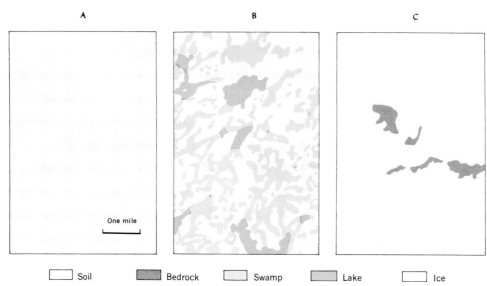

Figure 9.2   An example of contrast in the nature of surface material. *A* is from rolling prairies of northwestern Missouri, *B* from morainic plains of northern Minnesota, *C* from mountains of southern Alaska. *(From U.S. Geological Survey topographic sheets: Bethany, Missouri, Ely, Minnesota, and Seward A-8, Alaska.)*

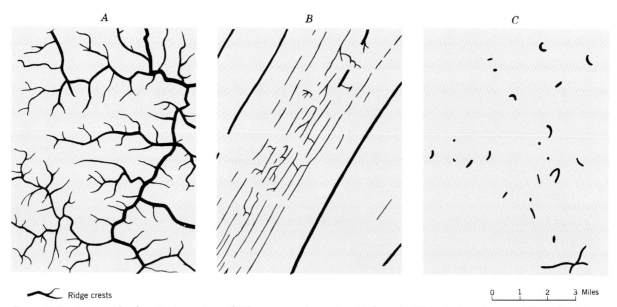

Figure 9.3   An example of contrast in pattern of ridge crests and summits. *A* is from the hill land of southwestern Wisconsin, *B* from the Appalachian Ridge and Valley region of central Pennsylvania, *C* from an area of volcanic cones in south central Oregon. *(From U.S. Geological Survey topographic sheets: La Farge, Wisconsin, Orbisonia, Pennsylvania, and Newberry Crater, Oregon.)*

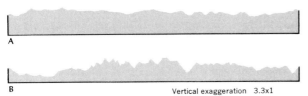

Figure 9.4 The continuously high crest line of the Sierra Nevada of California (*A*) contrasts with the deeply serrated crest of the Cascade Range in Washington (*B*). *(From Army Map Service series 1:250,000: Fresno and Wenatchee sheets.)*

discharge, and the effects of rock character upon the processes of erosion. The examples will suggest that these vertical arrangements may relate also to other aspects of geography, including potential utilization of the land by human beings.

Dimensions. Dimensions give scale to the characterization. Without a knowledge of the size of features, it is impossible to visualize a landscape that is being described.

Important dimensions in the horizontal plane are the spacings of valleys, ridges, and streams, the widths of patches of gentle slope, steep slope, or distinctive surface material, and the sizes of lakes and swamps. Areas similar in other characteristics are sometimes quite different in horizontal dimensions (Fig. 9.6). Areas in which widths and spacings of features are relatively large are spoken of as *coarse-textured*; those in which horizontal dimensions are small are *fine-textured*.

In the vertical direction, dimensions are given by various expressions of *local relief*. For a general expression of local relief, the difference in elevation between the highest and lowest points in a local area is often used. Another measure of relief indicates the average or prevalent height of crests above the adjacent valley bottoms. The relief along crest lines, on local uplands, and along valley floors or streams may also be of interest.

Local relief has considerable descriptive value, suggesting at once something of the scale of features and the degree of irregularity within the area being considered (Fig. 9.7). If the local relief in an area a few kilometers across is only 15 m (50 ft), it is evident that the surface must be either nearly flat or marked by only small roughnesses. But a local

relief of 1,500 m (5,000 ft) immediately suggests a landscape of considerable grandeur, although without specifying what form its great features may take. When combined with data on slope and profiles, local relief is one of the most revealing of all generalized expressions of terrain character.

Classes of Land Surfaces

Classifying land-surface form. The variety of land surfaces is so great that it is not only convenient but necessary to group them into a limited number of classes in order to discuss them. There is no single "best" way in which this grouping may be done; a scheme of classification should be keyed to the purpose for which it is made. In this book we are concerned chiefly with the current nature of the land surfaces, and thus we may use existing characteristics, such as those just discussed, as a basis for classification. Because we are interested in the land surfaces primarily as they relate to other environmental phenomena and to people, we should try to select properties that are significant to those relationships. Even so, the range of feasible classification schemes is large, and the choice must be somewhat arbitrary.

The classification that will be used here employs properties that are easily seen, measured, and understood. Simple as it is, it permits one to visualize roughly the appearance of the surface, to formulate highly generalized statements concerning

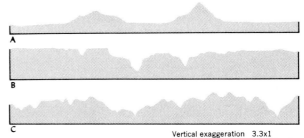

Figure 9.5 Contrasting transverse profiles in areas of high relief. *A* is from the Basin and Range province in Nevada, *B* from the Colorado Plateaus in northern Arizona, *C* from the northern Rocky Mountains in Idaho. *(From U.S. Geological Survey topographic sheets: Sonoma Range, Nevada, Diamond Creek, Arizona, and Lolo, Idaho.)*

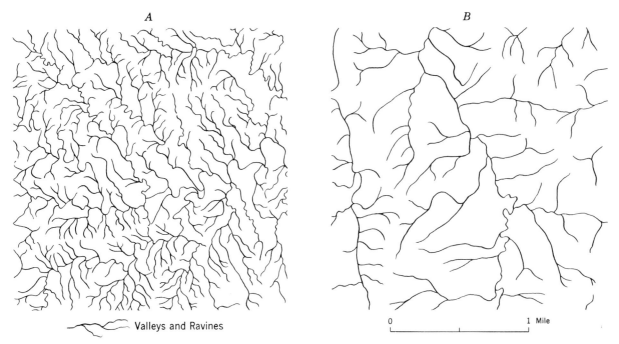

A

B

Valleys and Ravines

0   1 Mile

Figure 9.6 Example of contrast in texture, or spacing of valleys and ravines. The patterns are similar, but the textures are strikingly different. *A is from the White River Badlands of southwestern South Dakota, B from central Missouri. (From U.S. Geological Survey topographic sheets: Cuny Table East, South Dakota, and Nelson, Missouri.)*

possible modes of origin and current environmental functioning, and to begin speculative consideration of the potential utility to people. The classification appears as one major basis for organizing the discussion of land-surface types in Chapters 12 and 13. Each major class of surface distinguished by the classification, however, occurs in many varieties that differ chiefly through the kinds and internal arrangements of their crests, valleys, slopes, materials, and drainage patterns. These details are closely related to the principal gradational agents that have shaped the

particular sections of the surface. For that reason, the gradational agents and their work are discussed before the surfaces themselves and also enter strongly into the organization of the discussion of surface types.

Major classes of land-surface form. The scheme of classification to be used here is based upon three major characteristics: relative amount of gently sloping land, local relief, and vertical distribution of the gently sloping land. On the basis of the first two

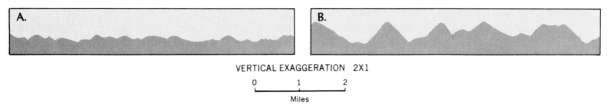

A.

B.

VERTICAL EXAGGERATION 2X1

0   1   2

Miles

Figure 9.7 Contrasting local relief in two areas of rough lands. *A is from the Missouri Ozarks, B from the Appalachian Highlands in central West Virginia. (From U.S. Geological Survey topographic sheets: Round Spring, Missouri, and Bald Knob, West Virginia.)*

characteristics alone we may distinguish among (1) *plains*, having a predominance of gently sloping land, coupled with low relief, (2) *plains with some features of considerable relief*—also dominated by gently sloping land, but having moderate to high local relief, (3) *hills*, with little gently sloping land and low to moderate relief, and (4) *mountains*, which have little gently sloping land and high local relief.

The second group, plains with some features of considerable relief, may be further subdivided on the basis of whether their gently sloping land occurs in the lower part of the profile or in the upper part. If most of the gentle slopes lie at relatively low levels, with steep slopes rising above them, the surfaces may be designated *plains with hills or mountains.* If, on the other hand, most of the nearly level land lies relatively high, with canyons or long lines of bluffs (escarpments) dropping down from it, the surfaces may be called *tablelands.* If the relief is slight or the amount of gently sloping land is not large, this criterion of vertical arrangement is less significant; so it is not used as a basis for subdividing plains, hills, and mountains. It is convenient, however, to separate out the flattest plains, which often have originated in a different manner from the rest and have distinctive potentialities for use.

Figures 9.8 and 9.9 give examples of the principal classes of land surfaces recognized in the

classification. The accompanying table shows schematically how the classes are defined.

It must be fully understood that within each of these major classes of land surfaces, which are defined here in terms of only two or three characteristics that seem particularly important to visualization or function, there exists a vast variety, based upon differences in other characteristics. The classification is intended to bring out only the most striking contrasts. Other differences will be noted and discussed in the succeeding chapters.

World distribution of land-surface types.   Plate 2 shows the distribution over the earth of the major classes of land-surface form. In addition to the seven classes defined above, the few broad icecaps have also been distinguished.

The following table, which was derived directly from Plate 2, shows that the major types of land surfaces are neither equal in total extent nor evenly distributed among the continents. The more irregular types of plains are especially widespread, suggesting that conditions favoring the development of such surfaces have been common in late geologic time. On the other hand, the formation of tablelands and flat plains requires sets of circumstances that have not occurred so widely. It will be seen later that these two latter types of surfaces demand rather

MAJOR CLASSES OF LAND SURFACES

Slope	Local relief	Vertical distrib. of gentle slope	Class
More than 50% gentle slope	0–100 m or 0–300 ft	Any	Plains (Flat plains if more than 80% gentle slope and 0–30 m or 0–100 ft local relief)
	More than 100 m or more than 300 ft	More than 50% of gentle slope is in upper half of elevation range	Tablelands
		More than 50% of gentle slope is in lower half of elevation range	Plains with hills or mountains
Less than 50% gentle slope	0–300 m or 0–1,000 ft	Any	Hills
	300–1,000 m or 1,000–3,000 ft	Any	Low mountains
	More than 1,000 m or 3,000 ft	Any	High mountains

A

B

C

Figure 9.8 Examples of the three smoother classes of land form. *A* is the gently undulating Gulf Coastal Plain near Austin, Texas. *B* is Canyon de Chelly and vicinity in northeastern Arizona, a well-defined tableland; *C* shows the Hopi Buttes, near Winslow, Arizona, a plain with hills and mountains. *(A, courtesy Exxon Corporation; B and C, Spence Air Photos.)*

A

B

Figure 9.9   Examples of the two rougher classes of land-surface form. *A* is hill land from the Allegheny-Cumberland section of the Appalachian Highlands in West Virginia; *B* is high-mountain country in the Alaska Range, central Alaska. *(A, J. L. Rich, courtesy of the Geographical Review, American Geographical Society, New York; B, Bradford Washburn.)*

LAND-SURFACE FORMS

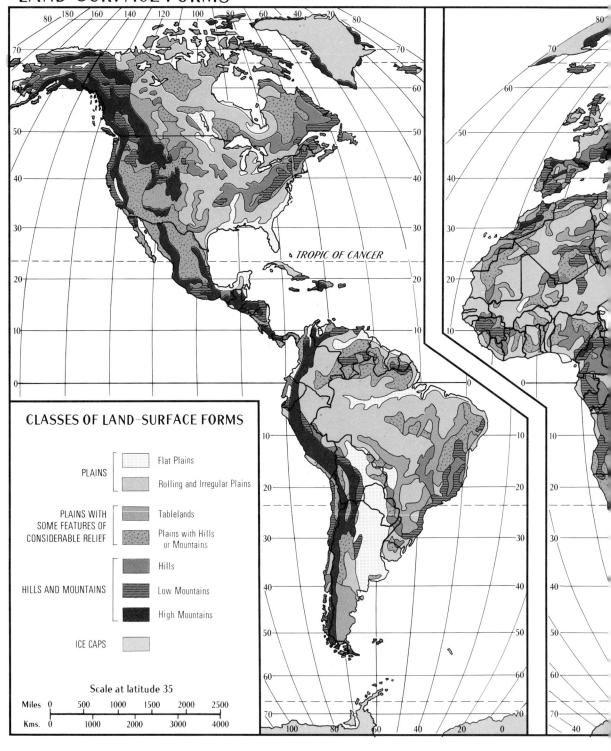

TROPIC OF CANCER

CLASSES OF LAND-SURFACE FORMS

PLAINS
- Flat Plains
- Rolling and Irregular Plains

PLAINS WITH
SOME FEATURES OF
CONSIDERABLE RELIEF
- Tablelands
- Plains with Hills or Mountains

HILLS AND MOUNTAINS
- Hills
- Low Mountains
- High Mountains

ICE CAPS

Scale at latitude 35

Miles	0	500	1000	1500	2000	2500
Kms.	0	1000	2000	3000	4000	

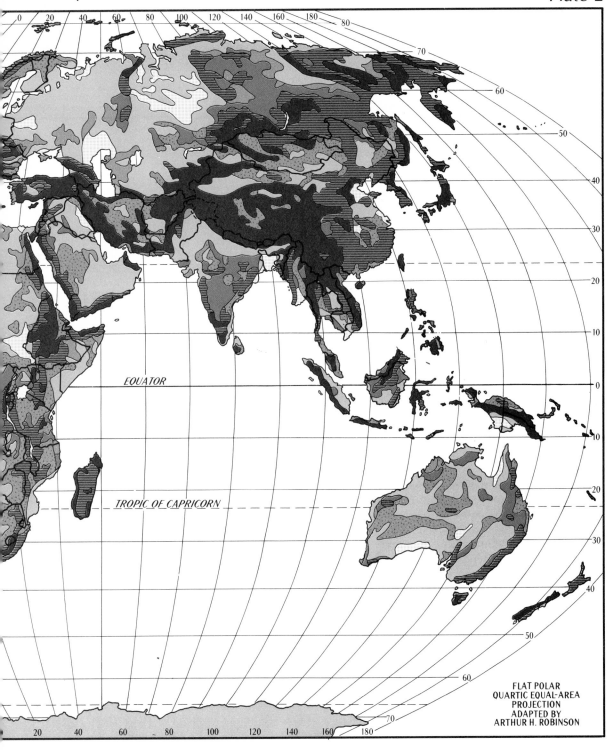

EQUATOR

TROPIC OF CAPRICORN

FLAT POLAR
QUARTIC EQUAL-AREA
PROJECTION
ADAPTED BY
ARTHUR H. ROBINSON

PERCENTAGE OF CONTINENTAL AND WORLD LAND AREAS OCCUPIED BY MAJOR LAND-SURFACE TYPES

	North America	South America	Eurasia	Africa	Australia; New Zealand	Antarctica	World
Flat plains	8	15	2	1	4	0	4
Rolling and irregular plains	23	30	30	44	51	0	30
Tablelands	9	10	3	5	1	0	5
Plains with hills or mountains	18	18	11	22	19	0	15
Hills	8	5	10	11	12	0	8
Low mountains	10	11	21	13	12	1	14
High mountains	16	11	23	4	1	1	13
Icecaps	8	0	0	0	0	98	11
Percentage of world area	16	12	36	20	6	10	100

specific and limited circumstances in order to develop at all.

REVIEW QUESTIONS

1. What is the aim of a geographical study of land-surface form as developed in this book?
2. What are the two principal sets of processes that shape the surfaces of the lands? In general terms, what does each accomplish?
3. In what sense may the land surface be considered as part of a dynamic, functioning, interconnected system? Discuss the principal activities of water in the functioning of the land-surface parts of the environmental system.
4. What are the principal materials involved in transfers of mass in the surface system? From what sources and in what forms does energy enter the surface system? Show an understanding of the occurrences of potential and kinetic energy in the surface system, including the transformations from one form to the other.
5. What is the advantage of considering specific characteristics in discussing or describing land surfaces? What five groups of land-surface characteristics are identified in the text? Show an understanding of what is included in each group.
6. How might one determine the slope of the land (a) from field observation and (b) from a contour map? What is local relief, and how might it be determined from a contour map? From what sources could information on the surface materials of an area be determined?

7. What is the difference between the pattern and the texture of a set of valleys or crest lines? Which one of the two is more difficult to describe quantitatively? What is meant by "vertical distribution of surface area"?
8. What three properties serve as a basis for the land-surface classification used in this book? On the basis of which one of these properties are plains distinguished from hills? Which one distinguishes hills from mountains? Which distinguishes tablelands from plains with hills or mountains?
9. Secure a number of assorted topographic maps and determine the classification of the land surface shown on each.
10. How much of the earth's land surface is made up of (a) all types of plains (flat, rolling, irregular)? How much is made up of all rough lands (hills, low and high mountains)? Which major classes of terrain are least widespread? Which of the continents has the largest percentage of rough land? Which two continents are especially smooth?

SELECTED REFERENCES: CHAPTERS 9 TO 14

Bertin, L. Translated by R. Bradshaw and M. M. Owen. *The New Larousse Encyclopedia of the Earth*, rev. ed. Hamlyn Publishing Group, Ltd., London, and Crown Publishers, Inc., New York, 1972. A lavishly illustrated encyclopedic volume providing useful examples of landforms and the operation of developmental processes.

Carter, D. B., T. H. Schmudde, and D. M. Sharpe. *The Interface as a Working Environment: A Purpose for Physical Geography.* Association of American Geographers, Commission on College Geography, Technical Paper No. 7, Washington, D.C., 1972. Effective statement of the importance of energy and work in the earth-surface system.

Chorley, R. J. (ed.). *Water, Earth, and Man.* Methuen & Company, Ltd., London, 1969. Valuable chapters on drainage basin characteristics, weathering, run-off and infiltration, stream channels, erosion, and sedimentation.

Continents Adrift. Readings from *Scientific American* with introductions by J. Tuzo Wilson. W. H. Freeman and Company, San Francisco, 1972. Collection of lucid articles tracing the rapid development of plate tectonic theory. Excellent maps, diagrams, photographs.

Dewey, J. F. "Plate Tectonics." *Scientific American,* Vol. 226, No. 5, pp. 56–68, 1972. A later article continuing the sequence begun in the preceding reference.

Dury, G. H. *The Face of the Earth.* Penguin Books, Inc., Baltimore, 1959. Brief, effective introduction to geomorphology. Especially good introduction to slope development.

———. *Perspectives on Geomorphic Processes.* Association of American Geographers, Commission on College Geography, Resource Paper No. 3, Washington, D.C., 1969. Brief introduction to major recent developments in geomorphology.

Fenneman, Nevin. *Physiography of Eastern United States.* McGraw-Hill Book Company, New York, 1938.

———. *Physiography of Western United States.* McGraw-Hill Book Company, New York, 1931. Classics of regional landform analysis. Though some interpretative material is outdated, these remain the most thorough sources on landform regions of the United States.

Flint, R. F. *Glacial and Quaternary Geology.* John Wiley & Sons, Inc., New York, 1971. Thorough and authoritative treatment of glaciation and Pleistocene history.

Gilluly, J., A. C. Waters, and A. O. Woodford. *Principles of Geology*, 4th ed. W. H. Freeman and Company, San Francisco, 1975. A challenging text in basic physical geology. Especially valuable, modern treatments of tectonics and the gradational processes.

Gross, M. G. *Oceanography: A View of the Earth.* Prentice-Hall, Inc., Englewood Cliffs, N.J., 1972. Modern, general text with valuable chapters on continents and ocean basins, the ocean floor, and shoreline processes.

Hammond, E. H. "Classes of Land-surface Form." *National Atlas of the United States.* U.S. Geological Survey, Washington, D.C., 1970. Pp. 61–64. Maps of the land-surface form of the United States, based on the properties discussed in Chapter 9.

Hart, P. J. (ed.). *The Earth's Crust and Upper Mantle.* American Geophysical Union, Washington, D.C., 1969. A wide-ranging assemblage of papers, generally technical, with useful maps and diagrams relating to world structure, tectonics, and the ocean floors.

Hunt, C. B. *Natural Regions of the United States and Canada.* W. H. Freeman and Company, San Francisco, 1974. An introduction to the regional physical geography of the United States. Excellent maps, diagrams, and photographs.

King, C. A. M. *Beaches and Coasts.* Edward Arnold (Publishers), Ltd., London, 1959. Sound, thorough discussion of shorelines and coastal processes.

Leopold, L. B., M. G. Wolman, and J. P. Miller. *Fluvial Processes in Geomorphology.* W. H. Freeman and Company, San Francisco, 1964. Scholarly treatment of modern advances in the understanding of running water and its work in shaping the surface.

Raisz, E. Map: Landforms of the United States. 6th rev. ed. Ginn and Company, Boston, 1957. Careful, surprisingly detailed, graphic portrayal of the landforms of the United States. Invaluable reference map for use with this book or with listed references.

Schumm, S. A. "The Development and Evolution of Hillslopes." *Journal of Geological Education*, Vol. XIV, No. 3, pp. 98–104, 1966. Brief, clear presentation of modern theories of slope development.

Sharpe, C. F. S. *Landslides and Related Phenomena.* Columbia University Press, New York, 1934. A short, classic, still-unequaled introduction to the various processes of mass wasting and their effects.

Shelton, J. S. *Geology Illustrated.* W. H. Freeman and Company, San Francisco, 1966. A lavishly illustrated introduction to physical geology, especially noteworthy for its magnificent collection of aerial photographs (many by the author) showing landforms and structural features.

Small, R. J. *The Study of Landforms: A Textbook of Geomorphology.* Cambridge University Press, London and New York, 1970. A particularly sound, modern textbook in geomorphology. Examples large British.

Steers, J. A. *The Coastline of England and Wales,* 2d ed. Cambridge University Press, New York, 1964. A classic application of coastal geomorphology by a master field investigator.

Stokes, W. L., and S. Judson. *Introduction to Geology: Physical and Historical.* Prentice-Hall, Inc., Englewood Cliffs, N.J., 1968. A sound, well-established introductory textbook of geology.

Thornbury, W. D. *Principles of Geomorphology,* 2d ed.

John Wiley & Sons, Inc., New York, 1969. A widely used, substantial textbook of geomorphology. Particularly strong in its treatment of classical theory. Examples largely from the United States.

———. *Regional Geomorphology of the United States.* John Wiley & Sons, Inc., New York, 1965. More recent than Fenneman's volumes, but briefer and more geologically oriented. Valuable bibliographies and illustrations.

Trewartha, G. T., A. H. Robinson, and E. H. Hammond. *Physical Elements of Geography,* 5th ed. McGraw-Hill Book Company, New York, 1967. A more inclusive, earlier text by the authors of this book. Designed for a one-year course.

Williams, W. W. *Coastal Changes.* Routledge & Kegan Paul, Ltd., London, 1960. Brief, modern treatment of coastal geomorphology.

The Earth's Crust: Nature, Processes, and Major Features

THE CRUST AND ITS MOVEMENTS

General Structure of the Earth

The crust and the earth's interior. We know nothing of the deep interior of the earth by direct observation. Our deepest mines are seldom more than 1,000 m deep, and even our deepest borings have rarely penetrated more than 7 or 8 km (4 or 5 mi)—scarcely more than $1/1,000$ of the way to the center. But geophysicists, by computing the speed of earthquake waves passing through the interior, mapping the pattern of terrestrial magnetism, measuring differences from place to place in the acceleration of gravity, and calculating the mean density of the earth, have been able to piece together a crude but revealing picture of what the internal structure of the globe must be. A simplified version of that picture is shown in Figure 10.1.

Although its temperatures are extremely high (possibly 1000 to 3000°C), the interior of the earth appears to be mostly solid. This is believed to be due to the raising of the melting point of its substances by the great pressure from the overlying materials. The exceedingly dense core, thought to be largely of nickel and iron, is solid toward the center but probably molten in its outer part. The thick surrounding mantle, less dense than the core, is evidently almost wholly solid. It is believed to be composed of some of the denser substances found in common surface rocks. The outermost shell of the earth, which varies in thickness from less than 5 to more than 40 km (3 to 25 mi), is low in average density and consists of the types of rocks familiar to geologists from surface exposures. This thin shell is called the *crust*, a curious term that reflects the earlier belief that everything below it was molten.

Although the crust seems very rigid, it is actually not so in relation to the tremendous forces, including the force of gravity, that act upon it. Furthermore, it rests upon a somewhat insecure underpinning. The outermost layer of the mantle, 100 km (about 60 mi) or so thick, appears to be at least as rigid as the crust; but below that the mantle is evidently much weaker and, although mostly solid, is capable of very slow flowage or other deformation, such as might be expected of an exceedingly viscous fluid. This combination of relatively weak crust and somewhat unstable substratum sets the stage for deformation of the crust, provided only that there are forces strong enough to deform it. Since there is abundant evidence that the crust has in fact been extensively warped, folded, and broken, it is clear that such forces do exist, although as yet they are poorly understood.

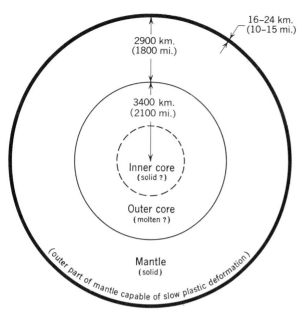

2900 km.
(1800 mi.)

16–24 km.
(10–15 mi.)

3400 km.
(2100 mi.)

Inner core
(solid ?)

Outer core
(molten ?)

Mantle
(solid)

(outer part of mantle capable of slow plastic deformation)

Figure 10.1 Diagram of the internal structure of the earth. The heavy outer line represents the crust, too thin to be shown at correct scale.

Continents and ocean basins. The continents are not simply upraised sections of a uniform crust, but fundamentally different from the low-lying ocean basins. The crust forming the continents has an average thickness of perhaps 40 km (25 mi), compared with about 6.5 km (4 mi) for that beneath the deep-sea floors. Also, the predominant rocks of the continental masses are much less dense than those of the ocean basins. The continents appear to be formed primarily of granites and closely related rocks, often overlaid with a thin skin of sedimentary strata. But beneath the ocean basins the crust appears to be composed largely of basalt, a fine-grained, dense, dark rock that is common in lavas (Fig. 10.2).

The surfaces of the continental masses stand higher than the ocean floors, but their bases lie deeper in the mantle underneath. The situation is comparable to that which would occur if a thick block of pine were floated in a tub of water next to a thin block of denser oak. The upper surface of the pine block would stand higher than that of the oak block, and its base would lie deeper in the water. All evidence suggests that this analogy is a reasonable one. The crust does behave as if it were buoyed up by a denser mantle

that is capable of plastic adjustment to the varying weights above it.

Origin of the extensive "rafts" of granitic rocks that form the continents is imperfectly understood. Much of their rock material is very ancient, and there seems little doubt that large masses of continental crust have existed for more than 2 billion years. Some continental rocks, however, are much younger, and it is thought that the continents have grown by accretion of crustal material of low density along certain parts of their margins. These added strips of low-density rock probably represent sections of oceanic crust that have been greatly altered by partial melting, recrystallization, chemical action of hot gases and groundwaters, and other complex reworking during periods of major crustal deformation. The nature and distribution of the thin sedimentary cover make it clear that from time to time parts of the continental platforms have been submerged beneath shallow seas. As will be seen later, the continental masses have also been pulled apart, moved relative to one another, and, in places, jammed together during the long course of geologic history.

Crustal Movements and Vulcanism

Evidence of Crustal Movements and Change

Most of our knowledge of what has happened to the crust in past times comes from observations of the rock layers and masses that are exposed at the surface or that have been reached by deep borings or excavations. Rock strata that were originally laid down horizontally are now gently or steeply inclined. Some layers of well-consolidated rock have been bent into sharp folds (Fig. 10.3) or shattered. Rocks containing fossils of sea animals are found in mountain

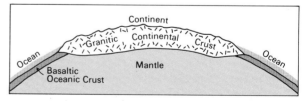

Figure 10.2 Continental crust differs from oceanic crust. Continental crust is thick and low in density; oceanic crust is thin and dense.

Figure 10.3 Portion of a small folded rock structure exposed in a stream valley. *(Stose, U.S. Geological Survey.)*

ranges thousands of feet above sea level. Great fractures sometimes cut through thick series of massive rock strata, and often there is clear evidence of slippage along the breaks, with displacements occasionally amounting to many feet or even many miles (Fig. 10.4). Such observations indicate clearly that the crust has been subjected to almost every conceivable form of bending, breaking, uplift, and depression. This crustal deformation is sometimes referred to as *diastrophism*.

Although rock structures provide most of the evidence for diastrophism, some of our knowledge comes from movements that have been observed in historical time. Slow vertical movements of the crust have been recorded at many places, usually along seacoasts, where the sea surface provides a ready reference level. Here such occurrences as the gradual submergence of ancient buildings, emergence of old harbor works, and progressive disappearance of low-lying coastal plains can be used to indicate the direction and rate of deformation. From this kind of evidence it has been determined, for example, that parts of the Baltic Coast of northern Europe are rising at about 1 m (3 ft) per century, while the outer part of the Mississippi River Delta in Louisiana is apparently sinking at a similar rate. More rapid movements have also been measured. Changes of level of several feet occurred along much of the south coast of Alaska during the great earthquake of 1964.

Displacements of rocks along fractures have been frequently observed, usually as rapid movements during earthquakes. The individual displacements are ordinarily quite small, but there have been conspicuous exceptions. In the violent San Francisco earthquake of 1906, a section of a road was offset laterally almost 6.5 m (21 ft). In northeastern India a sudden vertical displacement of more than 10 m (35 ft) occurred during a great earthquake in 1897.

Other evidence indicates crustal changes of a different sort. Rock materials of types known to develop by crystallizing from a molten state are found in masses and sheets within and upon the crust, lying in close association with rocks of wholly different kinds. The relationships make it clear that the molten materials have been forced or have melted their way into the other rocks from below. In some instances they have clearly emerged onto the surface before solidifying. All the diverse phenomena involved in

Figure 10.4 Fracturing and displacement of stratified sedimentary rocks. The fracture is a normal fault. *(Winchester, U.S. Geological Survey.)*

the formation, movement, and emplacement of these molten materials in and upon the crust are referred to collectively as *vulcanism*. The actual examples of surface vulcanism that have been observed are especially dramatic. Graphic accounts of ancient volcanic eruptions are among the earliest recorded observations of events that have significantly changed the surface of the earth.

Kinds of Crustal Movement and Change

Diastrophism. Because the structures and surface forms associated with warping and folding are often significantly different from those associated with fracturing and displacement, it is convenient to discuss the two aspects of diastrophism separately.

Warping and folding. In many places deforming stresses have been applied to the crust so slowly that the rock strata, confined by the great weight of overlying materials, have bent or buckled rather than broken. The resulting deformation ranges from the gentlest warping to tight and complex folding.

Few sections of the crust have escaped some warping. Even in such tectonically stable areas as the North American Middle West, southern England and northern France, and the central and western Sahara, the rock strata are gently warped into broad structural domes and basins, although inclinations are rarely more than a few degrees from the horizontal. Some parts of the continental platforms have been shallowly depressed below sea level, as in Hudson Bay. Elsewhere sections of the shallow sea floor have been upwarped, bringing fossil-bearing marine sediments well above the sea surface.

Some broad belts of the crust have been thrown into systems of folds that range from small wrinkles to great, wavelike structures measuring many miles from crest to crest and thousands of feet from base to top. The arch or crest of a simple fold is called an *anticline*; the trough is a *syncline* (Fig. 10.5). A one-sided simple fold is a *monocline* or *flexure*. In many mountainous areas, such as the Alps, the Himalaya, and the northern Rockies, deformation has been so vigorous that folds have been tightly jammed together, overturned, broken, and greatly displaced, producing structures of remarkable complexity. Such intense deformation can be explained only by extreme lateral compression of those sections of the crust, involving horizontal movements of many miles.

Fracturing and faulting. Like warping, fracturing of the crust is worldwide. Systems of cracks, often in roughly parallel sets, can be seen in almost all exposed rocks. Ordinarily there has been no appreciable displacement along these small fractures, which are known as *joints* (Fig. 10.6).

Where stresses have been more severe, however, there have been repeated vertical or horizontal slippages along the fracture planes, with cumulative displacements of hundreds or thousands of feet. Fractures along which displacements occur are called *faults*. Stresses producing the displacements may be compressional, tensional (stretching), or shearing (roughly parallel to the fault plane). The resulting displacements may be vertical, horizontal, or both.

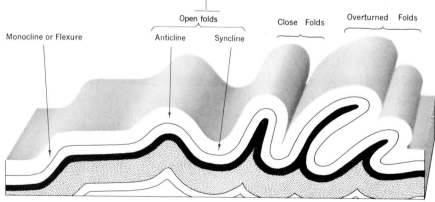

Open folds   Close Folds   Overturned Folds

Monocline or Flexure   Anticline   Syncline

Figure 10.5 Types of folds.

Figure 10.6 Jointing in granite. Three sets of joint planes are visible, roughly perpendicular to each other. *(Cross, U.S. Geological Survey.)*

Some simple types of faults are shown in Figure 10.7. If the displacement is vertical and extends to the surface, a cliff, called a *fault scarp*, is produced. If the displacement is largely horizontal, linear features such as roads, fence lines, and streams are offset along the fault.

Blocks of crust bounded on either side by faults are sometimes raised, lowered, or tilted. Raised blocks are called *horsts*; depressed blocks are *grabens*. Some of the small ranges of Nevada and western Utah are eroded horsts and tilted fault blocks. The Sierra Nevada of California is a huge tilted block with an immense fault scarp on its eastern side (Fig. 10.8). Death Valley in California, the great "rift valleys" of East Africa, and the trough occupied by the Red Sea are examples of grabens.

Of course, large-scale folding or faulting does not occur in single swift cataclysms. By human standards the time scale is slow. A great fault scarp like that of the Sierra Nevada was probably produced

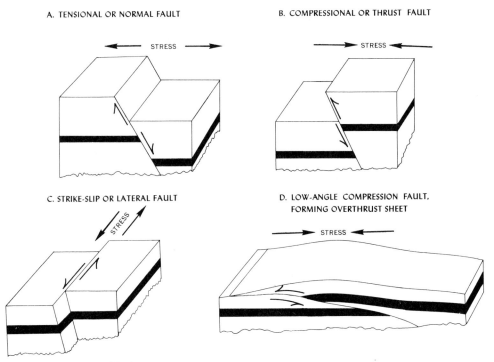

Figure 10.7 Types of faults.

Figure 10.8   The Sierra Nevada of California is an immense tilted fault block, strongly eroded by water and ice. The eastern fault scarp, at right, rises abruptly more than 3,000 m (9,000 ft) above the Owens Valley, while the dissected upper surface of the block descends gradually toward the left. Mt. Whitney, highest summit in the United States outside of Alaska, elevation 4,420 m (14,495 ft), is just outside the photograph at lower left. *(John S. Shelton.)*

by a long series of small displacements occurring over a period of many hundreds of thousands of years. Extensive systems of folds like those of the Appalachians or the Alps may have required millions of years for their development.

Vulcanism.   Normally both the crust and the layers of material beneath it are in the solid state, in spite of the high temperatures that prevail below the surface. Yet repeatedly during geologic history, large masses of material immediately beneath the crust or in the deeper crust have become molten and forced their way toward the surface. The development of these molten masses is not fully understood, but they appear to form most frequently in areas of active crustal deformation.

The molten rock makes its way upward partly by melting the rocks above it and partly by forcing its way into fractures. As it does so, hot gases are given off and groundwater is boiled into steam, generating high pressures. The various rising materials sometimes burst out upon the surface, causing the usually spectacular events known as volcanic activity

or *extrusive vulcanism*. Most of the molten material, however, cools and hardens into solid rock before reaching the surface. This subsurface part of the activity is called *intrusive vulcanism*.

Intrusive vulcanism.   Rock masses formed by intrusive vulcanism occur in a vast range of forms and sizes (Fig. 10.9). The largest, known as *batholiths*, are immense bodies of granite or similar rocks measuring tens or even hundreds of miles across and thousands of feet in thickness. Much of the unbroken expanse of mountains in the Rockies of central Idaho, for example, is carved out of a batholith measuring about 160 by 400 km (100 by 250 mi). Much of the Sierra Nevada of California is underlain by an even larger batholithic mass. Deep intrusive masses similar in character to batholiths but much smaller in size are called *stocks*.

When molten material under great pressure enters the rocks near the surface, it often makes its way into joints and other fractures, where it solidifies into vertical sheets known as *dikes*; or it works in between the layers of stratified rocks to form horizon-

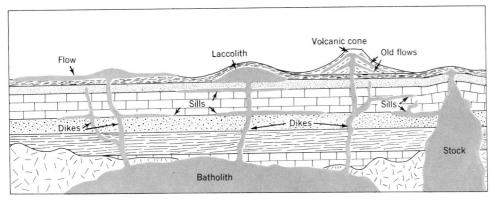

Figure 10.9 Characteristic features of intrusive and extrusive vulcanism.

tal sheets called *sills*. Sometimes in this situation, the overlying rock is bulged upward by the intrusive material, forming a great blister. The hardened filling of such a blister is called a *laccolith*. The filling of a volcanic vent forms a volcanic plug or neck.

Extrusive vulcanism. In extrusive vulcanism, rock material, along with quantities of gases and steam, is forced out onto the surface of the earth. This material may be emitted rather quietly as molten rock (lava) or may be vigorously blown out as semi-molten or solid rock in particles ranging from fine dust to large boulders (Fig. 10.10).

　Some volcanoes characteristically erupt in a series of explosions, often of tremendous force. This is especially likely to happen when the vent of the volcano has been sealed over by quick-hardening lavas, allowing extreme pressures to build up underneath. Vesuvius, near Naples, Italy, is a familiar example of an explosive volcano, which has been repeatedly active during historical time. Krakatau, in Indonesia, and Katmai, in Alaska, have produced two of the greatest explosions of human record, the former in 1883, the latter in 1912. Each mountain nearly destroyed itself by blasts of almost incredible violence. A similar explosion, which destroyed a considerable part of the island of Thira, southeast of Greece, in the fifteenth century B.C., is thought by some to have given rise, through a curious error, to the legend of the "lost continent of Atlantis" and may also have contributed to the destruction of the cities and palaces of the Minoan civilization on the neighboring island of Crete. In the products ejected by explosive volca-

noes, the percentage of solid material in small fragments or particles (ash) is naturally great.

　By way of contrast, many volcanoes emit slow-cooling lava that has little tendency to plug the vents. Eruptions of these volcanoes are quieter and normally produce a much lower percentage of ash. The volcanoes of Hawaii are of this type.

　Lava flows and ash deposits are the most extensive products of extrusive vulcanism. Near a vent these products may pile up to great thickness, forming a volcanic cone. Most lava accumulations cover no more than a few square kilometers of the

Figure 10.10 The volcano Paricutin, Mexico, in violent eruption. Typical steep-sided cinder cone. Note the thick cover of ash being eroded in the foreground. *(Segerstrom, U.S. Geological Survey.)*

Figure 10.11 Cinder cone and recent lava flow, north of Flagstaff, Arizona. The cone, SP Mountain, is 244 m (800 ft) high, with a crater about 90 m (300 ft) deep, and the lava tongue extends about 8 km (5 mi) from the point of emergence at the base of the cone. *(John S. Shelton.)*

earth's surface (Fig. 10.11). In a few places, however, layer after layer of highly fluid, slow-cooling lava, usually basaltic, has emerged through extensive systems of vents and has spread out over hundreds of thousands of square kilometers. In the Columbia Plateau region of the northwestern United States, successive flows over a long period covered an area of more than 260,000 sq km (100,000 sq mi) to an average depth of 800 m (½ mi). Similar accumulations cover large parts of peninsular India, Ethiopia, and southern Brazil.

Importance of Tectonic Activity

Importance of tectonics to land-form development. From the point of view of land form development, the tectonic processes, whether crustal deformation or vulcanism, produce, in the broadest sense, two significant kinds of results: surface irregularities and rock structures. Surface irregularities caused by tectonic activity are many and varied. Fault scarps, broad domes and basins, high-standing horsts and depressed grabens, anticlinal ridges and synclinal troughs—all are examples of diastrophic surface forms. Vulcanism produces cones and craters, laccolithic bulges, and tongues or plains of lava. Even the continents themselves owe their existence to complex tectonic events.

Rarely, however, do we find tectonic land-

forms in a "pure" state; usually they have been modified by gradation, sometimes so much that the original feature is scarcely recognizable (Fig. 10.8). The local differences in elevation produced by tectonics provide the energy required for the movements of streams, glaciers, and gravity-powered slides and flows of earth. As soon as these agents begin to act, however, they begin to destroy the very irregularities that brought them to life. By the geologic time scale, such destruction proceeds swiftly, erasing even great mountain systems in a few tens of millions of years and smaller features in much less time. Thus the surface irregularities produced by tectonics, though important, are not particularly long-lived.

On the other hand, warped, folded, and faulted rock structures, which reach deep into the crust, can persist for eons. The same is true of the continental rafts as wholes. Erosion may quickly strip off their upper parts, but the lower parts remain untouched unless later tectonic activity reworks them. As long as these structures remain, their distinctice arrangements of diverse rock materials affect the form and arrangement of the surface features that the gradational agents produce.

Tectonic events and human activities. Tectonic events, with a few local exceptions, proceed without human causation or intervention. On the other hand, earthquakes and volcanic eruptions have been responsible for some of the worst catastrophes that have befallen human beings. People have shown little inclination to avoid the tectonically active zones of the world, and in some parts of those areas the chronicles of disaster are long and full.

Earthquakes. The great majority of earthquake shocks are no more than dish-rattling tremors, but occasional quakes are sharp enough to cause minor structural damage, especially to plaster or masonry buildings. Truly violent earthquakes normally occur in any given locality only at long intervals, yet a year rarely passes without at least one severe and destructive quake somewhere in the world. Most earthquakes strike with little or no generally recognized warning, and relatively few buildings are designed to absorb intense shock without suffering heavy damage or complete collapse. Hence loss of life in earthquake-rocked cities is sometimes appalling. The largest recorded earthquake death toll during the present century was about 143,000 in Tokyo and neighboring areas in 1923. Some 74,000 were killed by a quake which destroyed Messina, Italy, in 1908, and nearly as many died in northern Peru in 1970. By comparison, loss of life in the most lethal quake that has hit the United States was 452, in San Francisco in 1906. Perhaps the most intense shock witnessed in

North America occurred in southeastern Missouri in 1811, but fortunately the sparseness of settlement in the area at that time kept the death toll small.

Not all destruction or injury is caused directly by the tremors themselves. Accompanying fires, landslides, floods from ruptured dams, and other related events may add greatly to the toll. In both the San Francisco and Tokyo disasters mentioned above, fires set by the quakes appear to have done much more property damage than the quakes themselves. In the Alaska earthquake of 1964, the city of Anchorage was heavily damaged by large-scale slumping and subsidence of the unstable saturated silts and clays on which it was built (Fig. 10.12), while the small coastal port of Valdez was almost overwhelmed by a seismic sea wave set up by displacement along a submerged section of the fault zone.

Volcanoes. Volcanoes in populous areas most commonly cause major damage by laying down thick blankets of ash that bury or break down houses and other low buildings. Sometimes large streams of lava move into inhabited areas, crushing buildings or setting them afire. More dangerous to human life than these relatively slow happenings, however, are the occasional violent outbursts of asphyxiating or scorching clouds of gases that rush down the flanks of

Figure 10.12 During the earthquake of 1964, much of the damage at Anchorage, Alaska, was caused by cracking, subsidence, and slumping of the saturated silty clay on which much of the city is built. *(U.S. Geological Survey.)*

a cone at high speeds, snuffing out all life that happens to be in their paths. In 1902 an incandescent cloud that burst from the erupting volcano Mt. Pelee, on the West Indian island of Martinique, swept over the city of St. Pierre, killing all but one of the nearly 30,000 inhabitants. In the year 79 A.D., the small city of Pompeii, near modern Naples, Italy, was turned into a tragically fascinating archeological object by an asphyxiating cloud from neighboring Mt. Vesuvius that instantly killed the inhabitants, after which a tremendous outpouring of ash quickly buried and largely preserved the city, which has since been excavated. It has even proved possible to make remarkably faithful casts of the bodies of a number of the victims by injecting wet plaster into the cavities which they once occupied.

As long as people continue to build their cities in coastal California, Central America, the Mediterranean peninsulas, and other tectonically active areas, there seems to be no way to avert repeated disasters. Nor, all considered, is abandonment of such otherwise attractive regions a reasonable alternative. There is little doubt, however, that increased understanding of the phenomena can lead to measures that will significantly reduce the loss of life.

Recent investigations have led some scientists to believe that it may soon prove possible to forecast both earthquakes and volcanic eruptions. Eruption forecasting might well permit the orderly evacuation of persons from the most immediately threatened danger zones and provide ample warning to others nearby to be alert and ready to move. It seems more doubtful that earthquake prediction is likely soon to achieve the precision with respect to time and location that would justify the mass evacuation of the citizenry of large cities. There is little question, however, that requiring quake-resistant construction in earthquake-prone areas, together with educational programs recommending sensible precautionary behavior, could save many lives when disaster strikes.

Plate Tectonics and the Larger Crustal Features

Plate Tectonics

World pattern of crustal disturbance. Crustal disturbance has not been evenly distributed over the

world in any given period of geologic history—nor, indeed, for the whole span of geologic history. The majority of the deformed rock structures that exist today were produced long ago. Thus, for example, the folds of the Rocky Mountains developed about 70 million years ago, while those of the Appalachians are more than 250 million years old. Many of the complex structures of central and eastern Canada date far back into early geologic time, some to more than a billion years ago. These records of ancient events exist now only because later diastrophism or erosion has not destroyed them. Some areas of the crust do not appear to have been subjected to anything more than mild warping for hundreds of millions of years. Others seem to have undergone strong and repeated disturbances over a long span of geologic time and are still being actively changed today.

Since earthquakes commonly accompany the fracturing and displacement of rocks, their pattern of occurrence should indicate where the greatest diastrophic activity is centered at the present time. Figure 10.13 shows that the principal earthquake regions lie in a belt which circles the basin of the Pacific Ocean and extends westward across southern Eurasia. Comparison with Plate 2 will reveal a close correlation with the high-mountain regions of the world, which is not surprising, since high mountains are themselves indicative of strong tectonic activity in late geologic time. Other areas of significant modern tectonic activity occur in the ocean basins, notably near the mid-line of the Atlantic Basin, along a curving line running from the South Atlantic into the western Indian Ocean, and in the eastern part of the southern Pacific Basin. Comparison with sea-bottom topography reveals that these strips of crustal activity correspond to broad, well-defined swells or ridges on the ocean floors.

Volcanic activity is much more localized than diastrophism, but it occurs chiefly in areas that are also diastrophically active (Fig. 10.14). Deep-seated masses of molten rock seem to develop most frequently in places where the crust is being profoundly deformed.

Continental drift and plate tectonics. Since the early part of the twentieth century, some scholars have suspected that the continents have not always been in their present positions relative to one another or to the poles of the earth. To these scientists it has

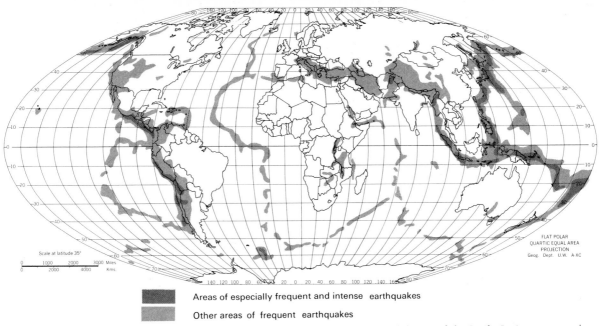

Areas of especially frequent and intense earthquakes

Other areas of frequent earthquakes

Figure 10.13 Medium and large earthquakes have been especially abundant around the rim of the Pacific Basin, across southern Eurasia, and along the mid-oceanic ridges. *(Adapted from Miyamura, in The Earth's Crust and Upper Mantle, P. J. Hart, ed., American Geophysical Union, Washington, 1969.)*

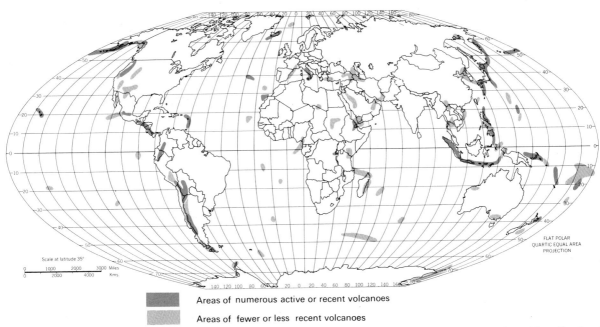

Areas of numerous active or recent volcanoes

Areas of fewer or less recent volcanoes

Figure 10.14 Volcanic activity is less widespread than earthquakes but occurs in parts of the same areas. *(Adapted from Horai and Uyeda [after Vening Meinesz], in The Earth's Crust and Upper Mantle, P. J. Hart, ed., American Geophysical Union, Washington, 1969.)*

209

appeared, for instance, that during the latter part of geological history, North and South America had pulled apart from Europe and Africa, swinging to the west and northwest, while India and Australia had moved eastward from Africa, and Antarctica had shifted southward. There was considerable supporting evidence, chiefly in the fact that the apparent past distribution of climates, as reconstructed from the fossil record, could not be otherwise explained, and in certain striking similarities between those parts of the continents thought to have been formerly joined.

This theory of "continental drift" did not receive wide acceptance, principally because there seemed no conceivable mechanism whereby the continental "rafts" could have been moved through or across the denser surrounding crust. At the same time, however, it was generally conceded that the intensely compressed structures of many of the great mountain systems could scarcely be accounted for except by horizontal movements of the crust of as much as several tens (or in some instances a few hundreds) of kilometers.

Since the late 1950s a series of remarkable new discoveries and perceptions has, with startling rapidity, generated a whole new body of theory concerning worldwide crustal movements. At the heart of the new theories is the realization, derived in large part from careful examination of the form and materials of the ocean floors, that at the great oceanic ridges, such as the Mid-Atlantic Ridge, the crust is indeed pulling apart, with new material moving up into the rift from below. Thus at these rifts new crust is forming and continuously spreading out symmetrically to either side. As new crust forms and spreads, the whole crust ahead of the spreading sheets must be pushed away from the rift zone. Since this process is occurring along several extensive lines or bands, it follows that the entire crust, together with the outer, most rigid layers of the mantle, must be in motion as a series of immense plates, each moving away from the nearest rifts (Fig. 10.15).

If, however, new crust is forming and expanding from the rift zones while the total area of earth crust remains unchanged, there must be other places where crust is being somehow consumed. The logical places to expect that to occur would be where the leading edges of two plates, each moving away from a different rift, are being jammed together. At

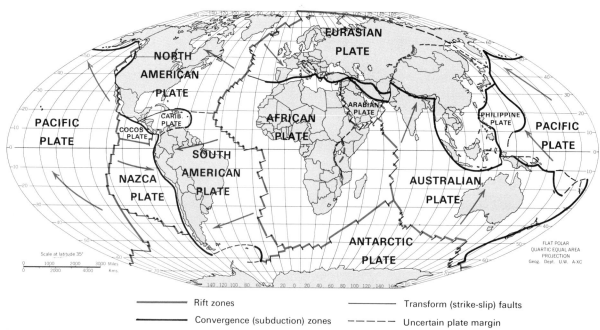

Figure 10.15   The earth's major crustal plates. *(Adapted from J. F. Dewey and others.)*

these places, the edge of one or both plates will be thrust downward into the mantle and consumed by melting. This worldwide scheme of movement of huge crustal plates, together with the accompanying deformations and alterations of the crust, is termed *plate tectonics.*

The causes of plate movements are not clear. Most students of the problem believe that the responsibility lies with slow convectional currents in the solid but deformable mantle underneath. Perhaps because of differences from place to place in radioactivity or in the rate of heat loss through the crust, temperature differences may occur deep in the mantle. Over "hot spots" rising currents might then develop, spreading out at the base of the crust, while over cooler areas currents would converge and sink. The horizontally moving currents in the mantle would tend to drag the crust (and probably the outermost shell of the mantle also) along with them.

The results of plate tectonics.   Plate tectonic theory vindicates those who believed that the continents have been displaced relative to one another. At the same time, it disposes of one of the principal stumbling blocks of the classical continental-drift hypothesis by noting that the continents do not move through the oceanic crust about them, but are simply parts of larger rigid blocks that may include great expanses of oceanic crust as well.

It now seems probable that most of the major structural features of the earth have been directly or indirectly produced by plate tectonics and that most current diastrophism and vulcanism can be in some degree related to plate movements. Those sections of the crust that show the greatest amount of current tectonic activity are generally at or near the edges of plates, especially the leading edges where crustal convergence and down-dragging is occurring. The mountainous rim of the Pacific Basin is one such zone, with the Eurasian Plate being jammed against the huge Pacific Plate on the western side of the Basin, and the South American Plate colliding with several smaller oceanic plates on the eastern side. The western margin of North America is a highly complex area lying partly on and partly just east of a major rift. Thus the Gulf of California is a rift; the famous San Andreas fault of California is an unusually long strike-slip fault associated with the rift; and the coast of the Pacific Northwest is a zone of convergence just

east of the rift. The extensive, complex-structured mountain systems extending across southern Eurasia and the Mediterranean zone are related to a jamming together of the broad Eurasian Plate, on the north, and the African-Arabian and Indian-Australian Plates on the south. Other relationships can be inferred from the map.

Where crustal convergence is occurring, dense oceanic crust evidently turns downward fairly readily and is thrust deep into the mantle, undergoing partial melting in the process (Fig. 10.16*A*). A zone of volcanic activity often develops above the area where melting is going on. Not infrequently this activity is so distributed as to give rise to a curving line or arc of partially volcanic islands, such as the Indonesian and Aleutian chains. When continental crust reaches the convergence zone, however, it resists being drawn down because of its low density. Under these circumstances, the outer margins of the continental block, often composed of unusually thick masses of sediments derived from erosion on the continents and deposited in the adjacent sea, are subjected to tremendously strong compressional deformation and thickening, sometimes accompanied by vulcanism (Fig. 10.16*B*). Farther back from the continental margin the crust is more mildly deformed. Many of the more massive mountain systems of the world, such as the Alps, the Himalaya, and the Andes, display the extremely complex deformation and unusually thickened crust believed to be characteristic of these leading edges of continental blocks in convergence zones. The immense bands of depressed, sediment-thickened, and subsequently compressed crust in which most major mountain systems have developed have long been called *geosynclines.*

An interesting problem is posed by the fact that other areas, such as the Appalachians, which are nowhere near the leading edges of present crustal blocks, display precisely the same type of complex geosynclinal structures. Their structures are known to be geologically ancient and thus provide ample evidence that the whole pattern of plates and plate movements has changed radically from time to time during the course of geologic history. The present system of plates and movements has probably been in existence for at least 200 million years. The separation of the American, Antarctic, Australian, and Indian land masses from Africa and Europe that was

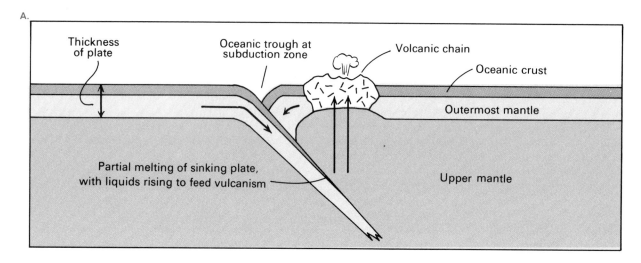

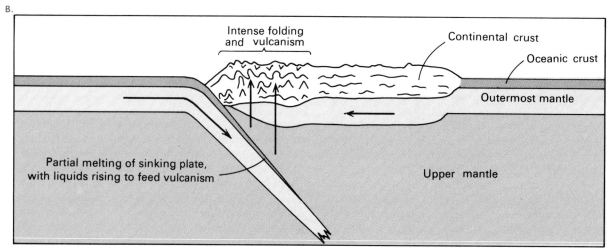

Figure 10.16   Crustal convergence zones. *A* involves only oceanic crust; *B* shows continental crust drawn into convergence zone. *(Adapted from J. F. Dewey, in Scientific American, May, 1972.)*

postulated by the early supporters of continental drift has occurred during that time (Fig. 10.17).

Unfortunately space does not permit more comprehensive treatment of this intriguing body of research. Much of it, especially the theories of causation, remains highly speculative. In spite of its recency and incompleteness, however, it already represents a prodigious scientific accomplishment. Without question it is one of the longest strides yet taken toward understanding the patterns and development of the largest of all geographical features: the continents, ocean basins, and cordilleran mountain belts.

World Pattern of Major Crustal Features

At the present stage of crustal evolution, the masses of continental crust are much less concentrated than they were in earlier geologic time, but they are neither evenly nor systematically distributed. A glance at a world map or, better, a globe will reveal the irregularities of the pattern. It is possible to divide the earth into two equal hemispheres, one of which contains over 80 percent of the total land area while the other is largely oceanic (Fig. 10.18). Eurasia contains as much land area as the next two smaller

Figure 10.17 Probable positions of continents at beginning of current sequence of plate movements, perhaps 200 million years ago. Present positions shown in dashed outlines. *(Adapted from R. S. Dietz and J. C. Holden, in Scientific American, October, 1970.)*

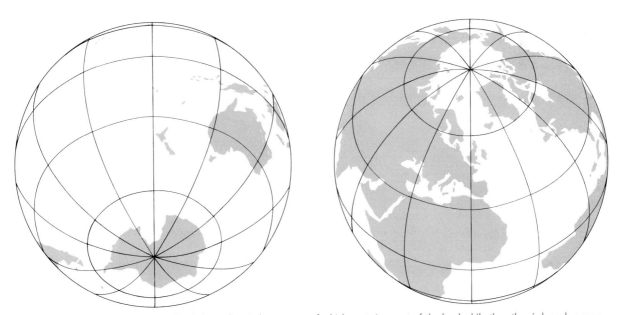

Figure 10.18 The earth can be divided into hemispheres, one of which contains most of the land while the other is largely ocean.

continents (Africa and North America) combined and more than one-third of all the continental crust. Conversely, the Pacific Ocean has roughly twice the area of the Atlantic and accounts for about 46 percent of the oceanic area of the earth. The four largest continents are all widest at the north and taper toward the south, and the greatest expanse of continental crust lies in the middle latitudes of the Northern Hemisphere.

In view of this lack of system in the overall distribution of continents and ocean basins, it is difficult to generalize meaningfully about the pattern of the world's major features. A beginning can be made, however, by emphasizing the pattern of the great cordilleran belts, which contain most of the world's great mountain systems, and the similarly massive mid-oceanic ridges, of which the Mid-Atlantic Ridge is the most familiar. As has already been noted, the true cordilleran belts correspond broadly to the zones of convergence of crustal plates, especially those in which continental crust is involved, while the oceanic ridges lie along the major rift zones where crustal plates are drawing apart.

Features of the ocean floors. As its name implies, the great crustal seam of the Mid-Atlantic Ridge

nearly follows the center line of the Atlantic Basin from the Arctic Ocean to the Antarctic (Plate 3), and from it the North and South American Plates on the one hand and the Eurasian and African Plates on the other are actively diverging. At its southern end, the rift zone swings eastward, passing midway between Antarctica and southernmost Africa, across the southern Indian Ocean, midway between Antarctica and Australia, and on across the southernmost Pacific Basin, finally turning abruptly northward across the southeastern Pacific to the west coast of Mexico and California. From this continuous rift a major branch reaches northward through the middle of the Indian Ocean and then northwestward into the Red Sea.

The mid-ocean ridges are features of impressive scale, rising 1 to 3 km (3,300 to 10,000 ft) above the adjacent sea floors and, in many places, exceeding 1,500 km (900 mi) in breadth. Parts of the ridge system, especially in the Atlantic and Indian Oceans, are crowned with a still higher and rougher crest, commonly split by a central trough (Fig. 10.19A). As previously noted, the ridges are foci of earthquake activity and locally exhibit volcanic phenomena as well.

The ocean bottoms apart from the mid-oceanic ridges are generally rather smooth, but by no

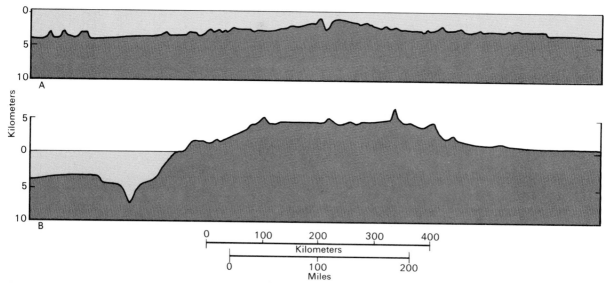

Figure 10.19 Simplified cross sections of plate boundaries. *A* is the rift zone of the Mid-Atlantic Ridge west of the Azores. *B* is convergence zone on western margin of South American Plate near latitude of 25° S. *(A, adapted from Vogt, Schneider, and Johnson in The Earth's Crust and Upper Mantle, American Geophysical Union, Washington, 1969. B, constructed from various sources.)*

means featureless. Sediment-floored basin plains occupy by far the largest area, but in many sections, most notably the western Pacific, Indian, and Arctic Oceans, these are interrupted by prominent isolated mountains (seamounts), series of parallel ridges and troughs, broad, gentle "rises," and various irregular ridges and plateaus. A number of long, curving strands of cordilleran structure, commonly accompanied by deep trenches on their outer margins, swing across the peripheral sections of the ocean basins, generally forming distinctive island arcs. These and other features of the continental margins are discussed briefly in Chapter 15.

Although the greatest depth of the sea (11,034 m or 36,201 ft) and the highest elevation on land (8,848 m or 29,028 ft) are not vastly different, the mean depth of the ocean floor (about 3,730 m or 10,600 ft) is far greater than the mean elevation of the lands (about 850 m or 2,790 ft). The extensive basin plains lie at depths of 3,000 to 7,000 m, with figures somewhat less than 5,000 m (16,000 to 17,000 ft) being especially common.

The cordilleran belts. A useful starting point in considering the structural pattern of the continents is the cordilleran belts, the great bands of strongly deformed crust in which most of the great mountain systems, together with various associated valleys, basins, and plateaus, are located. The principal cordilleran systems form a nearly continuous ring about the Pacific Ocean Basin, reflecting the convergence upon the Pacific crustal plates by the American plates from the east and the Eurasian and Indian-Australian Plates from the west. From this ring a long arm is thrust westward through southern Eurasia to the Atlantic, in accordance with the convergence of the Eurasian Plate with the African and Indian-Australian Plates (Plate 3).

Thus both of the American continents and Eurasia have long cordilleran segments running along one side of the continent, forming for each an immense "backbone," with the less rugged and tectonically less active remainder of the continent stretching out toward the Atlantic and Arctic Basins. Africa and Australia lack such well-marked cordilleran bands (except for the Atlas chain in extreme northwestern Africa), for these two continents are positioned within their crustal plates at considerable distance from convergent margins.

Both structure and terrain in the cordilleran belts are extremely varied, and major sections of the cordilleras differ greatly in character and complexity. Structures can vary from the most intensely folded, thrust-faulted, and intruded belts, such as are found in the Alps and Himalaya (Fig. 10.20), to broad, open folds and relatively simple fault blocks of the sort that occur in much of the western United States. Terrain similarly ranges from wide bands of mountains of great height and ruggedness to widely spaced, narrow mountain strands separated by broad, sediment-filled basin plains.

The simplest of the continental cordilleras is that of the Andes, which follows the western margin of South America without a break from the northern extremity to the southern. It lies along a well-marked and active zone of plate convergence. The actual subduction line is marked by a deep ocean-floor trench immediately offshore, and the band of crustal deformation is unusually narrow and continuous (Fig. 10.19B). The mountain belt itself is nowhere wider than 800 km (500 mi), generally much less, and is remarkable for the absence of low passes through the high divide.

By contrast, the North American cordillera reaches widths of 1,600 km (1,000 mi) and displays far greater variety in structure and surface forms. Generally speaking, the structures in the Mexican and United States sections tend to be relatively simple folds and fault blocks, and the terrain consists of a loose array of mountain strands, separated by broad valleys, basins, and tablelands. Toward the Canadian border the zone narrows, and from there northward crustal jamming is more intense and the terrain more continuously mountainous. Unlike the South American Plate, the North American Plate does not converge head-on with the oceanic plates to the west except in its northern part. Because of the shapes of the blocks and their relative directions of motion, the contact in California and southward involves more of a sideswiping movement, a fact which is probably responsible in part for the less intense compressional deformation in the southwestern part of the continent.

The Eurasian cordillera is not only the most extensive of all but by far the most varied. In the west it is only moderately wide but highly complex, being composed of loosely linked mountain systems, such as the Alps, Pyrenees, Apennines, and Carpathians,

MAJOR STRUCTURAL FEATURES

PLATE BOUNDARIES

Rift Zones

Transform (Strike-slip) Faults

Convergence (Subduction) Zones
Ticks on Side Toward Which
Descending Plate is Moving.

Uncertain Plate Boundaries

OCEAN BASINS

Continental Shelves

Mid-Oceanic Ridges

Other Ridges, Platforms, and
Closely-Spaced Seamounts

Deep Sea Floors

CONTINENTS

Cordilleran Belts

Folded and Faulted During Current
Sequence of Plate Movements
(Mesozoic and Cenozoic)

Folded and Faulted During Earlier
Sequences of Plate Movements
(Mostly Paleozoic); Subsequently
Reactivated

Ancient Shields Involved
in Cordilleran Reactivaction

Sedimentary Platforms and Basins
Included in Cordilleran Zones

Non-Cordilleran Areas

Folded and Faulted Before Current
Sequence of Plate Movements
(Mostly Paleozoic)

Ancient Shields

Sedimentary Platforms

Major Lava Plateaus

Areas Subject to Moderate Uplift
in Late Geologic Time

Scale at latitude 35

Miles 0   1000   2000   3000

Kms. 0   2000   4000

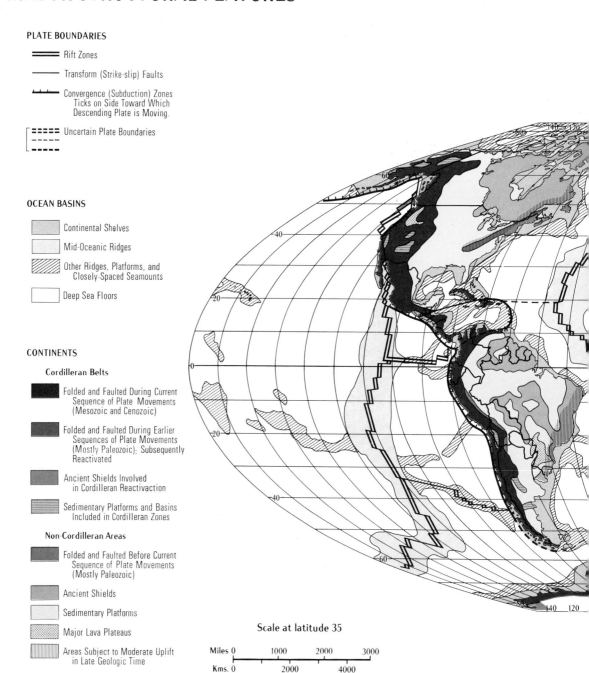

PLATE 3

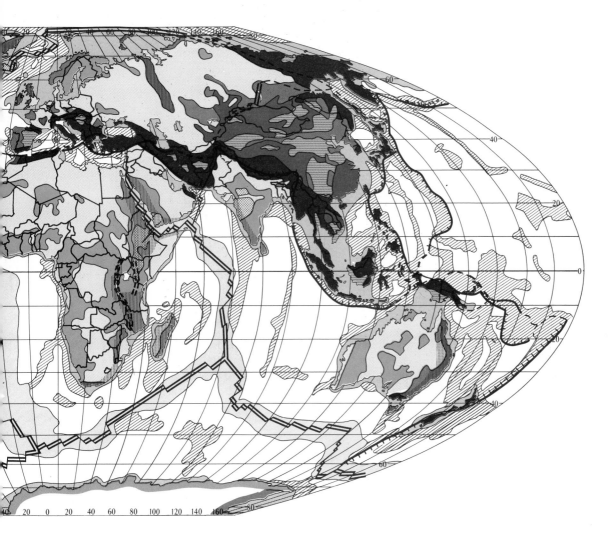

FLAT POLAR QUARTIC EQUAL AREA PROJECTION

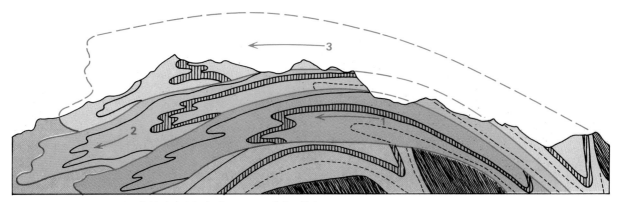

Figure 10.20   A complex folded and faulted structure of the Alpine type.

separated by broad, low basins—some drowned by the sea—and broken by numerous gaps. From Turkey eastward to Pakistan it somewhat resembles the cordillera of southwestern North America, both in structure and surface form, though with more intense compressional folding. From Pakistan eastward, however, it fans out to tremendous breadth, occupying practically all of central, southeastern, and northeastern Asia and flinging long strands along the great island arcs of the western Pacific. In general, the most intense deformation is occurring along the southern and eastern margins of the Eurasian Plate, where it is actively converging with the Indian-Australian and the Pacific Plates. Here the structures are those of a vigorous subduction zone—an intensely compressed band, in places complicated by vulcanism, fronted by a series of trenches and lowlands. In this zone lie the Himalaya, the Burma-Malaya-Indonesia arc, the Philippines and Taiwan, the Ryukyu and Japanese arcs, and the Kuril-Kamchatka arc. The remainder of the Asiatic cordillera is made up of ancient complex structures that have been variously reactivated and reworked by late tectonics. Compared with the marginal zone, the more recent deformation has been generally less intense, somewhat resembling that of the Middle East and southwestern North America in the breadth and spacing of its features, although many of the mountain systems and basin plains are on an even grander scale.

The noncordilleran sections of the continents. Structurally those parts of the continents not included in the cordilleras are composed of three kinds of elements: (1) old cordilleran structures, now subject only to intermittent, relatively mild uplifting; (2) platforms (shields) of ancient igneous and metamorphic rocks, covered only locally by later sediments and rarely subject to more than broad, regional uplift and warping; (3) platforms of thick series of sedimentary strata, usually gently warped into extensive domes and basins.

Examples of older cordilleran structures are found in the Appalachian-New England-Newfoundland zone, the mountains of northeastern Greenland, the highlands of the British Isles and coastal Norway, the Ural Mountains of the north-central Soviet Union, and the highlands of eastern Australia. The first three examples are believed to be parts of a single system, broken by the rifting of Eurasia and North America. Although all the areas named are now hilly or mountainous, their more recent tectonics have been largely confined to simple uplift.

Ancient crystalline-rock shields are broadly exposed in each of the continents. One such platform occupies most of central and eastern Canada and Greenland. Possibly the much smaller Scandinavian shield represents a part of the same ancient mass, separated hundreds of millions of years ago by the development of the Appalachian-Norwegian cordilleran structures. A broadly but shallowly veneered shield lies in central Siberia, and smaller sections reach into Manchuria and Korea. Other great shields form much of eastern South America, the southern three-quarters of Africa, western Arabia, peninsular India, western and central Australia, and much of

Antarctica. It is widely believed that all of the shields noted in the preceding sentence were once parts of a single ancient land mass (sometimes referred to in continental drift literature as "Gondwanaland") that became separated by the development of the currently active worldwide rift system. Virtually all of the shield areas of the continents show similar persistent patterns of extremely broad swells and gentle basins. The basins, such as the Congo and Kalahari Basins of Africa or the Amazon Basin of South America, and the Hudson Bay lowland of Canada commonly preserve a cover of later sedimentary materials and have the surface form of plains. The higher swells are largely clear of sedimentary cover and are in some instances carved by erosion into hill or mountain country, especially where they abut against the sea, as in Labrador, Greenland, or eastern Brazil. In several areas, notably the Deccan Plateau of peninsular India, the Ethiopian section of east Africa, and the Paraná Plateau of southern Brazil, extensive resistant lava sheets atop the shield rocks have given a tableland character to the eroded landscape. The East African-Arabian section is especially interesting in that its great swells and deep grabens represent the most extensive and striking example of a major crustal rift zone, comparable to a mid-oceanic ridge structure, that penetrates far into a continent.

Thick sedimentary platforms, no more than gently warped, occupy immense areas of northwestern Eurasia, interior and southeastern North America, interior South America immediately east of the Andes, north Africa and eastern Arabia, and the eastern interior of Australia. Like the shields, these areas have long been tectonically quiescent, and on their surfaces, together with the lower parts of the adjacent shields, are developed most of the world's truly extensive plains.

The relationships between structure and surface form will be developed further in the next three chapters, but comparisons of Plate 2, Plate 3, and the table on page 194 will reveal many general relationships that are useful in understanding the landform differences among the continents and their principal subsections.

REVIEW QUESTIONS

1. How does the earth's crust differ from the materials beneath it? How does the crust that forms the continents differ from that of the ocean basins? Why do the continents stand higher than the ocean basins?

2. How do we know that the crust has been significantly altered and deformed over a long span of geologic time? How do we know that such changes are still occurring? Specifically, locate the major zones of the earth that are tectonically active at present.

3. What are the direct results of diastrophism upon the surface of the land? What are the direct effects of (a) extrusive and (b) intrusive vulcanism upon the land surface? Upon the rock structure?

4. Why does a complex geologic structure usually last much longer than the surface irregularities produced by the same crustal disturbance?

5. What is the relationship of earthquakes to tectonic processes generally? In what ways do earthquakes cause property damage and loss of life? Can anything be done to decrease damage or death tolls in earthquakes?

6. What was the principal idea involved in the early theory of "continental drift"? How does the modern theory of plate tectonics differ from the earlier theory?

7. According to plate tectonic theory, what is happening along the Mid-Atlantic Ridge and corresponding zones in other parts of the world? With what parts of the moving system of plates does the most active crustal deformation appear to be associated? In those zones, how does oceanic crust behave? Continental crust? Why do the two behave differently?

8. Where do the following areas lie with respect to the system of crustal plates, rift zones, and convergence zones: (a) the Andes, (b) the Alps, (c) Japan, (d) the midwestern United States, (e) northcentral Siberia, (f) east Africa, (g) the Appalachians?

9. How can geosynclinal structures like those of the Appalachians, Scandinavia, and the Urals, which are not at the edges of continental plates, be reconciled with the idea of plate tectonics?

10. Characterize the form of the mid-oceanic ridges. What is the best example of a corresponding feature on a continent? What are the principal characteristics and features of the ocean floors other than the mid-oceanic ridges? How do the

depths of the seas compare with the elevations of the continents?

11. Which are the three "cordilleran continents"? What is distinctive, in structure or surface character, about the cordilleras of (*a*) the Andes, (*b*) southwestern United States, and (*c*) eastern Eurasia? What is the relationship between the sea-floor trench off the west coast of South America, the Ganges lowland of northern India, and the Marianas Trench in the western Pacific? Why is there no similar feature along the California coast?

12. What two continents conspicuously lack major cordilleran belts? What two kinds of structural elements predominate in those continents? What is believed to be the structural relationship among Africa, Arabia, peninsular India, western Australia, and eastern South America? Specify at least two other major structural features of the continental crust that have been broken by plate rifting. What is the general structural character of the North American and northwest Eurasian plains?

Gradation: Rock Breakdown, Running Water, and Mass Wasting

It was stated in Chapter 9 that the surfaces of the land masses are shaped by the interaction of the tectonic processes, which produce major surface irregularities and create specific arrangements of rock materials, and the gradational processes, which move materials about over the surface, producing various erosional and depositional landforms. The most active movers of earth materials are running water, glacial ice, wind, waves, and gravity. Gravity is not only an important earth mover in its own right but is also the direct or indirect source of power for all the other agents. Hence, when material is picked up and moved by any agent, it is most likely to come to rest at a point lower than where it began. The long-run effect is for the higher parts of the surface to be lowered by removal of material and for the lower sections to be raised by deposition, thus reducing the overall irregularity. It is for this reason that the earth-moving agents and processes are called *gradational*.

ROCK MATERIALS AND ROCK BREAKDOWN

None of the agents of gradation can work very effectively against solid, massive bedrock. Therefore the processes that break rock masses down into finer particles are highly important preliminaries to gra-

dational activity. Furthermore, because different kinds of rocks differ greatly in their response to the processes of breakdown and in the products which they yield, a basic knowledge of common rock types is useful to the study of land-surface form.

Rock Materials

The contrasts in the behavior of different types of rocks under the agents that break them down are due principally to differences in (1) the chemical composition of the minerals that form the rocks, (2) the size, arrangement, and cohesiveness of the grains or particles, and (3) the detailed structure of the rock, that is, whether it is thin-bedded, platy, or massive.

Minerals. Rocks are made up of particles or substances called *minerals*, each of which has its own well-defined chemical composition and physical properties. Some minerals are physically hard and difficult to break; others are easily crushed or split. Some are soluble or otherwise chemically unstable under conditions that are common near the earth's surface. Others are highly stable under normal surface conditions and thus resist decomposition. Although there are hundreds of known minerals, a relatively small number make up the great bulk of the crust. Some of the commonest of these are listed in the table below. Several of the entries in the table represent groups of closely related minerals (for example, the feldspars or the clay minerals) rather than single varieties.

Some common minerals are formed during the cooling and crystallization of molten materials. Others are usually products of the decomposition of more complex minerals. In the table, for example, the feldspars, micas, pyroxenes, amphiboles, and magnetite fall into the first class, while the clays, calcite, dolomite, hematite, and limonite belong to the second. Silica can develop in either way.

The great differences among minerals in hardness and chemical stability are transmitted to the rocks which they compose, and because of their varied mineral composition as well as the form and arrangement of the particles, the rocks themselves vary in physical and chemical resistance. Although it is not within the scope of this book to discuss the hundreds of recognized types of rocks, a general

familiarity with the nature and origin of rocks and with the characteristics of some of the commonest varieties helps one to understand the development of many distinctive features of land-surface form.

Rocks. Geologists usually classify rocks primarily by their mode of origin. The three principal classes are (1) *igneous* rocks, which have crystallized from a molten state; (2) *sedimentary* rocks, which have developed through the consolidation of loose sediments deposited by the various agents of gradation or through chemical precipitation of substances carried in solution; and (3) *metamorphic* rocks, which have been formed through the alteration of other rocks, chiefly by great pressure and heat or by the work of mineralized groundwaters or hot gases.

By definition, igneous rocks are associated with vulcanism and form the various intrusive bodies, lava flows, and ash deposits. Most are composed of interlocking particles or grains of the commoner igneous minerals, such as quartz, feldspars, micas,

COMMON ROCK-FORMING MINERALS

Name	Composition	Hardness	Chemical stability	Distinctive characteristics
Silica (quartz and related minerals)	Silicon dioxide	Very hard	Very stable	Transparent or various light colors
Feldspars	Aluminum silicates with potassium, calcium, or sodium	Hard	Moderately stable to moderately unstable	Pink or gray; smooth faces common
Micas	Aluminum silicates with potassium, iron, or magnesium	Soft	Moderately stable	Transparent or black; thin flakes and sheets
Pyroxenes and amphiboles	Silicates of calcium, magnesium, iron, and sometimes aluminum	Hard	Moderately unstable	Dark green or black
Clay minerals	Hydrous aluminum silicates	Soft	Stable	Earthy; light colors
Calcite	Calcium carbonate	Soft	Very unstable	Usually transparent, white, or light colors
Dolomite	Calcium-magnesium carbonate	Rather soft	Unstable	Usually transparent, white, or light colors
Hematite, magnetite, limonite	Iron oxides	Variable	Stable	Black, red, or yellow; often earthy

and amphiboles or pyroxenes. In general those of the larger and deeper intrusions, which have cooled slowly, are coarse-grained, while those of the more quickly cooled surface flows and narrow dikes and sills tend to be fine-particled. Among the abundant coarse-grained igneous rocks are granite (made up chiefly of quartz and feldspar), diorite (mostly feldspars), and gabbro (mostly pyroxenes, amphiboles, and feldspars). The fine-grained counterparts of these three are, respectively, rhyolite, andesite, and basalt. Except for lavas, ash deposits, and thin sills, the igneous rocks are massive rather than layered (Fig. 11.1).

In contrast, sedimentary rocks are characteristically stratified, with layers or beds of varying thickness (Fig. 11.2). One group of common sedimentary rocks, called *clastic* rocks, are simply deposits of loose gravels, sands, silts, or clays that have been compacted and cemented together by some substance—most commonly silica or calcium carbonate but sometimes iron oxides or clay. Conglomerate (cemented gravel), sandstone (sand), and shale (clay) are examples of this group. Limestones, dolomites, rock salt, and gypsum are examples of rocks formed by the precipitation or removal of the particular

mineral substance from solution, usually in lakes or shallow seas.

Metamorphic rocks, since they may be produced by various processes and from any kind of rock, are an extremely complex and diverse group. Some are distinctly foliated (divided into well-defined bands, sheets, or plates) while others are more massive (Fig. 11.3). Some, especially those formed from sedimentary rocks, may be stratified. Among the foliated types are gneiss (a coarse-banded rock commonly derived from granite, diorite, or conglomerate), schist (a more finely foliated rock that may develop from gabbro, basalt, shale, etc.), and slate (a firm-plated material usually derived from shale). More massive metamorphic rocks include fine-particled hornfels (from shale), coarsely crystalline marble (from limestone), and granular or nearly structureless quartzite (from sandstone).

Rock Breakdown

Processes of rock breakdown. The processes of rock breakdown are commonly referred to collectively as *weathering*, although the term is hardly appropri-

Figure 11.1   An immense mass of granite is laid bare in the uppermost 360 m (1,200 ft) of Longs Peak, the highest summit in Rocky Mountain National Park, Colorado. Note the absence of stratification. Dark bands in center are outcrops of an included body of schist.

Figure 11.2 Stratification is usually prominent in sedimentary rocks. *(National Park Service.)*

ate if applied to the diastrophic shattering of rock far below the surface. Two interrelated groups of processes are involved. One is simply mechanical breaking of the rock, or *disintegration*. The other is chemical alteration of the rock minerals, or *decomposition*. The two go on at the same time and actually aid one another, for the cracking of rock makes it easier for chemical agents (chiefly water) to penetrate, and conversely, decomposition weakens rock masses so that they can be broken more easily.

In spite of the basic simplicity of the disintegration process, the various ways by which it is accomplished in nature are imperfectly known. Probably the most important methods of rock breaking are (1) the formation of joints during crustal deformation or in response to stresses developed during the cooling or compaction of rocks, (2) the expansion of water as it freezes in rock crevices, and (3) the wedging effect of the growth of plant roots in rock crevices. In addition, all scraping, grinding, scouring, and striking of the rock surface by hard, heavy, or fast-moving objects may dislodge fragments from the larger mass. The extreme temperature changes that accompany forest

fires or lightning strikes cause enough uneven expansion and contraction to strain rocks to the breaking point.

Rock disintegration may thus be expected everywhere, but it is probably farthest advanced where crustal deformation has occurred, where plant roots are especially abundant, and where alternate freeze and thaw is frequent.

The principal agent of rock decomposition is water—especially water which contains certain dissolved substances, such as carbon dioxide, that make it more aggressive chemically. Most water in the ground does contain such impurities, which are washed down from the atmosphere, given off by plant roots, or released during organic decay. High temperatures also contribute to decomposition, not only by keeping water unfrozen, but by increasing the rate of chemical reactions of most kinds. The rotting of rock is therefore most rapid in moist areas, especially the humid tropics, and most retarded in arid or very cold regions. Some decomposition occurs, however, even where the climate is arid or cold.

The chemical processes involved in decompo-

Figure 11.3 Foliated schist. Lighter-colored band cutting across foliation is a granitic dike intruded after the schist was formed.

sition attack firm rock in several ways. Some minerals are actively removed in solution. The rest, as a rule, soften and swell and are eventually altered to yield substances that are softer, more soluble, or finer-particled than the original minerals, so that the rock is weakened or even destroyed. As an example, the hard mineral hornblende, one of the amphiboles, decomposes into carbonates of calcium and magnesium (which are soluble), iron oxides and clays (which are fine-particled), and silica in such fine-particled form (colloidal) that it is easily removed by water.

The end products of disintegration are simply rock fragments—usually, rather angular ones. Decomposition, on the other hand, characteristically produces a mass of fine soil particles and more or less rounded fragments of somewhat rotten rock. If erosion does not remove these products, they accumulate to form a surface layer of debris called the *regolith* (Fig. 11.4). In humid areas the regolith is composed

primarily of fine debris from decomposition. In dry and cold areas, however, the angular products of disintegration are more evident, not because disintegration is necessarily more active there than elsewhere, but simply because they are not hidden by finer debris (Fig. 11.5).

Rock resistance. It has already been emphasized that different types of rocks, because of their mineral composition and detailed structure, differ greatly in their response to the weathering processes. Some are very resistant in almost any environment; others are universally weak. Still others decompose readily in humid climates but prove surprisingly resistant in a desert environment.

In humid climates the most important factor in resistance is the chemical stability of the minerals which compose the rock. Thus rocks made up largely of silica are likely to be especially resistant; those composed chiefly of feldspars, pyroxenes, and amphiboles will be intermediate in resistance; and those composed of or cemented by the soluble salts and carbonates decompose readily. Other things being equal, massive, impermeable rocks resist decomposition better than jointed, thin-bedded, or foliated rocks containing the same minerals. The most resistant of all common rocks is quartzite, which is tightly structured and composed almost wholly of silica.

Among the rocks that are fairly resistant in humid climates are granite, rhyolite, gneiss, silica-cemented sandstones and conglomerates, and some dolomites that contain much silica. Lower on the

Figure 11.4 Bedrock grading upward into regolith of rock fragments and soil.

Figure 11.5 Angular rock fragments cover the steep upper slopes of Mt. Richthofen, in Rocky Mountain National Park, Colorado, at an elevation of about 3,700 m (12,000 ft). Repeated freeze and thaw at this high altitude favors rapid shattering of rock.

scale, but still moderately resistant, are gabbro, diorite, andesite, basalt, slates, and thicker-banded schists, most conglomerates, and some silica-rich limestones. Rather weak rocks include dolomites, thin-plated schists, thick-bedded shales, and lime-cemented sandstones. Weakest of all are pure limestones, marbles, rock salt, and thin-bedded shales. All the types listed, however, are subject to significant variations.

In dry regions, where chemical weathering is feeble, the physical structure of the rock appears to be particularly important. Massive, fine-grained rocks—rhyolites, basalts, quartzites, and even thick-bedded, fine-particled limestones—seem to endure better than coarse-grained granites, porous sandstones, all thin-bedded sedimentary rocks, and highly foliated metamorphic rocks. Weathering as a whole, however, proceeds much more slowly in arid regions than in humid ones.

THE PRINCIPAL GRADATIONAL AGENTS: RUNNING WATER AND GRAVITY

The Gradational Agents and Their Work

It is convenient to divide the work of any gradational agent into three parts: erosion, transportation, and deposition. This division is somewhat artificial, especially that between erosion, which is the detaching of

material from its initial position, and transportation, the carrying of material away from the point of erosion. However, the laws governing the processes do differ, and they can be understood best when they are examined individually. It is also necessary to consider the work of the different gradational agents separately, for each agent has its own peculiarities and produces its own distinctive results.

Before the 1930s, surprisingly little was actually known about the mechanics of erosion, transportation, and deposition by the different gradational agents. Most earlier students had based their concepts of the gradational processes largely upon inference drawn from observing the landforms themselves. Unavoidably, the inferences were not all correct. During the past few decades careful field observation, simulation of natural conditions in laboratory experiments, and the application of physical theory have greatly advanced our understanding of the agents, especially water and wind. Nevertheless, much still remains to be learned.

Running Water

For the world as a whole, running water is the most important long-distance transporter of earth material. In company with the short-haul activity of gravity-induced movement of regolith on slopes (known as *mass wasting*), it has been at work almost everywhere. Although some landscapes show the effects of some other agent more clearly, running water has left its marks on all but a few.

Origin and Mechanical Effects of Surface Flow

Water and energy.   As water that has been evaporated from the earth's surface is carried into the atmosphere by rising air currents, it acquires *potential energy* (sometimes referred to as *energy of position*). This energy is derived from the work done upon the water in moving it upward against the ever-present pull of gravity. As long as the water particles are small and are upheld by atmospheric turbulence, they retain that potential energy. If the particles grow too large to be sustained by turbulence, gravity will pull them downward, and the potential energy becomes progressively transformed into *kinetic ener-*

gy, or energy of motion, as they accelerate in their earthward fall.

When the drops strike the earth's surface, their velocity is abruptly checked, and in the impact, their kinetic energy is largely converted into heat. The water still retains a considerable potential energy, however, for gravity continues to urge it toward the center of the earth. If it lies on a slope, gravity will set it in motion down the incline, and again potential energy is converted into kinetic energy, this time expressed as flowing motion. As the water flows, a considerable part of its kinetic energy is used to overcome friction, either within the turbulent flowing mass or against the underlying earth material. The energy thus used is dissipated as heat. The water will continue to flow downslope, converting potential energy into kinetic and heat energy, until it reaches the sea or the bottom of some interior basin having no outlet. Because there is no adjacent lower place to which it can descend, friction drags it to a halt. Here, or at any other point it passes after reaching the ground, however, it may still respond to gravity by infiltrating down through the pore spaces or cracks in the soil, regolith, or bedrock beneath. In this infiltration process, as in surface flow, potential energy is converted into kinetic energy which, in turn, is dissipated by friction as the water passes through the small openings in the earth materials.

Thus water, falling upon the land surface, flowing across it in sheets or streams, percolating down through the surficial materials, and eventually being reevaporated into the atmosphere, plays a major role in the earth's mechanism of energy and mass exchange. The amount of kinetic energy developed by flowing water depends upon the mass of water involved and the velocity of flow. Thin films of water moving across the ground surface or down through pore tubes in the soil possess little kinetic energy and thus have small, but not negligible, capacity to dislodge and move particles of earth. Large, swift-flowing streams, on the other hand, possess great energy and can erode and transport immense quantities of solid matter, especially if one considers their cumulative work over considerable periods of time. In these processes, kinetic energy is transferred from the moving water to the earth materials as they are set in motion.

Infiltration, throughflow, and runoff.   As noted, water that falls to the land surface can follow either

of two downward paths (Fig. 11.6). Some of it flows down the surface of the slope as *direct surface runoff* or *overland flow*. The rest infiltrates into the regolith. The percentage of the precipitation that follows each path depends upon several factors. Much will soak in if precipitation is slow and gentle, if it occurs infrequently, if the regolith is highly permeable, or if surface movement is impeded by the levelness of the land or by a mat of vegetation. On the other hand, heavy and frequent downpours, regolith of low permeability, steep slopes, and scanty vegetation all favor larger amounts of direct surface runoff.

Direct surface runoff begins to move as a thin sheet of water on the upper slopes. Because it seeks the lowest places and the easiest lines of movement, it soon becomes concentrated into well-defined threads of flow. These join other threads in progressive fashion, forming larger and larger streams and rivers. The smaller streams are called *tributaries* of the larger streams they join. A major stream with all its tributaries is called a *stream system*, and the entire area of land drained by a given system is the *drainage basin* of that system. The line separating one drainage basin from another is a *divide*.

Of the water that infiltrates the ground, much is returned to the atmosphere by evapotranspiration. Most of the remainder, however, moves downward and laterally through the regolith and bedrock, eventually reappearing at the surface through seepages and springs on the lower slopes and in the valley bottoms. This movement of water is referred to as *throughflow*. Since most of the water finally reaches the streams, it may also be called *indirect runoff*. Direct and indirect runoff together constitute the total runoff (usually called simply the *runoff*) of an area. As noted in Chapter 8, direct surface runoff reaches the streams quickly and may cause the water level in channels to rise swiftly. Indirect runoff is paid out slowly and gradually and may account for nearly all of a stream's flow during the low-water periods between rains.

Water erosion.   Water dislodges particles from the land surface by five principal means: (1) the impact of raindrops striking against a bare soil surface; (2) the direct frictional drag of a flowing sheet or stream of water upon the underlying bed; (3) the work of eddy currents in the flowing water, which help to loosen particles from the bed and flip them up into the moving mass; (4) the impact or friction against the

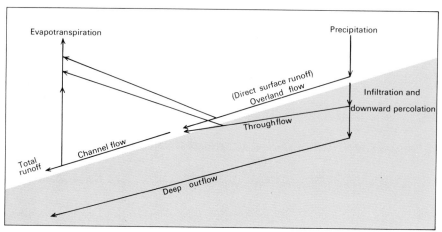

Figure 11.6   Some precipitation water runs off directly; some infiltrates. Water following either route may eventually reach streams, but some is lost by evapotranspiration.

bed created by particles already in motion; and (5) the dissolving of soluble minerals with which the water comes in contact.

Frictional drag, eddy current activity (turbulence), and the strength of particle impact all increase rapidly as the speed of the flowing water becomes greater. Speed of flow depends chiefly upon the steepness of the gradient, the depth and width of the flowing mass, and the roughness of the bed. Thus running water has the greatest erosional force in deep, wide, steep-gradient channels and is least effective in thin sheets and upon gentle slopes.

Erosion is also affected by the particle size and cohesiveness of the material over which the water flows. Up to a certain point, the smaller the particles, the easier they are to erode, with the maximum ease of erosion in the very fine sand or coarse silt range (0.2- to 0.5-mm diameter). But the finer silts and still finer clays are surprisingly difficult to erode, probably because the particles fit tightly together and tend to cling to each other. If particles are actually cemented, resistance is greatly increased.

Most of the land surface lies outside of stream channels. In these areas erosion depends strongly upon the vegetation cover, which not only protects the soil against raindrop impact but also slows the rate of runoff and increases the percentage of infiltration. A well-vegetated slope on which almost no measurable erosion has been occurring may

be disastrously stripped and gullied in a single rainstorm if the vegetation is removed (Fig. 11.7).

Erosion by solution, although it occurs almost everywhere, is especially rapid where such soluble rocks as limestone and dolomite are exposed. The work of solution by surface runoff is especially important as a gradational process, although solution by groundwater receives more attention in the literature.

Groundwater moving along joints and bedding planes may remove so much material in solution that the rock becomes honeycombed with cavities, large and small. Under particularly favorable circumstances huge caverns may be formed. With a few exceptions, it is only in such large solution cavities that freely flowing streams occur beneath the surface. Some of the solution cavities, especially those developed along vertical joints, are open to the surface as deep, steep-walled pits. In other instances surface depressions (sinks) are formed by collapse of the roofs of caverns (Fig. 11.8).

Transportation by running water.   Particles that have been dislodged from a slope or a stream bed are transported in several ways (Fig. 11.9). Materials too heavy to be raised from the bottom are simply rolled or shoved along by the force of the current and the impact of other particles. This load is said to be moved by *traction*. Somewhat smaller grains are thrown up into the current by eddies and then carried down-

Figure 11.7 Erosion by sheetflow and gullying on a slope whose grass cover has been thinned by overgrazing. (W. H. Lathrop, Soil Conservation Service.)

stream until they settle, strike the bottom, and bounce up again, thus proceeding by a series of leaps. This process is called *saltation*. Still smaller particles are so light that they can be kept off the bottom by the churning eddy currents. These particles are said to be *in suspension*. The load of particles moved along the bottom in traction, together with the heavier part of the load moving by saltation, is referred to as the *bed load*. The lighter part of the load in saltation is usually grouped with the load in suspension under the name of *suspended load*. Still other material is carried invisibly in solution.

Clay and silt particles are almost always carried in suspension, and even fine sands will move in suspension at modest stream velocities. Gravels, on the other hand, are nearly always moved as bed load. Usually, coarse sands are, too, except in the swiftest streams. A heavy bed load tends to "get in its own way": friction among its particles becomes excessive, and the particles underneath are masked by those above. For this reason, it seems probable that there are definite limits to the amount of coarse debris that a stream of given depth, width, and velocity can keep in motion at a given time. On the other hand, the concentration of suspended load can reach remarkably high values. Occasionally samples taken from

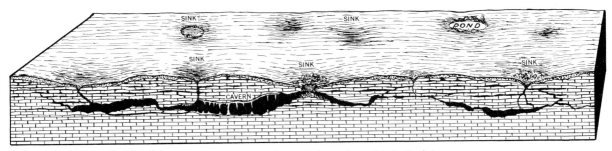

Figure 11.8 Sinks and their relation to solution cavities beneath the surface. (V. C. Finch.)

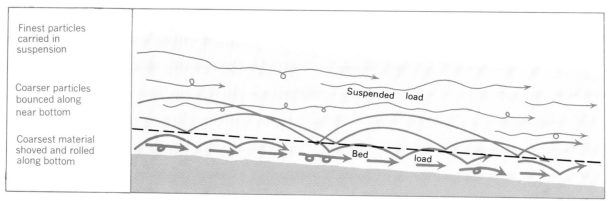

Finest particles
carried in
suspension

Coarser particles
bounced along
near bottom

Coarsest material
shoved and rolled
along bottom

Suspended   load

Bed   load

Figure 11.9 Ways in which solid material is transported by running water.

muddy streams in flood have contained several tens of kilograms of suspended matter per cubic meter of water (several pounds per cubic foot).

The concentration of load carried in solution depends chiefly upon the climate and the presence of exposed soluble rocks. Streams in the moister sections of the United States commonly carry as much as one-fourth to one-half of their total load in solution—a surprisingly high figure that indicates the importance of this often neglected process.

Deposition by water. Deposition occurs whenever (1) the velocity of flow drops below the value necessary to keep in motion all the material being transported, (2) the volume of water decreases below the amount needed to carry all the load, or (3) tributary streams, sheetflow erosion, or other agents dump more load into the stream than it can handle. Under any of these conditions the heavier and coarser elements of the bed load are most readily dropped, while the suspended load is most easily kept in motion. All stream-deposited materials are referred to as *alluvium*.

A particularly common location for deposition induced by decreased velocity of flow is in the slack water on the inner sides of stream bends, where accumulations known as *point bars* develop. Most extensive deposition occurs where the velocity is checked as the stream enters a lake or the sea, or as it emerges from a steep mountain canyon onto a gently sloping plain.

A downstream decrease in volume of water occurs chiefly in the dry lands. Rivers such as the Nile, the Colorado, and the Indus enter deserts from moister regions and receive no important contributions of runoff during their desert passage. Because of infiltration and evaporation (and nowadays, withdrawal for irrigation), the volume of water in the river shrinks, and deposition occurs all along the course.

Sometimes glaciers, rapid mass movements, unusually heavy local slope erosion, or the entry of steep, heavily loaded mountain tributaries (as well as artificial storm drains) will feed more coarse load into the main channel than the stream can transport. Under these circumstances deposition will occur along the channel for some distance below the point where the material enters.

Stream Channels

Channels and discharge. Well-defined streams of runoff carve elongated troughs or channels large enough to accommodate their waters. The volume of water that passes through a given cross section of the channel in a unit of time is called the *discharge* of the stream. The discharge of any stream fluctuates constantly, chiefly in response to the occurrence and intensity of precipitation or, in some cases, snow melt. A stream at high water in a humid region often discharges 5 to 15 times as much as at low water, and in the drier climates many streams dry up completely between rains.

The discharge of a stream is measured by the product of the cross-section area of the channel and the velocity of flow. The same discharge could be carried by a wide, shallow channel or a deep, narrow one. However, frictional drag is greater in a shallow channel than in a deep one, so that in a shallow stream a steeper gradient is needed to maintain a given velocity of flow.

During high-water periods a stream deepens and increases its velocity, thereby gaining increased erosional power, which it expends in scouring its bed and undermining its banks. By repeated erosion of this kind, the channel eventually achieves dimensions and a gradient that are adequate to handle the more frequently occurring high-water discharges. Observations indicate that most streams have channels just large enough to be filled bank-full once every year or two. The even greater discharges that occur less frequently cause the stream to overflow its banks, producing floods.

Channel form.   The typical stream channel is considerably wider than it is deep and has a more or less flat floor with inclined sides. The steepness of the sides and the ratio of width to depth appear to depend principally upon the materials that form the banks and bed (Fig. 11.10). Loose, easily caving sands yield wide, shallow channels with gently inclined sides. More cohesive clays or silts give narrower channels with steeper sides and greater depth. Channels cut in well-consolidated bedrock are commonly the deepest, narrowest, and steepest-sided of all.

Meandering and braided channels.   Nearly all streams of fluid that are not firmly confined show a clear tendency to develop rhythmic swings from side to side (Fig. 11.11*A*). Such sinuosities can be seen even in the atmospheric jet streams, as well as in

sharply defined ocean currents (e.g., the Gulf Stream) and in river channels.

Where these winding patterns are best developed in rivers, it has been discovered that successive bends are spaced quite regularly along the stream at intervals of about six or seven times the width of the channel. Similarly, it has been found that many channels develop alternate deep spots (pools) and shallow sections (riffles) at essentially the same spacings, that is, from one pool to the next. In winding channels the pools regularly fall at the outsides of the bends and the riffles in the straighter sections between. It is evident, therefore, that the sinuosity and the variations in depth are closely related in their development, but the reasons are uncertain, and the relevant theory is beyond the scope of this book.

The smoothest and most regular winding, called *meandering*, is most often found in streams that are flowing on broad surfaces of predominantly silty alluvium, although some sand may be present as bed load. Such materials permit the channel to shift laterally by caving of the banks without simply spreading and becoming excessively shallow. On the outside of any chance bend in the channel, the bank tends to be undercut and to cave in, while a point bar forms on the opposite side in the slack water just downstream from the sharpest curve (Fig. 11.12). In this way each bend tends to enlarge into a true meander and to migrate gradually downstream. Often one meander loop will break through to join the next loop downstream, thus cutting off the intervening segment of the channel, which then fills with sediment.

Channels cut in bedrock usually develop narrow and irregular bends rather than true meanders (Fig. 11.11*C*), although there are some conspicuous exceptions. The generally high but variable resistance of the bank materials inhibits and irregularizes the lateral movement of the channel that has to occur if free meanders are to form.

Streams flowing in loose sands and transporting quantities of sand as bed load form channels of a highly distinctive type. Because the banks cave so easily, the channel becomes wide and shallow. The heavy load of sand forms bars in midchannel, and the narrowed threads of flow to either side in turn erode their outside banks. In time these channels also develop bars, become subdivided, and widen by bank

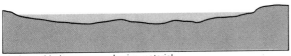

A channel in loose, non-cohesive material

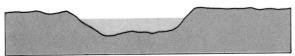

A channel in cohesive material or bedrock

Figure 11.10   *Stream channel cross sections depend chiefly upon bed and bank materials.*

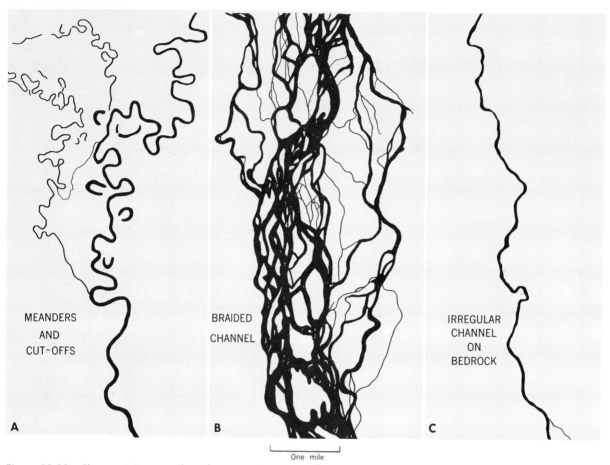

MEANDERS
AND
CUT-OFFS

A

BRAIDED
CHANNEL

B

IRREGULAR
CHANNEL
ON
BEDROCK

C

One mile

Figure 11.11   *Characteristic stream channel patterns. A: A stream flowing on fine-textured alluvium commonly displays a pattern of shifting meanders. B: A stream moving sandy or gravelly bed load often develops a braided pattern. C: Streams cutting in bedrock characteristically have relatively narrow, irregular channels. (From U.S. Geological Survey topographic sheets: Fairbanks D-1, Fairbanks C-1, and Fairbanks A-4, Alaska.)*

caving. The ultimate result, called a *braided channel*, is a wide band of many relatively narrow subchannels separated by bars (Fig. 11.11*B*). Because the frictional drag in the shallow ribbons of flow is so great, braided channels must maintain relatively steep gradients in order to move their sandy bed load at all.

Downstream variation in channels.   Streams in humid lands normally increase in discharge from head to mouth because of the water supplied by tributaries. To accommodate this growth, the channel must increase in width, depth, or velocity of flow.

Examination of many channels indicates that as a rule all three characteristics increase downstream: width most and velocity least. Until recently it was generally believed that because most streams decrease in gradient toward the mouth, their velocities must also decrease, but measurements disclose that this is not generally so. The greater width and depth reduce the frictional drag per unit volume of water enough to permit the mean velocity to rise slightly. Recent investigations also suggest that stream channels tend to develop toward a condition in which the downstream changes in width, depth, and

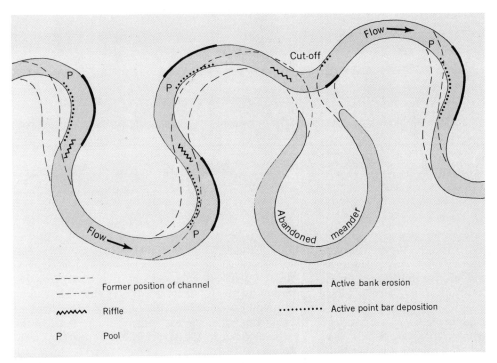

Figure 11.12 Characteristic features of a meandering channel.

velocity (and therefore gradient) are neatly adjusted to provide a near-constant rate of energy dissipation along the stream.

The reason for the characteristic downstream decrease in gradient (Fig. 11.13) is not wholly clear, although some contributing factors can be noted. For example, a stream cannot cut below the level of its mouth (baselevel). From the beginning of development, the lower reaches of a stream are closer to baselevel and thus have little vertical distance through which they can cut. Therefore one would expect those sections to achieve gentle and limiting gradients early, while the upper reaches are still far

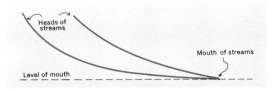

Figure 11.13 Stream gradients usually decrease gradually from head to mouth.

above baselevel and perhaps still steep. Particle size of the material in the stream bed also plays a part. Other things being equal, a stream can erode and transport fine material on gentler gradients than would be required for eroding and transporting coarse material. A section of the stream flowing on coarse bed material cannot cut down to the gentle gradients that a stream on fine materials can. Because of continued wear and tear, the average size of particles in the stream bed tends to diminish downstream, a circumstance which favors a corresponding decrease in gradient.

An actively eroding stream flowing over contrasting materials may have significant irregularities in gradient. As a result of differing rates of erosion, falls and rapids may develop on the resistant rocks, while gentler stretches occur on weaker materials (Fig. 11.14). Other irregularities in gradient may be caused by diastrophic disturbance of the channel or by blocking through lava flows or landslides. In time, however, all irregularities are normally smoothed out, and the profile assumes the familiar smooth, concave form.

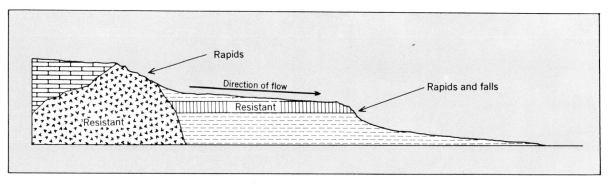

Figure 11.14 Rock resistance may affect stream profiles. Weaker rocks erode more rapidly and allow the stream to achieve gentler gradients, while resistant outcrops, because they yield more slowly and are undercut from below, develop steep gradients, rapids, and falls.

Changes in channels through time. Geomorphologists have long believed that stream channels undergo relatively rapid change until they reach some kind of balance or equilibrium, beyond which change is very slow or negligible. Classical geomorphology emphasized a sequence in which a stream cut down actively until it reached a gentle gradient near baselevel. It then ceased to cut down, but began to meander and to corrade laterally, thereby widening its valley floor.

Recent work suggests that a stream alters its channel rapidly by widening, deepening, and changing its gradient until each segment is nicely adjusted to carry the more frequent high-water discharges plus the sediment load fed to it from upstream. This condition of equilibrium does not necessarily involve a gentle gradient, nor need the stream be near baselevel. If the stream is flowing on coarse bed materials or is carrying a coarse bed load, the gradient will have to remain substantial. Furthermore, the channel may be adjusted by widening with little or no deepening or downcutting, especially if bank materials are loose. Widening of the valley may occur at any stage, with or without meandering, and is not dependent upon lateral corrasion by the stream itself. The rather small number of careful investigations of actual channels that have been made suggest that many channel segments, especially in the lower reaches of systems, are indeed well adjusted to the more frequent high-water discharges and loads they carry, and thus appear to be in a near-equilibrium state.

Nevertheless, the very fact that quantities of sediment are being passed through stream channels

to their mouths makes it clear that progressive erosion is occurring in some places in the drainage basins while deposition is going on in others. Probably erosion by small, steep, headwater channels and by unchanneled sheetflow and gravity movement of regolith on the slopes is responsible for most of the sediment load in the larger channels farther downstream.

Major changes in channel character. Any major and lasting change in a stream channel, whether in width, depth, gradient, or pattern, is brought about by some significant change in the environment of the stream. For example, diastrophic uplift of a drainage basin would raise its streams farther above baselevel and thus give them room and potential energy for further downcutting. At first, the only parts of the system affected would be those where the stream gradients were actually increased—most commonly around the margins of the uplifted area. In time, however, the downcutting would work its way progressively upstream into the headwaters of the basin.

Increased erosion could also be caused by increased high-water discharges. A climatic change, especially a greater intensity of downpours, or a thinning of the vegetation would allow more direct surface runoff. In some instances discharge might be augmented by the natural diversion of a neighboring stream into the drainage basin or by an invasion of the basin by a sizable glacier. Other things being equal, an increase in discharge will cause an erosional deepening or widening of the channel—commonly, both.

Finally, a channel could be forced to change its character and behavior by an increase or decrease in the supply of bed load. Increased direct surface runoff in the headwater area, especially if the vegetation cover were sparse, would stimulate erosion on the slopes and hence would increase the amount of sediment being fed into the streams. Unless the increase in discharge were proportionately even greater, the increase of bed load would cause extensive deposition in the channels. Deposition can also be induced in a given stream by damming (either natural or artificial) or by raising the water level at the mouth. In either instance, deposition will occur only in the section where the flow has been actually checked.

Valleys

Formation of valleys. Except on surfaces formed by deposition of alluvium, stream channels are usually more or less entrenched below the divide levels in well-defined valleys. Integrated systems of valleys, in fact, are the identifying mark of landscapes that have been shaped principally by stream erosion.

The widespread occurrence of valleys indicates that most streams pass through a period during which they progressively lower their channels by erosion. Not all the excavation of valleys is done by the streams themselves, however. As a stream cuts down, valley walls become exposed above the water surface. As soon as they appear, these walls become subject to attack by all available agents of erosion. Not only may the stream itself undercut them, but slope wash, gullying, and sliding or slumping of earth and rock will modify the form and steepness of the valley sides and may drive them back from the edges of the channel, thereby widening the valley.

The cross-section form of valleys varies from narrow and vertical-walled to wide with gently flaring sides, and these variations represent one of the most significant ways in which one stream-eroded landscape differs from another. It is probably true that, in general, narrow or steep-walled valleys are favored by rapid downcutting by the stream, massive and resistant bedrock in the valley walls, and little runoff down the walls. Conversely, slow downcutting, exposure of loose or thin-bedded materials in the walls, and large amounts of surface runoff down the walls tend to produce valleys that are wider and less steep-walled.

Although solution is an important means by which running water erodes, little is yet known about its specific effects upon the forms of stream-eroded valleys. Steep valley walls and smoothly meandering valleys appear to be unusually common in areas of soluble rocks, but they are not confined to such rocks, nor do all valleys in soluble rocks have them.

Stream and valley systems. Stream channels rarely occur singly and in isolation from one another. Except under arid conditions or in circumstances where downstream infiltration is unusually rapid, most channels join others to form larger streams, which join still others, thus forming integrated, branching systems. A channel system, in turn, begets a valley system by the downcutting of all branches.

For convenience in reference and for analytical studies of stream systems, various schemes have been devised for designating particular elements or segments of stream systems. In the most commonly used scheme, devised by A. N. Strahler, the smallest "fingertip" tributaries of a system are called *first-order streams*. Those segments formed by the confluence of two first-order segments, but receiving no tributaries of order greater than first, are *second-order streams*; those formed by the joining of two second-order channels and with no tributaries of order higher than second are *third-order segments*, and so on (Fig. 11.15). The valley systems in which the channels are located are similarly designated, and a drainage basin is designated as having the same order as its highest-order channel or valley.

The development of stream and valley systems is highly important to the evolution of erosional landscapes and has been the subject of considerable study and debate. Some of the theories of valley system development and their consequences are discussed in the latter part of this chapter and in Chapter 12.

Gravity as a Gradational Agent

Mass Wasting

The processes of slope evolution and valley widening are sufficiently complex and controversial to warrant further discussion. Before proceeding to that discussion, however, it is necessary to introduce the processes whereby earth materials are moved downslope

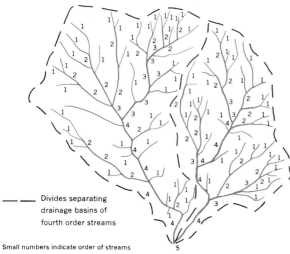

_____ Divides separating
drainage basins of
fourth order streams

Small numbers indicate order of streams

Figure 11.15 Diagram illustrating stream order according to Strahler's scheme. Two stream systems of fourth order are shown.

directly by gravity, for these rather obscure processes are usually important to the modification of slopes.

Gravity as an earth-moving agent. The force of gravity is well known as a contributing factor in the operation of all other gradational agents. Its work as an essentially independent gradational agent is much less familiar, however, and in the past, except for its more spectacular operations, it was given little attention. Now geomorphologists realize that the downslope movement of regolith under the largely unaided urging of gravity is one of the most widespread and effective of all the means of gradation, perhaps scarcely less important than running water itself. In the development of valleys, running water and gravity work closely together.

Gravity-induced earth movements, called _mass movements_ or _mass wasting_, can occur on gentle slopes and in dry regolith, but as a rule they are more active where slopes are steep and the regolith is wet. Saturation of the regolith is especially likely to occur during long-continued rains or seasonal melting of large amounts of snow. Actual flowage or rapid sliding of fine regolith is especially frequent in areas having a pronounced wet season or a major seasonal thaw.

Kinds of mass wasting. On steep slopes, masses of regolith and fractured bedrock sometimes break loose and fall, slide, or tumble at high speed into the valley

below. Such _landslides_ and _rockfalls_ are usually small, often involving only a few blocks. Some, however, are huge, sending tons of soil and rock thundering down the slopes. One of the larger recorded slides occurred in the Gros Ventre Mountains of western Wyoming in 1925 (Fig. 11.16). A mass of 50 million cu m of material moved about 600 m (2,000 ft) downslope and a short distance up the opposite side of the valley. The debris dammed a stream, forming a large lake which eventually overtopped its dam, washed out a part of it, and swept down the valley, causing damage and loss of life. The scar and the debris tongue are still prominent features of the landscape.

Landslides are often triggered by erosional or excavational undermining of the slope, by minor earthquake shocks, or simply by heavy rains that overload the regolith with water. Steeply inclined joints or bedding planes often provide breakaway points and slippage surfaces, especially when they have been lubricated by infiltrated water.

In areas with heavy clay or silty clay subsoils or substrata, long-continued rains can saturate the deeper layer, causing it to become plastic and to flow downslope, carrying the overlying material with it. Such movements, called _earthflows_, are slower than landslides and may occur even on relatively gentle slopes (Fig. 11.17). Like landslides, however, they usually involve a clearly defined mass of material and are sharply bounded.

In high-latitude and high-altitude areas, the deeper ground may remain frozen for some time after surface layers have thawed in spring or early summer. Since the water from melting snow and ice cannot escape downward by infiltration, the surface layers become so wet as to be jellylike. The soil may then ooze slowly downhill in lobes or across an entire broad slope. This process, known as _solifluction_, is a common and important gradational process in subpolar and high-mountain areas at present, and it appears to have been active around the margins of the great continental glaciers during the Ice Ages.

The most widespread and most continuous form of mass wasting is the slowest and least evident of all. This form, called _creep_, is not a single process, but rather the sum total of all those processes by which individual soil particles can be moved a fraction of an inch downhill by gravity. Cracks, burrows, and root cavities are slowly filled by particles which tumble into them, mostly from the uphill side. Frost

Figure 11.16   The Gros Ventre landslide of 1925, near Jackson, Wyoming, produced an immense scar on the mountainside and temporarily dammed the creek in the valley below. *(U.S. Forest Service.)*

Figure 11.17   Earthflow resulting from rain saturation of the ground on a shaly slope in eastern Ohio. The upper margin of the scar shows tension cracks; the lower section shows bulges from flowage beneath the sod. *(Soil Conservation Service.)*

crystals lift particles, which then settle farther down-hill with the next thaw. Soil expands or swells when it is wetted, heated, or frozen, and contracts again when it dries, cools, or thaws, and such expansion is greatest in the downslope direction because of gravity. Soil is forced downhill by the prying action of windblown trees and shrubs or by the weight of walking animals. In these and other ways the regolith on all slopes is moved slowly and steadily downward, grain by grain. The movement is imperceptible because of its slowness, but its results are visible in various forms (Fig. 11.18).

Aided only by unchanneled sheetflow and, occasionally, wind, mass wasting accomplishes all the gradational activity there is on the slopes and uplands between stream channels. Since these sections of the surface have a total area many times as large as that of the stream beds themselves, the accomplishment is great.

The swifter and more localized forms of mass wasting, such as landslides and earthflows, leave obvious marks on the surface. Normally there is a sunken scar on the upper slope where the material has broken loose, and at the lower end of the scar a jumbled, humpy accumulation of the debris that has come down. On cliffs, blocks of the exposed bedrock fall and roll to the base, where they may form accumulations known as *talus slopes* (Fig. 11.19).

These rapid and concentrated forms of mass movement are important chiefly in mountainous and hilly areas where steep slopes prevail. In many of those areas they undoubtedly account for a large part of the transfer of debris from the slopes to the valleys, where it may be carried away by streams or ice tongues. Because of their concentrated occurrence, landslides and earthflows are probably less important in worldwide result than the unobtrusive but more widespread creep.

The slower types of mass wasting produce less well-defined features. Solifluction sometimes forms definite lobes and troughs. More commonly, however, its effects are limited to the production of

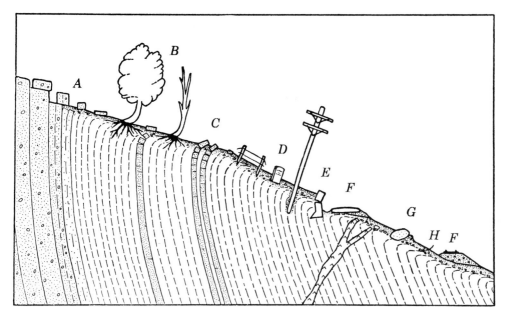

Figure 11.18   Common evidences of creep. *A:* moved joint blocks; *B:* trees with curved trunks; *C:* downslope bending and drag of fractured and weathered rock; *D:* displaced posts, etc.; *E:* broken or displaced retaining walls; *F:* roads and railroads moved out of alignment; *G:* turf rolls downslope from creeping boulders; *H:* stone line near base of creeping soil. *(From C. F. S. Sharpe, Landslides and Related Phenomena. Columbia University Press, New York, 1934. Reproduced by permission of author and publisher.)*

Figure 11.19 Talus slopes often accumulate beneath weathering cliffs. Near Lake City, Colorado.

minor hummocks, sags, benches, and sometimes long streaks of stones extending downhill from an outcrop. Creep, being even slower and less localized, produces few well-marked features but drives back the entire expanse of a slope. The material that has crept down may be carried away by streams or other transporting agents, or it may accumulate in a thickening sheet, gentling the lower part of the slope and masking it against further weathering and erosion. In humid areas that have a thick mantle of weathered material and a well-established cover of vegetation, creep may proceed at a significant rate even though surface erosion outside stream channels may be negligible. On the other hand, where the vegetation is sparse or open, surface erosion by rainwash is usually the more important process, although creep will still occur.

Slopes

The development of slopes. The majority of slopes, especially the steeper ones, have no doubt originated as stream valley sides. Others may have begun as tectonic forms (fault scarps, flanks of folds, volcanic slopes, etc.) or as erosional or depositional features produced by waves, glaciers, or the wind. Once formed, slopes are modified by the combined action of weathering, mass wasting, and channeled or unchanneled surface runoff. Weathering produces regolith, runoff and mass wasting move it downward, and streams or other gradational agents remove it from the foot of the slope.

Slope steepness appears to depend chiefly upon (1) the physical strength of the underlying material, (2) the coarseness of the regolith, and (3) the rate of downcutting or undercutting, if any, at the slope base. The strength and cohesiveness of the material set an upper limit to steepness, beyond which the slope will collapse and slump back to or below the limiting angle. The particle size of the regolith tends to set the lower limit of possible steepness, for the finer the material, the gentler the slope on which it can be moved. Rapid downcutting or undercutting by a stream, a glacial tongue, or wave erosion at the slope base will tend to keep the slope steep, while absence of this kind of attack may permit the slope to become gentler. Thus very steep slopes are usually associated with rapid deepening of valleys or with undercutting of slopes formed in strong, massive bedrock or highly cohesive sediments. Gentle slopes commonly indicate weak or loose materials or an absence of active downcutting or undercutting at the base.

Theories of slope development. For convenience the many existing theories of slope development can be gathered into two groups. According to the first group, slopes become progressively more gentle (Fig. 11.20). Throughout the course of development the characteristic slope form is convex in its upper part and concave below. According to the second group, slopes tend to be driven back without significant gentling, although as the steeper slopes retreat, they leave behind gentler footslopes, usually concave.

Recent thought suggests that these contrasting versions of the developmental sequence may in fact represent two special cases near the ends of a broad range of actual occurrences. Progressive gentling is probably characteristic where regolith removal is slow and debris can accumulate on the lower part of a slope, masking it against further attack, while the upper part continues to be eroded. These conditions might be expected on humid, well-vegetated slopes, especially if the inclination is relatively gentle to begin with and the soil is permeable, so that surface runoff and erosion are diminished. On such slopes, creep often appears to be the most active gradational process. On the other hand, if regolith is stripped from the slope about as fast as it is formed, no masking occurs, and the slope maintains steepness while retreating. These conditions would be favored

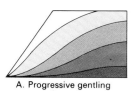
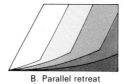

A. Progressive gentling   B. Parallel retreat

Figure 11.20 Two hypotheses of slope development.

by initially steep inclination, thin vegetation cover, heavy rains, low permeabilities, and, in short, all those factors that also favor large amounts of direct runoff. The dominant gradational processes are sheetwash and gullying erosion by surface flow, with some aid from rapid mass wasting. Convex rounding of the upper slope seems to be especially common where rocks are weak or weathering is rapid, for regolith then forms quickly. Active creep in the thick regolith then rounds off the slope near the crest above the level at which channeled slope erosion begins.

Developmental Sequences and Environment

The Cycle of Erosion Concept

Development of valley systems. The distinguishing features of land surfaces shaped primarily by the combination of stream erosion and mass wasting are integrated systems of continuous valleys and the higher-standing *interfluves* between them. Surfaces differ greatly in the numbers, spacings, cross-section forms, and patterns of their valleys. Traditional thought held that most of these differences could be explained rather simply in terms of progressive formation and headward extension of tributary valleys, combined with active valley widening during the late stages of development. This scheme has commonly been presented as an idealized sequence beginning with an uncut, recently uplifted, high-standing surface, proceeding through the stages of valley-stream growth and reduction of interfluves, and ending with virtually the entire area degraded nearly to baselevel. The sequence is called the *cycle of erosion*.

The classical cycle of erosion. In its simplest form, the cycle of erosion is conceived as beginning with the uplift of a smooth surface. The few larger streams quickly cut a set of relatively deep and narrow, widely spaced valleys (Fig. 11.21). Major

tributaries then cut niches in the walls of these few valleys and extend them progressively headward into the previously undissected interfluves. Additional tributary valleys develop in like manner until none of the original surface remains. First the major streams, and then progressively the tributaries, reach gentle gradients and cease to cut down. Widening of the valleys continues, however, much of it accomplished by lateral corrasion of the streams. Slopes, under the attack of wash, become progressively gentler and more mantled by debris. Eventually valleys and lowlands prevail; only low, narrow, gentle-sloped divides and occasional hills of especially resistant rocks remain above the nearly featureless surface. The erosion cycle is complete.

As long as there are few valleys and much uncut upland, the landscape is said to be "youthful."

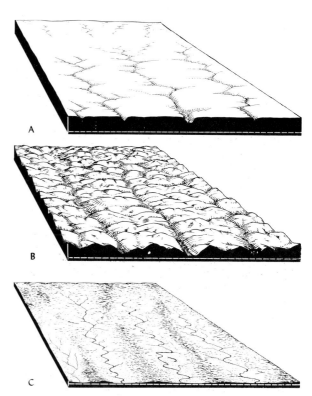

Figure 11.21   Ideal stages in the progressive development of a stream-eroded landscape. *A*: youth—few tributaries, broad, undissected interfluves. *B*: maturity—complete tributary network; valley sides everywhere. *C*: old age—broad lowlands; low, narrow divides. *(V. C. Finch.)*

When the network of tributary valleys is complete and no undissected upland remains, with the larger streams having reached gradients at which downcutting virtually ceases, "maturity" is at its height. When valleys and lowlands have so expanded that interfluves are narrow and inconspicuous, "old age" has been reached. The smooth, feebly sloped surface, mantled in regolith and alluvium, is termed a *peneplain* (i.e., "almost a plain").

Limitations of the classical cycle. Even those scientists who devised the erosion-cycle concept realized that many exceptions and complications could occur. In particular, they recognized that the rate of development could vary greatly from one environment to another and that the cycle could be interrupted at any time. The most likely intervention was a renewed uplift that would "rejuvenate" the area, increasing the potential energy and erosional capacity of the streams, thereby enabling them to resume downcutting and valley deepening. Because of the immense span of time required for valley widening and slope gentling, extreme old age was considered to be rarely achieved, especially in the present era, in which tectonic activity is probably well above average.

Continuing research upon stream behavior, valley development, and slope evolution has tended to emphasize other exceptions to the ideal erosion cycle. Among these are the following: (1) it is often difficult to conceive what the initial conditions of the cycle were, since rapidly upraised featureless surfaces are probably rare; (2) streams encumbered by coarse bed materials can become stabilized with steep gradients far above baselevel; (3) slopes and interfluves may become stabilized without reaching classical old-age forms; (4) lateral corrasion by low-gradient streams is probably relatively unimportant to valley widening; (5) environmental changes affecting discharge and bed load are probably more frequent and perhaps more crucial interrupters of the classical cycle than diastrophic uplift; and, particularly important, (6) the rates of tributary growth may vary so greatly under contrasting environmental conditions that "youthful" and "mature" surfaces can as reasonably be considered different in kind as different in stage of development. Although these problems may not warrant the complete rejection of the traditional sequence that some researchers have proposed, they do make plain

that it can be regarded only as a point of departure for further discussion and not as a picture of unvarying or even "typical" landscape evolution.

Environment and valley stream development. Wherever there is enough runoff to form well-defined streams, and where the gradient permits fast enough flow to move both the bed materials and any load fed in from upstream, the channel will cut down and form a valley. Hence runoff, gradient, and amount of bed load should be prime regulators of valley system development. Wherever direct runoff is large, gradients substantial, and shedding of coarse sediment by the slopes not excessive, a dense tributary net should develop rapidly. On the other hand, wherever direct runoff is slight because of high permeability, low gradient, thick vegetation cover, or low intensity of rainfall, only a few widely spaced channels are needed, and few will form. Thus completeness and spacing of valley systems may be more fundamentally a matter of environmental conditions than of time. There appear to be some environments in which maturity (in the sense of a complete valley net) is achieved almost at the outset of the erosional sequence and others in which youth persists for great lengths of time and classical maturity never occurs.

Problems of the advanced erosional stages. Even when a stream channel has become stable, the walls of its valley continue to be attacked by weathering, surface runoff, and mass wasting. These processes drive the walls back or wear them down so that the valley is widened or opened out. In the advanced stages of erosional development the valley floors expand into broad lowlands which eventually become the dominant elements of the surface.

Two different schools of thought have arisen regarding the nature and formation of old-age erosion surfaces. The two are intimately related to the contrasting theories of slope development discussed earlier in the chapter. According to one hypothesis, valley widening is accomplished by progressive gentling and rounding of slopes, aided by lateral corrasion by meandering streams. The end product, a smooth plain veneered with regolith and surmounted by low, rounded remnants (called *monadnocks* after Mount Monadnock in New Hampshire), is the classical peneplain. According to the second hypothesis, valley widening proceeds chiefly by parallel wearing back of the valley sides and the evolvement of a gently inclined floor, called a *pediment*, at the foot of the retreating slopes. The end product, consisting of greatly expanded, gently concave pediments surrounding relatively steep-sided interfluve remnants, is called a *pediplain*.

It has already been suggested that both forms of slope development probably occur, along with numerous variations between. Many modern geomorphologists are inclined to doubt, however, that lateral corrasion by meandering streams is an important means of producing broad lowlands. Thus even the lowlands formed under the first hypothesis of slope development should be very gently concave slopes, possibly shallowly dissected and mantled with fine regolith that has crept downslope, rather than flat, alluviated floodplains of great width. Such surfaces do occur, as do extensive surfaces of the pediplain type. Narrower alluviated valley bottoms occur with both.

Many of the ideas presented in the preceding sections are still highly conjectural. Changing understanding of stream behavior and the mechanisms of slope development have cast strong doubt on some classical concepts, but it is still too early to formulate a wholly coherent model of landscape evolution well backed by evidence.

Vertical Development and Relief

The amount of local relief on a stream-eroded surface depends upon (1) how much inherited relief the surface possessed when the current erosional sequence began and (2) the extent to which valleys have been deepened during the current sequence. The possible importance of inherited relief is easily understood and probably requires little discussion. It is often difficult to determine what the form of the surface was when the latest valley-cutting sequence began, but one cannot assume that each surface was originally an uplifted plane.

The maximum depth to which valleys may be cut is determined by the initial height of the newly developed channels above their baselevel. If erosion in a set of channels begins 1,000 m above the level of the sea into which the streams flow, valleys cannot be deepened more than 1,000 m unless there is further uplift of the land or lowering of the sea. It is entirely possible, however, that valleys may fall far short of

reaching 1,000 m in depth. The principal reasons are two: (1) the streams may not be able to develop gentle gradients, and (2) the crests of the divides between adjacent valleys may be lowered while the channels are still being cut toward baselevel.

The first point is readily illustrated. Suppose that a channel develops on sandy bed materials at an elevation of 1,000 m above sea level at a point 2,000 km from the stream mouth. The stream cannot achieve gentle gradients, for the bed materials cannot be moved except on relatively steep inclinations. A section of the stream 2,000 km from the mouth must remain poised at high elevation in order to maintain that considerable gradient. The situation of the Arkansas River in southwestern Kansas is essentially like that just described. The braided channel lies in a wide, shallow, sand-floored valley 1,000 m or more above sea level and shows no tendency to cut down.

The second point is perhaps best visualized from a diagram (Fig. 11.22). If valleys are widely spaced, they may achieve great depth without the divides between them being significantly lowered. If the streams are close together, however, their sides will soon intersect as the valleys deepen, forming sharp divides which will be continuously lowered as deepening proceeds. It may be seen that the steepness of the valley walls will also be important.

Chiefly because of these complications, it is difficult to state simple rules for the development of relief. It can be said that great relief cannot be produced by stream erosion unless the surface being eroded has been carried tectonically far above baselevel. High initial elevation, however, does not guarantee that great relief will develop. For that, the stream discharges and bed materials must be favorable to large-scale downcutting, and the stream spacings must be so wide that the divides will not be lowered as the valleys are cut down.

Effects of Climate

Relative rates of weathering and erosion. It is clear that temperature and precipitation, through their influence on runoff, infiltration, and chemical decomposition of the rock, affect erosion and mass wasting. On this basis, students of landform development have long tried to associate distinctive landsurface types or characteristics with particular climates. All attempts have been hampered by the lack

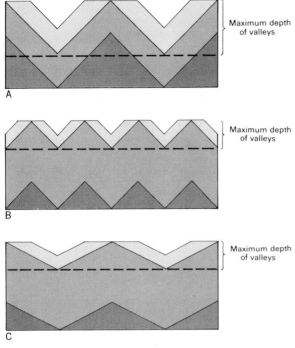

Figure 11.22 The depth to which valleys may be eroded depends upon the distance between valleys and the steepness of their sides.

of data that would permit careful analysis, and, even more fundamentally, by the fact that climate is but one of several factors that affect landform development. Certainly some of the common generalizations about land surfaces in dry versus humid climates or middle-latitude versus tropical climates are subject to so many exceptions that they are of doubtful value. Nevertheless, it is desirable to examine some of the principal effects of climate upon land-forming processes and from these to derive expected contrasts among the corresponding land surfaces.

Some of the important climatically affected land-forming factors are (1) rates of chemical and mechanical rock breakdown, (2) amounts, frequencies, and fluctuations of direct surface runoff, (3) effectiveness of vegetation protection of the surface, and (4) occurrence of conditions favorable to solifluction, earthflow, or creep. Considering these factors alone, a great variety of developmental possibilities exists.

Dry climates. In dry climates both chemical and mechanical rock breakdown are retarded, favoring slow production of relatively coarse surface debris. Precipitation is infrequent, and, with coarse regolith tending to favor infiltration, direct surface runoff is probably even less frequent. Channels are dry most of the time. If the occasional precipitation is of low intensity, surface runoff and erosion will be minimal, and landscape evolution will proceed extremely slowly. In many dry areas, however, high-intensity showers do occasionally occur, causing short periods of heavy direct runoff. At these times, the absence of protective vegetation may permit quantities of debris to be stripped from the slopes. Because the showers are short-lived and local, however, the discharge recedes quickly, and the load is soon dropped, clogging the lower reaches of the spreading channels. Integrated, through-draining channel systems are often absent, and the fragmentary systems that do exist often end in interior basins or on flat, permeable lowland plains. Hence in dry areas uplands and slopes are often sharply eroded, with relatively thin, coarse regolith and much exposed bedrock (Fig. 11.23). Lower parts of the landscape are commonly marked by broad, shallow channels and, in many instances, abundant accumulations of relatively coarse alluvium. Patterns of rock resistance, fracturing, and jointing are sometimes clearly reflected in both major and minor landforms.

It must be emphasized that this is an extreme and idealized picture, subject to great variation. For example, weak, fine-textured rocks may yield thicker, finer regolith, favoring more active creep, more rounded upland forms with fewer rock outcrops, and less spreading of channels in the valleys. If long-continued rains sometimes occur, longer and more integrated channel systems may develop, some of them carrying through to the sea. Toward the moister margins of the dry lands, the vegetation cover achieves sufficient density to inhibit slope erosion and allow more accumulation of regolith.

Humid areas of moderate or warm temperatures. In temperate or warm humid areas, chemical weathering is active, and a protective vegetation cover is normally present. Precipitation is usually frequent. In such circumstances, relatively fine-textured regolith forms, and surface erosion is generally slow

Figure 11.23   General view of Death Valley, California, from the south. The mountain slopes are strongly eroded, while the valley floor is buried beneath extensive alluvial fans. The portion of the valley shown is about 80 km (50 mi) long and 24 km (15 mi) wide. *(John S. Shelton.)*

except in stream channels. On slopes, mass wasting may, in fact, be the most active gradational process. Larger streams are usually permanent; lesser tributaries, commonly intermittent.

Compared with arid regions, one would expect less bedrock exposure and coarse regolith except where streams are cutting down rapidly, slopes are especially steep, or rocks unusually resistant to weathering. Because of the vegetation cover, slopes should be less gullied and stripped than in dry areas and lower parts of the landscape less conspicuously

drowned in coarse alluvium. The importance of creep and other forms of mass wasting might favor more rounding and smoothing of upper slopes and crests and more gentling of lower slopes by accumulation of finer regolith.

Again, however, there are so many possible variations in precipitation intensity, rock resistance, permeability, potential for downcutting, and form of initial surface that there is no such thing as a "typical" erosion surface for a humid climate. Furthermore, generalizations distinguishing tropical from middle-latitude surfaces appear to have dubious value except perhaps on the basis of greater statistical frequency of certain features, especially those associated with unusually rapid accumulation of fine-textured regolith.

Cold, humid areas. In the cold environments of high latitudes and high altitudes, controlling conditions of surface development are slow chemical weathering, frozen subsoils, and, in many areas, especially active frost shattering of rock. Apart from areas covered with glacial ice, the surface is seasonally snow-covered and may be exposed for only a few weeks or months during the summer. Regolith tends to be thin and coarse. Bedrock exposures are abundant, as are talus slopes and surfaces covered with angular rock fragments (Fig. 11.24). On gentler slopes where regolith is thicker, the various sorting phenomena associated with freeze and thaw of regolith are active, and solifluction may be the dominant gradational process. Surface erosion by water is commonly retarded because of the permeability of the coarse-textured materials, the tundra vegetation mat,

and, in some areas, the infrequency of heavy downpours.

Perhaps this environment of the subpolar and high-mountain regions is geomorphologically the most distinctive, although even here great variety is possible. During the times when great ice sheets expanded broadly across the Northern Hemisphere continents, many of the areas adjacent to the ice margins probably experienced environmental conditions much like those now found only in high latitudes or high altitudes.

Extremes and thresholds. Mean annual or monthly data often fail to convey the climatic information most important to landform development. A single, intense downpour may cause more erosion, sedimentation, and mass wasting than years of gentle rains, even if the yearly total is large. The occurrence of climatic extremes or the crossing of certain critical limits or *thresholds* may be crucially important; yet these events are rarely noted in brief climatic summaries.

On a given permeable soil there will be little

Figure 11.24 High-latitude and high-altitude areas often show thin, coarse regolith and much exposed bedrock. The upper slopes of Uncompahgre Peak, in southwestern Colorado, at an elevation of 4200 m (nearly 14,000 ft).

or no direct surface runoff as long as the rate of precipitation does not exceed the rate at which water can infiltrate through the soil. Once that rate is surpassed, however, direct runoff can occur, and surface erosion becomes possible. Thus a rate of precipitation equal to the rate of potential infiltration represents a threshold value of critical importance to surface runoff. In some humid climatic areas rains that greatly exceed threshold intensity (colloquially termed "gully-washers") are rare; in others they are frequent, and the spacings of channels and the rates of erosional modification should reflect the difference.

The vegetation cover also serves as a control and involves another threshold. Numerous measurements indicate that surface erosion on well-vegetated slopes, whether the cover is forest or grass, is usually slight even in heavy rains. If, however, the vegetation cover is even slightly open (i.e., some bare soil is exposed between plants), the rate of erosion jumps abruptly upward. Beyond that threshold, any rainstorm intense enough to generate much direct runoff may cause heavy erosion, while with an unbroken vegetation cover it might cause little or none. It is entirely reasonable that local erosion may be far more rapid in dry areas that receive occasional heavy showers than in most humid areas—a supposition that seems to be borne out by the unusually close gully net found on many dry-land slopes.

Temperature extremes and thresholds are also significant, the freezing level for water in the regolith or rock crevices being especially noteworthy. Long-continued freezing virtually prevents both chemical weathering and evapotranspiration. If it reaches to sufficient depth, it may favor solifluction during the melting season. Repeated oscillation of temperature across the freeze/thaw threshold speeds rock disintegration and, through the alternating growth and melting of ice crystals, causes a remarkable variety of churning and sorting phenomena in the regolith.

Seasonality. Surface-modifying processes in the land-surface system usually vary seasonally. These changes are more readily derived from the annual water balance account than from raw climatic data. In the majority of environments, precipitation reaches its maximum in the summer; but because of large evapotranspiration losses at that season, the maximum runoff, and hence maximum erosion, commonly

occur in late winter or spring. Soil moisture also is most abundant during the cool season. If winter temperatures are very low, that water may accomplish little weathering other than frost shattering. But in fall and especially in spring, when temperatures are more moderate, weathering and mass wasting may be particularly active. During the summer, biological activity is at a peak, but erosion and weathering may be slow or at a standstill except at times of unusually heavy showers. Unfortunately the early spring maximum of runoff and potential erosion often coincides with a time when fields are freshly plowed or protected only by stubble, so that erosional damage is especially likely.

Effects of Human Activities upon Gradation by Water and Gravity

Human activities have had and no doubt will continue to have a profound modifying influence upon the work of the major gradational agents. The most widespread of their modifying activities has been the thinning or clearing of the vegetation cover from immense areas, especially in the humid and moister semiarid parts of the earth. Obvious gullying and less obvious sheetwash on lands once protected by a natural vegetation cover demonstrate the tremendously enhanced rates of erosion that clearing and cultivation have brought (Fig. 11.7). Data from experimental plots in the humid midwestern and eastern United States suggest that replacement of a natural forest or grassland by an open-growth crop such as corn may be accompanied by as much as a 50 percent increase in direct surface runoff and a more than 100-fold increase in annual loss of soil through erosion. The increase in direct surface runoff enhances the rate and amount of fluctuation in stream discharges, including higher, more rapidly rising, and more frequent floods. The soil swept from the slopes is dumped into the streams, increasing their loads and contributing to their rates of deposition, some of which may occur on flooded agricultural lands farther downstream.

The building of dams creates lakes that trap the streams' sediment load, which will eventually fill the lakes. Below the dams the clearer waters are then able to erode more actively. Especially in the great metropolitan districts, huge areas of watershed are now largely roofed or paved, and the direct surface runoff and peak stream discharges have been significantly increased. Improperly designed bridges, culverts, and embankments sometimes so confine stream channels that during high waters the scouring of swift currents in the narrowed sections undermines and washes out the structures. The excavation of quarries, strip mines, road cuts, and building foundations often undercuts unstable slopes, triggering landslides that overwhelm the works below.

Even so brief and incomplete a catalog conveys something of the magnitude of the human role in changing the natural processes at work on the surface. Not all human activities result in disaster; many have been at least temporarily beneficial. Even for some that are known to upset the natural scheme of things, there seem no obvious and reasonable alternatives. For others, remedies are readily at hand. But in view of our far-reaching power to alter nature, it is critically important that we improve our knowledge of natural processes to the point where we can predict the long-term and indirect effects of our projects as well as the immediate and obvious ones.

REVIEW QUESTIONS

1. How are igneous, metamorphic, and sedimentary rocks formed? Are there consistent differences in characteristics between rocks of these three classes? Explain.

2. What are the two principal forms of rock breakdown? How is each produced, and what factors favor each? Are the two in any way causally related? What factors affect the relative resistance of different rock types to decomposition?

3. Why is coarse, angular regolith, as well as bare bedrock, generally more widespread in cold or dry areas than in humid areas?

4. In what general ways are rock types significant to landform development? Explain.

5. What are the five major gradational agents? Which are most widespread in their activity? Why are these various agents of land sculpture called "gradational"?

6. What is meant by the statement that precipitation water that has fallen on a high part of the land surface possesses potential energy? What force causes the water to flow down the slopes or

infiltrate the regolith? When these things occur, what happens to the potential energy? What happens to the kinetic energy of stream flow?

7. What is the difference between direct surface runoff and indirect runoff? What factors determine how much of the precipitation goes into each type of runoff? What effect does each type of runoff have upon stream discharge? What happens to most of the water that does not enter into either direct or indirect runoff?

8. In what different ways does running water erode? Generally speaking, what characteristics of flowing water favor rapid erosion? What is the relationship of particle size of bed material to ease of erosion?

9. What is the distinction between suspended load and bed load in a stream? Which of these most strongly affects the erosional capability of the stream? Why? What conditions may cause a stream to deposit part or all of its load?

10. What is meant if one says that the discharge of a stream is 80 cu m/sec? How can it be said that the size of a stream channel becomes adjusted to the discharge when the discharge is continually changing?

11. What is the characteristic form of a stream gradient profile from head to mouth? Does velocity of flow change correspondingly? Explain. In general, how is stream gradient related to erodibility of bed material?

12. What environmental changes might cause a stream to start downcutting more actively? Explain.

13. What does the abundance of valleys suggest about the erosional history of most streams? What is a valley system?

14. What is meant by mass wasting? Distinguish between landslide, solifluction, and creep. What specific effects does each have on landform? Which is the most widespread? What conditions favor the occurrence of the more rapid forms of mass wasting?

15. By what agents or processes are slopes modified? What conditions favor the occurrence of unusually steep slopes? What are two strongly contrasting theories of the developmental sequence through which slopes pass? What specific conditions would probably favor each?

16. Describe the evolution of erosional landscapes as

portrayed in the simplest form of the classical cycle of erosion. Discuss some of the principal problems of or exceptions to the classical theory. Discuss the concepts of peneplain, pediment, and pediplain.

17. What factors control the amount of local relief a stream-eroded landscape may have? Explain.

18. Specifically how and why might erosional landscapes in dry climates acquire characteristics different from those of more humid landscapes? Can you think of circumstances that might cause

major exceptions? Explain. Why are the cold environments often distinctive in their erosional landscapes? The tropical rainy areas have sometimes been said to have distinctive landforms. Discuss how such distinctive forms might develop and under what conditions.

19. At what season is each of the following likely to be most active: (a) erosion, (b) weathering, (c) mass wasting, (d) biological activity? Explain in each case, with reference to the seasonal water balance in various climatic regimes.

Land Surfaces Shaped by Running Water and Mass Wasting

TYPES AND FEATURES OF STREAM-ERODED SURFACES

As already noted, the distinguishing characteristics of surfaces that have been sculptured chiefly by running water and mass wasting are integrated valley systems and their associated interfluves. Valley depths, widths, shapes, spacings, and patterns differ widely from one stream-eroded surface to another, however, and such differences are closely related to the history of development, current functioning, and usefulness of the surfaces to humankind. In the discussion that follows, particular emphasis will be placed upon the differences among stream-eroded surfaces in local relief, degree of tributary development, and relative prevalence of steep and gentle slopes.

Low-Relief Types: Plains with Integrated Valley Systems

Origins and basic characteristics. Stream-eroded surfaces of low relief (generally less than 100 m or 300 ft) are probably the most widespread of all land-surface types. As a rule, low relief indicates a dominance of gradation over tectonics. Streams can cut deep valleys only if crustal disturbance has raised sections of the surface well above their surroundings. Where valleys are shallow, gentle slopes commonly predominate, not only on valley floors and interfluve uplands, but even on the valley sides themselves, especially if the materials are loose, thin-bedded, or otherwise physically weak (Fig. 12.1). Although some stream-eroded plains are formerly rough areas that have been eroded to low relief in late geologic time, the majority of extensive examples are found in sections of the crust that have been relatively quiet tectonically through tens or even hundreds of millions of years.

Kinds of stream-eroded plains. On the basis of the discussions in the preceding chapter, it is convenient to consider stream-eroded plains under three principal type headings: (1) those with incomplete valley systems and wide, undissected interfluves (traditionally called *youthful*); (2) those with complete valley systems, few or no broad uplands, and few broad valley floors (traditionally called *mature*); and (3) those with extensive erosional lowlands and only small remnants of higher ground (traditionally designated *old-age*). While these types have often been thought of as successive stages in an idealized developmental sequence, it has already been seen that in some instances, at least, the differences appear to result from fundamental differences in environment and materials and to be remarkably persistent. The types are not to be thought of simply as descriptive classes based upon static characteristics, but as classes that are different in circumstances of development, in current functioning as surface systems, and in the problems and potentials they offer to human use.

Youthful plains. The widely separated valleys, short tributaries, and broad, uncut interfluves that characterize the youthful stream-eroded plain appear in some instances to represent a truly young surface, in the sense of having been exposed to erosion for only a brief period of time. More often, however, they are plains for which the critical factor has not been shortness of erosional history, but slowness or feebleness of tributary valley development because of inhibiting conditions such as excessive flatness or permeability, reinforced by a protective vegetation cover or, less frequently, erosion-resistant surface material.

Thus, for example, the characteristically youthful outer sections of the Atlantic Coastal Plain in the Carolinas (locally called the "flatwoods") are indeed young in time of development. It is also true, however, that their nearness to baselevel, their extreme initial flatness, the permeability of their sandy surface materials, and their dense vegetation cover make it unlikely that stream dissection will progress at anything but a very slow pace. This surmise is supported by the fact that many sections of the higher, much older parts of the Coastal Plain farther inland are still so incompletely dissected as to merit the term *youthful*.

An unusually extensive youthful landscape is found in the High Plains, the vast smooth upland that stretches from the Platte River of western Nebraska southward into western Texas and eastern New Mexico, broken only at wide intervals by valleys crossing from west to east (Fig. 12.2). Most of the larger streams rise in the neighboring Rockies; little runoff is generated within the area itself. The semiarid climate, the permeable materials (originally al-

luvium from the mountains), the protective cover of grassland sod, and the initial flatness of the depositional surface have all helped to inhibit tributary growth. Although the plain has apparently been exposed to erosion at least as long as the more dissected plains to the north and some of those to the east, and although some valleys have achieved widths of several kilometers, the area remains obstinately youthful. The sand-floored channels show no tendency toward deepening their valleys. Short tributaries form narrow fringes of dissected "river breaks" along each major valley, but headward extension into the broad, uncut uplands seems to be proceeding no more rapidly than widening of the valleys themselves. Achievement of standard maturity appears unlikely, and the surface appears to be in close harmony with its environment.

In contrast, on the plains of south-central Illinois, developed on glacial deposits of clay and silt, tributary valleys appear to be undergoing progressive headward growth like that of the ideal sequence. Rainfall is considerable, and materials are not highly permeable, but direct runoff is slowed by the flatness of the upland surface. Where valleys have formed, however, water flowing down their rather steep sides can readily cut gullies in the weak material, and both surface and shallow subsurface inflow cause relatively rapid headward extension of the larger of these ravines.

In youthfully dissected plains, the broad, smooth interfluves are likely to be the principal sites of farmlands, towns, and transportation routes. Some uplands, however, are so flat that they drain very slowly, especially if their soils are fine-textured. Valley sides are normally well drained, but are sometimes too steep, gullied, or thin-soiled to be agriculturally useful. The bottoms of the principal valleys may contain usable land, although it may be poorly drained or subject to flooding. Minor valleys are usually narrow.

Mature plains. In contrast to the youthful surfaces just described, many plains have completely developed valley systems, with tributaries reaching into every part of the surface, so that the landscape is composed almost wholly of valley sides. In some instances these surfaces appear to have passed, in classical fashion, through youth and to be destined to continue to evolve, through progressive valley widen-

Figure 12.1   Elements of a stream-eroded plain.

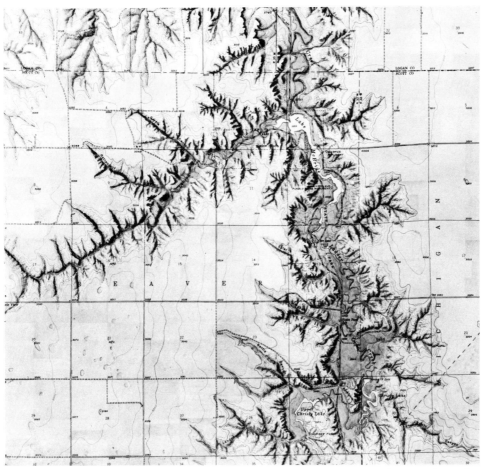

Figure 12.2 The High Plains of western Kansas are a youthful surface, with wide, smooth interfluve uplands and narrow fringes of river breaks along major valleys. The large squares are 1 mi across. *(Reproduced from U.S. Geological Survey topographic sheet: Lake McBride, Kans.)*

ing, into old age. In other cases, however, it seems probable that the surface achieved maturity very quickly and is likely to remain in that state for a very long time.

An example of the latter type is provided by the Appalachian Piedmont, which extends along the eastern foot of the Appalachian Highlands from New York City to beyond Atlanta, Georgia. The Piedmont is a rolling plain, in places almost hilly, with broadly rounded interfluves and narrow-bottomed valleys, an excellent example of a maturely dissected surface (Fig. 12.3). This landscape also appears to be essentially in accord with environmental conditions. Rain-

fall is abundant and frequently intense. The underlying granites and gneisses yield a sandy clay regolith of low permeability. With circumstances so favorable to runoff, it is hard to imagine that a youthful surface can have existed for any significant length of time. On the other hand, it is equally difficult to imagine that reduction of the relatively gentle, forested slopes and widening of the valleys cut in resistant rock will proceed at any but the slowest rates, although superficial erosion was rapid during the nineteenth and early twentieth centuries when agriculture was extensively practiced in the region.

By contrast, the strongly rolling plains of

Figure 12.3 The rolling surface of the Appalachian Piedmont is a maturely dissected, stream-eroded plain. *(Courtesy North Carolina State Highway Commission.)*

northwestern Missouri and southern Iowa are a mature surface developed largely on weak materials: old glacial till thickly mantled with presumably wind-deposited silt. Although the original surface was probably undulating rather than flat, stream dissection has carved out a new and substantially rougher terrain on the easily eroded, only moderately permeable materials. Wide valley floors along the larger streams support the expectation that relatively rapid continuing progression toward classical old age should occur in this environment.

During the early stages of maturity, the broad-crested divides may provide favored sites for roads, towns, and agricultural lands. In later maturity, however, when crests have narrowed and valley floors widened, the valley floors may be preferable. Overall suitability for agriculture, however, may depend heavily upon how steep and dissected the valley sides are, since they occupy the greatest percentage of the area.

Old-age plains. Extensive surfaces of the ideal peneplain or pediplain types that are currently near baselevel are either uncommon or not readily identifiable. Pediplains of lesser extent are abundant, however, and examples are discussed later in this chapter. Some scholars consider many of the broad upland surfaces of much of western, central, and southern Africa to be uplifted pediplains, as yet largely undissected.

Many pediments and pediplains are remarkably smooth, while others are corrugated by numerous shallow valleys or rills (Fig. 12.4). Some scholars prefer to restrict the term *pediplain* to the smoother type, which they consider to be a characteristic product of dry environments. It may be more meaningful, however, to extend the term to both varieties and to suggest that the differences stem primarily from the character of the sediment load carried by the streams which form them. According to this hypothesis, the smoother varieties, usually sloping bedrock plains thinly veneered by alluvium, may be formed if streams are heavily charged with bed load and so tend to develop broadly spreading, shifting channels of the braided type. On the other hand, if the streams carry little or no bed load, regardless of the climate, the channels may remain narrow and may therefore tend to cut well-defined rills and shallow valleys rather than to smooth the surface more broadly. If this concept is legitimate, the distinctions between pediplains, peneplains, and even mature surfaces of gentle slope and low relief become hazy and, from the developmental point of view, relatively unimportant. On resistant rocks crossed by streams carrying little bed load, truly smooth surfaces should be extremely rare because of the immense amount of time needed to erase the low interfluves. Perhaps the reason ideal old-age plains are so hard to find is that too much smoothness is expected of them.

Figure 12.4　Small, erosionally reduced mountain ranges surrounded by extensive pediments, near Oro Grande, Mojave Desert, California. The pediments show both smooth and corrugated sections. *(John S. Shelton.)*

Active and inactive surfaces. The foregoing discussions suggest that the distinctions among what have been called youthful and mature surfaces may in many instances be more profitably thought of as differences in kind than as differences in stage in an idealized developmental sequence. They also suggest that peneplains, pediplains, and certain low-relief, gently sloped mature lands may all be surfaces that have achieved near-stability in development, the differences among them representing contrasts in runoff and erosional potential on the slopes and in sediment load in the channels.

These considerations, in turn, suggest that in treating land surfaces as currently functioning systems, it may be particularly valuable to distinguish between "active" and "inactive" surfaces, i.e., those that are now undergoing significant change and yielding considerable amounts of sediment and those on which current change is so slow as to be inconsequential. Generally speaking, the active landscapes are those with relatively steep slopes, weak materials, and frequent direct surface runoff or rapid mass movements (Fig. 12.5). An open vegetation cover and high relief are also favorable to erosional activity. Areas with these characteristics account for a disproportionately large part of the sediment load carried by the world's river systems. Conversely, well-vegetated areas of gentle slopes, high surface permeability, and relatively resistant materials may be essentially inactive. In many large drainage basins, the major part of the erosional activity and sediment contribution is concentrated in relatively small areas of active landscape, most commonly located in the headwater areas.

Effects of Structure

Differential erosion. The concept of differential weathering, the weathering of different kinds of rocks at different rates in a given environment, was introduced in Chapter 11. Since potential rate of erosion is generally related to rate of weathering, differential weathering is commonly accompanied by differential erosion. Widths of channels, spacings of valleys, steepness of valley sides, and rates of valley widening are all affected by the character of the bedrock (or unconsolidated deposit) and the regolith it yields. In general, one would expect areas of resistant outcrop to be higher-standing and to have narrower and steeper-walled valleys and steeper stream gradients than the adjacent weak-rock areas, but variations on the theme are numerous and subtle.

The patterns in which rocks of varying resistance outcrop depend upon the geologic structure. Broad expanses of massive homogeneous rocks, for example, granite batholiths or horizontal rock strata, may show little place-to-place variation in erosional forms. Regions of complex igneous and metamorphic rock structure or highly deformed sedimentary strata, on the other hand, display highly irregular outcrop patterns and similarly chaotic arrangements of erosional features.

Figure 12.5   The rugged, closely gullied terrain of Badlands National Monument, South Dakota, is a highly "active" landscape, undergoing rapid erosional change.

Plains features due to differential erosion. Although the effects of differential erosion are usually more striking on high-relief structures than on low, they are not uncommon on stream-eroded plains.

An especially common structure is that in which stratified rocks, usually sedimentary, display strong contrasts in resistance between one stratum, or group of strata, and the next. If the strata are horizontal, a particularly resistant layer may become widely exposed at the surface through the erosional stripping of weaker materials from above it. Such a surface is called a *stripped plain*. On the other hand, if the strata are gently inclined so that they outcrop at the surface in wide, parallel bands of alternating resistance, differential erosion will produce a landscape consisting of parallel strips of highland and lowland. The higher strips, called *cuestas*, are usually asymmetrical in cross section, with a gradual rise along the surface of the resistant stratum (called the *dip slope*) and an abrupt drop on the other (the *escarpment*) (Fig. 12.6). In some cuestas the escarpment is steep and regular and the dip slope smooth and well defined. More commonly, however, especial-

ly if there is much runoff and the sustaining rock layer is thin, the cuesta is merely a belt of rougher country between strips of lower and smoother lands. Dip slopes always follow the inclination of the strata, while escarpments face in the opposite direction. Hence around a structural basin, cuesta escarpments face outward; while around a structural dome, they face toward the center (Fig. 12.7).

Much of the middle western United States is occupied by cuestaform plains. Throughout this area the strata are gently warped into a series of domes and basins that have suffered long erosion. Extensive formations of silica-rich limestones and dolomites and thick sandstones are the chief cuesta makers, and many of the escarpments can be traced for scores or even hundreds of kilometers. Other striking cuestaform surfaces are found in the Gulf Coastal Plain from Alabama to Texas, and in northeastern France and southern Great Britain (Fig. 12.7).

A more subtle result of differential erosion is a contrast, from one type of outcrop to the next, in closeness of spacing of the valley network. One may, for example, find a very dense, complete, "mature"

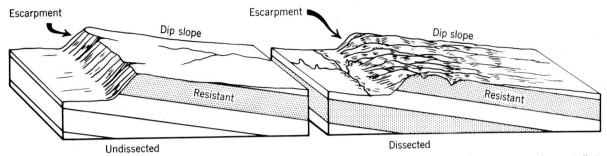

Figure 12.6   Form and structure of cuestas. Example at left is sharp and regular. Dissected form at right is more typical, especially in humid regions.

net of valleys on a broad band of weak shales that yield easily eroded regolith of low permeability. Next to it may be a band of permeable but strong sandstones on which valleys are far apart and steep-walled (a "youthful" landscape). Beyond that may be a zone of thick limestone on which there are few valleys at all, only undulating ground with numerous shallow sinks suggesting that most drainage goes underground.

On a smaller scale, differential erosion produces numerous details of slope form and valley pattern. Stream valleys sometimes follow narrow bands of weak rock or even major joints or faults along which weathering can proceed more rapidly

than the average. In fact, whenever one finds a pattern of valleys that is strongly linear or angular, in contrast to the randomly branching treelike (dendritic) pattern that most valley systems assume, one may reasonably assume that the underlying rock structure is making itself felt through differential erosion (Fig. 12.8).

High-Relief Types of Stream-eroded Surfaces

Origins and basic characteristics. The importance of strong uplift in relatively recent time to the development of high relief has already been noted, and in Chapter 11 attention was called to the broad correspondence between the patterns of current tectonic activity and the major belts of high-relief terrain. On stream-eroded surfaces of high relief, some of the local differences in elevation may be due to actual tectonics, but the majority have been produced by valley cutting since uplift took place.

Steep slopes naturally accompany high relief. Streams that have far to cut to reach stable gradients usually deepen their valleys rapidly, thereby producing steep-sided, often canyonlike cross sections. It does not follow, however, that all high-relief surfaces are made up largely of steep slopes. Some have extensive gentle uplands between the valleys, while in others broad valley floors and lowlands separate the high-standing and steep-sloped ridges or peaks.

Hills and Mountains

Hill and mountain lands are those high-relief surfaces in which steep slopes occupy a majority of the area.

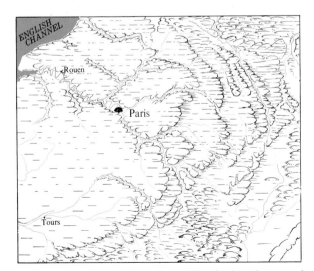

Figure 12.7   Paris lies near the middle of a broad structural basin, surrounded by cuestas with prominent out-facing escarpments. *(V. C. Finch.)*

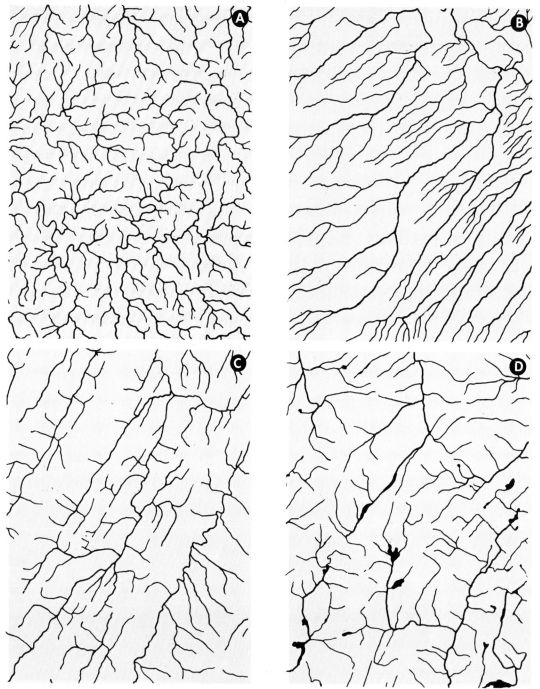

Figure 12.8 *A*: Random dendritic stream patterns develop where there are no strong local contrasts in rock resistance. *B*: If the original surface is strongly inclined, the dendritic pattern is drawn out in a downslope direction. *C*: Erosion on parallel bands of rock of contrasting resistance results in parallelism of many stream segments. *D*: Erosion on strongly fractured or jointed rocks sometimes produces angular stream patterns. *(From Army Map Service series 1:250,000: Charleston, Moab, Charlottesville, and Lake Champlain sheets.)*

While the two words are commonly used loosely, surfaces are designated *hills* in this discussion if the local relief amounts to a few hundreds of meters (several hundreds of feet) and as *mountains* if the vertical development is as much as several hundred or a few thousand meters. The prevalence of steep slopes, which signifies a predominance of valley sides rather than valley floors or interfluve uplands, indicates a type of surface in which dissection is essentially complete, and hence a steep-sloped, deep-valleyed analog to a "mature" plain.

Tectonic relationships. The high relief of hill and mountain lands reflects the occurrence of large tectonic uplifting or upbuilding in rather recent time. As a rule, the amount of relief depends chiefly upon the amount of late uplift; hills are rarely simply worn-down mountains. Mountains in advanced stages of erosional destruction tend to be distinguished more by the great width of their major valleys than by lowered relief.

Hill and mountain lands as we know them are, with some exceptions, best understood not as upraised folds, bulges, or blocks of the crust, but as erosional landscapes carved out of such raised structures, much of the carving having occurred during the course of the uplift. The structures of the upraised sections of the crust from which rough lands are sculptured range from gentle domes or anticlines (Fig. 12.9) or simple upheaved or tilted fault blocks (Fig. 12.10) to tightly folded, thrust-faulted, volcanically intruded masses of almost incredible complexity (Fig. 10.20). In some areas the principal structures (and hence the periods of most intense crustal deformation) are extremely ancient; in others they are quite recent.

It was noted in Chapter 10 that the zones of greatest current tectonic activity, and therefore many of the great mountain belts of the world, are located where major crustal plates are converging, and especially where thick, relatively rigid, low-density continental crust is being dragged into a subduction zone. The great rift zones experience less severe deformation and some extrusive vulcanism. Other mountainous areas not now located in either convergence or rift areas (the Appalachians were cited as an example) display ancient structures similar to those now developing in the convergence zones. It is clear that the pattern of plate movements has changed. Yet repeated uplifting, often in the form of broad, simple upwarping, continues to occur even in the ancient belts of deformation, probably because the thick masses of crumpled low-density crust continue to rise buoyantly as erosion strips off the upper layers. With each renewed uplift erosion carves a new generation of hills or mountains. Wherever hill or mountain terrain exists today, one may be sure that the latest uplift has occurred quite late in geologic time; otherwise, the high-standing features would have been destroyed by gradation. Thus, for example, the Appalachians are developed on structures more than 250 million years old, and the Rockies on structures 70 million years old. Yet the existing mountains in both areas are the result of uplift and erosion that have occurred, in all probability, well within the last 5 million years. Some rough lands are known to have been uplifted just before or during the last million years, and in some, uplift is going on actively today.

Surface features. The major mountainous zones of the continents are the cordilleran belts (Plate 3). These, in turn, are commonly made up of more or less well-defined *mountain systems*, such as the Rocky Mountains, the Alps, or the Himalaya. *Mountain*

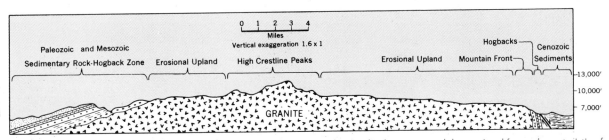

Figure 12.9 Cross section of the Big Horn Range, Wyoming, showing the anticlinal structure and the erosional forms characteristic of the ranges of the region. *(From U.S. Geological Survey topographic sheets: Cloud Peak and Fort McKinney.)*

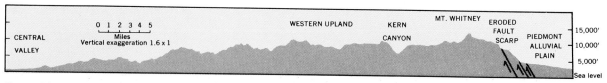

Figure 12.10 Cross section of the Sierra Nevada of California in its highest section. The range is a massive tilted fault block. Compare with Fig. 10.8. *(From U.S. Geological Survey topographic sheet: Sequoia and Kings Canyon National Parks.)*

ranges are elongated chains of ridges and peaks that possess an overall unity of form and structure (Fig. 12.11). *Mountain groups* are similar but more compact in outline. Ranges and groups may be isolated or they may form parts of the larger systems.

Valleys and slopes. Recent tectonic events have controlled the overall form and the drainage pattern of some mountainous areas, especially where the events have included large-scale faulting or extrusive vulcanism. More commonly, however, the patterns, features, and outlines of hill and mountain lands are the result of differential erosion upon an inherited structure of much greater age.

Because the latest uplift and associated environmental changes have disturbed their equilibrium, most streams in rough lands are actively cutting down. Their gradients are characteristically steep and irregular, with many rapids and falls. Valley widening is so slow relative to deepening, especially

in resistant rocks, that valley cross sections are commonly V-shaped or even slitlike. Where rocks are weaker, valley sides may be more widely flaring. If the principal streams have been able to achieve stable gradients, their valleys may have widened significantly and developed open floors. In this way the Alps, the Cascade Range in Washington, and the mountains of northern New England, all of which have open main valleys with gentle gradients, contrast with the Rockies, the Sierra Nevada, the Himalaya, and much of the Andes, where even the major streams flow through narrow gorges (Fig. 12.12).

The steep sides of rough-land valleys are liable to especially rapid erosion and active mass wasting. Hillside soils are typically thin and stony because of the continual stripping of the surface. Outcrops and cliffs of bedrock are common, especially on resistant materials, and blocks detached from such cliffs often roll down and form talus accumulations at the bottom of the slope.

Figure 12.11 The Sulphur Spring Range, northwest of Eureka, Nevada, a linear mountain range rising more than 600 m (2,000 ft) above its base. At the lower left are several well-defined shorelines of a lake that covered the basin floor in Pleistocene time. *(John S. Shelton.)*

Figure 12.12 Narrow gorge of Wind River through the Owl Creek Mountains, a range of the Rocky Mountains in Wyoming. Note railway at left and highway at right. *(William C. Warner.)*

Where there is little local contrast in rock resistance, slopes may be quite smooth (Fig. 12.13), especially if humid climate and abundant vegetation permit regolith to accumulate. On the other hand, contrasts in resistance of horizontal strata, or even strongly developed joint systems in resistant rocks, can produce steplike or architectural forms like those that give such spectacular quality to the northern Swiss Alps or the mountains of Glacier National Park (Fig. 12.14).

In general, slopes that are poorly protected by vegetation tend to become closely gullied, particularly if the materials are cohesive but easily eroded. The famed Badlands of the western Dakotas, carved out of weakly cemented sandy silts, are a striking example (Fig. 12.5).

In the majority of rough lands most major streams assume their courses in accordance with the pattern of slopes on the uplifted surface. Thus, if the uplift is a symmetrical arching, streams may flow down the two flanks from a central divide. If, on the other hand, the uplift has been strongly asymmetri-

cal—a gently tilted fault block, for example—the divide may be far off center, with long valleys on one flank and short, steep ones on the other. Deep valleys are sometimes found cutting completely through mountain ridges or ranges from one side to the other. These seemingly discordant features are called *dioric valleys*, if long, or *water gaps* if short (Fig. 12.15). The majority appear to have been formed by streams that assumed their courses on erosional plains or smooth sedimentary cover and then cut down into an underlying belt of resistant rock or a buried ridge following uplift of the plain. The uncovered belt of resistant material eventually came to stand above its surroundings because of differential erosion. Some dioric valleys, however, appear to represent the work of streams that have maintained their courses while fault blocks or anticlinal ridges have been slowly uplifted across their paths.

Crests and uplands. Most rough-land crests and uplands are simply what has been left by the cutting of adjacent valleys, although some owe their position and persistence to unusual resistance of their rocks. Crests are most likely to be continuous, high, and broad during the earlier stages of erosion; later they become narrowed to sharp edges, notched, and irregularly peaked. Many mountain and hill lands display smooth or rolling uplands that appear to be incompletely dissected remnants of the erosional surface that existed immediately before the last uplift. The higher peaks and ranges that sometimes rise above the upland level along the divides or on outcrops of especially resistant rock appear to be the remains of an earlier generation of mountains, incompletely destroyed during the last major epoch of gradation.

On some high mountains, frost shattering, solifluction, and glaciation have played major roles in sculpturing the surface. The work of those agents is discussed in the next chapter.

Effects of differential erosion. Rock structures, even ancient ones, may affect the landforms of the present generation of mountains because of differential erosion. In general these effects are not unlike those encountered in lands of lesser roughness. Because complex rock structures are almost the rule in mountainous areas, however, and because relief is great, the results of differential erosion are both more common and more strongly developed than in plains

Figure 12.13 Smooth mountain slopes developed in relatively homogeneous rocks, northeastern Washington. *(U.S. Department of Agriculture photograph.)*

lands. Some of the lesser effects upon valley pattern and slope have been noted previously.

Broad folds, domes, or fault blocks may bring to the surface large areas of rocks much more resistant than those about them. Some major mountain ranges and uplands owe their present existence to

Figure 12.14 Steplike mountain slopes developed on horizontal strata of varying resistance, Glacier National Park, Montana. *(National Park Service.)*

Figure 12.15 View southeastward across the Ridge and Valley section of the Appalachian Highlands toward Harrisburg, Pennsylvania. Note multiple water gaps of Susquehanna River to left of center in background. Ridge in foreground, rising 450 m (1,500 ft) above its base, is supported by a quartzite stratum in the crest of a sharp anticline. All other ridges shown are monoclinal. *(John S. Shelton.)*

differential erosion of such broad arrays of contrasting rocks. Relatively small resistant stocks, dikes, and volcanic necks that have been exposed by erosion may give rise to small, often spectacular mountain groups, peaks, buttes, or walls (Fig. 12.16).

    The most striking effects are found in the patterns of crests and valleys. Prominent joint systems or patterns of metamorphic foliation may pro-duce some degree of parallelism or rectangularity. Most remarkable, however, are the arrays of parallel ridges and valleys developed through deep erosion of parallel folds in sedimentary strata of contrasting resistance. Some of the structural relationships of ridges and valleys, together with the terms applied to them, are shown in Figure 12.17. Features of these kinds, especially monoclinal ridges, are common

Figure 12.16 Devil's Tower, in northeastern Wyoming, is all that remains of a small laccolith, uncovered and largely destroyed by erosion. The shaft, which rises 190 m (625 ft) above its base, is composed of immense prismatic columns of a basalt-like rock.

Volcanic mountains. While many of the world's rough lands are carved out of volcanic rocks, relatively few mountain chains have been constructed primarily by volcanic activity. The most truly volcanic mountains are the cones that have been built up by the accumulation of lava and ash about eruptive vents.

In a few places—for example, the island of Java—clusters or lines of cones form mountain-groups or ranges by themselves. More often, however, the cones are incidental features built upon mountains of diastrophic and erosional origin, as in the Cascade Range and the northern and central Andes. Some other mountains—for example, the San Juan Mountains of southwestern Colorado and the Absaroka Range of northwestern Wyoming—are made up largely of thick masses of extrusive rocks but are wholly erosional in their present form.

Cones form as essentially isolated features, ranging from insignificant hillocks to magnificent peaks thousands of feet high and several miles in diameter (Fig. 12.19). As a rule, cones formed wholly by explosive eruption of ash and cinders are steep-sided (Fig. 10.10), while those formed by the outpouring of slowly hardening lavas are broad and gentle. The majority of cones are intermediate between the two.

Fresh volcanic cones are usually smooth and symmetrical in form, with one or more well-defined

along the flanks and even in the interiors of many mountain ranges and systems. In some systems, however, linear crests and valleys dominate the landscape over extensive areas. Notable examples are the Jura of France and Switzerland and the long Ridge-and-Valley belt of the Appalachians, which stretches from eastern Pennsylvania to central Alabama (Figs. 12. 15, 12.18).

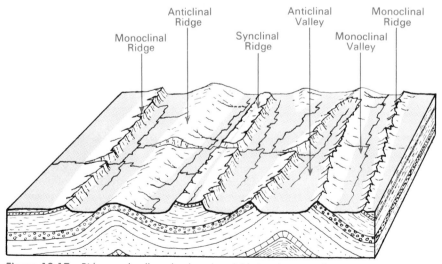

Monoclinal Ridge   Anticlinal Ridge   Synclinal Ridge   Anticlinal Valley   Monoclinal Valley   Monoclinal Ridge

Figure 12.17 Ridges and valleys developed on folded rock strata of varying resistance.

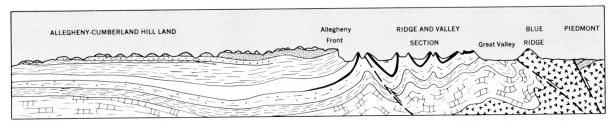

Figure 12.18 Schematic cross section of the northern Appalachian Highlands, showing general relationships of surface form to structure.

craters. After eruptive activity ceases, however, erosion soon breaches the crater and roughens the slopes. Occasionally destruction of a cone is hastened by collapse or explosion, which forms an immense *caldera*, larger than any normal crater (Fig. 12.20). Eventually extinct cones become so reduced that they can scarcely be recognized for what they are. Often nothing remains but the "skeleton"—the plugs and dikes of unusually resistant rock.

The hill and mountain environment. As a group, hill and mountain lands are the least habitable of the five major classes of land surfaces. Steep slopes, narrow crests and valley floors, thin and stony soils, and abundant rock outcrops make much of the land unfit for productive use. The small areas that are cultivable may be poor in quality and subject to destructive erosion if tilled. Some mountain lands, however, such as parts of Japan and southern China, support remarkably dense agricultural populations on broad alluviated valleys and lowlands. As a rule, though, most of the land that is not hopelessly barren is best kept in forest or grass cover, which both utilizes and helps to preserve the soil. Not surprising-

ly, lumbering and grazing are important activities in many rough lands.

The intense tectonic activity that produces the complex structures of many mountainous areas is often responsible as well for the formation of certain mineral deposits, especially metallic ores. These have been important attractions to settlement in some regions, but they are commonly spotty in occurrence and short-lived as bases for habitation.

The attractive scenery, clear air, and conditions favorable for camping, hiking, hunting, and fishing have come to be an economic resource of great value to some rough lands, especially those readily accessible to large centers of population. New England, the Catskills, the Colorado Rockies, and the Sierra Nevada are among the many notable mountain tourist centers. No doubt the most famous of all

Figure 12.19 The symmetrical cone of Mt. Fuji rises more than 3,600 m (12,000 ft) above the neighboring coastal lowland. *(H. Suito.)*

Figure 12.20 Crater Lake, Oregon, occupies a deep caldera formed by the collapse and destruction of the upper part of a great volcanic cone. Wizard Island *(center)* was formed by later eruptions. *(Oregon State Highway Department.)*

mountains are the Alps, a magnificent and intensively developed tourist attraction easily reached from anywhere in Europe.

Steep gradients, narrow and tortuous valleys, and high divides are among the numerous factors that tend to make hill and mountain belts barriers to travel and transport. Some ranges or systems, such as the Himalaya, the central Andes, and the southern Sierra Nevada of California, are unusually difficult to cross because of their continuously high crests and steep approaches. In others, for example, the Alps and the northern Rocky Mountains, crossing is made easier by open, low-gradient valleys that give access to relatively low notches or passes in the divide. The Columbia River gorge through the Cascade Range and the Hudson Valley through the New England-Appalachian Highlands are examples of dioric valleys that have become important trade routes (Fig. 12.21).

Tablelands

Surfaces of high relief that have deep, usually steep-walled valleys separated by broad expanses of relatively smooth interfluve upland are designated here

as *tablelands* (Fig. 12.22). Such surfaces are, in essence, nothing more than "youthful" plains with atypically deep valleys. In fact, most tablelands began as plains but have been altered by the deep valley cutting made possible by general uplift of hundreds or even a few thousands of feet.

Preservation of the uplifted plain surface against mature dissection during such deep cutting requires that tributary development be unusually slow. Hence the conditions that retard tributary growth—flatness, permeable surface materials, a continuous vegetation cover, light rains, and resistant surface strata—are even more crucial to the existence of tablelands than to the maintenance of youthful plains. It is not surprising that many tablelands are capped by unusually resistant rock strata or by sheets of permeable sand or gravel. Nor is it mere coincidence that most tablelands are found in rather dry areas. In many dry regions local runoff is slight, and canyon cutting can be accomplished only by a few permanent or seasonally active streams that enter the region from more humid areas nearby.

Surface features. The existence of canyons is favored by the very factors responsible for tablelands in general. Strong uplift permits rapid downcutting.

Figure 12.21 The Columbia River gorge, east of Portland, Oregon, is a dioric valley cut completely through a low section of the Cascade Range. Highways and railroads follow both sides of the river. View eastward from Vista House. *(Oregon State Highway Department.)*

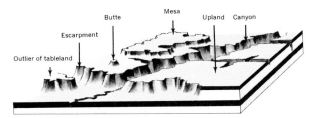

Figure 12.22 Characteristic features of tablelands.

States the latter are called *mesas* if large, *buttes* if small (Fig. 12.25).

The upland surfaces may exhibit any configuration of relatively low relief. Many are typical stream-eroded plains. Others are covered by alluvial deposits, extensive lava flows, or even glacial deposits. Some, developed in dry climates on horizontally stratified rocks, display miniature stripped plains, cliffs, mesas, and ravines closely akin to the larger forms of the tableland itself.

Limited surface runoff, slow weathering, and resistant caprocks inhibit valley widening. Although canyons are narrow and deep, the eye tends to exaggerate their proportions. The Grand Canyon of the Colorado is nearly ten times as wide from rim to rim as it is deep, and even the seemingly slitlike gorge of its tributary, the Little Colorado, is twice as wide as deep (Fig. 12.23).

The lines of cliffs, or escarpments, that form the margins of tablelands or separate one upland level from another originate either as canyon walls, bluffs produced by differential erosion, or fault scarps. They are continually driven back by weathering and erosion but retain their steepness (Fig. 12.24). Because of small-scale differential weathering and gullying, most escarpments are highly irregular, with many ravines and projecting buttresses or even flat-topped remnants of the upland (outliers) that have been detached by erosion. In the western United

The tableland environment. Functionally and environmentally the tableland may be a land of striking contrasts, the upland being one world and the canyons and escarpments another. In tablelands of especially great relief, the upland surface may lie in a different climatic realm from that of the valley bottoms or surrounding lowlands. The upland is simply a youthful plain, with the expected prevalence of gentle slopes and, almost by definition, a limited amount or frequency of direct surface runoff. Because of its relative smoothness, it may be readily traversable and in some instances cultivable. The canyons and escarpments, however, may provide troublesome obstacles to transport, and, in the drier examples, coarse surface materials, limited surface drainage combined with a deep-lying water table, and the difficulty of reaching irrigation water may inhibit agriculture, although grazing can often be carried on. The escarpments and valley sides, by way of contrast, are a hill

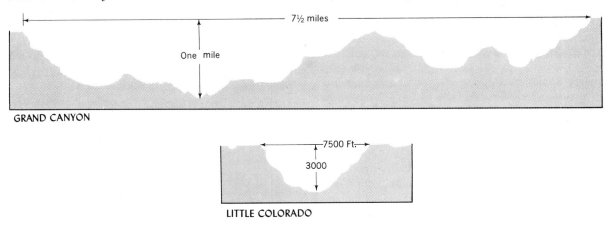

GRAND CANYON

LITTLE COLORADO

Figure 12.23 Cross-section profiles of the Grand Canyon of the Colorado at Powell Memorial and of the canyon of the Little Colorado about 3.2 km (2 mi) above its mouth. Vertical and horizontal scales are the same. *(From U.S. Geological Survey topographic sheet: Grand Canyon National Park, East Half.)*

Figure 12.24 The ragged edge of an escarpment that is being driven back by erosion. Painted Desert, northeastern Arizona. *(Spence Air Photos.)*

or mountain world, with steep slopes and active surface erosion and mass wasting—often a spectacular landscape but usually one of limited utility.

Examples of tablelands. Tablelands are not as widespread as other major classes of terrain. This fact is not especially surprising in view of the limited array of circumstances under which they can develop. Three North American examples illustrate the wide variety of tableland characteristics and origins.

The huge expanse of the Colorado Plateaus in northern Arizona, northwestern New Mexico, eastern Utah, and western Colorado is developed on gently warped sedimentary strata of contrasting resistance, under a dry climate. The area was uplifted as a great block, with marginal faulting, and has since been deeply cut by the Colorado River and several large tributaries, all of which originate in the higher plateau margins and the more humid surrounding mountains. The upland surface is a complex of cuestaform and stripped plains, with many rugged escarpments, rock terraces, mesas, and buttes. The larger canyons, notably the Grand Canyon of the Colorado, are among the most spectacular features of their kind (Figs. 12.23 and 12.26).

Another broad series of tablelands, occupying parts of southwestern Idaho, north central Oregon, and eastern Washington, has been carved out of an even more extensive area of immensely thick basaltic lava flows. In the areas specified, the Snake and Columbia Rivers and their tributaries, which

Figure 12.25 Mesa (*left background*) and buttes (*center*), Monument Valley, Arizona. *(I. J. Witkind, U.S. Geological Survey.)*

Figure 12.26   The Grand Canyon of the Colorado River, Arizona, is cut in nearly horizontal strata of varying resistance. View from North Rim. *(U.S. Department of the Interior, National Park Service.)*

emerge from the more humid mountains round about, have carved deep canyons and converted the lava plain into a tableland. Elsewhere the aridity of the climate and the high permeability of the lavas have preserved much of the surface against dissection.

The Cumberland Plateau, in eastern Tennessee, is the broadest tableland in the eastern part of the continent. Like most tablelands in moist environments, it is sustained by a resistant caprock, in this instance a massive conglomeratic sandstone formation. The gently rolling upland with its thin, sandy soils stands roughly 300 m (1,000 ft) above its surroundings and is slowly being dissected by short, steep-walled canyons working headward from the margins.

Plains with Hills or Mountains

Tablelands have been discussed as one type of surface in which high relief and large amounts of smooth land are combined. A second type, even more extensive in occurrence, is that in which the smooth land forms a floor and the relief is provided by widely spaced hills and mountains that rise above it. As with tablelands, the plain is ordinarily the product of widespread gradation, while the mountains or hills testify to tectonic activity that has at some time carried all or part of the area well above baselevel or above its surroundings.

At least two fundamentally different sequences of events combine gradation and tectonics in such a way as to generate surfaces of this class. In the first sequence, a high-standing surface is reduced by long-continued erosion to early old age; in the second, some kind of tectonic activity raises widely spaced irregularities upon an already existing plain.

Erosional types.   In earlier sections it was stressed that erosion of a mountainous area or other highland does not usually produce lower but still continuous mountains or hills. Instead, the valleys widen at the expense of the mountains between them, eventually becoming very broad and merging with one another to form a low-level plain of irregular outline. For a long time, however, numerous steep-sided ridges, isolated peaks, and small groups of hills or mountains may remain standing upon such a plain. The degree of erosional reduction and the detailed form of both plain and remnants vary considerably.

The most extensive development of mountain-studded plains of erosional origin has occurred in Africa and South America. Large parts of the hard-rock uplands of central and western Africa are smoothly rolling erosional plains surmounted by remnant ranges or groups, and in some areas by peaks so isolated as to resemble islands rising from the sea. Similar terrain, although generally less advanced in reduction, occupies the eastern parts of the Guiana and Brazilian Highlands of South America (Fig. 12.27).

In North America a narrow strip of the Appalachian Piedmont just east of the mountain front displays a similar granite erosional surface dotted with monadnocks (Fig. 12.28). Erosional plains surmounted by buttes, mesas, and hogbacks occur in parts of Wyoming, eastern Montana, and the western Dakotas. Many parts of New England and of central and eastern Canada are hard-rock erosional plains with monadnocks but have been much modified by glaciation. Essentially similar terrain occupies much of eastern Sweden and northern Finland.

Tectonically roughened types.   In the second sequence of development, the tectonically produced roughnesses may be volcanic cones, domes, anticlines, or, most commonly, horsts or tilted fault blocks. In some areas of the type, the plains between the mountains appear to have been little disturbed by diastrophism; in others they have been actively downwarped or downfaulted so as to form enclosed depressions.

The upraised features are attacked by erosion as soon as they begin to appear and are therefore usually found in more or less dissected form. It is not

Figure 12.28   Near the western edge of the Appalachian Piedmont, numerous monadnocks remain standing upon an erosional plain developed on igneous and metamorphic rocks. Big Cobbler Mountain in northern Virginia. *(J. L. Rich. Courtesy of the Geographical Review. American Geographical Society, New York.)*

uncommon for the mountains to have been much reduced by erosion and the plain thereby expanded through pediment formation. In this event the surface as it now exists represents a combination of the two sequences of development.

Plains with hills and mountains of tectonic origin are widespread, especially in the cordilleras of Eurasia and North America. One of the largest continuous areas of the type is the North American Basin and Range province, which occupies much of the southwestern United States and nearly all northern Mexico. From southern Oregon to Mexico City, this landscape of dry plains and generally small but rugged mountain ranges extends without a break and with only minor internal variation. Most of the ranges are believed to have originated as raised and tilted fault blocks, although there are some volcanic cones, chiefly at the extreme northwest and near the southern end of the province in central Mexico.

The principal internal differences in the Basin and Range province are in the degree of erosional reduction of the mountains and in the amount of alluviation and drainage integration on the plains. Thus in most of Nevada and western Utah and in parts of eastern California, the mountains are bold, relatively steep-sided ranges, and the plains are deeply alluviated basins with interior drainage (Fig. 11.23). In southern Arizona and southeastern California, on the other hand, the mountains are small, irregular remnants of once larger ranges, surrounded by extensive pediments (Fig. 12.4). Alluviation is

Figure 12.27   Remnant hills left standing upon an erosional plain developed on ancient resistant rocks in Guyana. *(D. Holdridge. Courtesy of the Geographical Review, American Geographical Society, New York.)*

much thinner, and stream systems are largely integrated, with few basins of interior drainage remaining. Evidence is strong that the Nevada-Utah area has undergone a relatively late renewal of tectonic disturbance which did not involve the long-eroded landscape farther south.

In the Asiatic cordillera the section from Turkey through Iran to Pakistan is similar to the Basin and Range province of North America. In central Asia the basins and ranges are on a truly grand scale, and Tibet is noteworthy for the fact that even its basin floors are at elevations of 10,000 to 16,000 ft. The central Andes of Peru, Bolivia, and northern Chile are remarkably similar to Tibet, though some of the prominent peaks are volcanic.

Plain and mountain surfaces of the tectonically roughened type appear to have formed most frequently in continental sections of the crustal plates inland from convergence zones in which continental crust is being severely jammed and deformed. In these areas farther from the convergence, deformation is less severe and more favorable to the open folding and block faulting on which this terrain type so often develops.

Environment. Because of the discontinuity and wide spacing of their peaks and ranges, plains with hills and mountains rarely offer serious hindrance to through transportation. Where soil, water, and climate are favorable, the plains also furnish valuable agricultural land. Unfortunately, large areas of the North American Basin and Range province, the central Andes, the Middle East, and central Asia are excessively dry, and many of their basins are floored with coarse alluvium and saline deposits. Some alluvial plains, however, have usable soils that can be irrigated by water from the adjacent mountains.

WATER-DEPOSITED SURFACES

Principles of Development

Streams will deposit wherever the load they are carrying exceeds the capability of the stream to keep it in motion. Deposition may occur within the channel or it may be spread beyond the banks or mouth. The process may be cumulative, with successive deposits added to those already there, or it may be temporary, with material being continuously shifted from one place of deposition to others farther downstream. Where cumulative deposition occurs, extensive aggradational surfaces may grow. Where noncumulative deposition occurs, there may be no more than a temporary and local shifting of channels and bars. Sometimes, especially along channels, a long period of cumulative deposition may be succeeded by an equilibrium situation, in which only shifting deposition occurs, or even by a period of active erosion in which the earlier deposit is partially or wholly removed. Some of the general circumstances leading to such changes were discussed in Chapter 11.

Cumulative deposition produces four characteristic types of land surfaces, depending upon where and how the deposition occurs. Deposition within or alongside channels in well-defined valleys forms long strips of valley-floor lands called *floodplains*. Deposition where streams emerge from steep mountain canyons onto gentle plains where they are no longer confined produces broad, flattened, half-conical accumulations known as *alluvial fans*. Streams flowing into lakes or the sea deposit their loads about the stream mouth, forming low-lying plains or *deltas*. Some of the sediment carried into the sea or lake may be spread broadly over the bottom beyond the delta itself by wave and current action. The smooth surfaces formed in this way become exposed only if the lake or sea levels decline or the coast is raised. Exposed floors of marginal seas are usually called *coastal plains*; those of lakes are *lacustrine plains*.

The surfaces of water-laid deposits are almost invariably plains—usually, conspicuously smooth ones. However, they are not featureless. Stream channels are present in various forms and patterns; and because channels are easily shifted in loose sedimentary materials, scars of abandoned channels are almost as characteristic as active streams. Usually there are also various slight swells and depressions resulting from unequal deposition. The depressions often contain swamps or shallow lakes.

Principal Types of Alluvial Surfaces

Floodplains and Deltas

Types and features of floodplains. It was formerly thought that floodplains were essentially erosional features, planed off by laterally swinging streams and only thinly veneered with alluvium. However, numerous borings indicate that in most instances the alluvial fill is relatively deep and has been laid down in a characteristic erosional valley bottom. The surface features of the floodplain, like the form of the stream channel itself, depend chiefly upon the particle size of the alluvium and the width of the alluvial strip relative to that of the channel (Fig. 12.29).

Silty floodplains with sinuous channels. Streams flowing on predominantly silty materials and carrying little coarse bed load usually develop undivided sinuous channels. If the alluvial plain is wide enough (more than about twelve to fifteen times the channel width), the stream can form sequences of

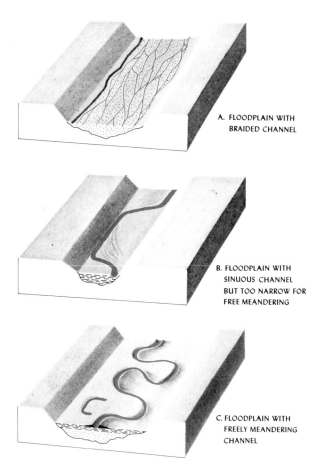

A. FLOODPLAIN WITH BRAIDED CHANNEL

B. FLOODPLAIN WITH SINUOUS CHANNEL BUT TOO NARROW FOR FREE MEANDERING

C. FLOODPLAIN WITH FREELY MEANDERING CHANNEL

Figure 12.29 Three kinds of floodplains. Type *A* usually develops in coarse alluvium; types *B* and *C*, on finer silty material.

smooth meanders which will shift and migrate as described earlier (Fig. 12.30). If, on the other hand, the alluvial strip is relatively narrow, meandering is distorted by contact with the bedrock valley walls. The channel will cross the floodplain, follow the base of the valley wall for a distance, and then swing back again to the other side (Fig. 12.29*B*). The crossover sections migrate rapidly, eroding their banks on the down-valley side and constructing bars on the up-valley side. On the wide floodplains, cutoff meanders in various stages of sedimentary filling are common features. On the narrower varieties, old channel scars are abundant, but they do not have the same horseshoe pattern.

On floodplains with sinuous channels, most deposition is probably in the form of point bars. During floods, however, some suspended load is spread over the entire surface. The accumulation is thickest where the velocity is abruptly checked as the overflow leaves the deeper channel and thins down farther from the stream. The thicker sections, called *natural levees*, are slightly higher and therefore better drained than the rest of the floodplain, which is sometimes called the *backswamp*. Narrower floodplains rarely have natural levees, presumably because the channel shifts too rapidly to allow them to form. The Missouri River Valley in central Missouri illustrates the narrower version of the silty floodplain, while the lower Mississippi is the classical example of the freely meandering stream with natural levees and backswamps.

Sandy floodplains with braided channels. The broad band of bars and channels characteristic of streams flowing in loose sand often occupies the entire width of a floodplain (Fig. 12.29*A* and 12.31). Although the active channels may not cover all the plain at any one time, the easy lateral shifting of such channels may cause all parts of the plain to be reworked in a period of several decades.

Braided channels are especially typical of the heavily loaded streams that drain glacial margins or that emerge from steep mountain valleys where erosion is active. Most of the streams of the Great Plains (such as the Platte and the Arkansas) and many Alaskan rivers (for example, the Copper River and upper tributaries of the Yukon) furnish excellent examples of braided channels and their related floodplain forms.

Figure 12.30 Broad, silty floodplain, showing meandering natural channel with cutoff meanders and meander scars (*top*). Straightened artificial channel (*center*) shows formation of point bars and beginnings of meander development. *(Production and Marketing Administration, U.S. Department of Agriculture.)*

Alluvial terraces. After a floodplain has been formed, the stream may start eroding again because discharge or gradient has increased or because the amount of bed load being fed into it has decreased. It will then cut down into its earlier deposit, leaving only shelflike remnants along the valley sides (Fig. 12.32). In some valleys several such alluvial terrace levels may be seen, indicating that the stream has repeatedly alternated between deposition and erosion. Alluvial terraces are sometimes preferred sites for settlements, roads, and farmlands because they stand above flood levels.

Deltas. Where a stream flows out of its confined channel into a lake or the sea, it quickly loses velocity and deposits its sediment about the stream mouth, forming a delta. The alluvium is usually dropped on either side of the main current and in a bar opposite the end of the channel. The channel then divides around the bar, and both branches extend seaward, eventually subdividing again in the same way. Thus the stream acquires numerous branching outlets known as *distributaries*, and the delta grows outward and laterally from the original mouth (Fig. 12.33).

Except for the distinctive distributary chan-

Figure 12.31 The braided channel of the Nelchina River, a glacially fed stream in the Copper River basin of southern Alaska. During flood the entire belt of channels and sand bars will be covered by water. (*J. R. Williams, U.S. Geological Survey.*)

Figure 12.32 Alluvial terraces are created by renewed downcutting in an older alluvial deposit.

nels, the surface features of deltas are usually much like those of floodplains in similar materials. Silty deltas—for example, the Mississippi's—are characteristically flat, with sinuous channels bordered by well-developed natural levees, which may provide the only well-drained land (Fig. 12.34). Between them are extensive backswamps, often permanently wet and usually grading into tidal marshes along the outer margin of the delta. In contrast, channels on sandy deltas are characteristically braided, gradients are steeper, and there are no natural levees and relatively little bordering marshland.

Some deltas reach great size. Those of the Mississippi, the Nile, the Volga, and the Ganges, for

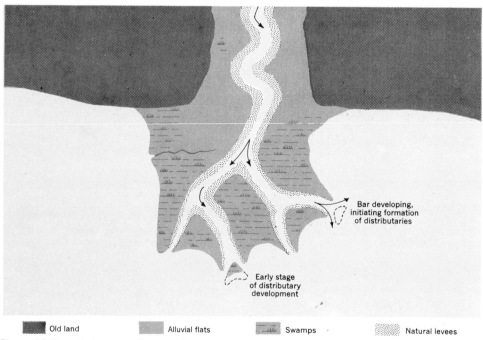

Bar developing, initiating formation of distributaries

Early stage of distributary development

| Old land | Alluvial flats | Swamps | Natural levees |

Figure 12.33 Characteristic features of a silty delta plain: alluvial flats with large swampy areas, natural levees, and branching distributaries of the stream channel.

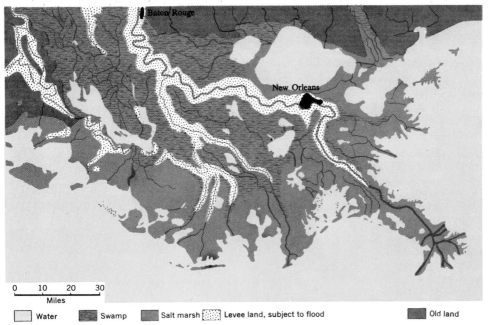

0 10 20 30
Miles

☐ Water   ▨ Swamp   ▩ Salt marsh ▦ Levee land, subject to flood   ▦ Old land

Figure 12.34 The Mississippi River Delta has fringing areas of salt marsh, areas of wooded swamp, and narrow strips of natural levee. Note that the levee lands grow narrow downstream and disappear. *(Adapted from V. C. Finch.)*

example, all exceed 160 km (100 mi) in width, and that of the Hwang is a plain more than 480 km (300 mi) wide. Many large deltas are not conspicuous on the map because they are built in the inner ends of arms of the sea. The Colorado, Sacramento-San Joaquin, and Tigris-Euphrates are examples.

Not every stream has a delta. Some carry little sediment to their mouths, either because the stream system is erosionally inactive or, more commonly, because most of the load has been deposited in lakes or segments of low gradient along the stream course. For example, most of the sediment from the headwaters of the St. Lawrence River is trapped by the Great Lakes, while that of the Congo is dropped in the shallow structural basin through which the river passes before plunging down the coastal escarpment to reach its mouth. Neither of these rivers has a delta. In some other streams the relatively small amount of sediment brought to the mouth is dropped into deep water or is spread across the sea floor or along the coast by waves and currents, so that no delta is formed.

The use of floodplains and deltas. Floodplains and deltas are often eagerly sought as agricultural lands because of their flatness, their loose and relatively fine material, and their easy access to water. Sometimes, although by no means always, their soils are more fertile than the older soils on the neighboring uplands. Floodplain agriculture, however, is always beset by floods, with their destructiveness to crops, buildings, and livestock. Even apart from floods, much of the land, especially in large deltas, is likely to be permanently swampy or subject to waterlogging by rains. Delta lands in hurricane areas are particularly vulnerable to flooding by the unusually high storm tides. While these problems can be attacked by various flood-control, drainage, and coastal protection programs, such measures are expensive and not always worth the cost and effort they involve.

Nevertheless, the pressure of population upon available agricultural land is so great in some parts of the world that marshy delta lands have been diked off and drained and are now able to support great numbers of people. This is true, for example, of large areas in the Yangtse and Ganges deltas. Perhaps the most remarkable instance of delta reclamation is in the Netherlands (Fig. 12.35). All but a small portion of that nation's territory is made up of formerly marshy land or even shallowly submerged sea floor in and adjacent to the great combined delta of the Rhine, Maas, and Scheldt Rivers. Over a period of many centuries small tracts have one after another been diked, ditched, and pumped dry, adding a total of several thousand square miles of agricultural land to this densely populated and intensively cultivated country. All such reclaimed land is called *polder land*.

Other Alluvial Plains

Alluvial fans and piedmont alluvial plains.

At high-water periods, the steep, swift streams of mountain canyons become heavily charged with coarse bed

Figure 12.36 Alluvial fans at the foot of a mountain range in the Mojave Desert, southeastern California. (*J. L. Balsley, U.S. Geological Survey.*)

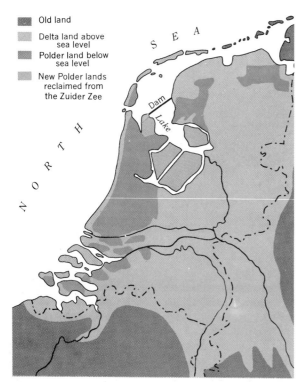

Old land

Delta land above sea level

Polder land below sea level

New Polder lands reclaimed from the Zuider Zee

Figure 12.35 Nearly all the Netherlands occupies low-lying alluvial land or reclaimed shallow sea floor on and adjacent to the delta of the Rhine, Maas, and Scheldt Rivers.

load and emerge upon the plains below as actively aggrading braided streams. As each channel shifts from side to side, pivoting about the canyon mouth, it constructs a smoothly semicircular alluvial fan (Fig. 12.36). Often several channels, diverging from the canyon mouth, are active at the same time. As a rule the coarsest material and steepest slopes are found at the apex of the fan.

At the foot of an elongated mountain range, many fans form side by side, eventually growing together to produce an extensive, gently sloping *piedmont alluvial plain* ("piedmont" simply means "foot of the mountain"). Some plains of this type reach great size, extending out several tens of miles or kilometers from the mountain front, with very gentle gradients on their lower slopes.

Piedmont alluvial plains often develop in association with pediments, which they sometimes resemble closely in surface form. In one common arrangement, a pediment extends out some distance from the mountain front, but the lower slopes of the plain are thickly covered with alluvium. However, if the rate of alluvial deposition is sufficiently rapid, alluvium accumulates in fans right at the mountain foot, and no bedrock pediment appears.

In dry climates, where fans and piedmont alluvial plains are especially common, water flows on the surface only during rainy spells or periods of snow melt. Low-water flow soaks into the alluvium near the head of the fans, but it is sometimes brought to the surface again by shallow wells and conveyed through ditches to the lower slopes of the plain, where it is used for irrigation. Sometimes the streams are dammed in the narrow canyons and their waters paid out from the reservoirs onto the fan surfaces as needed.

Piedmont alluvial plains are common features in the North American West, notably in the northern part of the Basin and Range province and in parts of the Central Valley and Coast Ranges of California. Much of Los Angeles stands on a plain of this type that has been built into the sea from the high mountains north of the city. Extensive piedmont alluvial plains are also abundant in the plain-and-mountain sections of southwestern and central Asia.

Complex alluvial plains. Several of the world's most extensive alluvial plains cannot be adequately discussed under any single heading. They combine floodplains, deltas, piedmont alluvial plains, and, in some cases, coastal or lake plains in a single smooth surface. Most of them have formed either in great structural depressions or immediately adjacent to high mountain systems, or both.

One of the finest North American examples is the alluvial plain of the lower Mississippi, which extends some 960 km or 600 mi southward from southern Illinois to the Gulf Coast, with a width varying from 48 to nearly 240 km (30 to nearly 150 mi) (Fig. 12.37). This great plain includes not only the floodplain and delta of the Mississippi but also the floodplains of several large tributaries, broad areas of older and slightly higher alluvial surfaces built by the Mississippi and its western tributaries at a time when their bed loads were heavy and their channels braided, and a number of still higher and older alluvial terraces. The plain has developed in a shallow crustal sag that has long received sediment from the north, west, and east. The present alluvial fill, which ranges in thickness from about 30 m (100 ft) at the north to 120 m (400 ft) in places near the coast, appears to have been laid down during and since the major rise of sea level that accompanied the melting of the last continental ice sheet. Beneath the alluvium is a typical erosional plain formed when the sea level was low.

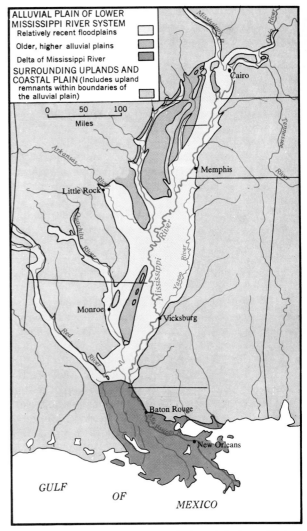

Figure 12.37 The complex alluvial plain of the lower Mississippi River system. *(After Fisk, Geological Investigation of the Alluvial Valley of the Lower Mississippi River. U.S. Army Corps of Engineers, 1944.)*

Other somewhat similar complex alluvial plains are found in the Central Valley of California, the Po Valley of northern Italy, the Tigris-Euphrates Valley of the Middle East, and the lower basins of the Indus and Ganges river systems in Pakistan and northern India. A combined piedmont alluvial plain, delta, and multiple floodplain complex, widely mantled with probably wind-blown silt, extends broadly eastward from the central Andes to the Paraguay River and the Atlantic.

Lake plains and coastal plains. On lake floors and coastal sea bottoms, sediments are spread broadly and evenly by waves and currents, forming surfaces that are unusually smooth, with only a gentle slope away from the shore. Many of the world's flattest and most featureless plains represent surfaces of this kind that have become exposed through the disappearance of the lake or a change in the relative level of land and sea.

Newly emerged coastal plains are especially widespread and extensive. Typically they are low, smooth, and poorly drained, with broad coastal marshes where the nearly level surface merges with the sea, and other swamps in shallow depressions in the depositional surface. Beach-lines and low, wave-eroded scarps mark the position of former shorelines. Stream gradients are extremely gentle, and erosion often makes little headway, even in the loose sandy, silty, or clayey materials. Extensive coastal plains rim the northern U.S.S.R., Hudson Bay, the Arctic fringe of Alaska, and the east coast of Central America. The outer zone of the Atlantic and Gulf Coastal Plain between New Jersey and the Mexican border is an excellent example of the type. This area contains nearly two-thirds of all the ill-drained lands of the United States exclusive of Alaska. This factor, together with the sandiness of much of the regolith, greatly restricts agricultural usefulness.

The exposed floors of former lakes are in most respects similar to newly emerged coastal plains. Abandoned shorelines, flatness, patches of swamp, and shallow remnant lakes are typical. Lakes are short-lived by the scale of geologic time, for they are inevitably subject to filling with sediment or draining by downcutting of the outlet. Some lakes have disappeared through evaporation because the climate has become drier. Other dry-land lake beds fill during periods of major runoff but become partially or completely exposed during dry periods. Lake plains are especially abundant in glaciated country; these will be discussed in the following chapter.

In North America most of the prominent lake plains outside the glaciated area occupy structural basins in the dry West. The lakes existed during times when the basins were receiving more runoff than they do now—probably at various moist periods during the glacial era, or, in some instances, even more recently. The two largest lakes, named Bonneville and Lahontan, covered huge areas in western Utah and western Nevada, respectively (Fig. 12.38). Great Salt Lake is a shrunken remnant of Lake Bonneville.

SELECTED LISTS OF UNITED STATES TOPOGRAPHIC QUADRANGLES

The topographic quadrangles listed at the ends of Chapters 12 through 14 have been selected from those published by the U.S. Geological Survey because they illustrate certain land-surface types and features described in the text.

Because of the great progress made during the last three decades or so in accuracy of representation, recently published sheets have been chosen wherever possible. To provide uniformity as well as adequate-sized samples of the terrain, the selection has been largely confined to sheets at the scales of 1:62,500 or 1:63,360. Where maps at other scales have been chosen, the scale is noted.

In recent years the Geological Survey has issued a number of sheets in shaded relief with contours, as well as in the regular contour editions. Because of the unusually graphic quality of these maps, they are especially useful for classroom teaching.

Attention should also be called to the series of contour maps at the scale of 1:250,000 published by the Geological Survey and now available for the entire United States. This set of maps is especially useful for regional study of land-surface form because larger features and regional contrasts are often shown much more effectively than on the larger-scale topographic sheets. Most maps of this set cover areas measuring 1° of latitude by 2° of longitude. Because of the diversity of features shown on each sheet, no attempt has been made to include maps of this series in the lists.

Copies of all topographic maps listed may be obtained from the U.S. Geological Survey. For maps of areas east of the Mississippi River, the address is

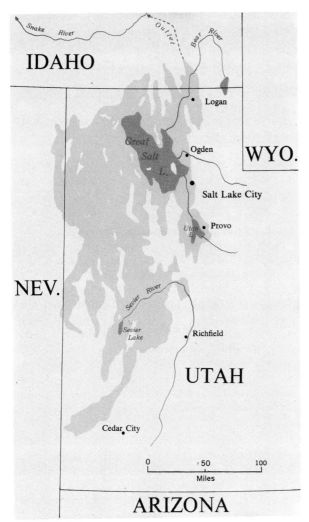

Figure 12.38 *Great Salt Lake, Utah Lake, and Sevier Lake occupy small portions of the area once covered by Pleistocene Lake Bonneville.*

1200 South Eads Street, Arlington, Virginia 22202. For maps of areas west of the Mississippi, the address is Federal Center, Denver, Colorado 80225. Also obtainable are index sheets showing the topographic maps published for each state, an index for sheets of the 1:250,000 series, and a folder giving instructions for the use of topographic maps and a key to the symbols employed.

MAPS SHOWING SURFACES SHAPED BY RUNNING WATER AND MASS WASTING

Erosional Plains

Youthfully Dissected Plains

Carlinville, Ill. (Smooth old-drift upland; sharply incised dendritic valleys suggestive of progressive headward erosion.)

*Rose Hill, N.C. (Smooth, newly emerged coastal plain; shallow dissection; early youth.)

†Sandon, Kans. (Smooth upland of High Plains; margin of river breaks at north edge.)

Maturely Dissected Plains

Chula, Mo. (Gently rolling; widening main valleys with meandering streams; carved in loess-covered old drift.)

Cowpens, N.C. (Strongly rolling section of Appalachian Piedmont; fine texture of dissection; monadnock hill.)

*Sherman, Miss. (Cuestaform plain on weak strata of Gulf Coastal Plain; western section rough mature; eastern section very late mature.)

Cuestaform Plains

Fredonia, Kans. (Two well-marked escarpments on indurated sedimentary rocks.)

*Sherman, Miss. (Much-dissected cuesta and smoother lowland; weak sedimentary rocks.)

*†Mammoth Cave, Ky. (Irregular sandstone escarpment overlooking limestone lowland; solution features.)

Plains Deposited by Water

Wide Floodplains; Meandering Streams

Caspiana, La. (Meanders; cutoffs; shifts of channel marked by county boundary.)

*Mellwood, Ark.-Miss. (Meanders of Mississippi River; artificial cutoffs; natural levees; meander scars; swamps.)

*Belle Plaine, Minn. (Meanders and cutoffs.)

*Sheets listed under more than one heading.
†Shaded relief editions available.

Narrow Floodplains; Sinuous Streams

Columbia, Mo. (Sinuous Missouri River confined by narrowness of floodplain; steep limestone bluffs; smaller meandering and sinuous streams; entrenched meanders in limestone.)

Hermann, Mo. (Missouri River floodplain among hills; bluffs; old channel scars.)

Floodplains with Braided Channels

*†Ennis, Mont. (Wide, braided channel; artificial lake; alluvial terraces; alluvial fans.)

*Tyonek (A-8), Alaska. (Braided channel below mountain glaciers.)

Fairbanks (C-1), Alaska. (Wide, braided channel of major stream.)

Alluvial Terraces

*†Ennis, Mont. (High gravel terraces at several levels; braided channel; alluvial fans.)

*Manito, Ill. (Broad outwash terrace above modern floodplain; sand dunes.)

Delta Plains

*East Delta, La. (Outer margin of Mississippi Delta; distributaries; narrow natural levees; backswamps; irregular shorelines.)

*Donaldsonville, La. (Inner part of Mississippi Delta; wide natural levees; backswamps.)

Rio Vista, Calif. (Agriculturally developed delta; diked and drained peat lands among distributaries.)

Alluvial Fans and Piedmont Alluvial Plains

*†Ennis, Mont. (Large, well-defined fan; alluvial terraces.)

*Wheeler Peak, Nev. (Several fans merging into piedmont alluvial plain; basin of interior drainage; alkali flat.)

Visalia, Calif. (Broad piedmont alluvial plain; fanwise channels and irrigation ditches.)

*†Sequoia and Kings Canyon National Parks, Calif.

(1:125,000) (Piedmont alluvial plain at foot of high fault scarp.)

Lake Plains and Newly Emerged Coastal Plains

Meldrim, Ga. (Swampy coastal plain; low terrace; beginnings of dissection.)

*Rose Hill, N.C. (Smooth coastal plain; low terrace; shallow valley system.)

Emerado, N.D. (Margin of former glacial Lake Agassiz; very smooth; several former beach lines.)

*Buckley, Ill. (Small, flat lake plain behind low marginal moraine.)

Complex Alluvial Plains (Lower Mississippi)

*Clarksdale, Miss. (Recent floodplain, now abandoned; many meander scars.)

Wynne, Ark. (Old higher alluvial plain originally formed by braided channels; strip of isolated bedrock upland.)

See also Mellwood, Ark.-Miss.; Donaldsonville, La.; and East Delta, La., listed above.

Tectonic Features of Hills and Mountains

Volcanic Cones

Lassen Volcanic National Park, Calif. (Cones in various stages and degrees of erosion; lava flows; most recently active volcano in conterminous U.S.)

*†Bray, Calif. (Several cones, variously eroded; craters; lava flows.)

*Mount Rainier, Wash. (1:125,000) (Large, glaciated, inactive cone among erosional mountains.)

Crater Lake National Park and Vicinity, Ore. (Lake-filled caldera; recent cone in lake; smaller cones; large dissected cones; photos and text.)

Fault Scarps

Hurricane, Utah. (Little-eroded fault scarp of Hurricane Cliffs; erosional scarps; monoclinal ridges; sand dunes.)

*†Sequoia and Kings Canyon National Parks, Calif.

(1:125,000) (High, rugged, dissected scarp of Sierra Nevada; glaciated mountain forms.)

*Wheeler Peak, Nev. (High, rugged, dissected scarp of tilted fault block; alluvial fans.)

Tablelands

Uplands and Canyons

†Portage, Mont. (Low tableland of northern Great Plains; smooth upland with low escarpment and outlier; narrow canyons.)

Canyon del Muerto, Ariz. (Broad, smooth upland of Colorado Plateaus; deep, steep-walled canyons.)

Bright Angel, Ariz. (1:48,000) (Deepest part of Grand Canyon of Colorado River; cliffs and benches; text.)

†Grand Coulee Dam, Wash. (Lava upland of Columbia Plateaus; wide canyon of Columbia River; abandoned channel of Columbia; great dam and lake.)

Escarpments

Johnson, Utah. (Two high escarpments in Colorado Plateaus; outliers.)

Agathla Peak, Ariz. (Ragged escarpment and outliers in Monument Valley area; volcanic neck.)

Plains with Hills and Mountains

Erosional Types

†Warm Springs, Ga. (Irregular remnant ridges rising above Appalachian Piedmont; water gaps.)

†Antelope Peak, Ariz. (Southern Basin and Range province; fault-block ranges much reduced by erosion; extensive pediments and piedmont alluvial plains.)

*Saponac, Me. (Residual mountains on rolling erosional surface; continental glaciation; esker.)

Tectonically Roughened Types

*Wheeler Peak, Nev. (High, rugged, tilted fault-block range in northern Basin and Range province; alluvial fans; piedmont alluvial plains; interior drainage; alkali flat.)

Sonoma Range, Calif. (1:250,000) (Large area of Basin and Range province; numerous fault-block ranges, variously eroded; basins of interior drainage.)

*†Bray, Calif. (Plain surmounted by several volcanic cones; northwest corner of Basin and Range province.)

REVIEW QUESTIONS

1. In general, what circumstances are responsible for most of the world's low-relief surfaces? Explain. What are the particular distinguishing marks of stream-eroded plains?

2. What is the distinction between "youthful" and "mature" stream-eroded plains? Discuss the statement, ". . . the ideal cycle is not always followed . . . some surfaces are persistently youthful while others are mature almost from the outset."

3. Why might the load-carrying characteristics of streams affect the smoothness of the pediplains they cross? Discuss the idea that ". . . peneplains, pediplains, and certain low-relief, gently sloped 'mature' lands may all be surfaces that have achieved near-stability in development."

4. What does the text mean by "active" and "inactive" surfaces? Locate probable examples of each. What evidence could you use to identify them?

5. What are cuestaform plains, and how do they develop? Identify in the photographs in the landform section of this book as many examples as you can of features produced by differential erosion.

6. What circumstances are necessary for high-relief surfaces to develop? Carefully discuss the circumstances that help to determine whether a high-relief surface will become a tableland, a hill or mountain land, or a plain with hills or mountains.

7. Why is it true that "hills are rarely simply worn-down mountains"? One sometimes sees the Appalachians referred to as "old, worn-down mountains" and the Rockies as "young, rugged mountains." Can this characterization be valid in

view of the probability that even major mountain systems can be erosionally destroyed in a few tens of millions of years? Discuss.

8. In what ways **may** dioric valleys and water gaps be formed? For **w**hat reasons do so many valleys in hill and mountain lands have steep sides and steep gradients?

9. Discuss two completely different roles played by vulcanism in the development of mountainous terrain.

10. What specific factors can contribute to the maintenance of tableland surfaces? Why are tablelands so much less widespread than other major classes of terrain? Describe the structure and surface characteristics of the Colorado Plateaus. What factors contribute to their existence as tablelands?

11. By what two different developmental sequences can plains with hills or mountains develop? How could one determine which of the two sequences a given example had passed through?

12. Describe at least two kinds of plains-with-mountains terrain in the North American Basin and Range province. Discuss the important aspects of the development of the area. Locate similar landscapes elsewhere in the world.

13. What are the four major classes of water-deposited surfaces? Indicate how and where each develops. What major characteristics do they all have in common?

14. How are silty floodplains and deltas likely to differ from those formed primarily of sand? Explain.

15. What is the difference between a pediment, an alluvial fan, and a piedmont alluvial plain? Is the Appalachian Piedmont a piedmont alluvial plain? If not, what is it? What are the nature and origin of the Lower Mississippi Alluvial Plain?

16. What are likely to be the advantages and disadvantages of floodplains and deltas for agriculture and other forms of human occupance? Why?

17. By what various means are lakes formed, and why are they commonly short-lived?

Surfaces Shaped by Groundwater, Ice, and Wind

The Marks of Groundwater Solution; Karst

It is probably true that on stream-eroded plains developed on limestones, dolomites, and calcareous sandstones, much of the valley cutting is accomplished by solution in the stream channels. Such erosion probably produces distinctive valley types, especially if the rocks contain insoluble residues that form bed load, but it has been little studied.

Much more attention has been given to the work of solution by groundwater, which in its more extreme forms may create landscapes bearing little resemblance to stream-eroded surfaces. It has already been mentioned that the most characteristic surface manifestations of groundwater solution are the depressions known as *sinks*. Most solution depressions are small and shallow, but where thick, pure limestones occur, progressive solution, aided by collapse, has led to the development of enclosed valleys and basins hundreds of meters across.

Sinks are rather common subsidiary landforms on the wider interfluves of stream-eroded plains in limestones and dolomites. But in some plains solution depressions occupy most of the surface, and integrated stream valley systems are practically absent. Runoff does not go far before disappearing into a sink or enlarged joint crack. Some of the

sinks are narrow-mouthed, open pits; some are broad, steep-walled, and flat-floored, with clayey soil; and some are plugged with clay so that lakes and swamps form in them. If the depressions are numerous and small, the landscape may closely resemble the terrain of glacial moraines (Fig. 13.1). The regolith, however, is generally thin and patchy, for pure limestones and dolomites yield little debris when they are weathered.

Subsurface cavities are not often large, although they may thoroughly honeycomb the soluble strata in which they occur. Great caverns, such as Mammoth Cave, in Kentucky, and Carlsbad Cavern, in New Mexico, can develop only in unusually thick and pure limestone formations. Some of these larger caves are many kilometers in length, with passages on several levels and rooms that may reach lengths of more than 100 m and heights of 30 m or more. The most spectacular caves are those with many pendants and pinnacles (stalactites and stalagmites), which are deposited by dripping water containing calcium carbonate in solution (Fig. 13.2).

Sinks are common in many parts of the United States, but only two large areas of almost purely solution terrain exist, one in central and northern Florida and the other in central Kentucky. The Florida region is low and gently rolling, with hundreds of shallow depressions, many of them filled with water. It has many large springs, as well as some areas of steep-walled solution valleys. Part of the Kentucky area is somewhat similar, but the section near Mammoth Cave is much rougher, with sinks of unusual size and depth.

Probably the most noteworthy area of solution topography in the world is in western Yugoslavia, where a truly mountainous surface of great ruggedness has been sculptured almost wholly by solution in thick limestones. The region is called *"the Karst"* (meaning "barren land"), and from this example the term *karst topography* has often been extended to cover all solution landscapes, however unlike the original they may be.

The Work of Moving Ice

Glaciers and Their Development

Development of glaciers. Glaciers are not simply inert masses of ice and snow, but rather tongues or sheets of ice so thick that they can actually be deformed and moved by the force of gravity. The deformation is much like the flow of very viscous liquids—the traditional "molasses in January." Glaciers rarely move more than a few inches per day, although exceptional rates of more than 30 m (100 ft) per day have been recorded.

Since ice must become 45 to 60 m (150 to 200 ft) thick before it will begin to flow, glaciers can form

only where ice accumulates over a period of years. If more snow falls during a cold season than can be melted during the following summer, the unmelted residue is added to the snow of the next year, and so on. The old, buried snow changes gradually into solid ice under the effects of compression combined with partial melting and refreezing. In this way a great thickness of ice can be built up in a relatively short time.

Circumstances favorable to glacier growth are most often encountered in areas having heavy winter snowfall but short, cool summers. At present most of the ice-covered area of the earth is in Antarctica and Greenland. Elsewhere, glaciers are confined to the moister and colder mountain regions. Dryness and summer heat are enemies of glacier development, and many high ranges and even some large areas within the polar circles have no glaciers at all because their snowfall is insufficient to last out the summer.

The ice in a glacier moves in response to gravity, flowing generally downslope and away from the center of thickest accumulation (Fig. 13.3). As it spreads beyond the region of collection into neighboring areas at lower elevation, where summers are warmer and longer or annual snowfall is less, its outer margins are attacked by melting. The ice continues to spread, however, until its edge reaches a point of balance between the rate of supply and the rate of melting. Thereafter, as long as conditions do not change, the edge of the glacier remains in the

Figure 13.1 Limestone plain with numerous small sinks, some containing ponds. Near Park City, Kentucky, south of Mammoth Cave. *(W. Ray Scott, National Park Concessions, Inc. Courtesy Kentucky Geological Survey.)*

Figure 13.2   Stalactites and stalagmites in Carlsbad Caverns National Park, New Mexico. *(United States Department of the Interior, National Park Service Photo.)*

same place, although the ice continues to move from the source to the edge. If climatic conditions change so that the supply of ice is lessened, or if the rate of melting is increased, the glacier begins to shrink. On the other hand, if melting is decreased or the ice

supply is increased, the edge of the glacier advances until it reaches a new point of equilibrium.

Existing icecaps.   It has been estimated that if the great icecaps that cover most of Greenland and Ant-

Figure 13.3   Nysne Glacier, Peary Land, northern Greenland. Note the collecting basins from which the glacier flows and the surface markings that indicate the flowing movement. Ridges of ice-deposited debris (moraines) border the ice tongue, and a braided stream of meltwater flows across the sand and gravel it has washed out from the ice margin. *(Geodetic Institute, Copenhagen, copyright.)*

arctica were to be completely melted, they would release enough water to raise the level of the oceans about 65 m (215 ft). The Antarctic ice sheet alone covers an area about $1\frac{1}{3}$ times as large as the entire United States. Both ice sheets reach extreme thicknesses of more than 3 km (2 mi).

The surface of each icecap rises rapidly from the coast to a high, plateaulike interior. In Antarctica the average elevation is about 1,800 m (6,000 ft), and the maximum is more than 4,300 m (14,000 ft). The highest elevation in Greenland is above 3,000 m (10,000 ft). Over large areas the bottom of each icecap

is below sea level, a fact which suggests that the land surface has been significantly depressed by the weight of the overlying ice.

For the most part, the surfaces of the icecaps are relatively smooth upland plains. Only near their margins and about the scattered mountain masses that project through them do they become rough and crevassed (Fig. 13.4). At their margins both icecaps descend toward the sea through gaps in mountain ranges, breaking into tongues and lobes as they do so. Where the ice reaches the sea, great masses split off from the edges to form icebergs, some of which drift

Figure 13.4   The undulating upland of the Antarctic icecap, with projecting mountain peaks. *(Official U.S. Navy photograph.)*

hundreds of kilometers from their source before melt-ing away. In a number of places the Antarctic icecap extends far beyond the shoreline as a thick, floating ice shelf ending in an abrupt cliff.

Existing valley glaciers.   Snows fall on almost all high mountains, but valley glaciers are found only in mountains that receive unusually heavy winter snowfall or have a short or cool melting period. Glacial tongues 8 to 16 km (5 to 10 mi) long are common in the Canadian Rockies and the Alps, while in southern Alaska and in the Himalaya and adjacent mountains, some glaciers reach lengths of 15 to 80 km (10 to 50 mi). In the Rocky Mountains and the Sierra Nevada of the western United States, on the other hand, long, warm summers restrict glacier develop-ment to a few tiny patches, generally around a kilometer (less than a mile) in length.

The snow that feeds mountain glaciers accu-mulates in high valley heads, into which it is swept by winds and by avalanches from the slopes above. From these collecting basins ice flows in great tongues down the valleys into the zone of melting (Fig. 9.9B). The upper parts of the glaciers are often concave, with snow-covered, sometimes smooth surfaces. Toward the lower ends, however, the snow cover disappears in the summer, exposing rough surfaces deeply slashed in places by open cracks or crevasses, especially at sharp turns and unusually steep gradients in the valley floor. Wastage of ice by melting and evapora-tion uncovers masses of rock debris that has been

carried upon and in the ice, so that the lower ends of many glaciers are almost obscured by a thick cover of rubble.

Former continental glaciers.   If glaciers had never been more extensive than they are now, they would not be familiar as sculptors of the land, for the surfaces beneath existing glaciers are effectively hid-den. However, it is well known that glaciers of tremendous size spread over large parts of the North-ern Hemisphere continents a number of times during the last million years or more (Fig. 13.5). In North America they originated to the east and west of Hudson Bay and, at one time or another, invaded all of Canada and the northeastern and north central United States. In Eurasia they formed in the Scandi-navian highlands and spread over most of northern Europe and northwestern Siberia. Most of eastern Siberia and much of Alaska were not glaciated in spite of their coldness, probably because of insuffi-cient snowfall. There were no continental glaciers in the Southern Hemisphere except on Antarctica, be-cause there are no large land masses in the upper middle latitudes where they could have grown.

At the same time that these continental ice sheets developed, there was a general expansion of glaciers in high mountain valleys all over the world. For example, in the western United States, the Rocky Mountains, which now are almost bare of glaciers, were heavily glaciated—to about the same degree that the Alps and Himalaya are now.

Why such immense glaciers developed during these great ice ages is not at all clear. Unquestionably there were climatic changes in the direction of cooler summers and possibly greater snowfall in the source regions, but the reason for these changes lies in the realm of hypothesis. The many possible factors that have been suggested include fluctuations in the output of energy from the sun, outpourings of volcanic dust into the atmosphere, and changes in the shapes and elevations of the continents and in the connections between the oceans.

Even the course of glacial history is most imperfectly known. Until recently it was generally believed that great ice sheets formed, spread, fluctuated, and melted away four times during an identifiable *Pleistocene epoch*, which was commonly estimated to have begun roughly 1 million years ago and lasted until the last few thousand years. More recent studies, however, suggest that there were considerably more than four major stages of glacial growth and that they began long before the Pleistocene epoch. As yet data are wholly inadequate to permit the establishment of anything approaching a clear glacial history reaching back beyond the last two or, in some places, three major glaciations.

The last Pleistocene icecap (called *Wisconsin* or *Wisconsinan* in North America) appears to have begun its expansion somewhat less than 100,000 years ago, to have reached its maximum about 18,000 years ago, and to have shrunk to approximately its present dimensions by 5,000 years ago. The edge of this last ice sheet did not disappear from the northernmost Great Lakes area until perhaps 9,000 years ago. Clearly the Wisconsinan expansion of continental ice sheets fell well within the period when human beings had become widely established over the earth, and it must have had profound effects upon their existence. By the time the last ice sheet had vanished, history had reached the early stages of the sedentary civilizations of Babylon and Egypt.

The effects of glaciation were widespread and complex. The surfaces actually covered by the ice were modified by erosion and deposition. Evidently they were also considerably depressed by the weight of the ice, rising again when the ice melted away. Valleys and plains adjacent to the ice were strewn with debris carried from the glacial edge by meltwater. Throughout the world sea levels dropped several hundred feet as more and more water was transferred to the ice sheets, then rose again as the glaciers wasted away. Accompanying the whole glacial sequence was a complex series of climatic changes which affected not only the glaciated areas but much of the rest of the world as well.

Gradation by Glaciers

Glacial erosion. The investigation of how glaciers erode and deposit is greatly complicated by the fact that it is impossible to see just what is happening underneath glaciers now in existence. Many of our notions of how glaciers rework the surface are in-

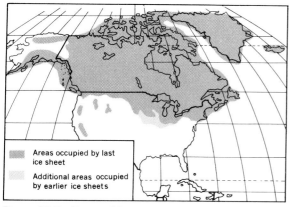
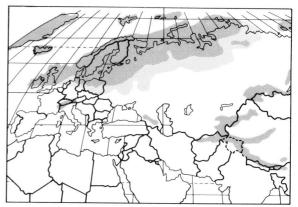

Figure 13.5 Extent of former continental glaciers in North America and Eurasia. *(Adapted from Flint, Glacial and Quaternary Geology, John Wiley & Sons, Inc., New York, 1971.)*

ferred from the forms left behind in areas where the ice has lately melted away. Hence knowledge has grown slowly, and strong differences of opinion remain.

Apparently glaciers can erode in three ways. First, and probably the most important by far, is the process known as *plucking* or *quarrying*. In this the plastic ice molds itself about particles of the regolith or blocks of bedrock and then drags them out of place as the ice mass moves forward (Fig. 13.6). Quarrying is most effective where the surface materials are loose, thin-bedded, or jointed. A second erosional technique is that of *grinding* or *abrasion*. Quarried rocks which are partly embedded in the lower surface of the ice are dragged across bedrock outcrops like grains on a giant sheet of sandpaper, scraping and gouging as they go. Grooved and polished rock surfaces show the work of this process. Third, and probably least important, is a bulldozerlike shoving effect, which may occur where the ice edge readvances over loose heaped-up debris dropped earlier.

Undoubtedly the chief accomplishment of glacial erosion is the stripping of the regolith from the surface over much of the area covered. However, the ice also quarries actively in strongly jointed or conspicuously weak bedrock. Projecting crags are removed or reduced in size. Bottleneck valleys lying in the direction of ice movement seem especially liable to strong erosion. But generally speaking, the

extensive and thick continental ice sheets were not strongly channeled, so that their erosional work was inclined to be patchy, producing irregular depressions rather than integrated valleys. Erosion by glacial tongues in mountain valleys, on the other hand, is narrowly confined and often highly effective.

Transportation by glaciers. Glaciers are highly competent and indiscriminate transporting agents, able to carry material of all sizes, including immense boulders. The debris eroded by the glacier itself is carried near the base of the ice. But mountain valley glaciers may also transport quantities of material that has been dumped onto them by mass movement or surface erosion on the valley sides above them. This material is concentrated near the surface of the ice, although some may eventually become covered by so much snow that it reaches considerable depth.

Glacial deposition. A glacier deposits its load by melting away from it. Melting occurs toward the outer margins of the ice and works both upward from the ground and downward from the upper surface. As a result of melting on the lower surface, the debris carried in the lower part of the ice is lodged beneath the glacier (Fig. 13.7). Melting downward from above exposes more and more debris on the surface of the ice, so that the lower ends of some mountain valley glaciers are almost completely obscured by a thick

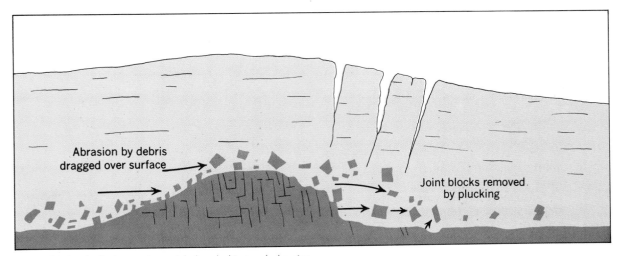

Abrasion by debris dragged over surface

Joint blocks removed by plucking

Figure 13.6   A glacier erodes mainly by plucking and abrasion.

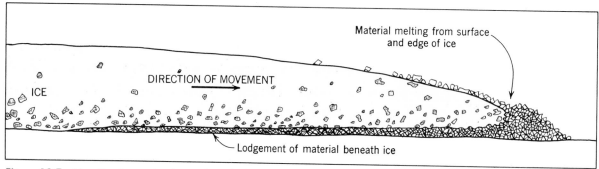

DIRECTION OF MOVEMENT

ICE

Material melting from surface and edge of ice

Lodgement of material beneath ice

Figure 13.7   Near its edge, an ice sheet melts on both upper and lower surfaces. Thus some of the debris it contains is lodged beneath the ice, while the rest is dropped at the outer margin.

cover of rock and sand. This surface debris is deposited at the edges of the glacier as the ice melts.

There is no mechanism for selectivity in either the transporting or the depositing process. Therefore glacial deposits are commonly jumbled mixtures of material varying in size from clay to huge boulders (Fig. 13.8). By this characteristic they can usually be easily distinguished from water-laid deposits, which almost always show some degree of sorting and layering. The unsorted debris deposited directly by the ice is called *till*. The specific deposits themselves are called *moraines*. The sheet of till believed to have been laid down by lodgement beneath the ice is the *ground moraine*; the thicker accumulations deposited along the ice edge are *marginal moraines*.

Moraines can be found throughout the glaciated area, for at some time or other every place overrun by the ice will have been in the vicinity of the glacial margin. Within the depositional area, however, the till is unevenly distributed in patches, heaps, ridges, and blankets of unequal thickness. The deposits are normally thickest in valleys, in areas "downstream" from sources of easily eroded material that furnish quantities of till, and in the outer parts of the glaciated area, where the melting zone may have remained longest. Deposits are often thin or absent altogether on hilltops, in areas of especially resistant rock, and in the source region from which the ice was continually moving outward.

Meltwater flowing from the ice margin may carry out quantities of debris, which are deposited as alluvium across plains or in valley bottoms. Such deposits, called *outwash*, are not strictly glacial, but

outwash and till deposits are both commonly included under the general term *glacial drift.*

In varying degrees, till deposition modifies the landscapes over which it is laid down. The resulting surface features depend upon the thickness and stoniness of the till and upon the form of the underlying surface. The tendency of moraine deposition to be irregularly heaped and to be concentrated in valleys has the effect of leaving behind an irregular surface of rises and depressions without well-organized valley systems. It was noted above that glacial erosion has somewhat similar effects.

Because there is a significant difference in

Figure 13.8   Exposure of glacial till, showing the unassorted clay, pebbles, and boulders of which it is composed.

age between early and late Pleistocene glacial depos-its, the surface features that the ice produced also show a considerable difference in their freshness and degree of preservation. Those formed by the late Wisconsinan ice sheets are generally clearly defined and little altered. Those formed before the Wisconsinan, and even some early Wisconsinan surfaces, are commonly so changed by stream erosion and mass wasting as to be unrecognizable. Only the distinctive character of the materials themselves reveals the glacial involvement of these "old drift" areas.

Surfaces Modified by Glaciation

Glaciated Plains

Glacial modification of plain surfaces.   The great continental ice sheets of the Pleistocene epoch covered about 30 percent of the land area of the earth, as compared with the 10 percent, chiefly in Antarctica and Greenland, now occupied by glaciers and icecaps. Within the area of Pleistocene glaciation, however, distinctively glacial landforms are well preserved only in those sections occupied by the last, or Wisconsinan, ice sheet. Not all these areas are plains, but their surfaces effectively illustrate the patchy, irregular, unchanneled erosional and depositional activity of the great ice sheets. That activity virtually obliterated the old stream courses and produced a surface in which there were many shallow enclosed depressions and few continuous valleys. For this reason lakes, swamps, and aimlessly wandering streams are found almost everywhere in the lately glaciated country, although they are uncommon in stream-eroded landscapes (Fig. 13.9).

Most of the glaciated area is dominated by depositional features. Only in scattered sections where there is no drift or where the drift is very

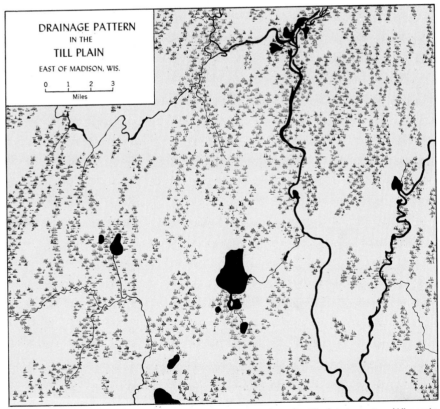

Figure 13.9   Typical aimless drainage pattern on a portion of a till plain in eastern Wisconsin.

patchy are scoured bedrock surfaces broadly exposed. By chance, both the Scandinavian and Canadian areas in which the glaciers originated are underlain largely by ancient "shields" of resistant rocks. Conversely, the broad outer zones of the glaciated plains in both continents are areas of weaker sedimentary strata. Since the weaker rocks yield more readily to weathering and erosion, it is not surprising that the areas which they underlie are in general more thickly covered with drift than are the hard-rock areas. However, the smoother sections of even the shields are also primarily drift plains, although the drift is relatively thin and bedrock outcrop is frequent.

In general drift deposition tended to make the surface smoother than it had been. Drift was deposited more thickly in valleys than on hilltops, while glacial erosion was somewhat more active on the crests than in the valleys. If the relief of the original surface was slight, the drift might completely obscure the older forms, producing an entirely new surface. If, on the other hand, the original terrain was hilly or the drift rather thin, the old hilltops may still protrude.

Because some glacial drift is put down underneath the body of the ice itself while some is deposited at the ice margin and some is laid down by the streams of meltwater flowing from the ice, a drift plain is a highly complex surface. The most extensive and fundamental element in this complex is the till plain or ground moraine, which covers most of the glaciated area. Marginal moraines are arranged about the margins of the till plain and also upon its surface, often in broad festoons, one behind the other. Bordering them, either beyond the till plain or upon its surface, are sheets of sandy and gravelly outwash or beds of fine sediments that accumulated in temporary lakes.

Till plains.   The till sheet or ground moraine is a widespread mantle of debris, in part lodged beneath the glacier and in part let down onto the ground when the ice edge melted back or the glacier wasted away. The till plain is characteristically a gently undulating surface produced by uneven deposition (Fig. 13.10). Broad, low swells and wide, shallow depressions are arranged according to no systematic pattern. Lakes and swamps accumulate in the depressions, and streams wander aimlessly from one depression to another. Even the larger lakes are quite shallow. In the till plains of North America, thousands of the smaller lake-filled basins left at the retreat of the last glacier have already been filled with sediment or drained by natural processes and converted into marshes or even dry land.

Rising above the undulating surface in a few localities are sizable groups of low, smooth, half-egg–shaped hills composed usually of till (Fig. 13.11). Each hill is commonly a kilometer or two in length and is elongated in the direction of glacier flow, with its steeper end facing the direction from which the ice came. These features, known as *drumlins*, seem to have been deposited beneath the marginal sections of the ice sheets and streamlined by ice movement, but the exact manner of their formation is not known.

Figure 13.10   The undulating surface of a till plain. *(Wisconsin Geological Survey.)*

Figure 13.11 Two drumlins in tandem on a till plain near Weedsport, central New York. Ice moved in direction from right background toward left foreground.

Extensive fields of drumlins occur in eastern Wisconsin, western New York, and several parts of central Canada.

While many areas of till plain, such as those in northern Iowa, Illinois, Indiana, and Ohio, are excellent agricultural lands, some others are not. Many sections are excessively sandy or stony, and nearly all are plagued with problems of poor drainage. Even in the productive plains of the middle western Corn Belt, thousands of hectares of land have arrived at their high value only through the installation of untold thousands of kilometers of drainage tile. Elsewhere great numbers of marshes and swamps have been ditched and drained. Unfortunately, vast areas of till plain, largely in the Soviet Union and Canada, lie poleward of the climatic limits of profitable agriculture and are further burdened with infertile soils and poor drainage.

Marginal moraines. Wisconsinan marginal moraines are relatively thick heapings of drift that accumulated around the edge of a glacier during periods when the ice margin remained nearly stationary for a considerable time. The location of marginal moraines reveals the position and pattern of the ice edge at various times during glacial wastage. Moraines put down where the ice was at its most advanced position are called *terminal moraines*. *Recessional moraines* are those built upon the till plain behind the terminal moraine during the general period of glacial wastage.

The surface of a well-developed marginal moraine is usually higher, stonier, and more irregular than that of the neighboring till plain (Fig. 13.12).

The depositional processes involved in the construction of a moraine are complex. Some material is dropped in heaps and ridges by melting; some is laid down in alluvial cones against the ice front by meltwater running off the glacier surface; and some is bulldozed up by brief local readvances of the ice edge. The gravel cones and piles of till form many small, rounded knobs or ridges, and between these are small hollows or depressions, some of which contain ponds or swamps. Generally speaking, moraines in stony and gravelly drift are more upstanding and have rougher, more broken surfaces than moraines in clay and silt drift. For example, the clay-silt moraines of northeastern Illinois, although large in volume, form low, gentle swells that would hardly be recognized as moraines by a person familiar only with the hilly, stony moraines of eastern Wisconsin or western Minnesota.

The highest and broadest marginal moraines represent situations in which either the ice edge oscillated over a limited zone for an unusually long time or a vast mass of drift accumulated in the narrow zone between two slightly separated lobes of the ice sheet. Oscillation of the ice edge accounts for the unusually broad belts of hummocky moraine in west central North Dakota and western Minnesota, as well as those across northern Europe south of the Baltic Coast. An example of an interlobate moraine is the remarkably high and rough Kettle Moraine of eastern Wisconsin.

Glaciated surfaces with little drift. In the rougher parts of the crystalline shields of Canada, Scandinavia, and Finland, the thin preglacial cover of regolith was stripped from large areas, and the resistant bedrock underneath, although it was vigorously scoured by the ice, yielded little new drift. As a result, naked bedrock is broadly exposed in rounded knobs and hills, steep, quarried bluffs, and more level expanses scarred by elongated grooves and innumerable shallow depressions (Fig. 13.13). Joints, fault lines, and other zones of weakness show unusually clearly because they have been etched out by selective erosion. Sparse accumulations of stony drift fill the bottoms of many of the valleys and basins. Drainage is in complete disorder. Lakes are even more abundant than in the areas of deeper drift (Fig. 13.14). Streams wander from one overflowing basin to the

Figure 13.12 Small kettle ponds surrounded by boulder-strewn knobs in marginal moraine near Whitewater, Wisconsin. *(V. C. Finch.)*

Figure 13.13 The scoured, bare uplands and rock basins of a glaciated surface with little drift. This site is in a rough section of the Canadian Shield near Great Bear Lake, Northwest Territory. *(Royal Canadian Air Force photograph.)*

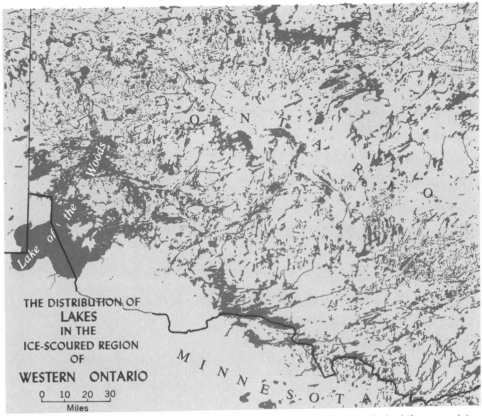

Figure 13.14 Sprawling lakes, mainly in rock basins, occupy much of the thinly drift-strewn plain of western Ontario. *(After Map 24A, Province of Ontario, Department of Surveys.)*

next in a wholly unsystematic manner. Falls and rapids are numerous and, in these areas of hard rock, are unusually persistent.

Ice-scoured surfaces of this kind offer little of value to humankind. Their thin, stony, patchy soils, irregular surfaces, and large amounts of standing water virtually exclude agriculture. Rapids and falls provide some waterpower sites, and valuable mineral deposits have been discovered in some areas; but for the most part they remain among the more thinly settled parts of the earth.

Outwash surfaces. Meltwater draining from the edge of the ice sheets usually carried a heavy load of sediment, much of it coarse, and therefore the meltwater channels were normally braided and actively aggrading. The finer suspended load was transported far beyond the ice edge, but the sands and gravels of the bed load were deposited in great quantity in the marginal zone (Fig. 13.15).

Some glacial streams flowed in definite valleys and for this reason laid down deposits, referred to as *valley trains*, that are in all respects like other floodplains formed by braided streams. Many channels, however, were not confined by valley walls, but were able to shift freely back and forth, spreading their debris fanwise to form smooth outwash plains similar to piedmont alluvial plains with particularly gentle gradients. This situation was no doubt especially common during the period of ice wastage, for then the meltwaters were released upon the surface of the till plains deposited shortly before.

During the wastage of the ice sheets, large blocks or masses of stagnant ice were left in front of

Figure 13.15 Glacial outwash is often composed of rudely stratified sand and gravel washed free of clay and silt. *(Wisconsin Geological Survey.)*

the retreating glacial margin by uneven melting. Outwash from the main ice front continued to be deposited around them and in some instances buried them. When each block or mass eventually melted away, often long after outwash deposition in that area had ceased, its disappearance left a steep-walled depression (*kettle*) in the otherwise smooth surface. Many of the small lakes of northern Wisconsin and southern Michigan are associated with pitted outwash plains of this type.

Some streams of meltwater built narrow deposits of outwash at the bottoms of deep crevasses or in ice tunnels through which they flowed beneath the outer part of the ice sheets. If the ice melted away without destroying the fragile feature, it remained as a sinuous ridge of gravel somewhat like an abandoned railroad embankment. Such ridges are called *eskers* (Fig. 13.16).

Because of the sandy and gravelly materials of which outwash plains are composed, they commonly have rather low agricultural value compared with the less stony varieties of till plain. They do, however, afford valuable and abundant sources of sand and gravel for constructional use. The large commercial gravel pits of the Great Lakes region are located mainly in outwash plains.

Glacial lakes and lake plains. Most of the numerous lake plains in the areas of late Pleistocene glaciation are no more than the sediment-filled relics of small postglacial lakes that formed on the irregular drift surface. Others, however, some of them very large, represent the beds of lakes that existed, usually rather briefly, in places where northward-flowing streams were dammed by the edge of the ice itself during the maximal and wasting stages of glaciation.

The largest of all these marginal lakes occupied much of the basin of the Red and Nelson Rivers in Manitoba and surrounding sections during the last major period of glacier recession (Fig. 13.17). At its greatest extent this lake, known as Lake Agassiz, covered an area larger than all of the present Great

Figure 13.16 The narrow, sinuous ridge of an esker, made up of stratified drift. *(John R. Randall.)*

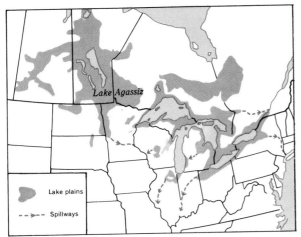

Figure 13.17   Glacial lake plains in the United States and Canada.

Lake plains

Spillways

Lakes combined and drained southward via the Minnesota and Mississippi Rivers. It finally disappeared when melting uncovered the outlets into Hudson Bay. Much of its bed is now the flat and fertile Red River Plain, although other sections are occupied by large swamps and lakes. The former outlines of Lake Agassiz are marked by beach ridges and other shoreline features.

The Great Lakes had a complex history during late glacial times. For a considerable period the ice blocked the St. Lawrence outlet and even covered the northern parts of the lake basins themselves. The lakes in the exposed parts of the basins rose and overflowed through various southern outlets, most of which led to the Mississippi River system. At their highest levels the lakes spread well beyond their present bounds. Chicago, Detroit, and Buffalo are among the many cities now located on the smooth plains that mark former extensions of the lake floors.

Where marginal lakes found new outlets across low divides into other drainage basins, the outflow carved large spillways that still exist although they are no longer traversed by streams. Some rivers blocked by the ice developed new courses that paralleled the ice front for long distances. Some of these new valleys were cut down to levels lower than those of the former channels, so that the rivers continued to flow in them even after the glaciers disappeared. The present courses of the Missouri and

Ohio Rivers are probably largely of glacial-margin origin, as are sections of the Mississippi Valley north of St. Louis. Similar marginal valleys, most of them not now followed by streams, run from east to west across the plains of Poland and northern Germany.

Glaciated Mountains and Hills

Effects of valley glaciation.   Valley glaciers tend to increase the roughness of mountainous areas, for, like streams, they tend to erode and enlarge the valleys in which they flow. They work vigorously, clearing weathered rock and talus from the valley bottoms and sides, plucking in jointed bedrock, scouring and quarrying on rock projections and spurs, and dumping their transported load farther down the valleys and along the edges of the ice tongues.

Because of this activity the walls of glaciated valleys are often steeper and freer of regolith than those of typical stream-eroded valleys. Frost shattering attacks these bare walls, driving them back and dropping the debris onto the ice below. Such steepened, smoothed, and straightened walls give some glaciated valleys a troughlike form with a crudely U-shaped cross section (Fig. 13.18). This form appears to be best developed in resistant rocks with prominent vertical joint systems.

Glaciated valley floors commonly descend in a series of irregular steps and are marked by lakes strung like beads along a cord. Some of the lakes occupy shallow depressions in the bedrock; others are dammed by moraines. Between the lakes the streams may plunge over waterfalls or rapids. These typically irregular profiles are probably due largely to differential erosion, in which the ice plucks most actively in weaker and more closely jointed rocks and on the steeper gradients of the preglacial valley floor. Tributary valleys often enter the main valley in discordant fashion, their mouths appearing as notches far up the valley side. The streams issuing from these "hanging" valleys must drop in waterfalls or cascades to reach the main valley floors.

Valley heads, like valley walls, are abrupt and steep, sometimes looking as though they had been scooped out of the mountainside by a gigantic power shovel. These features, called *cirques*, appear to be the result of glacial plucking, frost shattering, and talus removal at the headwall of the valley. Rapid retreat of the cliffed valley sides and cirque

Figure 13.18 Head of a glaciated mountain valley. A large cirque in background, with precipitous rock walls and a small remnant glacier. Characteristic stepped-down valley profile with lakes and waterfalls. *(Hileman, from Glacier National Park.)*

walls eventually leads to the formation of knife-edge ridges and rugged, sharp peaks on the divides between valleys or valley heads (Fig. 13.19).

Because of the quantities of debris that are carried onto the moving ice from the valley walls, mountain glaciers are often heavily laden with rubble, and consequently they build moraines that sometimes reach remarkable size. Lateral moraines are strung along the slopes at the sides of the ice tongues, and end moraines curve across the valleys like dams. Eskers, outwash deltas, and valley trains are also found, in all respects similar to those associated with continental glaciers.

This combination of abrupt slopes, sharp peaks and ridges, much exposed bedrock, numerous lakes, and prominent moraines gives glaciated mountains a spectacular quality that is further enhanced if glaciers are still present. Except for moraines, these characteristics can also be found in mountains that have never been glaciated, but the recurrent presence of several of them together is the special mark of mountain glaciation. Ranges in which the glacial features are notably rugged and in which glacial tongues still exist are called *alpine mountains*.

Effects of continental glaciation on hills and mountains. Many mountain and hill areas in the northern continents were completely overrun by the great Pleistocene ice sheets, with results generally similar to those on glaciated plains. The ice tended, in general, to smooth the surface by eroding away crags and small spurs and depositing drift in the valleys and ravines (Fig. 13.20). Where valleys in weak rocks were oriented in the direction of glacial flow, glacial erosion was unusually vigorous, sometimes excavating basins such as those occupied by the Finger Lakes of western New York. Lakes are common in all glaciated hill lands, especially in the drift-clogged valleys. The northern Appalachians and Adirondacks in New York State, the uplands and mountains of New England, most of the Laurentian highlands of eastern Canada, and most of northern Scandinavia are rough lands that have been modified by overriding continental glaciation.

The Work of the Wind

Where and how the wind works. The wind is a much less important sculptor of surface forms than water, gravity, and ice, chiefly because wind can erode only under certain limited conditions. Wind erosion is active only if the surface is nearly bare of vegetation, and then only if the surface material is fine and dry. For this reason the work of the wind is largely confined to deserts or semideserts and to those few areas in humid regions—such as beaches, wide

Figure 13.19 Valley-glaciated mountains of the alpine type, showing a large cirque, a small glacier, and the characteristic steep rock walls and sharp peaks and ridges. The large lateral moraines in the middleground indicate that the glacier was once larger than it is now. Mount Athabasca, Alberta, Canada. *(Canadian Pacific Railway Company.)*

river beds at low water, and, nowadays, plowed fields—which have little plant cover.

Where it is able to work, the wind erodes, transports, and deposits in much the same manner as running water, except that it does little channeling. It erodes by frictional drag, eddy currents, and the

Figure 13.20 Smooth, drift-covered slopes in glaciated section of the Appalachian Highlands near Syracuse, New York.

impact of particles already being carried (sandblasting effect). It moves material by rolling or bouncing particles along the ground or by carrying them in suspension. It deposits where surface irregularities, including vegetation, check its speed near the ground, or where its velocity decreases simply because of the atmospheric pressure pattern. Rain falling through the dust-laden air will often carry most of the suspended material down with it.

The wind can rarely move material larger than coarse sand. Sand is carried as "bed load" of the airstream—that is, by rolling or low bouncing—and seldom rises more than a few feet above the ground even in high winds. Silt and clay can be carried in suspension and thus may reach great heights and travel long distances. For example, fine red soil traceable to the plains of western Oklahoma has fallen on the decks of steamers in the Atlantic.

Wind erosion (deflation). Erosion by the wind, like that by ice, tends to be widespread or patchy rather than channeled. Thus it may lower the surface rather uniformly over a broad area without producing any pronounced surface forms. On occasion, however, deflation scours out shallow depressions in places where the vegetation has been destroyed, where the material is especially loose and fine, or where the wind velocity is increased by a natural bottleneck. It is common for the wind to winnow out the finer particles from mixed surface material, leaving behind a coarse-textured gravelly or stony cover sometimes called *desert pavement* (Fig. 13.21).

Wind deposition. The deposition of fine suspended material is so extensive and unconcentrated that it modifies the surface significantly only if it continues for a long time and leaves a very thick layer. Most of the widespread deposits of unlayered, buff-colored, calcium-rich silt called *loess*, common in the middle western United States, eastern Europe, and north China, are believed to have originated as wind-blown silt.

By contrast, sand tends to accumulate in heaps rather than smooth sheets, and thus sand deposition does produce distinct landforms. These features, known as *sand dunes*, are common in some desert regions and along many coasts.

Wind-eroded surfaces. Wind-sculptured lands are largely confined to the dry parts of the world, and even there the effects of wind action are usually less important than the work of water. Except for the few great "seas" of sand dunes, wind-produced features are mostly minor details on surfaces shaped primarily by other agents.

The most important effects of deflation occur where the wind picks up quantities of fine material

Figure 13.21 Sandblasted rock fragments and pebbles left behind by selective wind erosion on the floor of Death Valley, California. *(Eliot Blackwelder.)*

Figure 13.22 Bare surface lowered by deflation. Note mounds protected by shrubs and tufts of grass. *(A. M. Piper, U.S. Geological Survey.)*

from the bare floors of alluviated desert basins, thereby lowering the surface over a broad area. Only occasionally do clearly excavated depressions appear, usually on bare patches within otherwise vegetation-covered areas. Local destruction of the vegetation by animals, excessive alkalinity, or any other cause opens up a bare spot where deflation can go to work, producing a shallow *blowout* (Fig. 13.22). Generally, however, the wind erodes so broadly and so gradually that its importance can scarcely be estimated.

As a by-product of its selectivity, deflation is largely responsible for the widespread occurrence of gravel-clad surfaces in the deserts. Only the finer silts and clays are picked up; pebbles and coarse sand may not even be moved along the ground. In this way the coarser materials become concentrated at the surface. Where there is no coarse material in the regolith, however, the finer dust may be stripped off to considerable depth.

Sand-dune areas. The popular conception of the desert plain as a sea of wind-blown sand is considerably overdrawn. Not many large desert areas are so much as one-fourth sand-covered. Nevertheless, there are numerous regions of sandy desert, the largest being in the central and eastern Sahara and in southern Arabia, which derive their abundant sands chiefly from the disintegration of sandstone or granitic rocks or from accumulations of sandy alluvium in dry basins (Fig. 13.23).

Unlike the fine silt and clay, sand is rolled or bounced along the ground like the bed load in a stream and tends to accumulate in heaps, ridges, or sheets that assume a remarkable variety of shapes (Fig. 13.24). Where sand is thick and abundant, dunes commonly form as a series of great waves transverse

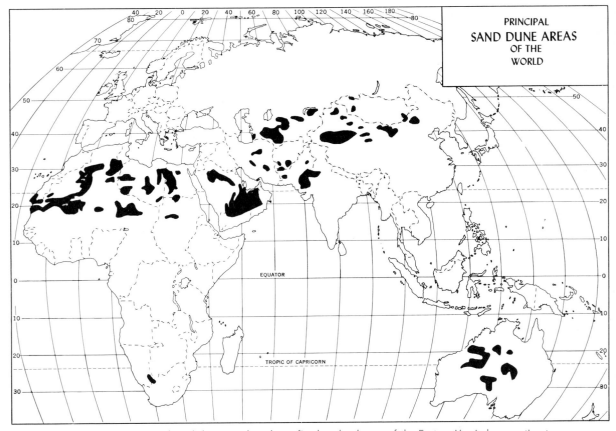

Figure 13.23   Extensive areas of sand dunes are largely confined to the deserts of the Eastern Hemisphere continents.

to the dominant wind direction, similar in form to wind-driven waves in the sea. Where strong winds may come from several directions, however, the waves are distorted into arrays of pyramids and other complex forms. Where the sand is less plentiful, the dunes are usually separated from one another. Some take the form of almost perfect crescents (*barchans*) with the horns pointing downwind. Others are long, peaked ridges (*seifs*), oriented parallel to the direction of strong winds (Fig. 13.25).

Most dunes that are barren of vegetation, and especially those occurring in areas of fairly constant wind direction, move quite actively. High winds drift sand up their gentle windward slopes and over their crests, where the grains drop in the shelter of the steep leeward slopes. By this process the dune

form is maintained while the whole feature slowly migrates. Rates of movement vary from imperceptibly slow to as much as 30 m (100 ft) per year.

In many regions of the world sand dunes have become fixed by the growth of a grass cover on them, in some instances indicating a long-term increase in rainfall. One such region forms a broad belt across Africa along the southern margin of the Sahara. In north central Nebraska a large area of once-active dunes, probably Pleistocene in origin, is now anchored by a thick cover of grass.

Loess surfaces.   The deposition of wind-blown loess may cover the land with an extensive blanket of silt several inches or even many meters thick. The thinner accumulations do not greatly change the form of

Figure 13.24 The complex, wind-rippled forms, primarily transverse and pyramidal, of one of the small patches of sand dunes in the American deserts. Death Valley National Monument, California. *(G. A. Grant, National Park Service.)*

the preexisting terrain. But thick loess deposits may reduce the unevenness of a plain somewhat, and may display low, inconspicuous dunelike features on their surfaces.

Loess has certain physical properties that permit the development of distinctive features by stream erosion and mass wasting. Owing perhaps in part to the angularity of its particles, it has the ability to stand in near-vertical faces when cut into by streams or artificial excavations. If the vegetation is thin, gullying is very likely to occur, leading to rapid and intricate dissection. Erosional slopes are steep and often much scarred by slumping, so that eroded loessial landscapes have an unusually broken appearance (Fig. 13.26).

Particularly extensive loess deposits occur in the interior of the United States (Fig. 13.27), the southern parts of the great plain of northwestern Eurasia from France into the U.S.S.R., the northern interior of China, and parts of the Pampa of Argentina. Some of these deposits appear to have been blown out from alluvial plains in neighboring dry regions; others are thought to have been obtained from broad

valley trains and outwash plains around the glacial margins during Pleistocene time.

Loessial soils are friable and often highly fertile. As a consequence the loess plains of the world are in most instances productive agricultural lands, although soil erosion is a perennial problem.

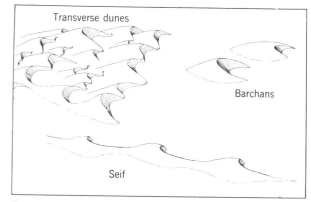

Figure 13.25 Common types of sand dunes. In all the examples the prevalent wind direction is from left to right.

Figure 13.26   An eroded and slumped hillside in deep loess in central Nebraska.

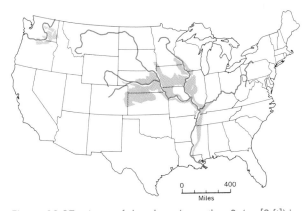

Figure 13.27   Areas of deep loess (more than 2.4 m [8 ft]) in the United States. *(From map: Pleistocene Aeolian Deposits of the United States, Alaska, and Parts of Canada. Geological Society of America, 1952.)*

MAPS SHOWING SURFACES SHAPED BY GROUNDWATER, ICE, AND WIND

Plains Showing the Effects of Solution

*†Mammoth Cave, Ky. (Small and large sinks on limestone plain and in hills of sandstone underlain by limestone.)

Interlachen, Fla. (Broad, shallow sinks, some with lakes; sand-covered limestone.)

Holt, Fla. (Smooth limestone upland cut by angular, steep-walled solution valleys fed by springs.)

Surfaces Modified by Glaciation

Till Plains

*Belle Plaine, Minn. (Undulating till plain; small lakes; incised by one broad valley.)

Madison, Wis. (Till over irregular bedrock surface; large lakes in partially drift-filled preglacial valley; marshes.)

Horicon, Wis. (Drumlins; lakes; huge marsh occupy-

*Sheets listed under more than one heading.
†Shaded relief editions available.

ing sediment-filled lake basin; stream course affected by drumlins.)

Marginal Moraines

*†Kingston, R.I. (1:24,000) (Rolling glaciated surface over irregular bedrock; hummocky moraine; shore features.)

*Jackson, Mich. (Broad belt of hummocky moraine; pitted outwash on east side; lakes and swamps.)

*Buckley, Ill. (Broad, low, smooth clay moraine; lake plain to northeast; beginning of dissection.)

Vergas, Minn. (Unusually broad and rough moraine; kames; kettles; no stream dissection.)

Outwash Features

*Jackson, Mich. (Pitted outwash area in broad morainic zone.)

*Manito, Ill. (Broad outwash terrain or valley train; sand dunes; modern floodplain.)

*Saponac, Me. (Prominent esker; bedrock control of drift surface.)

Mountain Valley Glaciers

*Tyonek (A-8), Alaska. (Numerous large glaciers; glacial tongue damming lake; medial and terminal moraines; braided meltwater stream.)

*Blying Sound (D-8), Alaska. (Large ice field with glacial tongues descending to sea level; fiord.)

*Mount Rainier, Wash. (1:125,000) (High, eroded volcanic cone among erosional mountains; radial glacier system.)

Mountains Modified by Valley Glaciation

†Rocky Mountain National Park, Colo. (Many cirques; troughs; cirque and valley lakes; stepped valley profiles; hanging valleys; huge lateral moraines.)

*†Sequoia and Kings Canyon National Parks, Calif. (1:125,000) (Cirques; deep troughs; sharpened crests; lakes, stepped valleys; huge moraines; eroded fault scarp; complete cross section of Sierra Nevada.)

Mount Bonneville, Wyo. (Many cirques; troughs; sharpened peaks and ridges; stepped valleys; hanging valleys; morainic terrain on upland to west.)

Rough Lands Modified by Continental Glaciation

Tully, N.Y. (Smooth, rounded slopes; open, troughlike valleys; large marginal moraines; small lakes; bedrock channels cut by meltwater; ice-contact outwash terraces.)

†Monadnock, N.H. (Smoothed knobs; ponds; swamps; Mount Monadnock, a large remnant of preglacial erosion.)

Surfaces Modified by Wind

Sand Dunes

†Ashby, Neb. (Large clumped, complex dunes, now grass-covered.)

*South Bird Island, Tex. (Coastal dunes on mainland and on broad offshore bar.)

*Saponac, Me. (Irregular small dunes on outwash terrace.)

*Provincetown, Mass. (1:24,000) (Irregular coastal dunes associated with beaches and spits.)

Loess Surfaces

Utica, Neb. (Smooth surface with shallow wind-formed irregularities; sharply dissected at edges.)

Broken Bow, Neb. (1:24,000) (Sharply dissected loess hills; small remnants of depositional surface.)

REVIEW QUESTIONS

1. What are the most common surface features that result from the work of groundwater solution? How are they formed? What is the principal factor that determines the areas in which groundwater solution will be highly active?

2. Under what circumstances will glaciers develop?

How do glaciers or icecaps move, and what makes them move?

3. Where are the largest existing icecaps? How extensive and how thick are they? Do they move? In what major mountain systems are valley glaciers especially large and abundant? Why are there no large glaciers in the Rocky Mountains or Sierra Nevada of the western United States?

4. Specifically, what parts of the continents were covered by icecaps during the great ice ages of the past few hundred thousand years? What percentage of the land area of the earth did they cover? Where were their source regions? Why were there no great icecaps in the Southern Hemisphere outside of Antarctica?

5. Of the areas at one time or another covered by icecaps, what part now shows distinctly glacially produced landforms? Explain. What has happened to the rest of the glaciated surfaces? When did the Wisconsinan glaciation reach its maximum extent?

6. By what processes do glaciers erode? Which of these is probably the most important?

7. Where and under what conditions do glaciers deposit? How is glacial till usually different from alluvium? Distinguish between terminal, recessional, and ground moraines. On which of these do drumlins often occur?

8. In terms of surface features, how do lately glaciated plains commonly differ from stream-eroded surfaces? Why? On glaciated plains, how do the surfaces of thick-drift and thin-drift areas commonly differ? Can one generalize about whether glaciation improved or damaged the land for human use? Explain.

9. To what other depositional material is glacial outwash most closely related? Explain. Do outwash features occur only beyond the terminal moraine of a glacier? Explain.

10. Why were large lakes common around the margins of the great ice sheets? Give examples.

11. Is there evidence that glaciers expanded in the high mountain valleys of the world during the periods of continental glaciation? What kind?

12. In general terms, how do the effects of mountain valley glaciation upon mountain landforms differ from the effects of continental glaciation that has overridden mountainous country? What specific kinds of landforms are often ascribed to the work of mountain valley glaciation? Of these, which provides the surest evidence of glaciation? For their size, mountain valley glaciers often seem to transport far greater quantities of debris than great icecaps. Why might this occur?

13. Why is the wind so restricted in the areas in which it can work as a gradational agent? In what environments is it now most active?

14. How and why do sand and silt behave differently under wind action? In general, how do the depositional landforms of the two materials differ? What distinctive features does wind erosion produce?

15. Are most of the world's deserts covered by sand dunes? Where are the most extensive dune areas? Upon what factors do dune forms depend?

16. What is loess, and how is most of it believed to have originated? Specify at least three major areas of the world where thick loess occurs. Do loess surfaces have distinctive depositional or erosional forms? Explain.

The Margins of the Lands

Factors of Coastal Development

Positioning of the Shoreline

Erosion and deposition by waves and currents, deposition by streams and glaciers from adjacent lands, organic accumulations, and various tectonic happenings have all left their mark on the landforms of the world's coastal zones. More fundamentally important than any of those, however, have been large changes in the relative levels of land and sea, for these changes have actively moved the shorelines about and are responsible for their present location and many aspects of their detailed pattern.

The continental shelf. That the continents end and the oceans begin at the shoreline seems obvious. But if this statement is changed to say that the continental platforms end and the ocean basins begin at the shoreline, it is neither obvious nor true. Along most continental margins the sea bottom does not drop off abruptly to great depths just outside the shoreline. Instead it usually falls away gradually to depths of 120 to 180 m (400–600 ft), and then plunges steeply for thousands of meters to a more gently sloping apron or to the relatively smooth floor of the deep sea (Fig. 14.1). The gently sloping shallow zone is called the *continental shelf*; its steeper outer mar-

gin is the *continental slope*. It is entirely reasonable to regard the shelf and slope as parts of the continents, for they are regularly underlain by sediments and other low-density rocks of continental type that differ sharply from the dense rocks beneath the adjacent deep-sea floor.

Widths of the continental shelf vary from less than 1 km to as much as 650 km (400 mi) (Fig. 14.2). The widest shelves are commonly found adjacent to low-lying plains on the continents. Mountainous coasts, on the other hand, are often bordered by narrow shelves or none at all.

Changes of sea level. A change in the relative levels of land and sea can be produced in two quite different ways. First, the land itself can be lowered or raised by crustal movement. Second, the sea surface can be raised or lowered, either by a change in the total amount of water in the oceans or by a tectonic alteration in the total volume of the basins in which the water rests. These things have all happened frequently and on a large scale in relatively recent time, producing two kinds of changes in the position of the shoreline. (1) If the land rose or the sea level sank, the shoreline migrated seaward across the continental shelf. (2) If the land sank or the sea level rose, the shoreline moved landward.

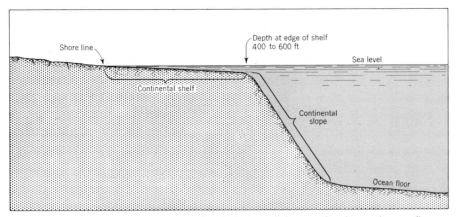

Figure 14.1   Relation of continental shelf and continental slope to shoreline and ocean floor.

The changes in sea level that accompanied the formation and disappearance of the great Pleistocene ice sheets were especially significant for the earth as a whole. Since the water that formed the glaciers originally came from the sea and was returned to the sea when the ice melted, the sea level sank as each ice sheet grew and rose again as the ice melted. When the last glaciation was at its maximum, the sea level is believed to have been nearly 120 m (400 ft) lower than it is now, thus exposing as dry land vast areas of what is now continental shelf. Thereafter the water rose irregularly, probably reaching its present level no more than 5,000 or 6,000 years ago. Tectonic raising and lowering of some coastal lands, especially in the far north and around the Pacific rim, have occurred even more recently.

As a result of these events, the shorelines have only lately attained their present positions; indeed, in some places the shore is still shifting because of changes in the level of the land. The effects

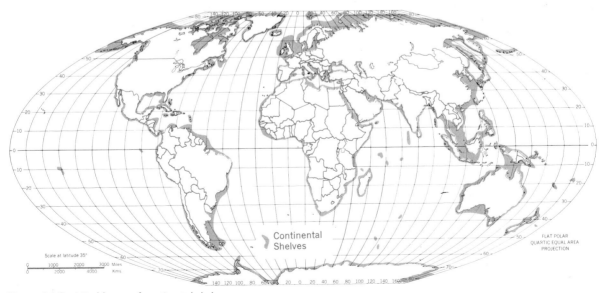

Figure 14.2   World map of continental shelves.

of these movements of the shoreline may be clearly seen in the present outlines of certain coasts and in various features repeatedly encountered in the coastal zones.

Modification of the Shoreline

Whether, in any given section of the continental margin, the relative levels of land and sea are changing or have become fixed, the shoreline is continually being modified by erosional and depositional processes. Any of several agents—streams, mass movements, glaciers, lava flows, winds, or waves—may bring material to the coast and dump it into the edge of the sea. But it is the unceasing activity of waves and currents that does most of the shifting about of loose debris and accomplishes most erosion in the coastal zone. In doing these things, it continually changes the form of virtually all the world's shorelines.

The work of waves and currents. Although waves and currents occur in the open seas, they can erode only along the shore and in shallow water, where their energy can be brought to bear against the coast or the bottom. Waves themselves probably accomplish little erosion at depths greater than 9 to 12 m (30 to 40 ft), although wave-generated currents can carry material along the bottom in much deeper water.

In waves of the open sea, the motion of individual water particles is a simple oscillation, with little net forward motion. The wave form moves forward without transporting the water itself, just as waves may be seen to move across a wind-blown field of grain or along a shaken rope. But when a wave enters shallow water, the lower part of the oscillation is retarded by frictional drag against the bottom. As a result, the wave form steepens, becomes higher, leans forward, and finally breaks, throwing a great mass of water violently forward and downward (Fig. 14.3).

Waves break when they reach water which is only slightly deeper than the wave height. On coasts where the water deepens gradually offshore, the large, more powerful waves break far out, and the plunging water scours upon the shallow bottom. Inside the breaker line, smaller waves continue landward, finally rolling or breaking against the shore and sending a swash of sand-laden water up the beach. Where the water maintains a depth of 3 to 6 m

Figure 14.3 A wave breaking. *(F. P. Shepard.)*

(10 to 20 ft) close to the shore, waves break only when they have almost reached the land and expend their energy directly against the shore itself. In either case, the water thrown onto the shore by waves or swash is drawn seaward again by gravity, flowing beneath oncoming waves as an undertow current which is sometimes strong enough to move debris along the bottom.

Large storm waves fling tons of water (and sometimes sand and rock as well) against the shore or the shallow bottom, probably generating as great an erosional force as any found in nature. Even relatively small waves can accomplish significant erosion. A few exposed coasts in weak materials are being driven back at rates of more than 10 m per century.

Material dislodged by erosion is transported and redeposited by the waves themselves or by undertow or other wave-generated currents. Much is cast up on neighboring beaches. Flat, gentle waves usually produce a net deposit of sand upon the beach, while the undertow accompanying wind-driven storm waves usually accomplishes net removal. Some debris may be transported long distances along the shore by currents. Considerable material may be spread over the zone between the breaker line and the shore, but as a rule only fine suspended material is carried out beyond the breakers. Coarse gravel and cobbles (shingle) as well as sand may be thrown up into a bar just inside the breaker line.

Where the direction of the wind is oblique to the shoreline, the diagonal shoreward motion of the waves and the direct offshore motion of the undertow combine to move both water and debris along the shore by zigzag in-and-out paths. If the prevailing winds come from one direction, there may be a large and continual longshore transport of material in the direction of the wind movement.

Other agents of shoreline modification.   Several other agents besides waves and shore currents contribute to coastal modification. Streams carry huge quantities of sand and mud to their mouths, where this debris may be either added to deltas that build the shore seaward or distributed along the coast on beaches and bars by wave-generated currents. Stream-borne materials are responsible for filling many shallow bays and lagoons.

Pleistocene ice sheets, moving beyond the shorelines as we know them today onto the then-exposed continental shelves, deposited large amounts of debris that now form shoreline features. Long Island, for example, is composed largely of moraine and outwash, while most of the numerous islands in Boston Bay are drumlins. In Antarctica and parts of Greenland and Alaska, glacial ice itself forms parts of the shoreline.

In volcanic areas, lava flows and unusually thick accumulations of ash sometimes encroach upon the sea. Some islands, such as Hawaii, are wholly volcanic.

Several types of floating or rooted plants thrive in sheltered waters and help to fill shallow inlets and lagoons with their own debris. But by far the most important organic modifiers of the shorelines are the corals, small colonies of tiny animals that secrete about themselves structures of calcium carbonate taken from the sea. Both living corals and the broken structures of earlier generations contribute to the growth of limestone reefs that may become very extensive.

Nearly all coasts have been formed by the combined action of several of the agencies thus far discussed. A single shoreline, for example, might bear the marks of wave erosion and deposition, stream deposition, and both a fall and a rise of sea level. For this reason, classifications of shorelines by origin are rarely satisfactory, and none will be attempted here.

Shoreline Features and Characteristics

Shoreline Features

Bays and gulfs.   Some deep gulfs, including the Red Sea, the Persian Gulf, and the Gulf of California,

occupy great structural depressions formed by sharp downfolding and downfaulting. A number of broader and shallower bordering seas, such as Hudson Bay and part of the Gulf of Mexico, appear to be the result of gentler downwarping of sections of the continental margin. But except for these and for some inlets or coves caused by differential wave erosion, most bays and gulfs have been formed through the drowning of erosional topography by a rising sea level. It is not surprising to find such coastal indentations so widely distributed, since the sea level rose perhaps 120 m (400 ft) all over the world during the melting of the last continental glacier.

When the sea level rises, a new shoreline is established on the former land surface. At first this shoreline will follow all the wanderings of a contour line upon that surface. If the submerged surface was a smooth alluvial slope, its contours were regular and the new shoreline will be similarly regular. But if the surface was an erosional surface, its contours were probably highly irregular, and the shoreline resulting from its drowning will also be irregular. The sea penetrates the valleys, forming bays, while the higher divides remain above water as peninsulas or headlands. Individual embayments resulting from submergence are called *drowned valleys*. Those at the mouths of rivers are called *estuaries*.

Drowned valleys: estuaries.   If the gradients of the valleys drowned are gentle, the resulting embayments reach far into the land. On the other hand, the drowning of steeply pitching valleys produces short indentations. Since the form and pattern of the bays follow the form and pattern of the valleys that have been drowned, some estuaries are dendritic, others are simple and parallel, and still others are highly irregular.

An especially fine example of an estuarine shoreline is the Atlantic Coast of the United States in Delaware, Maryland, Virginia, and North Carolina (Fig. 14.4). There the drowning of a dendritic system of broad river valleys having particularly gentle gradients produced estuaries of unusual size and length. Other strikingly estuarine coasts occur in northwestern Spain, Greece and western Turkey, western Ireland and Scotland, southern China, and southern Japan. The coasts of New England, Nova Scotia, and Newfoundland have an unusually complex outline as a result of the drowning of an irregular glaciated surface (Fig. 14.5).

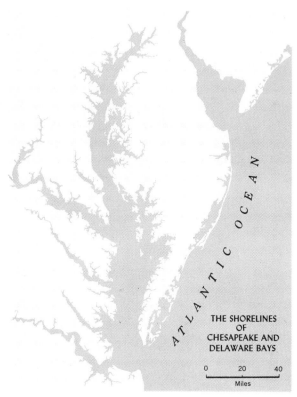

Figure 14.4 The middle Atlantic coast of the United States exhibits a remarkably fine development of estuaries.

The extensive stretches of the world's coastlines that are not impressively estuarine are rarely, if ever, completely free of existing or former estuaries. Most of these coasts have steep-gradient valleys that yielded only small estuaries, and in many instances even these have been filled by the deposits of swift-flowing streams. Thus, for example, the Pacific Coast of the United States, although it has few large estuaries, has many sediment-filled valley mouths that were once small bays.

Fiords. Several mountainous coasts of the world are distinguished by large numbers of narrow, deep, and spectacularly steep-walled bays, some of which penetrate unusually far into the land. These magnificent features, known by their Norwegian name *fiord*, are drowned, ice-scoured mountain valleys (Fig. 14.6). The principal regions of fiords are the coasts of (1) Norway; (2) Greenland, northern Labrador, and the eastern Arctic Islands; (3) British Columbia and southern Alaska (Fig. 14.7); (4) southern Chile; and (5) western South Island, New Zealand.

Some of the largest fiords are nearly 160 km (100 mi) long and 3 to 7 km (2 to 4 mi) wide and have depths in places exceeding 300 m (1,000 ft). Such extreme depths, together with the basinlike form of many fiord bottoms, suggest that glacial tongues of unusual thickness may have been able to erode even below the lowered sea levels of Pleistocene glacial maxima. The problem is complicated, however, by the fact that all the fiorded coasts were greatly depressed by the weight of the ice and have not yet fully recovered their preglacial level.

Cliffs and benches. Coastal cliffs and benches are produced chiefly by wave erosion. On exposed steep coasts, storm waves breaking directly against the land undercut the coastal slopes, forming sea cliffs (Fig. 14.8). If the materials are weak, the cliffs are usually fairly regular. In resistant rocks, however, joints and other local inequalities favor differential erosion, and the resulting cliffs are often spectacular, with many niches and caves, projecting buttresses, rock arches, and detached pinnacles and rocky islets.

As the sea cliff retreats landward, it leaves behind an eroded bench which inclines gently seaward a little below sea level. The material eroded from the cliff, together with other material carried in by streams or longshore currents, may be dragged seaward to the edge of the bench, where some of it may accumulate, extending the submarine terrace to seaward (Fig. 14.9). Wave-cut benches sometimes

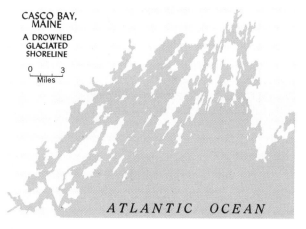

Figure 14.5 The drowned glaciated shoreline of Casco Bay, Maine, has many rocky islands, peninsulas, and narrow inlets.

Figure 14.6 Geiranger Fiord, a spectacular drowned glaciated mountain valley on the coast of Norway. *(C. d'Emery, Manugian Studio. Courtesy of Norwegian America Line.)*

reach widths of a kilometer or so—probably considerably more in nonresistant material; but as they widen, the wave attack on the cliff is likely to become weaker and eventually cease.

In many places sea cliffs and marine benches have been either submerged or left high and dry by changes of relative levels of land and sea. Submerged benches are often hard to identify because they have been obscured by later deposition. Cliffs and benches that are now exposed above sea level, on the other hand, are common and sometimes prominent coastal features. Some coasts display a whole series of such terraces, rising like steps from the present shore (Fig. 14.10).

Along tectonically active coastlines, raised shorelines are often warped and sometimes reach elevations of several hundred meters above the present sea level. Elevated shorelines also occur along stable coasts, however, and there they are usually at elevations well below 100 m (300 ft). Many of these terraces have been attributed to the high stands of sea level that occurred during the interglacial intervals of the Pleistocene. Because the successively lower shorelines appear to be successively younger, it has been suggested that the Pleistocene oscillations of sea level were superimposed upon a general lowering of the sea surface, which may have resulted from diastrophic depression of parts of the ocean floors.

Most coasts show evidence which is entirely compatible with the idea of an oscillating sea level

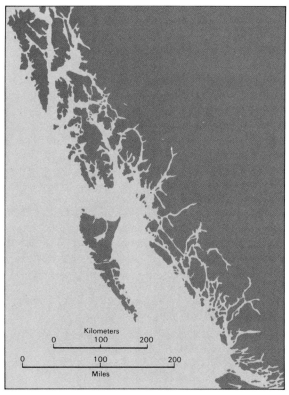

Figure 14.7 The intricate coastline of British Columbia and southern Alaska is typical of fiorded coasts.

Figure 14.8 A wave-cut cliff and rocky islets on the exposed coast of Anacapa Island, Channel Islands National Monument, California. *(Roger Toll, National Park Service.)*

during glacial times. Elevated shorelines, which indicate relative lowering of sea level, can and do occur along coasts that also display estuaries that indicate a late rise of sea level. This is true even on the remarkably estuarine coast of Virginia and North Carolina.

Beaches, bars, and spits. On protected sections of the coast, or even on exposed coasts that are not too frequently swept by destructive storm waves, relatively gentle wave action tends to move sand or gravel onto the shore, creating beaches. Along a smooth coast, the beaches may form a continuous strip many kilometers in length. On irregular coasts, however, the sediment is usually concentrated in the indentations, the headlands often being swept clear and subjected to active erosion (Fig. 14.11). Through the erosion of headlands and the accumulation of beaches in the indentations, an irregular shoreline is gradually straightened by wave action.

Debris that is moved parallel to the shore by obliquely striking waves and longshore currents continues to shift until it comes to an angle in the shoreline, to the sheltered or deeper waters of a bay, or to a protected position between a close-in island and the shore, where it is dropped (Fig. 14.12). Gentle waves that come more directly from seaward may then carry the material onto beaches or build it up into bars across the mouths of bays or between island and shore. Sometimes the line of a coast is extended

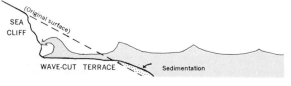

Figure 14.9 Development of sea cliff and wave-cut terrace.

Figure 14.10 Three well-defined marine terraces may be distinguished on this coastal hillside near Los Angeles, California. (W. P. Woodring, U.S. Geological Survey.)

beyond a major angle through the growth of a long, often curved bar or spit.

Some flat, relatively storm-free coasts that are abundantly supplied with alluvial sands have been built seaward for considerable distances by the successive formation of beaches or bars, one in front of the other. Conversely, some other coasts show evidence of a reduced supply of sediment, accompanied by gradual wastage of beaches and bars.

Offshore bars. Along coasts where shallow water causes the waves to break far from shore, long strips of sand, called *offshore bars*, form just inside the line of breakers. Such bars may touch the land at projecting points, but elsewhere they are separated from it by shallow lagoons a few meters to several kilometers in width. Most are broken at intervals by openings through which tidal currents pass (Fig. 14.13).

Many offshore bars appear to be simply elongated spits, built by longshore currents combined with constructive wave action. On the other hand, some bars are not in contact with the land and appear to be out of reach of land-derived sediments. These, at least, may have been formed wholly by constructive wave action just inside the erosional site of the breaker line. It is, however, difficult to understand how incipient sand bars could have survived their

Figure 14.11 A sandy beach has accumulated in this sheltered bay, while the headland beyond has been swept clear by wave action. Cape Sebastian, Oregon. (Oregon State Highway Commission.)

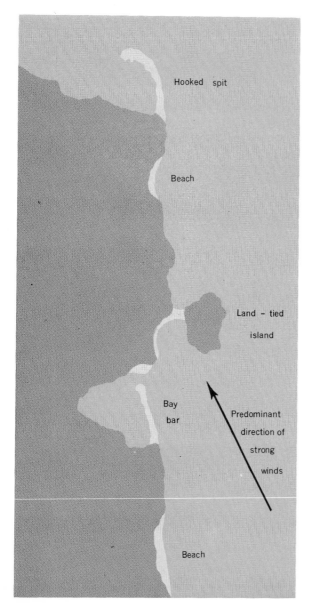

Figure 14.12 Characteristic types and locations of bars, spits, and beaches.

the famous beach resorts, such as Atlantic City, Palm Beach, Miami Beach, and Galveston, are built on them and are reached from the mainland by bridges and causeways. In North Carolina broad estuarine lagoons (sounds) are enclosed by an especially far-flung cordon of offshore bars, the outermost point of which is Cape Hatteras, famous for the number of ships that have been driven aground on its sandy shoals.

All beaches and bars composed of sand are subject to significant changes with time. They normally widen or lengthen during periods of gentle wave action, and they may be greatly altered, reduced, or even destroyed during violent storms. Shingle features are more durable and may grow even during storms.

In hurricanes the unusually high water levels and huge waves cause beaches and bars to be literally overwhelmed. The greatest loss of life in any natural disaster in the United States occurred in a hurricane at Galveston, Texas, in 1900. Wind-driven

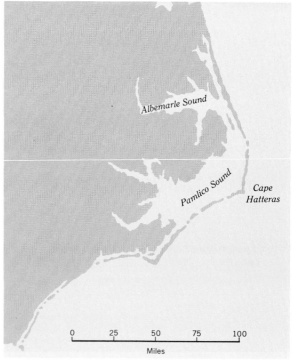

Figure 14.13 Offshore bars and sounds along the coast of North Carolina.

formative periods in such storm-swept waters as those at Cape Hatteras.

Offshore bars are unusually well developed along the south Atlantic and Gulf coasts of the United States, where they are almost continuous. Many of water completely covered the city to a depth of about 2 m, and nearly 5,000 people died. The construction of a high sea wall has thus far effectively forestalled a repetition of the catastrophe.

Coral reefs and atolls. Reefs of limestone comprised principally of the crumbled skeletal remains of colonies of corals are common features along tropical coasts. Most coral reefs form narrow coastal fringes in shallow water. Fringing reefs grow with such rapidity in clear, shallow, warm waters that they build a shoreline seaward in spite of wave and current erosion. Corals can also grow abundantly in shallow waters at a considerable distance from shore and thereby form a barrier reef separated from the mainland by a broad lagoon. The great reef that parallels the northeast coast of Australia for 1,600 km (1,000 mi) is the largest example.

Some small reef-encircled islands, mostly volcanic, seem to have undergone slow submergence while the coral fringe about them has continued to grow. The encircling reefs now appear at the surface as low, more or less complete coral rings, called *atolls*, which enclose shallow lagoons. Midway, Wake, Bikini, Kwajalein, and Eniwetok are all of this general type (Fig. 14.14). Borings and seismic investigations made in several Pacific atolls have revealed accumulations of coral rock more than 1,000 m thick atop the volcanic bases. This thickness represents the amount of subsidence that has occurred since the volcanic island was originally formed (Fig. 14.15).

Kinds of Coasts

Many schemes of nomenclature and classification have been devised for distinguishing among different kinds of coasts. No formal classification will be employed in this book, but some brief remarks concerning the general problem are appropriate.

Probably the most frequently used categorization of coastal types is that which divides all coasts into two groups, submergent and emergent, depending on whether coastal sinking or rising has been dominant. In classical American geomorphology, one

Figure 14.14 Coral reefs and sandy islets enclose a quiet lagoon at Wake Island, a small atoll in the central Pacific. Shallow reefs show as light-colored submerged areas ringed with a white strip of heavy surf, best seen in right foreground. *(Official U.S. Navy photograph.)*

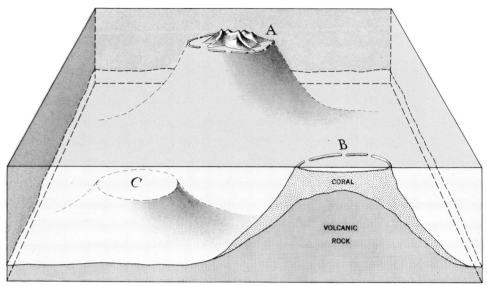

Figure 14.15 Volcanic islands and coral reefs. *A* is a modern volcanic island surrounded by a barrier reef, suggesting the beginnings of submergence. *B* is an atoll, formed by continued growth of coral above a volcanic island that has slowly submerged. *C* is a former volcanic island, its top planed off by wave erosion, which submerged too rapidly to permit the maintenance of coral growth.

finds submergent coasts described as being characteristically estuarine, with relatively deep water offshore and active erosion proceeding on the headlands. Conversely, emergent coasts are characterized as typically regular, with shallow waters and bars offshore and raised terraces indicating the relative rise of the land. This scheme, however, was devised before scientists realized the large-scale oscillations of sea level that had occurred during the Pleistocene epoch, which brought alternate submergence and emergence to all the world's coasts. An understanding of coastal histories and processes makes the submergence-emergence dichotomy largely meaningless, and examples such as the Carolina coast, which combines estuaries, shallow waters, offshore bars, and raised terraces, bear witness to the inadequacy of the system.

At the other extreme are systems which designate coastal types according to their dominant features or operative processes. Thus one might recognize estuarine coasts, cliff-and-bench coasts, coral reef coasts, mangrove coasts, etc. Or in terms of processes, one might speak of wave-eroded coasts, drowned glaciated coasts, alluvially prograded coasts

(those built seaward by alluviation), and others. These systems, especially those using dominant features, are quite satisfactory so long as they are kept flexible enough to accommodate the many combination types that occur in nature and so long as one is content to deal with a large number of varieties.

One of the more useful, simple schemes based upon actual characteristics is that which, at the primary level, separates flat coasts from steep coasts. Flat coasts are those along which the water deepens very gradually offshore and in which, as a rule, the land surface rises very gradually inland (Fig. 14.16). Along such coasts, destructive wave action is inhibited by the shallowness of the water, and accumulation of sediments and organic growths is common inside the breaker line. Offshore bars and reefs, lagoons, tidal marshes and mudflats, and sometimes extensive beaches and spits are common features. Because of their lowness and their normally somewhat protected state, such coasts are often subject to severe flooding and reworking during the severe storms that may occasionally occur. Examples are the Carolina coast, the Gulf coast of Louisiana and Texas, and the North Sea and Baltic coasts of the Netherlands, Germany,

Figure 14.16 Example of a flat coast, near Corpus Christi, Texas. Note broad offshore bar and shallow lagoon behind it. Depth contour of 30 ft (at right) is approximately 1600 m (1 mi) offshore. *(Reproduced from U.S. Geological Survey topographic sheet: South Bird Island, Texas.)*

and Poland. Steep coasts, on the other hand, are subject to constant attack by waves, and erosional features are their trademark. Sea cliffs, rocky islets, and wave-cut benches are common (Fig. 14.17). Beaches and bay bars form in coastal indentations and even on exposed sections where sediments are abundant. Such features, however, tend to fluctuate in size and form, growing during periods of good weather and shrinking because of vigorous erosion during storms or stormy seasons. This simple subdivision is only the beginning of a classification scheme, for each of the major classes exists in many subtypes, which can be designated as desired.

Islands

Islands of nonvolcanic origin. The existence of isolated masses and bits of land surrounded by the seas, occurring sometimes in groups or chains and sometimes quite alone in midocean, has never failed to stir human beings' interest and curiosity. It is hard to avoid feeling that such peculiar features, strangely rising from the open sea, must have some unique and startling mode of origin. Yet this is a false notion, for the processes that produce islands are not different from those that produce high-standing features on the continental masses themselves.

Some islands, for example, the British Isles, the islands of eastern Denmark, the Arctic Islands of Canada, Vancouver Island, Newfoundland, and Prince Edward, Cape Breton, and Long Islands, appear to be no more than detached portions of the continents. The often shallow channels that separate them from the mainland may well have been cut during low stands of sea level in glacial times and then drowned during the postglacial rise of sea level.

Other islands, however, have been formed by tectonic disturbance. Some are raised and tilted fault blocks. Santa Catalina and neighboring islands off southern California, the several islands of the Gulf of California, and, in a more complex manner, the

islands of Tasmania and Madagascar all originated in this way. Still others are complex folded and faulted masses similar to the continental mountain systems. Among these are the Mediterranean islands of Corsica, Sardinia, Sicily, and Crete; Cuba, Hispaniola, and Puerto Rico in the Caribbean; and Borneo, Celebes, and the islands of Japan in the western Pacific. Some of these lie off the coasts of similarly structured sections of the continents.

Volcanic islands. Many islands are wholly or in part formed by the upper portions of immense volcanic cones built up from the sea floor. Some form long, curving lines, usually near the edges of the continen-

Figure 14.17 Example of a steep coast, on Kodiak Island, Alaska. Land-surface and bottom contours in feet. Note numerous rocky islets near shore. Distance from Inner Right Cape to Outer Right Cape is about 2400 m (1.5 mi). *(Reproduced from U.S. Geological Survey topographic sheet: Kodiak (B-3), Alaska.)*

tal platforms; others occur in midocean. Isolated volcanic islands are very common, especially in the western Pacific. There the ocean floor is dotted with dozens of great cones (Fig. 14.18). These include not only the currently active volcanoes, such as those of the Hawaiian Islands, but also the many more inactive and eroded cones, such as those of Tahiti, Samoa, Ponape, and Truk. As previously mentioned, many cones have slowly become submerged after developing, leaving on the surface only the atolls maintained by the continuing growth of a cap of coral on the sinking peaks. Some cones sank too rapidly to permit the maintenance of coral growth and are now flat-topped features entirely submerged. Other isolated volcanic islands occur in the Indian and Atlantic Oceans.

These volcanic islands in midocean have evidently originated in at least two quite different situations. Some, such as Iceland, the Azores, Ascen-

sion Island, and Tristan da Cunha in the Atlantic, and the Galápagos Islands and Easter Islands in the Pacific, have formed along the great rifts where crustal plates are separating and new crustal material is rising from the mantle. They are presumably oceanic counterparts to Kilimanjaro, Kenya, and other huge volcanic peaks that have developed on or adjacent to the similar rift zone of east Africa.

Other volcanic islands, including most of those in the central and western Pacific, are nowhere near either rift zones or converging plate edges and must be accounted for by other means. The hypothesis has been advanced that the Hawaiian chain and its far-reaching northwestward extension of seamounts have developed sequentially as the huge Pacific Plate has moved northwestward over a localized hot spot in the mantle beneath. According to this concept, the currently active volcanoes of the Island of Hawaii, at the southeastern extremity of the series, are the

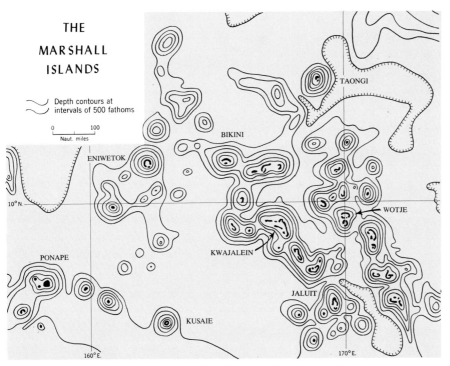

14.18   The Marshall Islands are coral atolls which have formed about the summits of volcanic cones that rise more than 4,600 m (15,000 ft) from the ocean floor in the west central Pacific. *(Modified from Depth Curve Chart of the Adjacent Seas of Japan, Maritime Safety Agency, Tokyo, 1952.)*

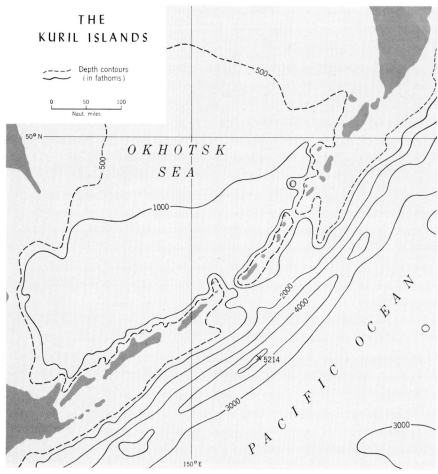

THE
KURIL ISLANDS

- - - - - Depth contours
(in fathoms)

Figure 14.19 The Kuril Islands, stretching northeastward from Japan, are a typical island arc, with an associated trough, or deep. *(Modified from Depth Curve Chart of the Adjacent Seas of Japan, Maritime Safety Agency, Tokyo, 1952.)*

latest to form and are approximately over the hot spot now. Other chains of islands farther south, including the Marshall, Gilbert, Ellice, Samoa, Cook, and Tuamotu groups, may have formed in similar fashion over other hot spots.

Island arcs. Many curving strings of islands, known as *island arcs*, festoon the borders of the continental platforms. They include the Aleutians, the Kurils, the Ryukyus, the Marianas, and the southern islands of Indonesia in the Pacific, as well as the lesser West Indies and the South Georgia-South

Sandwich-South Orkney chain in the Atlantic. These island arcs are largely volcanic, although some include complex folded and faulted structures. In most instances, they are bordered on their seaward sides by ocean-bottom trenches of tremendous depth (Fig. 14.19). The island arcs and trenches are known to be among the most active tectonic zones on earth. They appear to represent sites where deformation is proceeding actively because of convergence of crustal plates. The trenches probably form along the actual convergence line, where the leading edge of the oceanic crustal block is being thrust downward. Partial melting of that sinking crust gives rise to a band of vulcanism parallel to the convergence line but on the side toward the continent. It is this vulcanism, sometimes combined with compressional deformation of the leading portion of the continental crustal plate, that produces the island arcs. In many respects the arcs correspond closely to certain of the great, curving continental mountain systems, notably the Himalaya and the northern Andes.

Coasts and Human Activities

Human activities and coastal processes. Human activities affect and are affected by the dynamics of the coastal zone. Human beings seek and profitably use the coasts, whether for commercial shipping and fishing or for recreation and aesthetic reasons. But as they crowd the shorelines in ever-increasing numbers and build more numerous and more costly structures there, they also bring their own dynamism into continually intensifying conflict with that of the coastal sea. As in the tectonically active zones and along the floodplains of major streams, human beings have learned slowly and painfully the costs of living in areas of rapid and often violent natural change. Further, as they have tried to remake the coastal zone for their own purposes or have tried to counteract various natural processes of coastal change that run counter to their aims, they have often found themselves frustrated by their failure to understand the nature and strength of the processes they are striving to control.

Storms and seismic sea waves are responsible for the greatest human disasters along the shore. It has been noted that the overwhelming of Galveston, Texas, by the giant waves and storm tides of a hurricane caused the greatest loss of life in any natural calamity in the history of the United States. Other hurricanes and more general storms have caused immense property damage and have cost many lives along the low-lying and in part densely populated Atlantic and Gulf coasts of the country. These tragedies, however, seem almost slight in comparison with the loss of somewhere between 200,000 and 500,000 lives in the hurricane-driven flooding of the outer Ganges-Brahmaputra delta in present-day Bangladesh in 1970, probably the worst natural dis-

aster of the century. But even relatively minor storms can strongly erode beaches and drive back the shoreline where materials are weak, undermining homes, highways, and commercial structures and causing millions of dollars' worth of damage, not to mention the actual destruction of valuable land. Seismic sea waves are less common and usually much more localized in their effects, yet they have caused severe damage and significant death tolls in many places, especially around the margins of the Pacific Basin and on some of the Pacific islands.

Human activities such as the dredging, filling, and building of dikes have reshaped the coast extensively in some populous areas. Many of these works have been reasonably effective and long-lived, although some are open to criticism for their disturbance of major coastal ecosystems, such as those of salt marshes and estuaries. Where such works are exposed to strong wave action or tidal currents, however, they may require continual maintenance and in some instances may be destroyed over a period of time or even during single severe storms. Especially unsatisfactory and often futile have been the efforts to prevent erosion of beaches, shifting of bars, and closure of harbors or inlets in places where under natural conditions movement of sediment is especially active.

Coasts and harbors. Among the more significant relationships between coastal characteristics and human activities are those involving navigation and the development of harbors. Clearly the configuration of the shoreline and of the bottom close to the shore are factors that must be taken into account in locating or improving ports or channels. It must be kept in mind, however, that a port is a result of human needs and effort rather than a feature of physical geography. The value of a harbor depends upon its own physical characteristics, but even more upon whether it is located where a harbor is needed.

A deep and well-protected bay with access to a productive or populous hinterland is a resource of incalculable value. It is only natural that many significant ports have developed on estuaries and fiords or in waters sheltered by reefs, bars, or offshore islands. But even such magnificent "natural" harbors as those of New York, San Francisco, Rio de Janeiro, and Sydney have required much dredging and re-

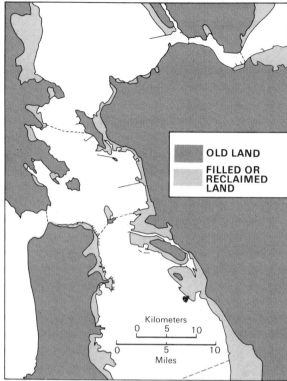

A. SAN FRANCISCO HARBOR

OLD LAND

FILLED OR
RECLAIMED
LAND

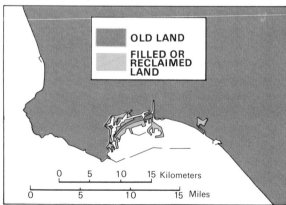

B. LOS ANGELES HARBOR

OLD LAND

FILLED OR
RECLAIMED
LAND

Figure 14.20 *A* is the "natural" harbor of San Francisco, showing filled land and dredged channels. *B* is the largely artificial harbor of Los Angeles.

shaping to provide enough deep-water docking space to handle their immense traffic (Fig. 14.20*A*).

Some of the most commodious and sheltered bays are of almost no value as harbors because the land behind them is unproductive, sparsely settled, or inaccessible. The great fiords of southern Chile, for example, are almost unused because they are backed by a wild, storm-swept, mountainous, and nearly uninhabited land.

On the other hand, some of the world's busiest ports have been developed where no natural harbor existed, because the hinterland required a shipping and receiving facility for its products and imports. The harbor of Los Angeles—and, to an even greater degree, that of Callao, the port of Lima, Peru—are largely of human construction (Fig. 14. 20*B*). At both places long breakwaters have been built to protect an otherwise exposed section of coast. At London, Rotterdam, Bremen, and Hamburg, shallow estuaries have been heavily dredged to provide sufficient entrance depth, and basins that can be closed off by lock gates have been excavated to provide docking space unaffected by the excessive rise and fall of the tides.

MAPS SHOWING SHORELINE FEATURES

Bays and Gulfs

Estuaries

*Kilmarnock, Va. (Branching estuaries of dendritic valleys; low terrace; small spits; bottom contours.)
*Point Reyes, Calif. (Branching estuary; drowned erosional valley along fault zone; spits; cliffs; small delta.)
Boothbay, Me. (Highly irregular coast of drowned, rock-controlled, glaciated surface; many drowned valleys; islands.)

Fiords (All sheets have bottom contours.)

Sumdum (D-5), Alaska. (Long, twisting, narrow fiord; deep basin and shallow mouth; small mountain glaciers; stagnant ice tongue; cirques; troughs.)
*Blying Sound (D-8), Alaska. (Large fiord with deep basin and shallow sill; smaller fiords; large ice field and glacial tongues.) Blying Sound (C-8) extends coverage southward, showing mouth of fiord.

*Sheets listed under more than one heading.
†Shaded relief editions available.

Features of Marine Erosion and Deposition; Steep and Flat Coasts

Sea Cliffs

*Point Reyes, Calif. (Steep coast; high sea cliffs; offshore rocks and islets; estuaries; spits.)

Point Sur, Calif. (Steep coast; mountainous with sea cliffs; offshore rocks; islet tied to land by bar.)

Beaches, Bars, and Spits

*Provincetown, Mass. (1:24,000) (Large hooked spit; bay bar; smaller spits; beaches; dunes; bottom contours.)

*†Kingston, R.I. (1:24,000) (Several spits and bay bars; beaches; drowned glacial coast; moraine.)

*Point Reyes, Calif. (Steep coast; spits and bay bars; sea cliffs; estuaries.)

*South Bird Island, Tex. (Flat coast; broad offshore bar with dunes; lagoon; large estuaries; dunes on mainland; bottom contours.)

Elevated Shorelines

Redondo Beach, Calif. (1:24,000) (At least six marine terraces discernible on coastal hillsides.)

*Kilmarnock, Va. (Relatively flat coast; low terrace; smooth plain below and dissected plain above; estuaries.)

*Rose Hill, N.C. (Low terrace; youthful dissection.)

REVIEW QUESTIONS

1. How does a rise of sea level or a sinking of the land affect the shoreline? What is believed to have happened to worldwide sea levels during the Pleistocene epoch? Explain. What, then, has happened to most of the world's coastal areas during the last 15,000 to 18,000 years?

2. Assuming a 120-m (400-ft) lowering of sea level during the last glacial maximum, try with the aid of a map showing ocean depths or continental shelf areas to gain an idea of what areas now submerged may have been exposed previous to that time. Estimates suggest that if all present ice were to melt, the sea level would rise 60 to 65 m (215 ft). What continental areas and cities would be submerged if that occurred?

3. What are the continental shelves? Structurally are they part of the continents or of the ocean basins? Explain.

4. Once the shorelines have assumed relatively fixed positions, what two agents are especially active in modifying them? What are the principal effects of streams on shorelines? What are the principal effects of waves on shorelines? On beaches and bars, how may the effects of gentle wave action differ from those of strong wave action?

5. What process is responsible for most of the world's bays? What is the difference between a fiord and a typical estuary? With the aid of an atlas, locate a number of large estuaries, both in the United States and elsewhere. State one major reason why some coasts seem conspicuously devoid of estuaries.

6. Under what conditions are sea cliffs especially likely to develop? Why? What type of submarine feature is often associated with sea cliffs? Under what conditions are offshore bars especially likely to develop? Why? What general range of depths would you expect to find in lagoons behind offshore bars?

7. Under what conditions and in what parts of the earth do coral reefs develop? What are atolls, and how do they appear to have formed?

8. Why is a subdivision of coasts into "submergent" and "emergent" classes unsatisfactory? What processes and features might characteristically occur on "flat" coasts? On steep coasts? With the aid of a good atlas or other maps, locate several examples of flat and steep coasts.

9. What are the characteristics of "island arcs" and the sea floors that lie adjacent to them? How are they believed to have formed? Some think that the formation of an island arc represents an early stage in the addition of a strip of land to the continental margin. How might this happen?

10. Would you expect the danger of severe damage and loss of life from storms to be greater on steep coasts or flat coasts? Why? Why is the prevention of beach erosion so difficult? Why is it so common for the mouths of bays and inlets through bars to become obstructed or closed?

11. Discuss the relationships between coastal forms and ports.

Natural Vegetation on the Land

Viewed from space, the earth ball tends to appear a mottled blue-green with considerable areas of brown, tan, and white. This patchwork complexity is partly due to land-water-ice contrasts, but much of the variety is supplied by the covering of the continents, large portions of which are clothed in a seemingly bewildering array of vegetative forms. In this chapter we shall examine this floristic covering of the land in order to observe its systematic distribution and its relation to other patterns of physical geography.

The entire biosphere (plants and animals) occupies a relatively thin layer, perhaps 15 km (approximately 10 mi) thick, which envelops the earth and in which all life exists. The greatest share of this life occurs relatively close to sea level, ranging from perhaps 6,000 m (a little less than 20,000 ft) in mountain areas to relatively shallow depths in the oceans. In this zone occur the primary requisites for photosynthesis, namely, sunlight as the source of energy and carbon dioxide and water, out of which carbohydrates such as glucose are formed. This fundamental process for sustaining life on the earth is accomplished by phytoplankton and higher forms of plant life in the sea, by freshwater algae and higher forms of vegetation in the waters on the land, and by the more complex flora on the "dry" land. Those areas of the land which can support vegetation sustain a great variety of plant life. Some of this is "artificial" in that human beings are responsible for it. We will not be concerned with that portion; instead we will focus on the patterns of what we can call *natural vegetation*. Natural vegetation cannot be precisely defined but may be loosely characterized as that wild, i.e., undomesticated, floristic assemblage occurring in uncultivated and not intensely managed grazing areas.

Since human beings learned to cultivate the land in order to simplify the process of obtaining food, a considerable portion of the land has been systematically managed. Some of this takes the form of the controlled grazing of food animals, and some the orderly cultivation of plants. The latter occurs primarily in those areas which support dense populations. In the aggregate, cultivation does not occupy a very significant proportion of the total land area, the cultivated sections of the earth being estimated at only a little more than 9 percent of the total land area.[1] Considerable portions of the continents are not suitable for intensive grazing or food cropping for a variety of reasons, much being too dry, too wet, too

---

[1] Lieth, Helmuth. "Über die Primärproduction der Pflanzendecke der Erde." *Zeitschrift für Angewandte Botanik*, Vol. 46, pp. 1–37, 1972.

hot, too cold, or too steep. Consequently, very large areas of the land are covered by natural vegetation. One should not infer, however, that the vegetation of all such areas has not been at all affected by human beings. On the contrary, people have induced many changes. For example, the flora of some grasslands has been greatly modified as a consequence of the depletion of the vast herds of wild herbivores which used to graze there; the need for lumber and pulp has modified many forest areas; and so on.

The Grouping of Plants

Plant communities. When the geographical diversity of plants is closely studied, it is seen that a particular combination of species tends to occur in an area, existing in a systematic interrelationship with one another and with the animal life of the area, all in apparent harmony with the environment. Such a floristic assemblage is called a *plant community*. The study of the life communities, plant and animal, and their interdependence with one another and with the other aspects of the environment is the objective of ecology.

Because the environmental conditions of the earth are dynamic, its plant communities change. The plant varieties which invade a newly developed mud bank, volcanic island, or recently glaciated area die out and are replaced as the environmental conditions are modified as a consequence of the development of soil, of continuous ground cover, of animal life, and of all the other changing attributes of the area. Ultimately, if the climate and a well-drained landform condition remain stable for a considerable period, a plant community will develop which has a competitive advantage over any other combination. This is called a *climatic-climax community*. This is the vegetative steady state toward which the evolving plant cover is striving in the life systems of the earth. The concept of a climax vegetation is a bit misleading, however, if it implies an end to change. On the contrary, "change is the order of nature," and a climax vegetation simply means that a near-steady state has existed for some time; one state cannot persist forever.

Some areas of the earth support what apparently approaches a climatic-climax plant community, but a larger proportion of the areas of natural vegetation is in a transition-community stage, either be-

cause of human activity or because of the natural changes that are always occurring in the environment. For example, large areas of North America and Eurasia have only recently emerged from burial by continental glaciers; on the other hand, large areas of the Congo and Amazon basins have apparently persisted with relatively little change for millions of years. Because the earth is so dynamic and our understanding of the ecological relationships is so meager, we cannot predict with confidence the climatic-climax communities which would occupy each area if the elusive environmental steady state were to occur.

Formation types. Another way of characterizing the plant cover of an area is to describe it in terms of the form elements of the assemblage. These consist of a large array of physical and organic forms, the more important of which, for descriptive purposes, are the following:

Plant type, such as trees or shrubs (predominantly woody plants) and grasses and other herbaceous (nonwoody) plants.

Size, such as tall or short trees or grasses.

Leaf character, such as broadleaf or needle-leaf.

Branching character, such as high-branching (as many trees) or low-branching (as shrubs).

Leaf tenure and life character, such as evergreen or deciduous, annual or perennial.

Horizontal density, such as close-growing or widely spaced.

Vertical arrangement, such as tree crowns producing a canopy, or an understory growth beneath tree crowns, or a ground cover.

If the physical and organic form characteristics of the vegetation are generalized at a high level, we can recognize several principal classes, such as forest and grassland. In turn, a major class may be separated into divisions and the divisions separated into formation types. For example, the major class, forest, may be separated into two subclasses: evergreen forest and deciduous forest. The deciduous forest may then be subdivided into the formation types: rain green forest and summer green forest. Within a formation type, a variety of geographical formations and associations of genera can be recognized. The relation among formation type, formation, and association is shown in Figure 15.1.

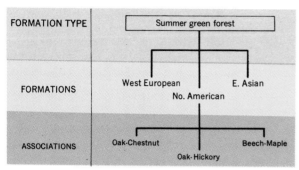

Figure 15.1 The subdivisions of one formation type. For simplicity, only North American associations are shown in the diagram; Europe and East Asia have other summer green forest associations.

Causes of Regional Variations

The remarkable diversity of the earth's mantle of vegetation is a result of the interaction of heredity or evolution, natural environment, and the effects of human activity.

Evolution

The first land plants were simple primitive forms such as algae and fungi. From these the present complex vegetation forms have evolved over eons of time. The prime cause of the development of higher and more complex plant species from lower forms, and of the differentiation of these species over the earth, is believed to be a natural selection of inheritable characteristics that are beneficial in the struggle for existence with other plants. In the competitive struggle of any and all life forms, including plants, it is those individuals which possess advantages, however slight, in structure or function over their fellows that come to prevail. Among the characteristics most important in the evolutionary process are migrational abilities, potential for adjusting to climatic change, and habitat preferences.

Environment

The present broad patterns of distribution of great plant associations or vegetation types appear to be closely related to environmental factors, such as solar energy, climate, underlying bedrock, soils, water, terrain, and the wild fauna and flora. Together these elements compose a complex of mutually interacting phenomena called the *ecosystem* or *biotic complex* (Fig. 15.2). Unlike animals, plants do not have the power of locomotion, cannot improvise shelters, and do not generate heat, so they are unable to escape the effects of the surrounding environment.

Climate. For the earth as a whole, climate is the most important of the environmental elements affecting the distribution of vegetation. Perhaps the most obvious relation between climate and vegetation is that of total productivity. Everyone knows that much of the land area in the near-polar regions has only a sparse vegetation because of the inhibiting cold. Similarly, some desert areas are also essentially devoid of plant life because of persistent dryness. In between these extremes are varying combinations of the climatic factors which are more or less conducive to vegetative production. The total productivity, as expressed by the number of grams of carbon fixed annually per square meter by photosynthesis, is shown in Figure 15.3. Although other factors, such as

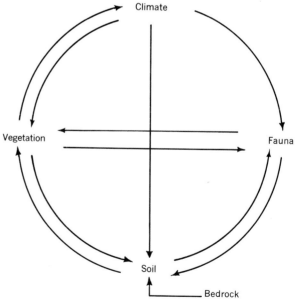

Figure 15.2 The complex of interacting and interdependent natural phenomena may be referred to as the *ecosystem* or the *biotic complex*. (After Eyre.)

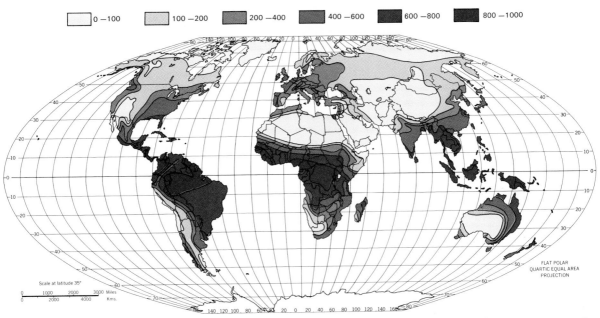

Figure 15.3   The estimated annual carbon fixation on land areas in grams per square meter. A very approximate average conversion factor for forest areas is that in areas where the rate of carbon fixation is greater than 600 grams/m^2, fixation of 200 g C per m^2 represents production of 3 m^3 of wood per hectare (a little less than 2 yd^3 per acre). *(After Lieth.)*

some unusual characteristic of the soil, are likely to be extremely important in some (generally small) areas, a comparison of Figure 15.3 with the world maps of temperature and precipitation clearly reveals the close relationship between total productivity and the elements of temperature and precipitation.

Not only does climate operate directly through its components of light (sun energy), temperature, precipitation, and wind, but it also affects plants indirectly through the weathering of rocks, the soil-making and leaching processes, and organic decay. Still, climate is only a permissive factor, for many plants which could otherwise flourish are eliminated by competition. For example, grass can be quite at home in the climatic conditions which exist in most forest regions; in many such areas it has been excluded, not by the general climate, but by a microclimate developed by the vegetation, for grasses cannot tolerate the shade beneath the tree cover.

As we saw earlier, if the climate remains fairly stable for a relatively long period, a characteristic community or formation may become established. Over large and perhaps separate areas a series of formation types similar in character may develop, and they may correspond generally with the major types of climate. Examples of widespread climatic-formation types are the tundra of the poleward margins of North America and Eurasia, the evergreen forests of the boreal climates of the same continents, and the rainforests of those equatorial latitudes which have abundant rainfall and little or no dry season. But although a plant formation type, such as rainforest, may be similar in general appearance throughout the world because its dominant species are alike in physical form, actually its different continental subdivisions may contain quite unlike species. Neither plant communities nor formation types are sharply delimited; rather, they merge imperceptibly through zones of transition called *ecotones*, where the species of one class are intermingled with those of another.

It should not be assumed that a homogeneous vegetative assemblage is bound to prevail everywhere within a general climatic type, even though the climate remains unchanged over a long period of time. In some parts of a climatic region, a variety of specific factors (such as slope, exposure, soil, and drainage) may operate to cause variations from the standard community for formation type. Thus, in a region of varied relief there may be a complex patchwork of vegetative forms. For example, the thin soils of the uplands in the subarctic glaciated areas support trees; on the steeper slopes the soil cannot accumulate to much depth, and low-growing plants and mosses may flourish; and on the flatter, low areas the land may be so poorly drained and marshy as to inhibit the development of larger trees. Human activity in the form of set fires, logging operations, tillage, and the grazing of domesticated animals are other varieties of interference with the development of homogeneous vegetation.

Among the more important climatic elements acting on plants are sunlight, temperature, and precipitation. Each of these influences vegetation directly and indirectly in a great many ways, through processes too complex for much elaboration here.

Solar energy provides the energy for the functioning of the vegetative life processes. Light is essential for photosynthesis, and in most plants the rate at which the process occurs is closely related to the intensity of the energy receipt. The variations in amounts of energy (its intensity and duration) which are received in various parts of the earth have much to do with the variations in productivity.

Temperature is critically important, since it affects the speed of the chemical activity that goes on within the plant and so conditions the life processes. For example, temperature is closely connected with photosynthesis. To a significant degree temperature determines the growing, reproductive, and dormant periods of plants. As a consequence the great world vegetation zones appear to be closely aligned with temperature belts. Temperature also indirectly affects the water requirement of plants, because it is a major factor determining the rates of evaporation and transpiration.

Different species resist cold in a variety of ways. Some make the adjustment by retarding growth and arresting certain functions during the period of low temperatures. This may result in a marked external change, such as leaf fall from middle-latitude deciduous trees. Certain other plants, such as coniferous trees, lapse into dormancy during a cold season without showing any outward change. In *annual* species the plant completes its entire life cycle

during the warm period. The vegetative portions perish completely during the season of cold, and it is only by means of a seed, which is capable of greater and more prolonged resistance to low temperatures, that the plant survives. They stand in contrast to the *perennials*, some parts of which live on year after year.

Precipitation supplies the necessary soil water for land plants. Water, taken in mainly at the roots, is the principal ingredient of sap, in which soil nutrients are dissolved and can then be assimilated by plants. Loss of water by transpiration, which occurs chiefly through the leaves, aids in the circulation of sap inside the plant and is also associated with certain chemical changes furthering assimilation of nutrients.

Drought-resistant plants have a variety of structures which provide a defense against their arid environments. Roots commonly are long or spreading. To reduce evaporation, leaves may be small and thick, may have a covering of wax or hairs, or may even be replaced by thorns or scales. By contrast, plants which are adapted to humid environments have scarcely any defense against evaporation and water deficiency.

Soil. The soil environment affects plant life chiefly through its chemical composition and moisture characteristics. Porous, coarse, and stony soils may induce a drought-resistant vegetation even in regions of moderate rainfall, while water-logged soils tend to support a vegetation quite different from that of adjacent better-drained areas. Soils with excessive amounts of salt or lime support only meager or special communities of plants, and the same is true of soils covered with raw and highly acid humus. Generally, soil variations produce local details within the broader patterns of distribution.

Biotic factor. Vegetation communities are modified profoundly by the activities of organisms in a variety of ways: the browsing of wild or domesticated animals is selective and often tends to reduce the number of woody plants with edible leaves; pollinating insects are indispensable in maintaining reproduction in many plants; and birds carry seeds from one area to another. But human beings themselves, as herdsmen, cultivators, fire carriers, and constructors of cities and transportation systems, have been the most widespread and drastic modifiers of the earth's vegetative mantle. By their activities a portion of the earth's original plant cover has been literally replaced by tilled crops and other areas have been exploited and depleted in varying degrees, so that over extensive areas only vestiges of the natural vegetation remain.

Principal Classes of Natural Vegetation

In a classification based largely on appearance or physiognomic character, the earth's main classes of land vegetation are forest, woodland, grassland, desert shrub, and tundra. *Forests* are those assemblages of trees whose crowns (in season) form a more or less continuous canopy shading the ground beneath. *Woodland* is a more or less continuous cover of woody plants but with no continuous canopy. Many areas of woodland are made up largely of what may be called *brush or scrub* vegetation in contrast to trees. *Grassland* has a nearly continuous cover of herbaceous plants, sometimes with widely scattered trees, but often with little or no woody plant growth. *Desert shrub* is characterized by a discontinuous cover (often less than one-third) of both evergreen and deciduous types of shrubs and may contain succulent plants (juice-filled, fleshy tissues, such as cacti). *Tundra* is made up of a variety of combinations of dwarf shrubs, grasses, sedges, lichens, etc., and is particularly characterized by a lack of trees. The main types of natural vegetation and the extent of the areas occupied by each are shown in the accompanying table.

The distribution of these classes over the earth is mostly, although not entirely, controlled by environment—chiefly climate. Tundra is largely confined to climates where the summers are so cool and short as to exclude trees and, to some extent, grass. Desert shrub is a product of climates that are extremely deficient in rainfall. On the other hand, some arid regions have a sparse plant cover which is more grass than shrub, so it is not always true that shrub indicates greater aridity than grass. Scrub woodland and chaparral are found in areas which have a distinct, severe dry season but in a climate which cannot be classed as dry.

One of the more interesting problems is the explanation for the distribution of forest and grassland. It was once thought that they occupy mutually exclusive types of climate, but the weight of evidence appears to be against such a hypothesis. Instead, it seems that grasses are meager or absent in forested regions primarily because most grasses cannot tolerate the shade beneath a continuous forest cover. Consequently, grass has difficulty competing in environments where the more complex and exacting tree thrives. Trees, on the other hand, have certain characteristics that make them less tolerant of certain environments than grass. The very height of a tree makes it more susceptible to drying winds. This same height requires large amounts of water to transport mineral nutrients from roots to crown. In addition, the soft green shoots annually produced by trees require a sufficiently long growing season free from cold, drought, or fire to be able to mature. It is correct to say, therefore, that grasses tend to dominate in those environments which permit vegetation but are hostile to trees. The worst conditions for trees are dry subsoils, desiccating winds, and periodic burning of the vegetation cover.

World Map of Vegetation Types

The necessary simplification of the complexities of the plant cover of the earth onto a small map, such as Plate 4, may mislead an uninformed user. Consequently, a student must use Plate 4 with several facts carefully kept in mind. First, what are portrayed as homogeneous vegetation regions are composed of intricate patchworks of plant communities that are combined only because they fall in the same basic formation type. Second, the small size of the map makes it impossible to show small areas of plant communities which do not belong to the formation type which surrounds them, even if such depictions were desirable. Furthermore, on Plate 4 no try has been made to show (*a*) the areas of desert without vegetation, (*b*) the cultivated areas and the innumerable smaller lakes, (*c*) the settlements of human beings, and (*d*) the distinctive vegetation of marshes and swamps. Instead, these have been incorporated in the delineation either as the areas which surround them or as they were (or probably were) before people began their cultivation of the land. The entire land surface, except for the icecap areas, has thus been shown to have some kind of cover of upland natural vegetation. The purpose of preparing Plate 4 in this way is to make more apparent the broader distribu-

TABLE 15.1 MAIN TYPES OF NATURAL VEGETATION ON THE LAND AND THEIR APPROXIMATE AREAS

	Millions of square kilometers*		Percent of total
1. Forest			
a. Evergreen			
a^1 Tropical rainforest	17.0		
a^2 Temperate mixed forest	5.0		
a^3 Boreal forest	12.0		
b. Deciduous			
b^1 Summer green forest	7.0		
b^2 Rain green forest	7.5		
		48.5	32.5
2. Woodland			
a. Scrub and thorn woodland	7.0		
b. Chaparral woodland	1.5		
		8.5	5.7
3. Grassland			
a. Tropical grassland	15.0		
b. Temperate grassland	9.0		
		24.0	16.1
4. Desert shrub		18.0	12.1
5. Tundra		8.0	5.4
Other land areas (dry and ice deserts, lakes and streams, settlements, cultivated land, swamps and marsh, etc.)		42.0	28.2
		149.0	100

*After Lieth.

tions so that they may be related to the other general patterns of physical geography—chiefly climate but also soils and land-surface forms.

Forests and Their Distribution

Evergreen Forests

Tropical rainforest. This most luxuriant and widespread (see preceding table) type of forest is the climax vegetation of tropical lowlands and slopes where rainfall is both abundant and well distributed throughout the year. No long dry season can be tolerated. There are three distinct regional formations of rainforest: American, African, and Indo-Malaysian. The American sector is the largest, with its most extensive development occurring in the Amazon Basin (see Plate 4 for other regions).

This forest type has three principal charac-teristics: (1) There is a great variety of different species of trees—far greater than in middle-latitude forests. But although species are numerous, rainfor-est trees are remarkably similar in general appear-ance and structure. (2) Vertical stratification in the forest is developed to an unusual degree. This feature arises from the fact that the various species have different height limits and arrange themselves in several layers (Fig. 15.4). The result is a forest with a number of tree tiers, each lower one reflecting an increasing tolerance for the shade imposed by the canopy above. (3) The number of climbing plants, lianas, and epiphytes is unusually large. The giant lianas have the appearance of great cables interlacing the branches of the forest crown and binding the individual trees together. Even when a large tree breaks off near the base, it may be prevented from falling by the lianas that entwine it.

Luxuriant, complex, exuberant—such is the

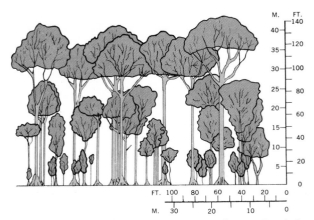

Figure 15.4 Profile diagram of tropical rainforest in Trinidad, West Indies. Note the several stories of trees. Under such a dense canopy there can be little undergrowth on the forest floor. *(After Beard.)*

character of the rainforest in the tropics. In external appearance it presents a richly varied mosaic of many shades. Rainforest is evergreen broadleaf. There is no dormant period when the forest as a whole is bare and without foliage: leaf shedding is a sporadic event rather than a seasonal one for all species. Individual trees without leaves may be observed at any time.

From the inside, the rainforest is dense, with trees which vary greatly in height and diameter. The tallest ones rarely exceed 50 m (approx. 165 ft). Trunks are relatively slender and do not branch until near the top. Their bark is thin and smooth. Such a multistoried forest produces a dense canopy of shade. The forest floor is deep in gloom, with a light intensity less than 1 percent of that at the top of the forest crown. Because of the deep shade, the forest undergrowth of low shrubs and herbaceous plants is poorly developed, so that one can proceed in all directions without following paths or chopping new ones. Typical *jungle* conditions, with a thick and impenetrable undergrowth, are characteristic chiefly of sections where more light reaches the forest floor—as, for example, along rivers and coasts, on precipitous wet slopes, and in abandoned agricultural clearings. Reflecting the abundant moisture in the surface soil, tropical rainforest trees are relatively shallow-rooted and consequently highly susceptible to uprooting and damage by storm winds.

Resource value of the tropical rainforest. Wood from the rainforest is a principal source of fuel in many underdeveloped areas, but up to the present commercial development of the wood resources has lagged. While reserves of timber in the tropical forest are enormous, there are serious handicaps to the exploitation of this resource. Chief of these is associated with the great number of tree species. If only one or even a few particular kinds of trees are desired, they are so widely scattered that the selective logging required is very expensive. And if clear-cutting of the forest (*i.e.*, cutting down all timber in a given area) is resorted to, there is the serious problem of marketing the great variety of woods obtained. Currently the main commercial varieties of timber logged from tropical forests are hard, durable cabinet woods such as mahogany, teak, and rosewood, whose high value justifies the expense of selective logging.

There is reason to believe that the rainforest has persisted relatively unchanged since remote times. Recently it has been rudely disturbed by the spread of settlement in the tropics, especially in Amazonia, with associated clearing of the forest for an expanding agriculture. It is estimated that the rainforest may comprise as much as half of the earth's remaining timber; but at the accelerated rate at which it is being destroyed, much of it may disappear within a few generations.[2]

Temperate mixed forest. In several areas there are extensive forests of mixed broadleaf and needleleaf trees in which the broadleaf varieties are also largely evergreen. They are especially widespread in the Southern Hemisphere, where they occur in southern Chile, southeastern Brazil, South Africa, and southeastern Australia (Plate 4). In the Northern Hemisphere, they occur primarily in southeastern United States and southern Japan.

These mixed forests occupy diverse areas of climate—for example, the very wet, cool regions of southern Chile, the much drier and warmer areas of South Africa, and the warmer and wetter areas of southeastern Brazil. Although it is difficult to generalize, the Southern Hemisphere's mixed evergreen forests contain considerable proportions of widely

[2]William M. Denevan. "Development and the Imminent Demise of the Amazon Rainforest." *The Professional Geographer*, Vol. 25, No. 2, pp. 130–135, 1973.

NATURAL VEGETATION

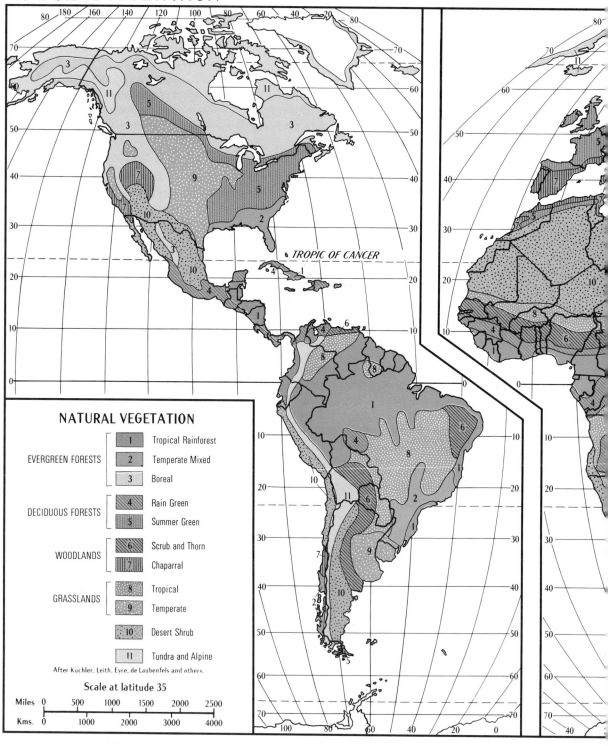

TROPIC OF CANCER

NATURAL VEGETATION

EVERGREEN FORESTS		
	1	Tropical Rainforest
	2	Temperate Mixed
	3	Boreal

DECIDUOUS FORESTS		
	4	Rain Green
	5	Summer Green

WOODLANDS		
	6	Scrub and Thorn
	7	Chaparral

GRASSLANDS		
	8	Tropical
	9	Temperate

| | 10 | Desert Shrub |
| | 11 | Tundra and Alpine |

After Küchler, Leith, Eyre, de Laubenfels and others.

Scale at latitude 35

Miles	0	500	1000	1500	2000	2500
Kms.	0	1000	2000	3000	4000	

PLATE 4

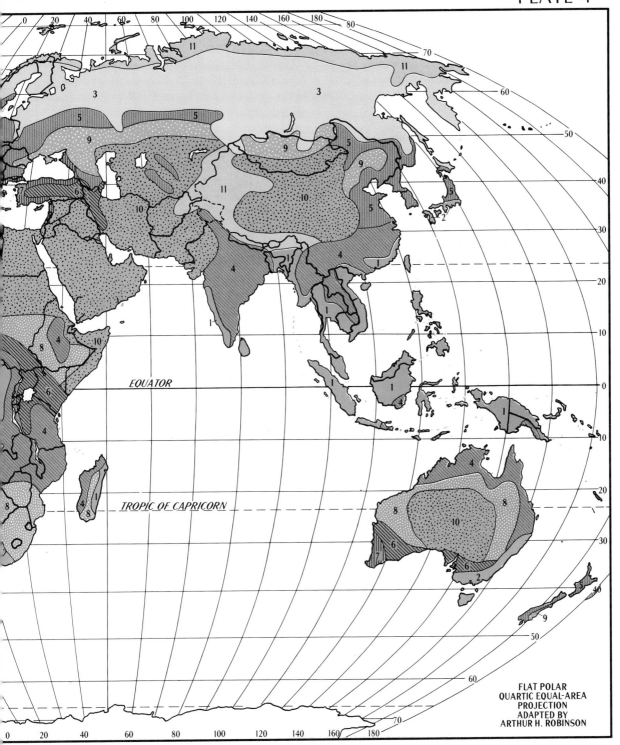

FLAT POLAR
QUARTIC EQUAL-AREA
PROJECTION
ADAPTED BY
ARTHUR H. ROBINSON

varying pines and other coniferous trees combined with evergreen species of broadleaf beech and cypress-and-magnolialike varieties.

In the subtropical southeastern United States is a conifer-dominant forest which coincides more or less with the Atlantic and Gulf Coastal Plain, where sandy soils, which are low in mineral nutrients and do not retain water, are widespread. The prevailing species are pines—loblolly, shortleaf, pitch, longleaf, and slash. Still, many broadleaf trees (oak, hickory, and poplar) do grow in this forest area. The southern pine-dominant forest apparently does not represent a climatic-climax type, for the subtropical humid climate appears highly suitable for broadleaf varieties. In conjunction with the soil-terrain environment of the Coastal Plain, fires, both natural and human-set, seem to have been the decisive factor in maintaining the pine dominance, for such trees suffer less injury from fire than do most broadleaf varieties. If protected from fire, it is likely that much of the southern pine forest would be replaced by an oak-hickory association. The Coastal Plain conifers are one of the nation's main sources of lumber and pulpwood.

Boreal forest. Not quite as extensive as the rainforest, but still far more extensive than any other class is the boreal forest (see preceding table). This largely needle-leaf, coniferous forest coincides generally with the severe boreal climatic areas in North America and Eurasia, although important extensions occur southward in western North America.

Coniferous trees are predominantly evergreen; larch (tamarack) is the important exception. The growth and fall of needles are continuous processes and not confined to a single period or season; hence this forest never appears bare. Unlike broadleaves, most of which permit rapid transpiration, the hard, narrow needles of conifers retard water loss. Thus leaf shedding is not necessary to protect the conifer against a season of drought or of severe cold with frozen ground. On the whole, conifers are less demanding as regards both climate and soil than most broadleaf trees, and consequently they tolerate a wider range of environmental conditions.

The boreal forests reach their maximum extent in the severe climates of subarctic northern North America and Eurasia, where they exist in wide and continuous east-west belts stretching from the Atlantic to the Pacific. On its northern frontier, along a sinuous transition, the boreal forest gradually grades into tundra, where, chiefly because of the cool and short summer, the climate is hostile to all trees.

Within the harsh subarctic environment, the more tolerant conifers greatly predominate over broadleaves, although varieties of the latter, such as birch, aspen, alder, and willow, are scattered in groves and thickets, especially in the equatorward margins. Among the most common needle trees are spruce, fir, pine, and larch, with the combinations of species varying from region to region and from locality to locality. In these boreal climates growth is slow, so that trees are relatively small in both girth and height (Fig. 15.5). Over extensive areas where strong ice scour occurred and bedrock is widely exposed, the forest cover is usually thin and in places even absent.

On the margins of openings where light is available, brush may be dense; but on the shaded floor of the boreal forest, undergrowth tends to be scanty, in part stifled by the thick blanket of slowly decomposing needles. Little organic matter is incorporated in the soil, for needle leaves are a poor source of humus to begin with, while the low temperatures and deep shade act to retard decomposition and to discourage the activity of soil fauna.

Since enormous areas of the boreal forest in North America and the U.S.S.R. remain sparsely populated, much of the tree resource is as yet unused. But along parts of this forest's southern margins which border on regions of denser settlement, there has been large-scale logging for pulpwood during the last half-century, so that extensive cutover and burned-over areas exist.

South of the great belts of subarctic conifers, and therefore in climates which are less severe except at high altitudes, there are other less extensive areas of needle trees which represent a valuable forest resource. Not only are they composed of larger trees and superior timber species, but they lie closer to important markets.

In dry western North America, broken belts of conifers extend southward from the subarctic following the rainier highlands and, continuously, the moist coastal lowlands and lower slopes. In the highlands the harsh climate of the subarctic is duplicated in modified form. Vertical zonation of forest types is a prominent feature. In general the highland forests,

Figure 15.5 Side view of boreal forest in Canada. Note the small size of trees. *(U.S. Forest Service.)*

with their thinner stands of usually smaller trees, are not as valuable for timber as the forests on the lower slopes and in the coastal areas, which form a continuous belt extending from southern Alaska southward as far as California. In this rainier and milder climatic environment, large trees, dense stands, and good-quality timber combine to make the forests of the western coastal regions the most extensive areas of high-grade conifers anywhere in the world (Fig. 15.6).

Dominant varieties in this coastal forest are western hemlock, western red cedar, Sitka spruce, and, in California, the gigantic redwood. Douglas fir, although widespread and very valuable, is considered a subclimax resulting from depredations by human beings and fire. In such a mild and humid climate, it may be wondered, why is there not a broadleaf

deciduous forest instead of conifers? Summer dryness in the southern half of this forest area may be a partial answer. Another possibility is that the broadleaf species were largely exterminated by the rigors of the Pleistocene ice-age climate while the conifers were able to survive.

East of the Rockies, the boreal forest extends southward from the subarctic into humid southeastern Canada and adjoining parts of the northern United States—Minnesota, Wisconsin, Michigan, New York, and northern New England. Because of its fine-quality timber this forest area of white pine, red pine, hemlock, beech, and maple suffered such rapid and complete cutting in the late nineteenth century and later that little of the original stand has survived. Regeneration has been minor. Today much of this forest region is a mixed evergreen-deciduous land, whose second growth of poplar and shrub has only modest commercial value as wood. In scenic value it contributes to an extensive tourist and recreation industry. In Eurasia, before logging reduced them, valuable coniferous forests south of the subarctic usually occupied highlands, although they were occasionally found in some sandy lowlands as well.

Figure 15.6 Interior view of the Douglas fir forest in the United States Pacific Northwest. The stand is dense and trees are large. *(U.S. Forest Service.)*

Deciduous Forests

Summer green forest. In the humid subtropical and temperate climates of middle latitudes in eastern North America, western Europe, and eastern Asia, the warm summers promote rapid growth, but the winters are severe enough to create a dormant season for vegetation. The response of the deciduous tree is a lush foliage of thin and delicate leaves in the warm, humid summer and the shedding of leaves in winter when low or subfreezing temperatures are common. In consequence, a formation type of largely deciduous trees has evolved in these areas. The summer green forest areas are bordered, both to the north and to the south in North America and to the north in Europe, by an area of mixed summer green-evergreen forests. Since the climatic environments and soils of both the summer green and the mixed summer green-evergreen forests are suited for agriculture, in extensive areas much of the forest cover in these areas has been swept away by agricultural activity. The most extensive remnants exist in rough slope lands which are less suited to farming.

Mature trees of the broadleaf deciduous forest usually range in height from about 15 to 30 m (approximately 50 to 100 ft) and in diameter from 60 to 120 cm (2 to 4 ft). The variety of different kinds of trees is by no means so great as in the tropical rainforest; three or four species usually predominate. The forest canopy, bright green in color, lets a considerable amount of sunlight through to ground levels, where it stimulates a moderately abundant undergrowth and activates a relatively rich soil fauna. One of the most spectacular events in the earth's annual cycle of change is the display of brilliant autumn colors just before leaf fall in many of the broadleaf deciduous and mixed forests. At this season different species, and even individual trees, show striking color variations.

In North America the main block of the broadleaf deciduous forest, situated between mixed forests on both the north and the south, stretches from the Appalachians in the east beyond the Mississippi River, except for an eastward thrust of prairie in Illinois. This same forest is continued further westward along the river valleys. It is unusually rich in species, with oak and hickory most prevalent, although maple, basswood, birch, and beech are also common. In the United States, three main forest associations, each distinguished by its combination of dominant species, are usually recognized: oak-hickory in the central and western parts (Fig. 15.7); birch-beech-maple in the north and northeast; and oak-yellow poplar in the south and southeast.

Rain green forest. In several areas in the tropical regions the forest trees respond to a dry season by dropping their leaves in the same way that middle-latitude deciduous trees respond to a cold season. These forests are called *rain green* in contrast to those called *summer green*. Sometimes they are referred to as "monsoon forests." Several major areas of rain green forest formation types can be identified (see Plate 4): the American, covering much of the West Indies, the western side of Central America, and northern South America; the African, comprising large areas of the south central and southeastern regions, as well as more local areas south of the Sudan; and the Asian-Australian, the first covering large areas of the Indian subcontinent and Indo-China, and the second, the northern sections of Australia. The limits of these areas are drawn in the *ecotones*, or transitional areas, where the rain green merges into the evergreen rainforest on the wetter

Figure 15.7 A dominantly summer green forest (oak-hickory) in northern Indiana. Much of this type of forest occupied potentially good agricultural land and as a consequence was displaced in the process of settlement. *(U.S. Department of Agriculture.)*

sides and into the shrub and thorn woodland on the drier sides.

It is not easy to describe the rain green forest because there are considerable variations from place to place. Generally there are two distinct canopies, the higher usually less than 20 m (60 ft) and generally deciduous, and a lower 3 to 10 m (10 to 30 ft) high which may be composed of many evergreen varieties. Lianas and epiphytes (plants which grow on others for support but are not parasitic) are generally absent. The African formations are distinctive in that there is a larger proportion of grasses in the ground cover.

Woodland

Scrub and Thorn Woodland

In several sections of the humid tropics there are considerable regions of a transitional formation type of woodland. It is characterized by small trees or lower-growing shrubs with only some grasses or other herbaceous plants. The majority of the plants are deciduous, trees are small and may be gnarled, and many of the trees and shrubs carry spikes and thorns. There is no continuous canopy, and bare ground is not uncommon in the drier areas. Their type of location is in the transitional areas between the rain green forest on the humid side and the tropical grasslands on the drier side. However, not only does the rainfall tend to be less in the scrub and thorn woodland than in the summer green forests, it also tends to be more variable and seasonal. These woodlands usually have a distinct and fairly long dry season.

In the American West a woodland formation occupies a transition zone in the flanks of highlands, lying between the evergreen forests of the upper levels and the chaparral or desert shrub below. This woodland is dominated by such plants as the evergreen variety of oak, piñon, and juniper.

Chaparral Woodland

This formation type is closely identified with areas of subtropical dry-summer, or Mediterranean, climate (see Plates 1 and 4). It is a woodland that is predominantly both evergreen and broadleaf, but it is able to tolerate summer drought and heat. This is

accomplished through a variety of structural adaptations which aid in conserving water—dwarf forms, thick bark, small, leathery, often shiny leaves, and extensive or deep root systems.

It is a formation predominantly composed of wood shrubs and widely spaced dwarf trees (Fig. 15.8). Tall trees are rare. This bush thicket is called *maquis* in the Mediterranean lands, and there it is composed of a great variety of evergreens, prickly shrubs, and some herbaceous plants. In California the complex is called *chaparral* and includes a variety of dwarf and bush oaks. It can grow up to a height of 6 m (18 ft). It burns easily in the dry season but can quickly send up new shoots, so the formation is resistant to fire.

Grassland

Grasses are able to tolerate a wide range of environmental conditions—from tropical to polar temperatures, and from desert lands to swamplands. Compared with the more complex tree, grasses suffer less from the vicissitudes of climate, fires, and the depredations of animals. Their wide range is also fostered by the smallness and lightness of their seeds.

Tropical Grassland

There is a great variety of tropical grassland. Much of it incorporates widely spaced trees or shrubs as well as grasses and sedges. When this occurs it is usually referred to as *savanna*, although that term has also often been used simply as a synonym for tropical grassland.

Tropical grasslands differ from middle-latitude grasslands in certain respects: They more frequently contain some trees; they do not have a continuous sod cover—the grasses occur in discontinuous tufts; and the grasses are markedly coarser (Fig. 15.9). Tropical grasses vary greatly in height, reaching 3 to 4 m (10 to 12 ft) in the more luxuriant stands found in parts of Africa. The blades of the mature grasses are harsh and leathery; mainly it is the fresh young shoots which are palatable to grazing animals. Although grazing is often the principal economy of these areas, no important commercial livestock industry has developed there. It has long been the common practice among the inhabitants of tropical

Figure 15.8 Chaparral consisting of drought-resistant evergreen woodland and shrub in California. *(U.S. Department of Agriculture.)*

Figure 15.9 Tall coarse grass with some low trees in the tropical grassland of Africa north of the equator. Height of the grasses is about 2.5 m (8 ft), so that they reach into the lower branches of the short trees. *(From Shantz and Marbut, 1923; courtesy of American Geographical Society.)*

grasslands to burn off the dead material toward the end of the dry season in order to make room for new growth at the beginning of the rains.

Most of the world's extensive low-latitude grasslands coincide with tropical wet-and-dry climates. But that climate type may not necessarily be the cause of the formation. It is debatable whether there is such a thing as a tropical grassland in which the grasses represent the true climatic climax. Increasingly, plant geographers have tended to conclude that many, if not most, of these grass areas are a consequence of human intervention in the form of set fires and livestock grazing. In some areas, however, the grass vegetation seems to be the result of waterlogging of the soil in the wet season followed by extreme soil dryness in the dry season.

Temperate Grassland

The grasslands in the middle latitudes typically are located in subhumid climates (Plates 1 and 4); and some ecologists view them as the climatic-climax

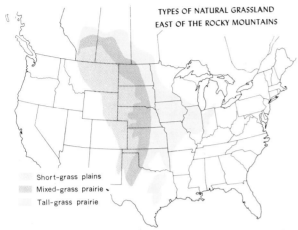

TYPES OF NATURAL GRASSLAND
EAST OF THE ROCKY MOUNTAINS

Short-grass plains
Mixed-grass prairie
Tall-grass prairie

Figure 15.10 Tall-grass prairie, short-grass plains, and a two-story mixed-grass prairie transition zone are found in the midcontinent grasslands. *(After J. Richard Carpenter.)*

vegetation of such environments. In this respect they may differ from tropical grasslands. They also differ in that they generally have fewer trees, except along stream courses and along their zones of contact with forest.

In the midcontinent grasslands of interior North America east of the Rockies, two, or sometimes three, subdivisions are recognized (Fig. 15.10). The tall-grass prairie, or true prairie (which has mostly been replaced by farmland), used to occupy the more humid eastern parts, and the short-grass steppe, or plains, still exists in many of the drier western parts. Between them is a transition zone called the *mixed-grass prairie*, which consists both of midgrasses 60 to 120 cm (2 to 4 ft) tall and of shorter grasses, which together form an upper and a lower story (Fig. 15.11). It is possible that the two-story mixed-grass prairie originally also prevailed on the plains area farther west, and that the midgrass species were largely killed out by overgrazing. West of the Rockies extensive vegetation areas of the original short bunchgrass still exist, mainly in Washington, Oregon, Idaho, and California.

The tall-grass prairie was dominated by tall, luxuriant, deep-rooted grasses which reached heights of 1.5 to 2.5 m (5 to 8 ft) in the more humid eastern parts. Usually there were many showy flowering plants intermingled with the grasses. A notable fea-

ture of the American prairie, and one difficult to explain, is the far eastward thrust of grassland. It extends in the form of a wedge even into central Illinois and western Indiana (Fig. 15.10), where the climate is humid and therefore seems favorable to forest development. Some authorities maintain that this humid prairie has a higher concentration of summer rainfall variability and regional drought than the forested regions both to the north and to the south. Others believe that the humid prairie region was climatically capable of supporting forest, but was prevented from doing so by grass fires (set both by lightning and by human beings) which killed the woody plants but not the grass, and by the effects of grazing animals.

Outside Anglo-America, important middle-latitude grasslands formerly existed in southern U.S.S.R. and in northeastern China. In the Southern Hemisphere, they were mainly in Argentina–Uruguay–southeastern Brazil, and the southern island of New Zealand. In all of these areas, large parts have been converted to tilled land.

Desert Shrub

Some extremely dry or soilless, windswept, rocky deserts and some areas of moving sand dunes may be devoid of all vegetation, but these are the exception. Most desert regions have some plant life, although almost invariably it is sparse. Desert plants are of several types, and each has a different way of surmounting the handicaps of its arid environment.

Desert shrub is the most widespread form of arid-land vegetation and covers a large area (Table 15.1). The deciduous species make use of leaf shedding in order to withstand drought. The evergreen varieties have protective structures such as small, thick, and leathery leaves with shiny, waxy surfaces. In both types of shrub, root systems are unusually well developed—some in depth and others in breadth. In the United States the two most widespread desert shrubs are sagebrush and creosote bush, the latter growing chiefly in the hotter and more arid Southwest.

Arid-land vegetation also includes leafless, thorny succulents such as the cacti, certain salt-

Figure 15.11 Midgrasses on the Great Plains in Colorado at the end of a season of exceptional rainfall. Ordinarily, only short grasses grow this far west. *(U.S. Forest Service.)*

tolerant plants, and a variety of short-lived transients (Fig. 15.12). The shallow-rooted cactus is distinguished by its large water storage capacity, which permits it to survive between infrequent rains. In addition, its outer surface is hard and waxy, which reduces losses of water by transpiration, while its spines protect it against animals attracted by its interior water supply. Fleshy, succulent, salt-tolerant plants are characteristic of areas which have highly alkaline soils as a consequence of poor drainage. Like the cacti, they are able to store water in leaves and stem. The so-called transients, usually small, include many flowering annuals, but also grasses and tuberous plants. They are able to tolerate the aridity chiefly because growth is rapid and their life cycles can be completed in a brief period of time. In the form of seeds, tubers, or corms, they are able to remain dormant during periods of drought. Subsequently they are stimulated to germination and growth by a period of showers.

Tundra

The lowly dwarf vegetation comprising the Arctic tundra of northernmost North America and Eurasia is a reflection of the harsh environment. This includes strong drying winds, a short growing season of only a month or two with occasional summer frosts, and shallow, infertile, poorly drained soils underlain by permanently frozen ground.

In the climatically more favorable parts, the climax vegetation usually is one in which grasses and sedges dominate, with an understory of lichens and mosses. Where the environment is harsher, grasses and sedges decline, while lichens, and to a lesser extent mosses, become dominant. Dwarf shrubs are scattered throughout both communities in protected areas and may become the dominants in some local areas. Tundra vegetation also includes a great variety of ephemeral plants with bright flowers. Yet even at the height of the short growing season when many

Figure 15.12 Desert shrub and cacti in the vicinity of the Superstition Mountains in Arizona. *(U.S. Forest Service.)*

species are in flower, the general color of the tundra is drab or yellowish. On its southern boundary, the tundra makes contact with the boreal forest along a very complex zone, with tundra communities dominating the exposed interfluves, and with forest growing in the protected valleys and on the lower slopes. Throughout the tundra, the pattern of vegetation distribution is likely to be very patchy; plant groupings change with minute variations in slope, exposure, and drainage. Tundra vegetation has little economic significance except in connection with the grazing of reindeer.

Vegetation in Mountain Areas

Mountain areas are characterized by an unusual variety of local environments existing in close juxtaposition. The vegetation responses to these variations are so complex that it is impossible to describe them in detail or to represent them on a small-scale map

such as Plate 4. Only a few broad generalizations about mountain vegetation are given here.

On the lower slopes of highlands, the vegetation cover may resemble that of the surrounding lowlands. But with increasing altitude, temperature decreases rapidly, while solar energy, moistness, and winds increase. Changes of vegetation fall into a rough vertical zonation of plant life, but with many interrupting local variations.

Conifers, with their strong tolerance for the vicissitudes of mountain climates and soils, comprise the largest element of mountain forests in middle latitudes, and they are also found at high elevations even in the tropics. Within the coniferous zone, pines usually predominate at lower elevations, but fir and spruce take over near the upper climatic limits of forest. Above these limits, which vary in altitude, trees will not grow because of low temperatures, a short growing season, diurnal freeze and thaw, strong winds, and thin soils that alternate between saturation and aridity. Alpine pastures and meadows predominate in this zone and furnish summer grazing for flocks and herds brought up from farms or ranches at lower elevations. Above the alpine pastures, the meager, lowly mountain vegetation bears considerable resemblance to that of the Arctic tundra. But it is by no means uniform, since there are important variations in the plant associations on sunny and shady slopes, on wet and dry flanks, and in windy and protected locations.

REVIEW QUESTIONS

1. Compare the concept of an ecotone as a spatial phenomenon with transition through time.
2. Suggest several ways humans may cause modifications in the plant cover without actual cultivation.
3. How might vegetative forms arrive at a newly built volcanic island in the tropical seas?
4. The distribution of solar energy available for photosynthesis may vary along any one parallel of latitude at the surface of the earth. Why?
5. Compare the competitive characteristics of grass and trees in given environmental conditions.
6. Suggest several reasons why the tropical rainforests have not been heavily logged for lumber.
7. There seems to be a somewhat greater area of evergreen temperate mixed forest in the Southern Hemisphere than in the Northern. Suggest possible reasons why.
8. Describe and account for the extent of the commercial utilization of the various parts of the boreal forest.
9. Grasslands apparently are often a result of "disturbance," either by humans or by nature. What does this mean?

SELECTED REFERENCES

de Laubenfels, David J. *A Geography of Plants and Animals.* Wm. C. Brown Company Publishers, Dubuque, Iowa, 1970. A rather short, untraditional, but logical look at the subject.

———. *Mapping the World's Vegetation.* Syracuse University Press, Syracuse, 1975. A thorough, modern and readable treatment of the complex problem of mapping vegetation. Many maps.

Detwyler, Thomas R. (ed.). *Man's Impact on Environment.* McGraw-Hill Book Company, New York, 1971. A selection of articles by specialists. Contains several dealing especially with the plant world and the human modification of it.

Eyre, S. R. *Vegetation and Soils: A World Picture.* 2d ed. Aldine Publishing Company, Chicago, 1968. A geographically arranged treatment of these two related elements of physical geography. Emphasis is on vegetation. Contains detailed maps.

——— (ed.). *World Vegetation Types.* Columbia University Press, New York, 1971. An interesting collection of scholarly essays characterizing or examining problems in connection with a plant formation or community.

Grass. Yearbook of Agriculture, 1948. U.S. Department of Agriculture, Washington, D.C. A thorough reference work typical of the series. Many articles by experts on a variety of topics.

Haden-Guest, Stephen, John K. Wright, and Eileen M. Teclaff (eds.). *A World Geography of Forest Resources.* The Ronald Press Company, New York, 1956. A large collection of chapters describing the forests and inventorying the product-potential of 24 regional areas of the earth.

Küchler, A. W. *Potential Natural Vegetation of the United States.* Special Publication No. 36, American Geographical Society, New York, 1964. Detailed map with accompanying manual (156 pp.), comprising text, bibliography, and legend descriptions, and 118 illustrations of vegetation types.

———. World Natural Vegetation. Colored map in *Goode's World Atlas.* 14th ed., Rand McNally and Company, Chicago, 1974. Pp. 18–19. A good reference using a systematic legend on a world scale.

Polunin, Nicholas. *Introduction to Plant Geography.* McGraw-Hill Book Company, New York, 1960. An extensive treatise, with emphasis on the botanical aspects.

Trees. Yearbook of Agriculture, 1949. U.S. Department of Agriculture, Washington, D.C. Like *Grass,* a collection of many articles by experts. An excellent reference.

Weaver, J. E. *The North American Prairie.* Johnsen Publishing Company, Lincoln, Neb., 1954. A thorough study put together by an expert after a lifetime of research on the subject.

The Pattern of Soils

The interface between the land and the atmosphere is the most biologically active portion of the land area. Here grow the plants which nurture almost all other terrestrial life. Parts of the plants grow below the interface and draw some of their sustenance through their roots from the mineral-organic matter complex of the land. Other plant parts grow in the air above, where solar energy drives the photosynthesis process and where carbon is obtained from the gas CO_2. Except for the areas of bare bedrock or ice, the land area lying beneath this interface is covered by a layer of disintegrated rock material.

Much of this more or less loose veneer is residual, that is, it has accumulated on top of the bedrock from which it was formed. Some of it, however, has been moved—either locally by mass movement, or for some distance by gradational agents such as glaciers, running water, and wind. Except when solidly frozen, this mantle is porous, so that both air and water circulate among the particles. Normally, this loose material becomes a dynamic complex of inorganic and organic substances teeming with life. This complex is called *soil* when it includes disintegrated rock, air, water, organic material, and living organisms. The processes which form it include many that go on only under the influence of organisms. For this reason the soil is considered to extend downward only so far as life and its contributions do, which is usually no more than a few meters.

It would be difficult to overemphasize the significance of soil to human beings. The many chemical elements on which human life depends are primarily needed in the form of organic compounds, such as proteins, fats, carbohydrates, and vitamins; and these, as well as minute quantities of trace elements, come from the soil either directly by way of plant parts that people consume, or indirectly through animal products. The soils of some areas can support a large and healthy human population, but in even larger areas the reverse seems to be true. In many instances poor yields are due to human ignorance of proper soil management rather than the soil itself.

The soil as an open system. Like all dynamic entities, the soil can be considered as a system in which there is a continual exchange of materials and transformation of energy. Most of the energy is derived, directly or indirectly, from the sun, but a little is heat conducted upward from the interior of the earth. Energy exchanges are very intricate within the soil because of the complex of life processes which take place there. The soil is continually cycling a variety of organic and mineral materials, being a part of the total complex ecological system involving plants and animals, including human beings at the interface between land and the atmosphere. Like all other systems on earth, the soil is "striving" toward a steady state but does not ever reach it. Nevertheless, in its process of evolution in some areas it may appear to be stable, that is, to have reached a sort of climax condition and without much change taking place. From a long-term point of view, this is an illusion.

The Elements of Soil

The critical properties of soil, like the elements of climate, are those qualities which combine to produce the uniqueness which distinguishes one soil from another. The most important are: (1) fertility—that is, the supply and balance of plant nutrients available; (2) texture—the proportion of different sizes of particles, including the smallest and most active, the colloids; (3) structure—the arrangement of the particles in cohesive units; (4) organic components; (5) water and air relationships within the soil; and (6) the profile—the distinctive arrangement of horizontal layers that commonly develops in a soil.

The elements of soil character differ systematically from place to place according to the operation of the controls of soil development just as the elements of climate vary according to the action of the climatic controls.

Fertility. The existence of all life on land is ultimately dependent upon the ability of plants to obtain from the soil many of the chemical elements required for their photosynthetic construction of carbohydrates and their biosynthetic production of protein and other essential foods. A large supply of these elements—that is, a high level of fertility—does not necessarily mean a productive soil; a dry-land soil may be very fertile even though it is too dry to be productive.

Plants need some chemical elements in relatively large amounts: these include oxygen, carbon, hydrogen, nitrogen, calcium, potassium, phosphorus, sulphur, and magnesium. Others, no less essential but required only in very small amounts, are iron, manganese, copper, zinc, chlorine, molybdenum, and boron. Although some of these are available directly from the gases of the atmosphere (e.g., carbon), others are derived from the water in the soil, the organic

material in the soil (e.g., nitrogen), and the soil's inorganic matter (e.g., the metallic elements, such as calcium).

Many factors affect the complicated process of plant growth, but a basic requirement is that the essential minerals be present in the soil: if a sufficient supply is not there to begin with, the soil cannot be fertile unless the minerals are added artificially.

Supply and removal of fertility elements. The supply of essential minerals in a soil may be reduced in several ways: by erosion; excessive use, or over-cropping; and especially, by *leaching*, that is, the removal of elements in solution by percolating soil water which becomes part of the groundwater. A deficiency may be partially remedied in several ways: by appropriate mineral fertilizing; by fallowing, that is, letting the land lie idle so that natural decomposition provides an additional supply of minerals; and by manuring, that is, returning a major proportion of the plant material to the land in the form of animal excreta and plant refuse.

Certainly, the most universal factor affecting the fertility of soils is leaching. Although to some extent temperature, vegetation, and other factors contribute to leaching, it is caused mostly by the water from precipitation. Thus humid regions tend to have less fertile soils than dry regions.

Acidity and alkalinity. Some of the molecules in the soil solution occur as hydrogen ions, H, and others as hydroxyl ions, OH. If there is a preponderance of H ions, the solution is said to be *acid*. The degree of acidity or alkalinity of a solution is expressed by the pH scale, which extends from 0.0 to 14.0, with the midpoint, 7.0, indicating neutrality. pH values below 7.0 indicate acidity, which increases as the pH numbers become smaller.[1] The availability to plants of many elements is affected by the pH of the soil solution, and the microorganisms in the soil function best when the pH of the soil is near neutral. Each kind of plant has its individual pH preference and range.

[1]A pH value is the reciprocal of the logarithm of the concentration of hydrogen ions. Therefore, a pH value of 5.0 indicates ten times the concentration of hydrogen ions of a pH value of 6.0, and a pH value of 4.0 indicates ten times the concentration of a pH value of 5.0—and, accordingly, one hundred times the concentration of a pH value of 6.0.

From an overall point of view, the most important factor affecting the pH of a soil is the amount of leaching to which it has been subjected. Humid lands usually have acid soils, which tend to favor the production in plants of bulk carbohydrates such as starches, sugars, fats, and cellulose, as opposed to the proteins that are nutritionally more significant to animals.

Texture. The potential productivity of a soil depends upon several physical characteristics in addition to its chemical fertility. One of the more important is its texture—the relative proportions of the various sizes of particles that constitute the inorganic part of the soil complex. These weathered rock fragments, which commonly occupy nearly one-half the volume of the upper portion of the soil, are grouped in size classes ranging from sands (the coarsest) to clays. The accompanying table shows some class limits. The various combinations of percentages of the textural classes that occur in a soil are given specific names. *Loam* is the general term assigned to combinations that include moderate amounts of all three. Figure 16.1 shows the relative proportions of sand, silt, and clay in the various textural classes.

The texture markedly affects the retention and movement of water within a soil. For example, the amount of water that a soil can hold varies inversely with the average size of the particles. Hence sandy soils have relatively poor water retention, so that they dry out quickly after rains.

Usually the texture of a soil varies with depth. Downward-moving water may carry with it some of the smaller soil particles—mostly the clays—and deposit them at a lower level. This process of mechanical washing of clay downward is called *lessivage.* The mechanical and chemical removal of material is called *eluviation.* Importation of material into a portion of the soil is called *illuviation.* Because this translocation is accomplished by water, the upper portions of the soils of humid lands commonly tend to be eluviated as well as leached.

Colloids. The smallest particles in the soil are called *colloids,* ranging downward from 0.001 mm in diameter, with many particles as small as 0.5 and even 0.2 microns (1 micron = 0.001 mm). There are two distinct types of colloids, inorganic and organic. The inorganic colloids consist almost entirely of tiny

TEXTURE CLASSES*

Name	Diameter, mm
Sand:	
Very coarse sand (fine gravel)	2.00–1.00
Coarse to medium sand	1.00–0.25
Fine to very fine sand	0.25–0.05
Silt	0.05–0.002
Clay	Less than 0.002

*U.S. Dept. of Agriculture system.

particles of various kinds of platy, crystalline clays, while the organic are complex, amorphous substances comprising part of the soil component called *humus,* material derived from dead tissues that have been incorporated in the soil. The importance of colloids stems partly from the fact that, being so small and numerous, they present an extraordinary amount of surface area on which chemical reactions important in plant nutrition can take place. It has been estimated that the surface area of the clay fraction of the plow layer of 1 hectare (2.5 acres) of representative clay loam soil may actually exceed half the land area of the United States!

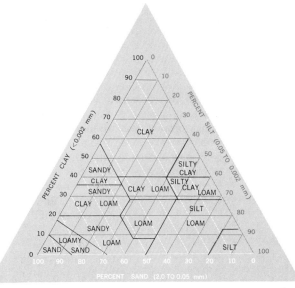

Figure 16.1 The textural triangle used by the soil scientists of the U.S. Department of Agriculture. In order to find the textural class, enter the percentage of sand, silt, and clay on the appropriate scales and follow the hatch lines to the intersection of the three lines.

The minute colloidal particles, both inorganic and organic, carry a negative charge on their surfaces, and as a consequence innumerable positively charged ions, called *cations*, are attracted to them. These swarms of cations are one of the two main sources of nutrients absorbed by the root hairs of the plants in intimate contact with the colloids. The other source is the soil solution itself, which derives its nutrient content from the surfaces of the colloidal particles. Consequently, the greater the colloidal content of a soil, the greater the potential "feeding area" and the supply of cations. The different types and amounts of colloidal clays and organic matter vary greatly in their capacity to attract and hold (adsorb) cations. This is called the "exchange capacity" of soils and is a measure of the soil's ability to make nutrients available to plants. Colloids are also important in relation to the water-holding capacity of the soil and its reactions to wetting and drying, such as swelling or shrinking and cracking.

Structure. The term "structure" refers to the character and arrangement of the small clumps or groups of individual soil particles that develop in most soils. These units, called *peds*, are very significant to the productivity of a soil because peds permit pore space to develop between them, allowing air, water, and root penetration. A favorable structure greatly eases problems of management—that is, the treatment of the soil in order to develop its maximum productivity.

There is a variety of ways in which primary particles may become aggregated in peds that maintain their identity when a soil is shattered. The principal distinct forms of peds are spheroidal (granular or crumb), blocky, prismatic, and platy (Fig. 16.2). In some poorly structured soils the amount of pore space may be less than 20 percent of the soil volume, whereas in highly structured clays it may exceed 60 percent. Most topsoils are granular or very fine blocky and include amounts of pore space comprising 35 to 50 percent of the soil volume.

Good structure, which provides a high percentage of pore space, commonly is found in soils of fine texture that have considerable organic content. A favorable structure is promoted by the presence of lime, colloids, and organic material that form gluey films which help the soil particles to stick together. However, a good soil structure may be destroyed by improper treatment.

Organic components. It is the presence of living organisms and dead organic matter that makes soil different from mere disintegrated rock. The role played by this organic content in a functioning soil is critical. It includes the following actions: (1) During decomposition organic material releases plant nutrients—especially nitrogen[2] and some of the essential mineral elements, such as calcium, magnesium, and phosphorus. (2) One important product of the decomposition of tissue is the supply of organic colloids. (3) The dead organic tissues provide the major food source for the living microorganisms of the soil, which in turn affect the health and quality of the higher forms of organic life supported by the soil. (4) Organic decomposition yields complex acids which contribute to further weathering of mineral matter. (5) The dead tissues have a high water-holding capacity, which helps the soil retain a supply of water for the soil solution and at the same time retards the leaching of dissolved minerals. (6) Organic matter promotes the development of a favorable soil structure.

The soil microorganisms (bacteria, fungi, and protozoa), which may total more than 1,100 kilograms per hectare (approx. 1,000 lb per acre), perform many functions in addition to helping make nitrogen available. For example, they rot organic matter, and they produce antibiotics which promote the quality and health of plants. Higher forms of life, such as earthworms and many kinds of insects, are also active in the soil. Insects help in the disintegration of plant remains. Insects and earthworms together affect the porosity of soil with their burrows and galleries, as well as by carrying out extensive transporting and overturning of the soil. The many thousand earthworms which may be in a hectare (2.5 acres) of soil may bring 50 metric tons of material to the surface in a year. This is an important aid in the vertical mixing of the soil materials.

---

[2]Plants must have nitrogen in rather large amounts. They get it in the soluble form of nitrates. These can be added artificially in chemical fertilizers; in nature, nitrates are produced through the work of some microorganisms which are able to take nitrogen gas and transform it. Legumes and some other plants play an important role in this connection, since their roots act as hosts to these nitrogen-transforming bacteria (Rhizobia). Other soil organisms make nitrogen available through their ability to decompose the remains of plants and animals, which are then incorporated in the soil.

Figure 16.2 The principal forms of soil structure: upper left, prismatic; upper right, blocky; lower left, platy; lower right, spheroidal (granular). In each photograph the white line represents 1 in. The peds in the photographs at upper and lower left are in place in the soil; those at upper and lower right have been removed from the soil and spread on a flat surface. *(Photographs by Roy W. Simonson.)*

The decomposed plant and animal remains of the soil are called *humus*. They break down to a jellylike consistency, which ultimately reaches the colloidal state.

Regional variations in humus accumulation.
Some soils have very small amounts of humus; some are richly supplied with it. Generally, other things being equal, the production of humus is closely associated with moisture and temperature relationships. For the earth as a whole the creation of vegetative matter (plant growth) takes place only above freez-

ing, and the amount of volume produced tends to increase with annual temperature up to about 25°C (approx. 80°F). At higher temperatures it decreases. This general relationship is graphed in Figure 16.3, which also shows that in a moist and aerated environment the organic material which has been produced tends to be destroyed by microorganisms during the process of decomposition. These aerobic microorganisms (i.e., microorganisms which thrive only in the presence of free oxygen) begin to function around 5°C (approximately 40°F), and their destructive ability increases with temperature well beyond the level of

25°C. Until such temperatures are reached, however, the relative rate of destruction remains below that of production. When translated into latitudinal terms, this means that humus can accumulate in all non-polar humid climates, except in those low-latitude regions where average annual temperatures are approximately 25°C and higher.

The curve in Figure 16.3 representing the destruction of organic matter in environments without air, such as swamps, shows that anaerobic microorganisms (i.e., microorganisms which can live without free oxygen) are much less active as agents of decomposition. Hence there can be a continuous accumulation of humus in such environments at any latitude. This accounts for the relatively large accumulation of organic material in swamps, both now and in former ages.

In a subhumid climate the volume of vegetative production by the characteristic grasses and shrubs is, of course, below that of a humid climate, but the activity of the microorganisms is proportionately even less as a result of the lack of moisture (Fig. 16.4). Consequently, humus can accumulate in subhumid climates at any latitude.

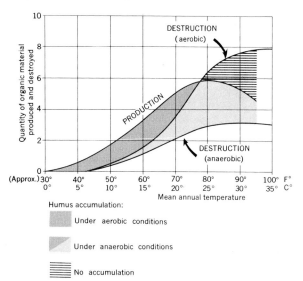

Figure 16.3 In humid climates, these are the relative rates of production of vegetative matter and its destruction by aerobic and anaerobic microorganisms (decomposition) as generally related to average temperatures. Thus in regions with average temperatures above about 25°C, no humus is likely to be produced. *(After Senstius.)*

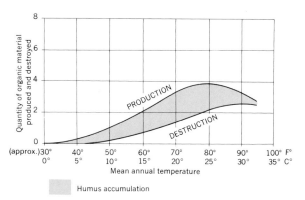

Humus accumulation

Figure 16.4 In semiarid climates, these are the relative rates of production of organic material and its destruction by aerobic microorganisms. Less organic material is produced than in a humid climate, but the soil microorganisms are proportionately even less active owing to the decreased moisture. The result is that humus production can take place at higher temperatures than in humid climates. *(After Senstius.)*

Water and air. Perhaps only 50 percent of the volume of an average, good-quality surface soil consists of inorganic particles, dead organic material, and living organisms. Water and air circulating within the pore spaces occupy the other 50 percent. Water and the gases of the air play an integral part in the inorganic and organic chemical reactions that occur in the soil, and hence are just as much constituents of soil as the solids are. Although plants derive much of their food from the soil solutions, relatively few types of plants are able to thrive in soils in which the pore space is always filled with water; most of them require soils which contain air as well.

Immediately following a rain, the pore spaces of a soil may be filled with water which displaces the air. In this condition some water will move rapidly downward. This is sometimes called *free* or *gravitational water* (Fig. 16.5). The water which remains in capillaries is held relatively tightly to the surfaces of the soil particles and in the voids between them by surface tension. This is the persistent soil solution. When the amount of capillary water is diminished by plant use or direct evaporation, capillarity may cause some water to move horizontally, or even to creep upward a short distance, from zones where it is more abundant. During a drought, when the supply of capillary water has been depleted, there is still a molecular film called *hygroscopic water* on the surfaces of the soil particles, especially the colloids (Fig. 16.5). It adheres firmly, does not move from one place to another, and is resistant to both evaporation and absorption by plant roots.

The supply of soil water varies from region to region and depends upon the ratio of precipitation to evapotranspiration and the amount of free drainage there is. Where precipitation is relatively high in proportion to evapotranspiration, there will be more downward-moving water and hence more leaching, and the soils will tend toward an acid reaction (pH below 7.0). On the other hand, in arid regions water only occasionally moves downward, and then only a short distance, carrying with it dissolved salts, and then moves upward again through capillarity, to be lost by evapotranspiration. In this way lime and other salts may accumulate in definite layers or even at the surface in dry-land soils. Consequently, the soils of sub-humid areas tend to have an alkaline reaction (pH above 7.0).

Profile. In the development of soil, one set of processes—such as the accumulation of organic matter, illuviation, or eluviation—tend to produce more or less distinct layers called *horizons*, which have different chemical and physical properties. These are designated as A, B, and C horizons, reading from the top down. The thicknesses of the horizons vary greatly; in some types of soil they are thin, in others so thick and irregular that for purposes of better description each horizon is further subdivided as A_1, A_2, A_3, etc. (Fig. 16.6). The horizons within a profile are distinguished from one another in appearance, texture, structure, chemical characteristics, and many other qualities.

Organic life and debris are most abundant in the A horizon.[3] In humid regions the A horizon is usually subjected to leaching and eluviation and is left poorer in soluble substances and coarser in texture as a result. The B horizon, in contrast, may be one of illuviation as well as a zone of nutrient enrichment, since some of the materials carried in solution from the layer above may be deposited in it. The C horizon is the little-changed parent material from which the inorganic fraction of the soil was derived.

Another set of developmental processes tend to churn or mix the soil materials, so that distinct and contrasting horizon development is inhibited. These processes include the mixing of soils by animals; tree tipping; expansion and contraction, which occurs in freezing and thawing or when certain clay-rich soils are alternately dried and moistened; mass movements; and the like. Some clay soils, for example, are known as "self-plowing" and hence have simple profiles; yet they may have been in existence ten times as long as the Michigan forest soil diagrammed in Figure 16.6 with its clearly defined horizons.

Color. Among the more obvious characteristics of the surfaces and horizons of different soils are their distinctive colors. Since color is generally significant as an indicator of the soil's physical or chemical condition, it is usually included in the descriptions of horizons.

The commonest subsoil colors are shades of red, brown, or yellow, which are caused primarily by the iron and manganese in well-oxidized soils. Iron oxides are red or brown, but the hydrous form is yellow. In areas where insufficient oxygen occurs in the soil, as, for example, in waterlogged situations, the blue and gray tints of the reduced form of these same elements are common. Mottling or alternate streaks of oxidized and reduced materials indicate zones of good and poor aeration. In some humid regions a gray tint often indicates a loss of iron oxides as a consequence of strong leaching. In arid regions, on the other hand, light colors may denote a concentration of soluble salts. In some areas black and dark-brown surface soil colors indicate a considerable content of organic matter. In many soils two or more

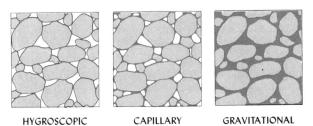

HYGROSCOPIC   CAPILLARY   GRAVITATIONAL

Figure 16.5 Forms of soil water. Gray areas represent individual soil particles greatly magnified; colored margins, water; white areas, air spaces.

[3]The organic horizon, the upper part of the A horizon, is now sometimes called the O horizon. In the O_1 the original form of the vegetative matter is readily visible; in the lower O_2 the original form is not recognizable.

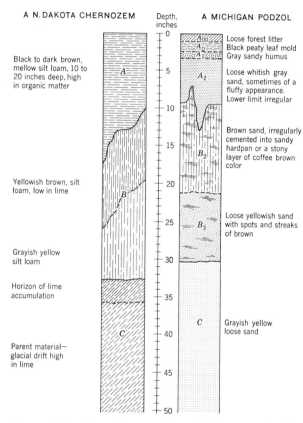

CONTRASTING SOIL PROFILES

A N. DAKOTA CHERNOZEM

Black to dark brown, mellow silt loam, 10 to 20 inches deep, high in organic matter

Yellowish brown, silt loam, low in lime

Grayish yellow silt loam

Horizon of lime accumulation

Parent material—glacial drift high in lime

Depth, inches

A MICHIGAN PODZOL

Loose forest litter
Black peaty leaf mold
Gray sandy humus

Loose whitish gray sand, sometimes of a fluffy appearance. Lower limit irregular

Brown sand, irregularly cemented into sandy hardpan or a stony layer of coffee brown color

Loose yellowish sand with spots and streaks of brown

Grayish yellow loose sand

Figure 16.6 Some characteristic profile elements within the profiles of two different soils. The organic horizon, formerly the upper portion of the A (A_{OO}, A_O), is now sometimes designated as the "O" horizon.

color-forming agents are present, giving rise to intermediate color, such as yellowish-brown or grayish-brown.

Pans. Some soils develop a dense or compact horizon known as a *pan*. This layer can markedly affect soil productivity because of its interference with root penetration and, in some instances, water penetration. There are many kinds of pan layers, and they are caused by a variety of factors, the two most common being deposition in the subsoil of clay and sesquioxides[4] by large amounts of percolating water

[4]Sesquioxides are oxides containing three atoms of O and

in humid regions, and by the precipitation of carbonates from small amounts of water in dry regions. Both of these conditions result in a strongly illuviated or cemented horizon.

One widespread kind of pan is called a *fragipan*. It is a compact layer of weakly cemented fine material, which may be created either by a high concentration of clay in the original subsoil or by illuviation. Fragipans are relatively widespread in the very smooth or flat lands of the humid forest land soils of the upper middle latitudes.

Another kind of pan is the result of chemical cementation. These occur widely in all latitudes. In humid regions, the cementing agents are commonly silica or iron and aluminum sesquioxides. In the tropics the pan may develop into an ironstone called *laterite*. Pans in dry regions are typically cemented by caliche, i.e., calcium, and magnesium carbonates with associated silica.

The Controls of Soil

The characteristics of an individual soil, that is, its distinctive assemblage of components, result from the interaction of a number of controls, the most important of which are (1) the initial or parent material, (2) climate, (3) land-surface form, and (4) biotic factors.

Each control varies in its effect and relative importance from place to place on the earth. Some of these variations are quite systematically arranged, such as those deriving from climatic factors, while others are less so, such as those which primarily depend upon the biotic factors. Generally, world patterns of soils show much more internal variation than do world patterns of climate.

In the sense that soils develop and change in the same way that successions of plant communities do, time is a kind of control. It is impossible, however, to specify with any degree of certainty just how the soil of any considerable area will develop. The constant ecological change which is characteristic of the biosphere is one variable factor. Furthermore, there seems to be no specific period in which a soil develops its particular characteristics. Some may reach a condition of relative balance with the environment com-

two of another element—iron, aluminum, or manganese. In most soils they are very insoluble.

paratively quickly, possibly in less than 100 years; others may require thousands of years.

Initial material. The thin, loose, inorganic layer at the earth's surface, however it may have come into existence, contains a combination of rock particles of particular chemical composition which have weathered to a particular array of fragment sizes. Whatever are the processes of development in a soil, they are not likely to erase completely the fundamental qualities deriving from this initial or parent material.

The textural characteristics of the initial material are significant, and the mineral, or chemical, content is extremely important, since under natural conditions (i.e., without changes made by human beings) it is largely the source of the soil's fertility. Thus the initial material may be thought of as a limiting factor with respect to some of the soil's textural and most of its initial fertility characteristics.

Climate. Climate directly affects the rate and depth of weathering of rocks and the amount of water percolating through or evaporating from the soil. Prevailing high temperatures promote deep weathering and other rapid chemical activity in the soil, while cold temperatures slow these down. Alternating wet and dry seasons develop soil characteristics which differ from those of continuously rainy regions, and the total amount of precipitation is directly related to the leaching of the important bases—that is, the salts of calcium, phosphorus, potassium, etc.—from the soil. Furthermore, as observed earlier, the temperatures which occur in a region have an important effect on the rate of accumulation of humus (Figs. 16.3 and 16.4). Climate also acts as an indirect control through its influence upon the organic life of a soil and on the plants (and animals) which subsist on it.

Land-surface form. Differences in slope can have a great effect on moisture and air conditions within the soil. Even more important, they influence the rate of surface erosion. Maximum development of soil profiles, called *mature profiles*, such as those shown in Figure 16.6, will ordinarily take place only on undulating, well-drained uplands with free underdrainage and only slight surface erosion. The slow rate of erosion on such sites allows the soil-forming processes

to penetrate relatively deeply below the surface. The soils of steep slopes generally fail to develop mature characteristics, because accelerated surface erosion restricts the profile development by thinning the horizons and by limiting the vegetative cover so that the organic content is reduced. Soils of poorly drained or marshy areas develop quite different profiles from other soils, primarily because they remain waterlogged.

The sequence of related soils of a limited area, such as from hilltop to valley bottom, that vary in character because of differences in slope and the level of the water table, is sometimes called a *soil catena*. A full set of variations may include soils which range from the well-drained soils of the rolling uplands, to the moderately well-drained soils of the lower flanks, to the waterlogged soils of wet depressions.

Biotic factors. As we saw in the previous chapter, distinctive formation types of wild vegetation are regionally arranged on the earth. Because the totality of organic and inorganic phenomena in any area constitutes an integrated functioning system, or ecosystem, it is obvious that the vegetation affects the soil, and vice versa. The effects of vegetation are many and complex. They include the fact that the root systems, upon dying, are incorporated in the soil as organic matter, sparingly, as in dryer areas, or in profusion, as in lush grasslands; their leaf forms (broadleaf, needle-leaf, grass blades, etc.) provide organic material to the surface of the soil where it can decompose rapidly or accumulate and perhaps provide strong acids to percolate downward; or deep-rooted plants bring minerals up from the subsoil and hold them in their tissues. When the plants die and decay, these minerals are then returned to the upper soil layers, constituting a kind of biocycling process.

Animal as well as plant forms are incorporated in the soil. The microorganisms (bacteria, protozoa, fungi, etc.) in the soil are primary agents in the decomposition of these remains. Some microorganisms also are able to change atmospheric nitrogen into a form that can be utilized by plants. Burrowing organisms as well as plant roots add to the porosity of the soil by their penetration of it.

Human beings are, of course, a primary agent in modifying the total environment and thus the soil. Since they became numerous they have made changes in all the classes of controls. They have altered the parent material by adding mineral fertilizers, removing salts, taking out more nutrients by cropping than are replaced naturally, or even adding toxic herbicide and insecticide materials. They have changed the land-surface form relationships by checking or accelerating erosion, and they have caused subsidence by draining or mining. They have affected the climate in many ways, such as by adding carbon dioxide to the atmosphere, creating smog and toxic gases, or clearing and burning vegetative cover, which in turn affects wind velocities and humidities. They may have added organic matter by manuring, or they may have removed it by overcropping, burning, or plowing.

All soils are, of course, always undergoing change; change is characteristic of the environment. But because people have been so active in their tilling of the soil, it is likely that nearly mature soils in relative equilibrium with natural controls are largely restricted to those which have never been cultivated. On the other hand, it is important to keep in mind that the immature or human-modified soils of cultivated areas may have qualities closely related to those of the actual or hypothetical mature soil of the region.

Soil Classes and Regions

In many ways a soil is similar to a living organism: for one thing, some of its characteristics are hereditary, such as those derived from its inorganic ancestry, while others are due to environmental influences. Generally, the environmental controls, especially climate and living organisms, tend to be dominant in the development of a soil. But the number of combinations of important soil properties is very large, and the systematizing help of a classification is needed to study their occurrence over the earth.

Soil classification. Because soils are very complex assemblages of numerous constituents and properties, and because they are so important to people as the growth medium of their food-producing plants, a variety of classification systems have been developed to simplify their study.

At the one extreme is the essentially evolutionary approach which identifies the soil characteristics in terms of their presumed genetic pathway of origin and recognizes three major classes of soil: Zonal soils, Intrazonal soils, and Azonal soils. *Zonal soils* are assumed to have well-developed characteristics based largely upon the dominance of climate and vegetation among the soil-forming processes. *Intrazonal soils* may have more or less well-developed characteristics, but their development was dominated by factors other than climate and vegetation—for instance, excessive or poor drainage, unusual parent material, or excessive salts. *Azonal soils* do not have well-developed soil profiles; windblown sand areas or recent alluvium are examples of the Azonal order.

This system of classification then proceeds through suborders to divisions called *great soil groups*, of which there are approximately 40 in the United States. Each great soil group is composed of families, which are in turn composed of series, which are divided into types. The soil type is the fundamental element in the classification system.[5] This general system was adopted in the United States in 1938 and revised somewhat in 1949.

More recently in the United States an entirely different system has been developed which emphasizes the properties of the soils themselves as the differentiating characteristics with little regard to their presumed evolution. Definitions are precise and quantitative and are based on diagnostic horizons, both surface and subsurface. The classification system, first developed and summarized by the Soil Conservation Service in 1960, with supplements published in 1964 and 1967,[6] contains six categorical levels, beginning with orders, then ranges downward through suborders, great groups, subgroups, families, and finally series. The soils of the world are divided into 10 orders, while there are perhaps 10,000 series in the United States alone. This system has gained general acceptance in the United States.

[5]There are thousands of soil types. A type is distinguished by a surface-textural term added to a series name which is a geographical name: for example, a Miami silt loam. Soil types can be further described as divided into phases: for example, stony phase or steep phase.

[6]Soil Survey Staff. *Soil Classification, A Comprehensive System: 7th Approximation*. Soil Conservation Service, U.S. Department of Agriculture. U.S. Government Printing Office, Washington, D.C., 1960; *Supplement to* [same], 1964; *Supplement to* [same], 1967.

DIAGNOSTIC HORIZONS OF SOILS

Surface layers	Characteristics
Mollic	Dark layer at least 17.5 cm (7 in.) containing an aggregate of more than 1 percent organic matter. Not massive or hard structure; base saturation over 50 percent.
Anthropic	Thick, dark, soft layer. Acid reaction.
Umbric	Thick, dark, layer like mollic.
Histic	More than 30 percent organic matter to a depth of 40 cm (16 in.). Water-saturated part of the time.
Ochric	Light and/or too thin or too low in organic matter to be mollic, anthropic, umbric, or histic.
Subsurface layers	
Argillic	Clay-rich illuviated layer beneath eluviated layer. Usually acid; not strongly alkaline.
Agric	Clay and humus-rich argilliclike layer but formed immediately beneath plow layer.
Natric	Clay-rich, argilliclike layer but with prismatic or columnar structure; strongly alkaline.
Spodic	Sesquioxide-rich illuviated layer with considerable organic carbon.
Cambic	Weakly argillic or spodic but insufficiently developed for either.
Oxic	Highly weathered, rich in sesquioxides. Oxide, clay-rich layer at least 30 cm (12 in.) thick, with low cation exchange capacity.

A world view of soils. In order to provide the reader with a worldwide view of soil as a component of the geographical environment and to aid the study of how the soil relates to the other elements of physical geography, the distribution, environmental relationships, and distinctive characteristics of each of the 10 orders will be examined. Plate 5 is a very simplified portrayal of the distribution of the soil orders. Like Plate 4 showing vegetation, many locally important variations are too limited in extent to be shown on the map, which is intended to show the basic pattern of soil distribution. Very much abbreviated listings of the names and descriptions of the major diagnostic horizons are given in the first of the two accompanying tables and the employment of these in identifying the 10 orders is given in the second table. It should be noted that the diagnostic layers ("horizons") listed in the first table constitute a key to the soil orders but do not necessarily coincide exactly with the specific A, B, or C horizons as these might be recognized in a particular family or series belonging to that order.

Because the climatic and vegetative biotic controls of soil formation are naturally somewhat systematically arranged on the earth, we can expect the soil orders to show some system as well. Figure

DOMINANT SOIL ORDERS

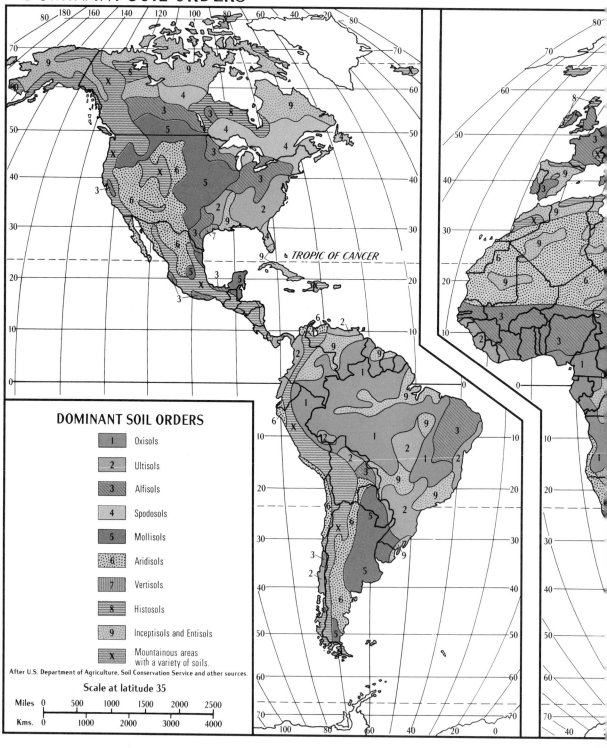

DOMINANT SOIL ORDERS

1	Oxisols
2	Ultisols
3	Alfisols
4	Spodosols
5	Mollisols
6	Aridisols
7	Vertisols
8	Histosols
9	Inceptisols and Entisols
X	Mountainous areas with a variety of soils.

After U.S. Department of Agriculture, Soil Conservation Service and other sources.

Scale at latitude 35

Miles	0	500	1000	1500	2000	2500
Kms.	0	1000	2000	3000	4000	

TROPIC OF CANCER

PLATE 5

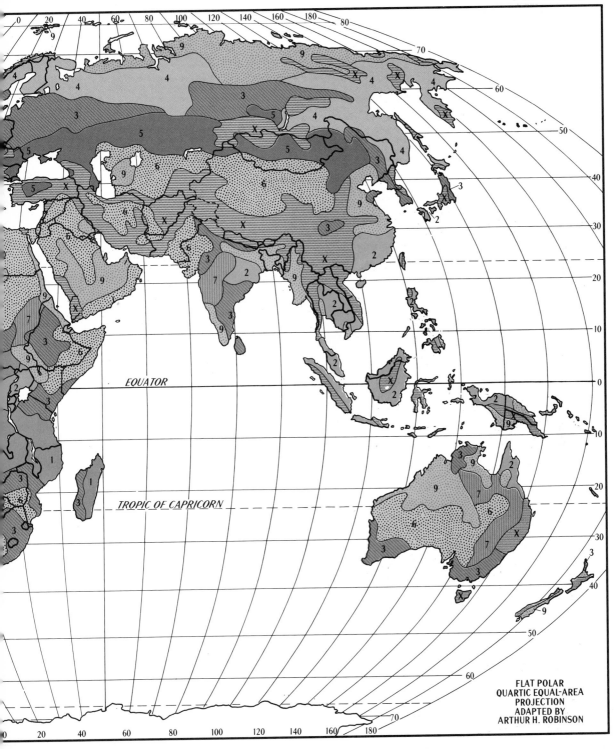

FLAT POLAR
QUARTIC EQUAL-AREA
PROJECTION
ADAPTED BY
ARTHUR H. ROBINSON

THE SOIL ORDERS

Order name	Diagnostic characteristics
Oxisol	An oxic horizon.
Ultisol	An argillic, but no oxic or natric, horizon. Low base supply.
Alfisol	An argillic or natric, but no mollic, spodic, or oxic, horizon. Medium to high base supply.
Spodosol	A spodic horizon.
Mollisol	A mollic, but no oxic, horizon.
Aridisol	An ochric or argillic, but no oxic or spodic, horizon. Usually dry.
Vertisol	More than 30 percent clay to 1 m (40 in.). Swells when wet and cracks upon drying.
Histosol	More than 30 percent organic matter to a depth of 40 cm (16 in.).
Inceptisol	A cambic or histic, but no spodic, argillic, natric, or oxic, horizon.
Entisol	Only weakly developed horizons, commonly with an ochric horizon.

16.7 shows, in a diagrammatic way, the very general relation among various combinations of temperature and moisture and the seven orders associated with them (compare Plates 5 and 1). Note that Alfisols can occur in a wide range of environments. Note also that Entisols, Vertisols, and Histosols are not shown; their occurrence is less related to the basic climatic parameters.

Because the controls of climate, and associated vegetation, are so significant, a few generalizations about the main differences between the soil-forming processes of humid and dry areas can be made.

Soil formation in humid areas. Many soils of humid regions have developed under a natural cover of forest or woodland. Except in areas with very high temperatures, the production of organic matter exceeds its destruction; consequently humus accumulates. Humus is formed primarily on the surface, however, and is therefore incorporated into the soil rather slowly. Also, there is a net downward movement of soil water in humid regions; accordingly the

soils as a whole are much leached, usually light-colored, and have an acid reaction (pH values less than 7.0). The net result is that they tend to be comparatively low in both organic matter and mineral plant foods.

The chemical soil-forming processes, and the resulting soil profiles, are notably different between

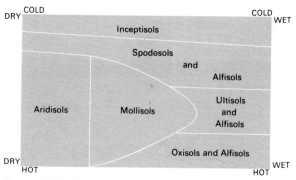

Figure 16.7 Diagram showing the general relation between soil orders and the major climatic parameters. The distribution of Entisols, Histosols, and Vertisols is not closely related to climate.

warm and cool humid regions. In general, in the humid tropics there is little surficial humus accumulation, and solution and eluviation dominate. Weathering is deep, and the basic minerals and much of the silica have been leached, leaving a concentration of sesquioxides in the upper sections. Horizon differentiation is poor.

By contrast, in the cooler humid regions of middle and higher latitudes, the soil-forming process commonly yields abundant decaying organic material. The organic compounds combine with iron and aluminum and make them more mobile, facilitating the removal of these metals from the A horizon and their deposition in an illuviated B horizon. The soils generally have an acid reaction. Horizon differentiation tends to be marked.

Soil formation in dry areas. Leaching is not a major factor in the development of dry-land soils. Consequently they have a considerable, and in some places excessive, content of soluble alkaline compounds. Calcium, magnesium, sodium, or potassium may be plentiful, and the soils usually have neutral or basic reactions (pH values of 7.0 or more). Because there is a delicate relationship between any downward-moving water heavily charged with salts and the precipitation of the salts as a result of water loss by evapotranspiration, an actual horizon of concentration often develops.

Although there are some significant differences between the soils of the warm dry regions and those of the cool, the most important differences are those between the soils of the very arid or desert regions and the soils on the subhumid margins of the dry regions. The typical soil of desert areas is light-colored, high in saline or alkaline minerals, and low in organic matter. On the other hand, the soil of the barely subhumid region is likely to have formed under grass and may be dark-gray or brown, neutral or only moderately alkaline, and high in organic content.

The Soil Orders

Oxisols

Oxisols are the mineral soils that have an oxic horizon within 2m (80 in.) of the surface. They are most often found in the tropics, where they occur at rela-

tively low elevations in regions having quite high and uniform temperatures. In these areas they occur under rainforest, rain green woodland, and in some wooded, tropical grassland areas. The development of the oxic horizon requires considerable time, and consequently, although Oxisols are found mostly in the tropical areas, by no means do all soils of the tropics fall in this class. Oxisols have developed and persisted only in the older landscapes, undisturbed by erosion or recent deposition.[7]

The high temperatures and abundant precipitation of the tropics combine to promote deep and intense weathering, and horizon differentiation is poor (Fig. 16.8). This results in the removal of the iron and aluminum combined with silica, as well as the bases, from the surface soil, while quartz and the reddish sesquioxides of iron and aluminum remain. The texture is commonly clay, but the soil is surprisingly porous, with a tendency toward granular structure. These soils are not very subject to erosion. The high temperatures and moist conditions are favorable to the activity of microorganisms as well as to plant life. There is little humus accumulation where temperatures are continuously high (Fig. 16.3). Because of the heavy leaching, the soils are predominantly acid, commonly with pH values around 5.0.

Because of the extreme weathering and great leaching of Oxisols, most of the nutrients in the soil-vegetation system are likely to be concentrated at any one time in the plant tissues. Consequently, there is a rapid exchange of the nutrients between the vegetation and the litter. These soils are obviously adapted to the growth of deep-rooted crops, such as oil palms, which utilize the deeper supply of nutrients in lower C horizons, the intense tropical sunlight, and the abundant rains for the production and storage of fats, starches, sugars, and other carbohydrates instead of proteins. "Shifting cultivation" is practiced widely in Oxisols, but it cannot support much population. This is the practice of clearing a patch of land, growing crops until the available nutrients are exhausted (a few years at most), and then moving on to clear a new patch and repeat the cycle.

Laterite. *Laterite* is a term with a variety of meanings, but most often it has been used to refer to a layer

[7]The great soil groups of the 1938 classification which generally fall in the Oxisol order are Laterite soils and Latosols.

Figure 16.8 Profile of an Oxisol formed from gneiss northwest of Rio de Janeiro, Brazil. There is some darkening of the upper portion by organic matter. Plant roots extend to depths below 1.5 m (5 ft) in this soil. Numbers on the scale show feet. (*Photograph by Roy W. Simonson, Soil Conservation Service, U.S. Department of Agriculture.*)

of concentrated iron and aluminum oxides. In this sense it can occur in other than tropical areas.[8] It has, however, most often been associated with Oxisols and other soils which occur in the tropics. In a more restricted sense the term *laterite* has also referred to the sesquioxide-rich horizon which, upon exposure

[8]T. R. Paton and M. A. J. Williams. "The Concept of Laterite." *Ann. Assoc. Amer. Geographers*, Vol. 62, No. 1, pp. 42–56, 1972.

and wetting and drying, hardens irreversibly to a hard pan. It is sometimes even used for building material (Fig. 16.9).

Ultisols

Ultisols are characterized by a strongly eluviated surface horizon and a clay-rich, illuviated (argillic) horizon below it. The profiles are deep because of long and active weathering, but the clay-rich horizon has not become oxic. The base saturation of Ultisols is low, being below 35 percent. This reflects the extensive leaching characteristic of Ultisols.[9]

These soils occur in some areas of humid subtropical climate and in some tropical regions. Like the Oxisols, the Ultisols can maintain an undisturbed forest vegetation through the recycling of nutrients by such deep-rooted plants. The evergreen and mixed forests of southeastern United States flourish on these soils. If the forest cover is removed, the fertility

[9]The great soil groups which fall in the Ultisol order are Red-Yellow Podzolic, Reddish-Brown Lateritic, associated Planosols, and some Half-Bog soils.

Figure 16.9 A stack of laterite bricks cut from a layer about 2 m (6 ft) thick near Colombo, Ceylon. The handle of the small pick is about 50 cm (18 in.) long. (*Photograph by Roy W. Simonson, Soil Conservation Service, U.S. Department of Agriculture.*)

drops rapidly and can be maintained only by extensive manuring or mineral fertilization. Ultisols are much more subject to erosion than the more porous, granular Oxisols, and erosion has been and is a serious problem in many areas of Ultisol soil.

As shown on Plate 5, Ultisols dominate in only a few areas of the subtropics, but they occur in regions of considerable agricultural importance, such as southeastern China and the United States. In these areas the upper horizons generally are brown clays and loams (ochric horizons). Their B horizons usually are deep, with colors varying from red to yellow and often showing mottles of laterite (i.e., iron concentrations), and fragipans are common in areas of poor drainage. The generally lighter colors of these soils as compared with Oxisols result from less complete oxidation of the iron content. In many areas the sesquioxides have been removed from the upper horizon and deposited in the B, so that the ochric surface layer of darker organic material is commonly underlain by a lighter A_2 horizon and an illuviated acid B horizon of clay-enriched material. The inherent agricultural capacity of these soils is not high, but with careful management they are productive. They are generally low in calcium and other alkaline substances, and the supply of organic matter is seldom abundant. Under cultivation, the red and yellow colors of the B horizon usually predominate, becoming distinctive elements of the landscape.

Alfisols

Like the Ultisols, Alfisols are soils with clay accumulation in the B horizon (an argillic horizon), but Alfisols have a medium to high base supply. They form under a variety of climates and are extensive in middle-latitude regions in areas of both humid and subhumid climate where the landforms have been stable for several thousand years. They also occur in tropical areas. They form under a variety of vegetation.[10]

Alfisols in the middle latitudes tend to have a darkened surface layer (ochric horizon) of organic material, but it is either too light or too thin or too low

[10]The great soil groups which fall in the Alfisol order are Gray-Grown Podzolic, Gray Wooded, Noncalcic Brown, Degraded Chernozem, and associated Planosols and Half-Bog soils.

Figure 16.10 Profile of forest soil in the middle latitudes. Note the ochric surface horizon, the leached zone immediately beneath, and the darkened illuviated B horizon. *(Photograph by G. A. Hills, Ontario Department of Lands and Forests.)*

in organic matter to qualify the soil for one of the other orders (Fig. 16.10). Plant roots provide the organic material in grasslands, while in forest areas this is provided by leaf fall to the surface. Surface horizons are often nearly neutral (pH 7.0) but, except in subhumid areas, subsoils are generally quite acid. Generally, the A horizon of a forest Alfisol is stained with a brown hydroxide of iron, and the admixture of organic matter gives it a grayish-brown color. The illuviated B horizon is commonly yellowish-brown and heavier in texture than the A horizon. The C horizon is the little-changed parent material of the soil.

On the whole, the Alfisols formed under middle-latitude forests have better structures than other forestland soils, maintain them better under cultivation, and respond more readily to the application of lime and organic fertilizers. However, they lose their quality under continuous cropping unless they are managed carefully, limed, and well fertilized. Alfisols formed under grass in the middle latitudes generally have better structures than those developed under forest.

Alfisols occupy many areas in regions of subtropical dry-summer climates. In the Mediterranean region it is likely that many of their characteristics are inherited from the soils that formed under the extensive mixed evergreen forests that were apparently widespread in this region before humans upset the balance and turned them into scrub woodlands. In the tropics Alfisols occupy a number of areas where, for one reason or another, the weathering and other soil-forming processes have not been able to operate long enough to produce an Oxisol or Ultisol.

Associated soils in the Northern Hemisphere. A surprising variety of soil types and variations, often comprising drainage catenas, occur in the glaciated areas where Alfisols have developed. Among these are Entisols, formed on either fertile river deposits or the infertile sands and gravels associated with glacial outwash. Entisols lack any marked horizon development and tend to be low in humus, and those that are sandy dry out quickly.

Also common are types of soils that have been affected by poor drainage, such as the dark-colored Histosols formed in marshy or boggy places where peat and muck have accumulated. In them the surface layers are composed largely of organic matter derived from the remains of grasses, sedges, and other marsh plants. They commonly are underlain by sticky compact clays that are light shades of gray tinted with blue. These plastic clays are termed *gley*, and they occur where a high groundwater table allows the formation of ferrous iron compounds, which cause the blue tints. The process of *gleization* can occur anywhere if the soil is periodically water-logged. Such soils are common in the numerous kettle depressions and high-water-table areas of glaciated plains. If drained, many can be productive.

Spodosols

A spodic subsurface horizon is characteristic of the Spodosols. This sesquioxide-rich subsurface layer with organic complexes with iron and aluminum is a consequence of the accumulation of organic matter on the surface, which becomes strongly acid, and the downward-moving acid soil water heavily leaching the A horizon. Clay is also removed from the eluviated A horizon and accumulates in the B. The general process, which encompasses a variety of chemical and mechanical activities, is called *podzolization*, taking its name from the Russian words *pod* (beneath) and *zol* (ashes), because of the ashy gray layer directly beneath the darker surface (Fig. 16.11). Cementation often occurs in the spodic layer, and fragipans and hard pans are common in Spodosols.[11]

Spodosols occur in areas of cool humid climates under a boreal forest cover. Conifers do not require abundant bases for their growth; and since they are mainly shallow-rooted trees, they draw only small supplies of the soil bases to the surface, even where these are available in the parent material. Thus there is little mechanism to oppose the tendency toward soil acidity, and pH values are generally in the vicinity of 5.0. The long, cold boreal winter and moderate summer temperatures, as well as the forest litter of highly acid resinous needles, act to retard bacterial action and to allow the formation of a surface layer, often thin, of acid, half-decomposed humus. Spodosols also occur in poorly drained areas of the coastal plain of southeastern United States.

Spodosols are used for cropping, for pasture and hay land, and for forestry. Without improvement, they are poor soils for most farm crops. Under cultivation the top layer of organic matter is soon lost, and the grayish surface soil requires lime, fertilizer, and good management to keep it productive and to prevent its poor structure from becoming a hindrance to tillage.

---

[11]The great soil groups included in the Spodosol order are Podzol, Brown Podzolic, and Groundwater Podzol soils.

Figure 16.11 Profile of a Spodosol in Ontario. Note the typical heavy leaching of the light-colored lower A horizon and the strongly illuviated dark-colored spodic horizon beneath it. *(Photograph by G. A. Hills, Ontario Department of Lands and Forests.)*

Mollisols

Mollisols are characterized by a dark surface layer containing at least 1 percent organic matter with neither massive nor hard structure and with a base saturation of more than 50 percent. They occur in large areas in central North America and in a broad band across central Eurasia (Plate 5). In the Southern Hemisphere they occur extensively only in southeastern South America.[12]

Subhumid grasslands communities are the principal natural vegetation under which Mollisols have developed, and the combination of climate and vegetation accounts largely for their character. The grass roots provide an abundant supply of organic material, and this produces a large and deep supply of humus (Fig. 16.12). It has been estimated that each year from 300 to 1,000 kg of raw organic matter (dry weight) per hectare (approximately 250 to 900 lb per acre) are added to a representative Mollisol in a short-grass prairie area. Since there is relatively little leaching, sufficient lime is available to combine with the large amount of organic colloids and clays in these dark soils, thus promoting excellent structural conditions in all the soil horizons. These soils occur under a range of precipitation amounts, and, as one would expect, the transition from the subhumid to the semiarid is accompanied by changes in the character of the Mollisols. Less moisture means less leaching, less vegetative cover, and therefore less humus and a lighter-colored and shallower mollic horizon.

Mollisols are widely used for cropping because they have good structure and a high base saturation, which is desirable for grains. Because they occur over extensive plains areas, their cultivation is relatively easy. Their major drawback is related to their origin, namely, that they occur in areas where precipitation is highly variable and where droughts are not uncommon.

Chernozem soils. One of the best-known and most productive of the Mollisols has often been called a *Chernozem*, from Russian words for "black" and "earth." It is formed under a dense vegetation of somewhat shorter prairie and steppe grasses. Average annual precipitation in these areas is sufficiently low, about 50 cm (20 in.), so that this soil contains an abundance of lime and the less soluble basic minerals. The deep mollic horizon of the Chernozem is very high in humus and is black or very dark-brown. The B horizon is lighter-brown or yellow. Horizon differentiation tends to be gradual. The soil structure is granular and porous; when tilled, it crumbles into a fine

[12]The great soil groups included in the Mollisol order are Chernozem, Chestnut, Brunizem, Rendzina, some Brown, Brown Forest, and associated Humic Gley and Solonetz soils.

Figure 16.12 Profile of a Mollisol formed from glacial till in South Dakota. The divisions on the rule are feet. The A horizon extends to a depth of a little over 1 ft, while the B horizon extends to nearly 2¹/₂ ft. The white spots in the bottom of the B and in the C horizon are carbonate accumulations. *(Photograph by Roy W. Simonson, Soil Conservation Service, U.S. Department of Agriculture.)*

seedbed; and it has a large capacity for holding water. The pH values usually range from 7.0 to just below 7.0. In a Chernozem soil, the horizon of lime accumulation generally lies 1 to 1.5m (3 to 5 ft) beneath the surface—still within reach of the grass roots, which find in it an inexhaustible source of calcium.

Aridisols

The surface horizon of Aridisols (ochric horizon) is too light-colored, too thin, or too low in organic matter for them to be included in any other class. This situation primarily results from their occurrence in dry regions where the sparse desert shrub vegetation can provide only a limited supply of organic material. Because of the small amount of organic matter, the light reds, browns, yellows, and grays of weathered-rock particles are widely exposed. Their light colors are accentuated by the accumulation of carbonates, salts, and other whitish substances near the soil surface, or even upon it (Fig. 16.13).[13]

The lack of water inhibits the use of Aridisols. Most Aridisols have more than sufficient amounts of the needed fertility elements, with the exception of nitrogen, and with irrigation some areas can be productive. The process of irrigation can itself lead to the accumulation of salts in the surface horizon. Without irrigation, Aridisols support only enough vegetation to provide some seasonal grazing.

Vertisols

Some areas of dark-colored soils with a high content of swelling clays are found on several continents lying between 45° N and S lat. These are called *Vertisols*, from the Latin *verto*, "turn," because the clay content of these soils causes them to shrink and crack open when dry (Fig. 16.14). Rainfall then tends to drain into these cracks rather than moistening the entire soil. thus wetting a lower layer, which may then expand. As a consequence, the soil heaves about instead of remaining *in situ*. Generally, the parent material of Vertisols is basic and the reaction of the soil is alkaline. Vertisols have a variety of origins: some of them weathered from basic igneous rocks with an unusual mineral content, such as the Regur soils of central India; many others developed from limestones. They are commonly formed under grass with scattered woody vegetation, and many have a dark-colored A horizon which resembles Mollisols. But in many instances, this darkness may be caused

[13]The great soil groups included in the Aridisol order are Desert, Reddish Desert, Sierozem, Solonchak, some Brown, Brown Forest, associated Humic Gley, and Solonetz soils.

some engineering difficulties with buildings, pipelines, utility poles, and fences.

Histosols

Widely distributed, but not covering a large area in the aggregate, are soils in which the rate of production of organic material exceeds the rate of its destruction. By definition Histosols are soils dominated by organic accumulation, and this will ordinarily occur only when they are continually saturated by water, which greatly inhibits the supply of oxygen. By definition these soils must contain more than 30 percent organic material to a depth of 40 cm (16 in.) (Fig. 16.15).[15]

[15]The great soil group included in the Histosol order are Bog soils.

Figure 16.13 Profile of an Aridisol formed on alluvial sediments in Nevada. Although the regolith is deep, horizon differentiation is low. The scale of the rule is in feet. Carbonate accumulation occurs at depths below 14 to 16 in. *(Photograph by Roy W. Simonson, Soil Conservation Service, U.S. Department of Agriculture.)*

by a complex of factors not directly related to organic accumulation.[14]

Although some Vertisols are used for crops, the largest area is used for pasture. The cracks that develop can be hazardous for animals and present

[14]The great soil group included in the Vertisol order are Grumusol soils.

Figure 16.14 Cracks in a clay soil in Arizona as a result of drying. The average width of the cracks is about 8 to 10 cm (3–4 in). *(Photograph by Soil Conservation Service, U.S. Department of Agriculture.)*

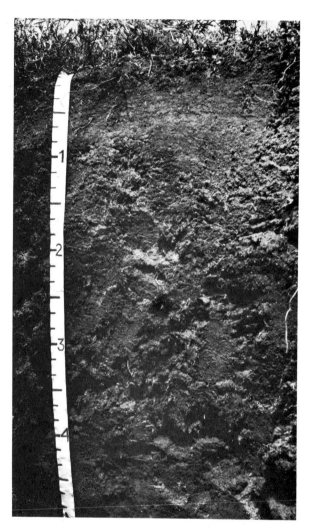

Figure 16.15 Profile of a Histosol from the Kenai Peninsula in Alaska. Numbers on the scale indicate feet. The peat is more than 2.5 m (8 ft) thick at this point. *(Photograph by Roy W. Simonson, Soil Conservation Service, U.S. Department of Agriculture.)*

Inceptisols and Entisols

These two orders comprise soils that have not developed diagnostic features which would place them in another order. In that sense they are "immature" soils, although it would be a mistake to say that they are "on the way" to being mature. Many will never develop the features characteristic of the other orders because of continually changing circumstances, climatic inhibitions, and the like. Of the two orders, Entisols show the least development. They do have an ochriclike surface horizon in many cases. Inceptisols have more features of maturity but are also commonly much like their parent material. Inceptisols are widespread in the tundra and in areas of volcanic ash.[16]

Soils developed on new and older alluvium, mostly Inceptisols but some Entisols, probably support a larger proportion of the world's population than any one other soil order. There is great variety among these soils because their character is largely derived from the source materials of the specific alluvial products. Their textures may range from sands through silts to clays; their color may range from the light-colored gray, buff, or reddish alluvium derived from Aridisol soils to the dark-colored alluvium derived from Mollisol soils; and they may be more or less rich in plant nutrients. They are usually free from stones and easily cultivated, but in many areas they are poorly drained and, of course, subject to flood. In general there is little horizon development except where surface cultivation has provided it.

Not all alluvial soils are productive. In many areas they are too wet or too dry; or they occur where the growing season is too short; or they may be too subject to flooding. In Far Eastern areas, where rice is commonly grown in alluvial paddy lands, the alluvial soils are probably more intensively utilized than elsewhere in the world.

REVIEW QUESTIONS

1. Compare the roles of the elements and the controls of soil in our understanding of them.

[16]The great soil groups included in the Inceptisol order are Ando, Sol Brun Acide, some Brown Forest, Low Humic Gley, and Humic Gley soils. Those included in the Entisol order are Azonal soils and some Humic Gley soils.

Numerous, relatively small areas of Histosols are very common in the areas of more recent glaciation in old lake bottoms and kettle holes in North America and Europe. They are often used for vegetables. Dried blocks of the organic material, called *peat*, are used for fuel in some areas.

2. How many different ways can the parent material of soils accumulate?

3. How can a soil be fertile but not productive?

4. How may the fertility elements be added to or removed from the soil artificially?

5. What is the relationship between texture and water retention? Why?

6. What is the difference in meaning between leaching and the eluviation-illuviation processes?

7. Compare the roles of living and dead organisms to the soil.

8. Compare the probable rates of production and destruction of vegetative matter at latitude 20° and latitude 50° in (*a*) humid climates and (*b*) subhumid climates.

9. List all the ways a soil profile can be inhibited or prevented from developing.

10. How do people function as a control of soil formation?

11. Contrast the likely consequences of the climatic and biotic controls of soil development as they might take place in the following climates: (*a*) warm-humid, (*b*) cool-humid, (*c*) warm-dry, and (*d*) cool-dry.

12. Under what conditions could a Spodosol occur in a low-latitude area?

13. Why can an Oxisol be used for cultivated crops for only a short time?

14. Areas of Mollisol soil are likely to be productive but are subject to what hazard? How is this "related" to their formation?

SELECTED REFERENCES

Albrecht, W. A. "Physical, Chemical and Biochemical Changes in the Soil Community." In William L. Thomas, Jr., (ed.). *Man's Role in Changing the Face of the Earth.* The University of Chicago Press, Chicago, 1955. Pp. 648–673. A fascinating review of the profound effects on the soil of the earth's rapidly growing and first dominant species— human beings.

———. "Soil Fertility and Biotic Geography." *Geog. Rev.*, Vol. 47, pp. 87–105, 1957. Examines this fundamental relationship in a refreshing way.

Bidwell, O. W., and F. D. Hole. "Man as a Factor of Soil Formation." *Soil Science*, Vol. 99, pp. 65–72, 1965. A summary account of this important subject.

Buckman, Harry O., and Nyle C. Brady. *The Nature and Properties of Soils*, 6th ed. The Macmillan Company, New York, 1960. An elementary college text in soil science. Useful as a reference.

Bunting, B. T. *The Geography of Soil.* Aldine Publishing Company, Chicago, 1965, A useful reference source which employs the great soil group framework.

Buol, S. W., F. D. Hole, and R. J. McCracken. *Soil Genesis and Classification.* The Iowa State University Press, Ames, 1973. A rather technical but thorough survey of the named topics, incorporating the terminology of the *7th Approximation.* Contains detailed descriptions of the soil orders.

Eyre, S. R. *Vegetation and Soils*, 2d ed. Aldine Publishing Company, Chicago, 1968. A thorough regional account of these associated phenomena. Contains maps.

Soil. Yearbook of Agriculture, 1957. U.S. Government Printing Office, Washington, D.C. Many articles by experts on a variety of topics. Written largely for the layman.

Soil Survey Staff. *Soil Classification, A Comprehensive System: 7th Approximation.* Soil Conservation Service, U.S. Department of Agriculture, U.S. Government Printing Office, Washington, D.C., 1960. *Supplement to* [same], 1964; *Supplement to* [same], 1967. A complete description of the new classification system in the United States. Highly technical.

Index